Computer Simulation
in
Genetics

Computer Simulation in Genetics

JACK L. CROSBY

Reader in Genetics,
University of Durham

JOHN WILEY & SONS

London · New York · Sydney · Toronto

Library of Congress catalog card number
72-5715

ISBN 0 471 18880 8

Printed in Belgium by
Ceuterick, printers since 1804
B 3000 Louvain

To the memory of

FERDINAND

with whom I spent many happy,

if anxious, evenings

Preface

When, many years ago, I began to study the population genetics of the primrose, electronic computers had not been invented. My theoretical calculations were simple enough, but involved a great deal of iteration, and many long and weary hours were spent turning the handle of a calculating machine (our only machine was hand operated, we did not even have an electro-mechanical one). But in the late nineteen-fifties the installation of an electronic computer (known affectionately as Ferdinand) in the Newcastle Division (as it then was) of the University of Durham not only provided a means of much more rapid and much less laborious calculation, but also suggested possibilities of quite new methods of approach to the theoretical study of evolution, in particular the substitution of stochastic for deterministic treatment, and the introduction of complexity far outside the range which had hitherto been practicable.

I am very much indebted to the Director of the Computing Laboratory at Newcastle, Professor E.S. Page, and to his colleagues for help, instruction and encouragement during the early days. Later on, when their second and much faster machine was installed, I spent a very enjoyable and profitable year there on sabbatical leave.

I am also grateful to many of my students at Durham, who were willing, interested and intelligent guinea-pigs while I was developing my genetics teaching programs and evolving techniques for their presentation to classes.

It is not particularly difficult to learn to program computers for genetic simulation. Once I had been helped through the novice stage and had acquired the knack of computer programming, it was largely a matter of teaching myself (with willing help available if I ever ran into difficulty), profiting greatly from experience and discovering new tricks and techniques as I went along. It was great fun and I thoroughly enjoyed myself.

This book begins at the beginning, as I did, and assumes no knowledge of computing, and only very elementary mathematics (and for most of it not even that is necessary). It presents a personal view of genetics simulation, since it is based almost entirely on my own experience. I hope that it will be of interest to population geneticists, undergraduates, research students, university teachers, school teachers and their senior pupils, and to anybody else who thinks that models are valuable and valid tools in the investigation or exposition of biological systems, and that they will readily be convinced that electronic computers are admirable devices for the construction of such models. I hope that some will be persuaded to indulge in computer simulation, and that they will enjoy it as much as I have done. I also hope that they will first discard any notions of orthodox mathematical treatment of evolution theory, and will approach the matter with a completely fresh outlook. You do not need to be a mathematician to simulate genetics on an electronic computer; indeed, you will be better off without mathematics. The introduction of mathematical devices will rarely improve genetic models and will often have the opposite effect. Nor should anyone be put off by the esoteric aura which surrounds the world of computing and gives many people the impression that computing is only for members of the cult who know the jargon. Anyone can learn to program computers. It is the genetics which is difficult.

J.L. Crosby

Durham, September 1972

Contents

CHAPTER 1

Introduction

Evolution has long provided a happy hunting ground for the armchair biologist. Of all fields of biology, it is perhaps the one which lends itself least readily to the experimental verification (or otherwise) of ideas and hypotheses. From the great body of facts about the organic world, or about parts of it, it is easy to draw 'obvious' conclusions and make hypotheses which can often only be tested by reference to other facts; such tests tend to be subjective because like the original conclusions they depend on personal interpretations of the facts. And this of course is one of the reasons why there has been so much argument in the field of evolution theory. The armchair biologist no doubt enjoys this situation.

For the more serious biologist, who is prepared to come to closer grips with his problem in the field or the laboratory, the special difficulties imposed by the limited possibilities of experiment present a challenging situation requiring special adaptations in outlook and technique.

The major difficulty of course is time, and this operates against us in several ways. It is hardly possible to conduct long-term evolutionary experiments except with organisms which have a short generation time, and for some of us these are not the only organisms of interest. There are a number of animals of whose evolutionary history we have a detailed knowledge from the fossil record, and (we believe) some theoretical understanding. But how, for example, can we demonstrate not only that the evolution of the foot and of the tooth in the horse really was connected with a change from living among and browsing on trees to living in and off the open grassland (where speed of movement and teeth which could cope with the more abrasive grass would appear to have been highly desirable), but also that stages in the evolutionary development of the new foot and the new tooth really did confer a selective advantage on the horses which exhibited them? Appropriate environments may still be available, but we cannot recreate the genetical situation; the animals concerned are extinct, and we have no way of evoking in their ancestors the genotypes we would require for experiment, quite apart from any other difficulties.

With living organisms, short-term experiments to test hypotheses of selective advantage and to determine its nature and magnitude may sometimes be possible and have been successfully carried out. It is not too difficult to show that melanism does confer an advantage on certain species of moths in the smoky regions of England by making them less conspicuous to predators (Kettlewell, 1956); that *Agrostis tenuis* growing on copper mines in Wales shows a much higher tolerance to copper than is normal for the species and that this is due to strong selection (McNeilly, 1968); that under experimental conditions slugs and snails preferentially eat acyanogenic forms of *Lotus corniculatus* rather than the cyanogenic forms (Jones, 1962), and thus the latter have a selective advantage in certain habitats; and that under experimental conditions slugs and snails have no preference as between acyanogenic and cyanogenic forms of *Trifolium repens* and thrive equally well on either (Bishop and Korn, 1969), so any selective advantage of cyanogenesis in that species requires some quite different explanation.

Everybody 'knows' that the gorgeous tail of the peacock helps to endear him to a likely peahen, but has anybody ever proved that the peacocks with the most gorgeous tails are the most successful in terms of the number of eggs fertilized? And even if this could be demonstrated, would it prove that this was the basis of the selective advantage responsible for the evolution of the tail of the peacock? Or even that this evolution was a selective process at all?

The white flash from the tail of a startled rabbit may warn its companions of danger, but how can it help the rabbit that is first startled? What could have been the selective advantage to the first rabbit which had a little white on its tail? Put in this way, the question is too naive. But a quite serious question is there, and it is by no means unique; it is not easy to see how one could begin to tackle it experimentally, though it is not at all difficult to produce a plausible but apparently unverifiable answer.

How can we prove that the ancestors of the willow-warbler and chiffchaff (*Phylloscopus trochilus* and *Ph. collybita*) were recently members of a single continuous gene pool, and how can we determine the way in which the present genetic discontinuity between them arose? The role at present played by song in maintaining this discontinuity seems to be obvious, but how can we demonstrate incontrovertibly that song is as important for species discrimination to the birds concerned as it is to ornithologists?

Whether we have experimentally determined the selective facts about a situation, reached highly probable conclusions on the basis of a critical study of circumstantial evidence, or merely have an intuitive hunch based on experience, the result can directly relate only to the situation as we now find it. If it is to make any contribution of real evolutionary significance, we have to extrapolate from it both backwards into the past history of the system we are studying and forwards into the future; to use an analogy, this is rather like trying to extrapolate from a point when we only kwon the slope of the curve at that point. We hope we can do this accurately, and we may try to verify our extrapolation by reference to similar systems which we hope may now correspond to past or future states of the one we are studying, and we must also understand these thoroughly in the present.

Such extrapolation is a theoretical procedure. Because it can only rarely be tested experimentally and must usually be tested by comparison with analogous situations, which is itself a theoretical operation, we need to be confident of the validity and accuracy of the theoretical treatment. Theoretical understanding of population genetics is therefore essential equipment for progress in the study of evolutionary systems, and such progress will depend on the proper integration of theoretical, observational and experimental elements.

When, rather superficially, we were discussing experiments in evolution, the only kind of experiment considered involved real living systems. When we bear in mind that the application of conclusions drawn from evolutionary experiments in the laboratory or experimental field to the same organisms under natural conditions may sometimes be of doubtful validity, the difficulties involved in experimental approaches to the study of evolution become even more severely limiting.

An alternative approach, which is at the same time both theoretical and in a sense experimental, is to construct models of evolutionary systems and study their behaviour. Again there are limits, but they are of a different kind. Argument from analogy is always a dubious procedure, and it is clear that great caution must be used in applying the results from experiments on model systems to systems actually existing in nature, or in generalizing such results and incorporating them into evolution theory. But the knowledge that we have been working with an unreal or substitute system should be sufficient guard against uncritical application of our conclusions, and the danger is for that reason less than the danger that we may allow ourselves to be misled by results derived from experiments with natural systems which, because they are natural, we may tend to think have an authority which they do not in fact necessarily possess.

On the other hand, model systems are less limited in the range of situations with which they can deal, and often provide the only possible way in which we can attempt any kind of experimental approach.

Evolutionary models may be of two kinds. The models may themselves be living systems in which we use one (or more) species of organism either to represent a hypothetical generalized organism, or to represent some other species which is experimentally intractable. For this purpose, we choose organisms about which we know a great deal, which are easy to maintain and control under laboratory or field conditions, and which have a short generation time. The most obvious example of this is the much used *Drosophila*. How far we can make valid generalizations in evolution theory from the hundreds of experiments which have been performed with members of this genus, or whether the results do no more than tell us something about *Drosophila*, is arguable.

There are features about living models which must be clearly understood. We cannot know everything about the organism we are using, not even *Drosophila;* can we ever be sure that the results we obtain are not due to some unknown peculiarity of the experimental organism rather than to some general property of the evolutionary system? Any living system is highly complex; many of the complexities may be irrelevant to the problem we are studying, some may have an indirect relevance. To what extent can we know and control the relevant structural elements and all the possibly relevant variables in a living model?

There can however be no doubt that experiments with living model systems have made important contributions to evolution theory, and that they will continue to do so.

The second kind of model is purely abstract, and while it has its own peculiar limitations it also has its peculiar advantages. Because we determine them, we know the basic genetic properties, parameters and variables of abstract models. We can limit the number of them to those which we believe to be relevant to the problem under consideration. There need be no unknown variables of unknown effect.

Abstract models provide analogies of real or hypothetical biological situations. Their main requirements are that they must be biologically sensible, and that we must understand both the structure of the model and the biology of the natural system being modelled if the analogy is to be considered valid and if the conclusions we draw from experiments with the former are to have any useful meaning when applied to the latter. Their proper use demands a clear understanding of the theories, ideas and principles of population genetics. In the development of these they have themselves in the past played a major role. Their potentialities for the future have greatly increased over the last ten years or so with the development of techniques by which electronic computers can provide the abstract raw materials for the construction of evolutionary models of much greater complexity, fidelity and speed of operation than could be achieved in any other way.

This book is about the use of electronic computers in the construction of abstract models and their use in the simulation of evolutionary systems. It will assume no knowledge at all of computers or computing. For mathematics, it will assume little more than an elementary knowledge of algebra at school level, which is indeed about as far as the author's own knowledge goes. Familiarity with the basic ideas and language of statistics will be an advantage; lack of such familiarity need not be a serious difficulty, for it can be made good by reference to such excellent books as that by Moroney (1951). A knowledge of mendelian genetics and the basic principles of population genetics, as well as a general familiarity with the ideas of evolution theory, will be assumed, although it is hoped that much of the book will be intelligible to other people with a broad interest in computer simulation techniques; certainly, some of the procedures described in this book have an application to a wider area than the field of genetics.

The book is primarily aimed at those people who wish to write simulation programs for their own use. Some of them will have little or no knowledge of computers or computer programming, and will probably imagine that the art of programming and its application to genetics are matters of great difficulty. This is not really true, although certainly a lot of hard work may be involved, and it is hoped that this book will demonstrate that the difficulties lie rather in understanding genetics than in writing a computer program. It is a salutory experience to write a program which works admirably and accurately but which in so doing demonstrates to the programmer that his knowledge of genetics was not quite so good as he thought it was.

Other readers will have experience of computers and programming, possibly in statistical or other biomathematical operations. They may well have a general idea of how to set about the simulation of genetic systems, though possibly with some doubts about the first steps. It is hoped that this book will make it easier for them, and by taking them quickly and without stumbling through the first steps and then in detail through various examples, will soon get them to a stage at which they can leave the book behind and progress directly into programming for their own problems, equipped with a useful repertoire of techniques at their programming fingertips.

There may be some readers already well experienced in this field. They will doubtless derive pleasure in reflecting how much better some of their own procedures are than the author's, and may occasionally derive benefit when the relative merits are in the reverse direction. So little is published of actual programming techniques that have been used that it is inevitable that different workers will have provided different solutions to similar problems, and some of these solutions will be better than others.

Those intending to write simulation programs may include senior workers who feel that they are not too old to learn new tricks (and this book should mean that, unlike the author, they will not have to teach themselves), as well as graduates and others just entering seriously the complex field of population genetics.

The author's experience has shown that computer models can play a useful part in genetics teaching (Crosby, 1961) both at university level and in schools. The number of schools which possess computers is increasing, and it is hoped that this book may be useful to biology teachers in schools as well as to lecturers in universities and colleges of technology. There is no reason why a biology teacher at school should not be able to learn to write a simulation program for himself or herself, and it is the author's intention that this book should help to make it possible; he has borne in mind the fact that while some of his readers will have access to large fast machines with virtually unlimited store capacity, others will have access only to small and slow machines, perhaps second-hand and obsolescent and with a limited repertoire of instructions. In Chapter 9 there are detailed flow diagrams and quasi-programs corresponding to programs which the author has used successfully in practical genetics classes; it should not be difficult to produce working versions of these for any machine which may be available.

Some university teachers may find the book useful for their undergraduate courses, even though they may not wish their classes to do any programming. One of the best ways of getting to understand a system is to try and make a model of it; a successful model cannot be made of a system which is not properly understood, and the act of making a model may both expose deficiencies in understanding and help in the clarification of ideas. Making and using simple models by a genetics class can be a valuable teaching method, and the models do not have to be electronic (there is some advantage in their not being, in that context). The kind of model demonstrated in Chapter 3 is very effective for this purpose, and some of the flow diagrams elsewhere in this book can readily be translated into models of this kind. Where computer models are being used in practical classes to simulate genetical or evolutionary experiments, the best students will want to know the principles on which the models are constructed and should be able critically to consider their validity; this book should be of some use to them.

There are people with the sort of mind that enjoys intricacy and delights in problems and brain-teasers. They may indulge in programming for programming's sake. They should enjoy this book, and perhaps derive pleasure in working out better ways of doing almost everything.

This is an instructional book, and its primary purpose is to teach its readers how to write genetics simulation programs for themselves. All the examples in which program construction is analysed and explained in detail will be taken from the author's own work. This is not because he thinks that his own work is likely to be better than anybody else's (which it certainly is not), but because effective detailed exposition of a program requires thorough familiarity with it; this involves not only having available the original written program, but also knowing how it was developed and the reasons for using particular procedures. One can only have that kind of familiarity with one's own programs. It is also an advantage to be able to criticize faulty programming techniques in one's own programs, without fear of giving offence or of subsequently finding that somebody else's technique was not faulty after all. Occasional reference will however be made to simulation experiments by others.

There is one point which must be made. When one writes a computer program, the presence of errors in it will almost always be revealed when it is run on the computer (indeed, this is in some ways the best method of detecting errors, both in original writing and in punching, as well as the laziest and the most expensive). The flow diagrams and quasi-programs presented here are generalized without reference to any real computer, and therefore cannot have been directly tested in this way. They have been carefully checked, but some programming slips are very easy to overlook, and it would not be surprising if one or two have escaped detection. The author would be grateful if his attention were drawn to any such errors which appear to have evaded it. But this does require care, for an apparent error may sometimes be an unappreciated subtlety, and if any part of a program does appear to be wrong it is best to put oneself in the position of a computer and go through it operation by operation. This is an excellent exercise, and the reader is encouraged to do this always when any section of a flow diagram or quasi-program does not appear clear to him.

Finally, this book will not by itself make the reader into an expert programmer, and it is not intended that it should. The best teachers are practice and experience of programming. The first aim should be to get the 'feel' of computer programming, and to develop as normal mental equipment a common way of thinking about genetic systems and computer models. Once this has been achieved, real expertise will begin to come as the reader leaves the limited field of genetic systems exemplified here and begins confidently to write his own programs for his own problems, working out his own techniques and learning from and profiting by his own mistakes.

CHAPTER 2

The Basic Ideas of Genetic Simulation

There are two quite different ways of making abstract models of genetic systems. One of these, which we may call the algebraic method, has developed quite naturally from the classical mathematical approach to population genetics. This book deals mainly with the other which in its purest form avoids mathematics, creating instead individual model organisms and inducing them to behave in a way analogous to the behaviour of real organisms. Arrays of such organisms form the model populations.

This method is, for most biologists, the simplest to understand and apply and has many real advantages, but an account will first be given of the algebraic method so that the essential differences between the two may be appreciated.

The Mathematical Approach to the Study of Evolution

If we accept the view that, fundamentally, evolution is a change in gene frequency, then it is natural to suppose that since we ought to be able to express such change mathematically and establish mathematical relationships between the causes of change and the rate of change, then we ought to be able to represent evolutionary systems in mathematical terms.

The first application of mathematics to genetics seems to have been made by Maupertuis in the middle of the 18th century (Glass, 1947). The next of any significance was by Francis Galton in the second half of the 19th century. Important though his work was, it certainly helped to sow confusion during the early days of genetics. In its early development, genetics suffered because many of its important facts were discovered in the wrong order. The bitter controversy in the early part of this century between the biometricians (led by Pearson and Weldon) and the mendelians (led by Bateson), culminating at the famous meeting of the British Association in 1904, was largely due to a failure by both sides to appreciate that the differences between continuous (biometrical) and discontinuous (mendelian) variation were differences not of kind but of degree (though Galton himself appreciated this, his followers do not appear to have done so). The controversy became very much involved with ideas about the mechanism of evolution, and evolution theory remained for some time in a state of confusion.

Clarification came in 1930 with the publication of R. A. Fisher's *The Genetical Theory of Natural Selection*. The subsequent mathematical studies of Fisher, Wright, Haldane, and others who came after them, led to the firm establishment of population genetics and to progress in evolution theory based on the development and interpretation of mathematical models.

The principles involved in the construction of mathematical models of evolutionary systems are fairly simple. Their construction and interpretation may not be.

The basic idea is that the genetical properties of a population (or that part of the genetical properties in which we are for the time being interested) can be described in terms of the relevant variables (e.g. gene frequencies) and parameters (e.g. selection pressures), and that the relationship of these may be defined by algebraic expressions in such a way that the course of any change to be expected in the genetical constitution of the population may be calculated. Putting this another way, if for example the relevant variables in the population are $p\ q\ r\ s$ and we know these values in one generation and the way in which they interact with one another and are affected by the parameters, then in principle we can construct algebraic expressions which will allow the calculation of the values $p_1\ q_1\ r_1\ s_1$ to be expected in the next generation. These algebraic expressions are the model of the system.

We may consider a simple example. Imagine a randomly breeding population; we are interested in one gene with two alleles, **A** and **a**, occurring in three genotypes **AA**, **Aa** and **aa**. We will suppose that these three genotypes have equal survival values, that **AA** and **Aa** are equally fertile, but that **aa** individuals have only half the fertility of the others, the reduction in fertility being the same on male and female sides. We may construct either of two models (which would be equivalent) according to whether the variables we are primarily interested in are the genotype frequencies or the gene frequencies.

In the former case, if the frequencies of **AA Aa** and **aa** in any one generation are $r\ s$ and t, respectively $(r+s+t = 1)$, and those in the next are $r_1\ s_1$ and t_1, it can easily be shown that $s_1 = 2(2-2t-s)(s+t)/(2-t)^2$ and $t_1 = (s+t)^2/(2-t)^2$. These two equations are sufficient to provide a model of the system, since $r_1 = 1-s_1-t_1$ and therefore does not require a separate equation. (Any of the three variables could have been treated in this way but we are usually more interested in the genotypes containing the disadvantageous allele, and may not wish to consider r and r_1 at all; for this reason, r has been eliminated by substitution from the two equations which constitute the model.)

By substituting the determined values of s_1 and t_1 for those of s and t in the equations, the values of s_2 and t_2 (and r_2 if required) may now be calculated for the next generation, and so on iteratively for as many generations as desired.

If our primary interest is in gene frequencies, we may use a much simpler model. If the frequency of **a** in our specified population in one generation is q, then in the next generation its frequency $q_1 = (2q-q^2)/(2-q^2)$, and that equation is the population model. If at any time we require the genotype frequencies, then since the population is assumed to be randomly breeding these can be obtained by application of the Hardy–Weinberg rule that the frequencies of **AA**, **Aa** and **aa** are $(1-q)^2$, $2q(1-q)$ and q^2, respectively.

This exemplifies in a very simple way the basic idea of the mathematical approach to population genetics, on which the development of modern evolution theory has very largely depended. But valuable though this approach has been, it has severe limitations.

The algebra of the example we have dealt with was quite simple, though some readers who have left most of their algebra behind at school may have felt a little uneasy about it. The situation itself was an extremely simple one, involving only one stated parameter (the relative fertility of **aa**) and one independent variable (the frequency of one allele; the genotype frequencies are not independent of this when the breeding system is stated and fixed).

Obviously, the interesting evolutionary systems are less simple than this. More genes may be involved, and there may be more than two alleles at a locus. The genes may not segregate independently; in their determination of the phenotype and its viability of fertility they may interact with one another. Selection pressures may be variable, dependently or independently of the genotype frequencies within the population or of its 'average genotype'. The breeding system may vary, again dependently or independently of the genotype frequencies. It is evident that even a moderate increase in complexity in the systems we are studying will require a considerable increase in mathematical complexity, and it is fair to use a mathematical analogy and say that the complexity of the mathematical techniques required increases exponentially rather than linearly with biological complexity.

There are several consequences of this. Most evolutionary systems, unless they are dealt with in a very over-simplified manner, are outside the reach of sensible mathematical treatment because, like most biological systems, they are very complex, much more so for example than non-living physical or chemical systems. Even those to which mathematics can be applied will require some degree of simplification and approximation, for biological operations will not always correspond precisely to mathematical ones, and the mathematics itself will require simplifications and approximations if it is to remain manageable. Mathematics quickly tends to become the master, because it is the way in which the mathematics has to be treated that determines the mathematical interpretation of the biology. There is always danger that approximations, even apparently reasonable ones, may lead to biological nonsense unless there is at the same time a clear understanding both of the mathematics and the biology, an uncommon combination in one individual.

But even when the mathematical model provides a reasonable and sensible analogy of the system, one difficulty remains. Most biologists have only an elementary knowledge of mathematics, and cannot really understand even the moderately sophisticated interpretations by biomathematicians of evolutionary systems. Much of the work of Fisher, Wright and Haldane is incomprehensible to the average biologist, even to many of those interested in the processes of evolution. It is doubtful whether the majority of those who read mathematically-oriented papers on population genetics to gatherings of geneticists realize that many of their audience will have little understanding of what is said, and that few will understand it thoroughly. One of the difficulties is unfamiliarity with mathematical techniques; another, perhaps more serious, is lack of knowledge of the language of mathematics and of the meaning of its symbols. Quite often, a mathematical expression on the page of a book is saying something which would be easily comprehensible if expressed at length in plain English, but is meaningless or interpreted only with difficulty by a reader unfamiliar with mathematical symbols. It is possible that some readers of this book may not easily be able off-hand to explain the meaning of one of the simplest mathematical expressions of an evolutionary process, $\Sigma(\alpha dp) = \Sigma(pqa\alpha)\, dt = W dt$, which is the fundamental theorem of natural selection as it appears in the first edition of *The Genetical Theory of Natural Selection* (Fisher, 1930). (Fortunately, this should prove no disadvantage in dealing with the rest of the present book.)

The consequence of this is that most biologists are often in no position to be able to judge for themselves the validity of mathematical representations of evolutionary systems in which they are interested, which is a situation that would hardly be tolerated in any other branch of biology. The situation is made worse when, as sometimes happens, it is the mathematical techniques which are of primary interest to the biomathematician, who may use the biological system mainly as a vehicle for the exercise of mathematical expertise, and take liberties with the biology (not always consciously) which cannot easily be recognized by those at a lower mathematical level.

Even among the biomathematicians themselves there is not always agreement about the validity of mathematical interpretations, and it is not surprising that there has been much argument in the history of population genetics, of which the best known, longest (it has outlived Fisher and still continues) and most vehement was that between Fisher and Wright on the evolutionary importance of random fluctuations. Sometimes, arguments have forgotten the biology and been about the mathematics. An example was that between Wright, Fisher and Moran involving a problem concerned with the breeding system of *Oenothera organensis*, which hardly entered into the later stages of the argument; the problem in fact was solved quite easily by using a non-mathematical model (Crosby, 1966) of the kind on which this book is concentrated.

Valuable though the application of mathematics has been in the development of the theories and ideas of population genetics, it has also undoubtedly had some bad effects. It has not only meant that many biologists interested in evolution have been unable fully to follow and understand the development of population genetics and have as a consequence tended to ignore something which is an essential foundation for the real understanding of evolutionary processes. It has also meant that many biology students, already made somewhat unhappy by mathematics at the level of mendelian genetics and recombination theory, have been thoroughly scared away from genetics on meeting the mathematics of biometry and its application to population genetics.

The operation of mathematical models of the kind we have been talking about is an iterative process, since it involves a series of calculations of the genetical situation at one particular time from that at an appropriate preceding time—the time interval commonly (but not necessarily) being a generation. With the use of orthodox calculating machines this can be a lengthy and laborious operation, very liable to arithmetic error. By the use of electronic computation, time and labour can be enormously reduced and the operation becomes a simple and fast one practically free from errors of calculation. The electronic computer, used primarily as a very fast calculating machine, is obviously a valuable tool in the operation of algebraic models of evolution. The labour of iteration has in the past called for the development of mathematical methods of proceeding directly from generation t to generation $t+n$, without the need for iterative calculation of the intervening generations. This requires considerable knowledge of mathematical techniques both to carry it out and to follow the way in which it has been carried out by others. Again, there is the difficulty for most biologists of assessing the validity of the mathematical methods. The use of an electronic computer can avoid these difficulties because usually there will no longer be any point in evading the generation by generation calculation.

On the other hand, the fact that the use of electronic computation so greatly reduces the time and labour of the calculations allows the development of much more complex mathematical models which are even further from the comprehension of the average biologist.

Deterministic and Stochastic Models

There is one important aspect arising from a consideration of algebraic simulation which is of relevance to the whole field of simulation and which we have not so far considered. In the simple example of a mathematical model, it was shown how from the genotype frequencies $r\ s\ t$ in one generation we could calculate those of the next, $r_1\ s_1\ t_1$. There are few things in biology which we can predict with certainty; but we can be almost certain that in a real population corresponding to the simulated one the actual values for the genotype frequencies in that next generation would not agree precisely with the calculated values $r_1\ s_1\ t_1$. It hardly requires even an elementary knowledge of statistics to apply the well-worn penny-tossing analogy to this situation. Tossing a penny up n times will more often than not fail to produce the expected ratio of $n/2$ heads:$n/2$ tails; the higher the value of n the less likely is the expected result, although if a number of such series of tosses is carried out the results will cluster around the expected value in a way which in general terms is predictable. This is because penny-tossing, as we are considering it, is a random process and no random process can be specifically predictable in terms of an individual event.

Returning to the model which has been taken as an example, the change in genotype frequencies from one generation to another is the result of a number of processes most of which have basically a random element for which penny-tossing or some similar random process may provide a good analogy. Reproduction which produces the new individuals of the next generation begins with the formation of male and female gametes, some of which will be **A** and the others **a** in a ratio which we can attempt to predict. We will begin by simply considering gamete formation in terms of the products of meiosis, taking the sperm first. **AA** individuals will produce only **A** sperm, **aa** only **a** sperm, and **Aa** will produce from each meiosis equal numbers of **A** and **a**. Knowing the proportions of the parental genotypes in the population and assuming that the individuals are hermaphrodite or that the proportions are the same for the two sexes, and assuming that **aa** individuals are only half as fertile as the others, we can calculate the expected ratio of **A** to **a** among the sperm as $(2r+s)$ **A**:$(s+t)$ **a**. But in an actual situation, even if no other factors interfered, chance would ensure that the realized fertilities (evaluated in terms of gamete output) of **AA** or **Aa** individuals would not all be exactly the same, and that **aa** individuals at about half the fertility level would also show variability. So although the proportions of **A** and **a** among the sperm of the whole population would approximate to the predicted ratio, they would rarely be identical with it.

On the female side there is another source of random variability. In most animals and in flowering plants only one of the four products of a meiosis leads to the formation of an egg, so that in the heterozygote the allele carried in any egg is in effect the result of a random selection from $2\mathbf{A}+2\mathbf{a}$ and quite independent of the allele in any other egg. Accordingly, the **A**:**a** ratio among eggs produced by **Aa** will be variable, though approximating to equality.

The effect of chance continues beyond the output of gametes. The individuals produced for the next generation develop from n zygotes resulting from n fertilizations, involving n sperm and n eggs. If the breeding system is at random (as specified in the example model), then although we can easily state the expected frequencies of the different kinds of matings (r^2 **AA** × **AA**, $2st$**Aa** × **aa** or its reciprocal, etc.), chance will again ensure that the expected frequencies are rarely achieved, that some individuals will mate more frequently than others and some perhaps not at all, and that the zygote outputs of the different matings will tend to vary from those expected on the basis of parental fertility. Further, in any mating the effective gametes (that is, those which actually produce a zygote) will usually be only a random sample from the whole production of the parents (a very small sample in the case of sperm), and for a heterozygous parent the gametic ratio in the effective gametes will therefore usually not be the same as the ratio produced in gametogenesis.

In effect, each zygote produced results from the fertilization of a female gamete chosen at random from the whole array of generated female gametes, by a male gamete similarly chosen, chance operating at various stages between meiosis and fertilization.

Bearing all this in mind, we could hardly expect these zygotes to appear precisely in the 'expected' genotype ratios. Even with breeding systems which are not random, there will always be enough randomness somewhere in the reproductive process to ensure that precise conformity with prediction will be the exception rather than the rule.

Not all the zygotes produced in a real population normally survive to maturity. In our example we initially postulated equal survival value for all genotypes, that is there was no differential selection at the development and survival levels. In practice, the survivors would be a random sample—often a very small sample—from the zygotes produced, and the genotype ratios of the mature individuals in the population would rarely be identical with those of the zygotes; they would be even less likely to coincide with the ratio of $r_1:s_1:t_1$ calculated from the preceding generation by using the equations of the model. The same argument would apply where selection at the level of development and survival was involved—many zygotes would be eliminated by chance rather than by selection.

If we proceed to a further generation, the actual genotype frequencies for that are less likely still to conform to the originally expected $r_2\ s_2\ t_2$, since these would have been calculated from the hypothetical values r_1 s_1 t_1 and not from the values which actually occurred.

The use of algebraic simulation in the way which has been described cannot therefore provide an entirely realistic representation of evolutionary change, and may sometimes be quite unrealistic. Models of that kind are deterministic. Calculation of the course of evolutionary change from the generating equation or equations which form the algebraic model of a system will indicate one route leading to one endpoint; there will be one answer to the evolutionary problem which the model is designed to solve.

But biological systems are not like that. Their processes are not deterministic but stochastic, and their realistic simulation requires stochastic rather than deterministic models.

A stochastic process is one which is subject to the effects of chance variation, and about which therefore we can make no accurate prediction from one stage to the next. While we may be able to calculate from the state of the system at any one time an expected state at some future time, the actual state reached will almost certainly differ from the expected one. The probability of any expected state occurring at the relevant time may, in principle, be calculated. What we can never say is which of the many possible states will in fact occur. Further, just as we cannot with certainly predict forwards in a stochastic system, so we cannot work backwards and deduce precisely the earlier states of the system from its present state.

Evolutionary systems provide a perfect example of stochastic processes; there is not just one answer to a particular evolutionary question, but many answers all equally correct in one sense, though not all equally likely to be achieved in practice. These answers may be very similar to one another, clustered closely around what we may perhaps refer to as the 'ideal' answer; or there may be considerable differences between them such that we cannot obtain a single generalized solution to the problem under consideration. A stochastic process may reach many possible endpoints by many possible routes, and even an improbable endpoint may be a possible one. It could be a biologically significant one too. There has been ample time since life began for the improbable to have happened very often.

The usefulness of any general prediction about a stochastic process will depend on the properties and behaviour of the system, which will determine both the extent and consequences of divergence from the predicted route, and how far the likely divergences will be of any significance to us. We may sometimes be able to make useful predictions for long distances ahead, while at others predictions over quite short intervals of time may be valueless.

Some evolutionary systems have negative feedback characteristics; that is to say, a deviation from the predicted path may produce a change in the evolutionary pressures which tends to push the population back towards the predicted path, the only significant effect of the deviation being possible loss or gain of time. In a somewhat similar category would be the situation where the population did not tend to move back onto the previous path but kept moving along a new path (no more permanent than the other) in a direction different from the previous one but converging towards the general area of the predicted endpoint. The difference is only one of degree; whatever the divergence from expectation at any point, or however much time is lost or gained, so long as the population parameters remain unchanged the evolutionary behaviour of the population should bring it eventually to the neighbourhood of some predictable endpoint, a point of equilibrium about which the genetic constitution of the population may fluctuate (unless genetic fixation is reached) but near which it will remain. (There are exceptions to this, such as 'endpoints' which involve cyclical changes in genetic constitution, but they do not affect the argument.)

In a situation of this kind, deterministic models can certainly make useful contributions, in that they can provide a general picture of the course of evolutionary change and predict the equilibrium state to which the population will eventually approximate. Their usefulness has been successfully exploited many times. But how can we be quite sure, with any evolutionary system, that its properties really do conform to the pattern we have been discussing? The deterministic model merely reassures us by providing uncritical confirmation of our belief that they do. It might sometimes happen that a stochastic model would raise interesting doubts.

Even where the population will reach the neighbourhood of the predicted equilibrium, stochastic deviations in pathway or in rate of evolutionary change may be of significance, and a deterministic model would be inadequate. An interesting example of this, which is presented in more detail in Chapter 10, occurred in a system of natural populations which apparently had negative feedback characteristics as far as the predicted pathway and final equilibrium were concerned, but positive feedback characteristics for speed along that pathway; the faster it went, the faster still it went. Variation in genetic constitution between a large number of populations was thought to be due to different rates of evolutionary change resulting from random deviations from the calculated pathway; only a stochastic model could have provided an adequate simulation of that system and allowed the validity of the hypothesis to be tested.

A different kind of evolutionary system is one showing positive feedback characteristics such that deviations from a predicted pathway induce such changes in the genetic structure or the evolutionary pressures that the population diverges even further from deterministic prediction. Examples of this would include the evolution of polymorphic systems, and of that genetic discontinuity which is the fundamental process in speciation.

Systems of this kind are among the most interesting from the evolutionary point of view, and are quite out of the reach of investigation by the use of deterministic models. If algebraic models are to be used, they must be in a stochastic and not a deterministic form, and the problem arises of how to transform a deterministic algebraic model into a stochastic one. This is more difficult that it might seem to be at first glance.

Since the problem arises from random variability, which can be treated by statistical methods and expressed in statistical terms, it might be thought that a model which simply expressed its results in statistical terms would be adequate, but this is by no means true. The obvious way of expressing the results in this form would be to give the deterministic answer together with a statistical expression of the variability to be expected, in the same sort of way for example that we can express the result of a series of measurements as their mean together with its standard error. This may sometimes give us the information we need, but if the particular problem we are considering has broader evolutionary implications we will be faced with the task of interpreting the results and assimilating them into the broader situation. This will require a thorough understanding of the implications of the statistical results and will usually have to be a mental process, carried out theoretically without help from models and unverifiable by any kind of experiment. Another difficulty is that just as the deterministic algebraic model may be complex and its validity difficult to assess even with a relatively simple system, so the introduction of statistical treatment into the model will also involve considerable complexities and these will be even less amenable to critical assessment by the average biologist. Since even statisticians may disagree strongly about statistical procedures, how can the average biologist have confidence in the validity of algebraic models which contain a substantial element of statistical mathematics?

The best known of the early attempts to introduce random variability into deterministic models was the work of Wright (1931), who analysed the effects of random fluctuations on gene frequency in populations of finite size. He determined, for different population sizes, selection pressures and breeding systems, the chance of a population having a particular genetic constitution at a particular time; or, putting it another way, the expected frequencies of the different genetic constitutions to be expected in a large array of equivalent populations. From this work arose the valuable (but much disputed) concept of genetic drift, and Wright's results have been applied by himself and others to purely theoretical considerations of evolution in species split up into geographically distinct populations, to the evolution of genetic discontinuity and to some of the problems of speciation.

But genetically speaking the systems which Wright treated in this way were almost as simple as they could have been. More complex systems would hardly be within reach of this sort of statistical approach except through approximations and simplifications which would render them of very doubtful validity.

For systems with positive feedback characteristics, the application of statistical procedures to algebraic models is practically useless. From each possible outcome of one generation we would get a series of diverging possibilities for the next, and so on. It would not be practicable even if it were possible to produce an expression which would allow the calculation of the probabilities for all possible population constitutions even after only two generations. Even if it were, it would not necessarily give the information required. We are no longer interested in the 'likely' outcome (the deterministically calculated one); we want to see some examples of the sort of thing that may happen to the system.

The answer to all this (to the negative feedback situation as well as to the positive) is not the use of statistical procedures in the algebraic model, but the application of randomization operations to the result of each calculation of a stage in evolutionary progress. Instead of performing a single experiment with a basically deterministic model which will produce a single answer showing a 'likely' result with an estimate of the possible variability (which may or may not be immediately comprehensible), we will perform a series of experiments with a stochastic version of the model and will obtain a different answer each time it is operated. That is, the stochastic model will provide a sample of the many possible answers to the evolutionary question that is being asked.

The principle of this kind of stochastic transformation of a deterministic model is quite simple, though its application may not be. From the values of the variables of a population at one stage, say $p\ q\ r\ s$, we calculate their values $p_1\ q_1\ r_1\ s_1$ at the next stage from the appropriate generating equations which form the algebraic model. This is an ordinary deterministic calculation. However, the answer required is not $p_1\ q_1\ r_1\ s_1$ but some set of values $p'_1\ q'_1\ r'_1\ s'_1$ which could have been arrived at by chance when the expected answer was $p_1\ q_1\ r_1\ s_1$. Occasionally, of course, the two may be the same. The stochastic transformation, then, involves the random choice of a set of values $p'_1\ q'_1\ r'_1\ s'_1$ in such a way that the chance of choosing that set is equal to the statistically expected frequency of its occurrence when the expected values are $p_1\ q_1\ r_1\ s_1$. For the calculation of the next stage we use $p'_1\ q'_1\ r'_1\ s'_1$ and not $p_1\ q_1\ r_1\ s_1$.

We will not proceed in this chapter with an account of the technique of stochastic transformation, which is dealt with more appropriately in Chapter 10, but will simply point out that it is likely to be very time consuming. Whereas the deterministic operation of an algebraic model will often be practicable (even if tedious) with a desk calculating machine, stochastic transformation in that way would usually be quite impracticable and the use of electronic computation is essential. Even with electronic computation, the need for stochastic transformation removes one of the main advantages which algebraic models have—their speed of operation when used deterministically.

A more detailed account of algebraic models is given in Chapter 10. It is sufficient for the present to say, with the proviso that the algebra should be intelligible and ascertainably valid as a representation of the system under investigation, that stochastic algebraic computer models may provide very satisfactory simulations of evolutionary processes. They do not seem to have been used a great deal, and for that reason do not occupy a very large proportion of this book, but there may well be situations when it would be worth while considering whether there might not be some advantage in using them. For example, they would have an advantage for the simulation of large populations using a computer with limited storage capacity. In some cases, such as the difficult problem of linkage, they may provide the best simulation method.

Stochastic Models by Individual Genotype Simulation

A completely different way of making models of genetical and evolutionary systems avoids mathematical representation entirely. It is intrinsically stochastic from the beginning, so that the problem of stochastic transformation does not arise.

An individual organism is simulated by the representation in some suitable way of its genotype. This is a familiar enough procedure. **Aa** written on a blackboard during a lecture is a model of a heterozygous organism, though we may not think of it as one at the time. It would be more obviously a model if we wrote **Aa** on a card or a piece of paper, when we could regard that as the model and the letters as the genotype it carries. Visible models of one kind or another are familiar in their use in providing visual demonstrations of mendelian segregation—**Aa** may become two playing cards with backs of different colours, two differently coloured balls, or a block of wood with two differently coloured pegs inserted. A population is simulated by a number, small or large as desired, of simulated individuals.

Passage from one evolutionary stage to the next consists in using the model organisms in a way which simulates the essential elements of behaviour as parents (essential for our purpose, that is) and causes through the simulation of reproduction the formation of new model organisms of the next generation. This is a stochastic process because the appropriate random element is necessarily present at each stage where a choice of action is possible.

For example, consider a single gene and two organisms each heterozygous for it. Each heterozygote may be represented by two playing cards with differently coloured backs indicating the different alleles of the gene. We can then simulate reproduction satisfactorily by taking at random one card from each pair (segregation and gametogenesis) and bringing those cards together (fertilization) to form a new pair which represents a new individual whose genotype is indicated by the colours on the backs of those cards. It is easy enough to make the random choice; we can shuffle the two cards of each pair until we think we have lost count of which is which and then blindly take one of them; or we can toss a penny and take the appropriate predetermined action according to the result; or we could refer to a table of random numbers and take action according to whether for example the next number to be chosen was odd or even.

The random choice from **Aa** of either **A** or **a** is a sufficient simulation for our purpose of the process of meiosis in the heterozygote. The one essential element is that each meiosis produces two haploid nuclei containing **A** and two containing **a**, and that the gamete required from that individual for a single act of reproduction is derived from one nucleus taken at random from the products of a meiosis. The simulation provides a statistically rigorous and sufficiently precise analogy (there being no fundamental difference between choosing one from **A a** and one from **A A a a**). Gamete production by the other parent is performed in the same way, with a result which is entirely independent of that from the first parent.

In this case, fertilization is a non-random part of the reproductive process.

Repetition of this simulation of reproduction by the playing card model will produce a family; as a point of technique, because each parent is now going to be used several times, we would not remove the chosen card from the parent each time for fertilization, but would use a card of identical colour to represent the gamete. Subsequent simulations of gametogenesis from that parent will produce results quite independent of that from the first and from each other. It does not matter whether we produce all the gametes of one sex first and then those of the other, subsequently bringing them together at random, or whether we produce egg and sperm alternately and combine them as we go along. The variability we can expect in a series of such families will be the same in the two cases.

We can use n pairs of playing cards to provide a simulated population of n individuals, and reproduction of this population can be simulated by a series of single acts of reproduction for each of which two such pairs (individuals) are chosen at random to represent the parents (that is, if the breeding system is panmictic; otherwise with a randomness restricted by the specifications of the breeding system). Reproduction of a single offspring by the chosen parents is then performed as previously described by producing a gamete from each parent. In a population, of course, not all the individuals will be heterozygous (except in special cases), and the production of a gamete from a homozygous parent does not require simulation of segregation, since no real choice of allele is involved.

We can use this example to provide further illustration of the difference in basic principle between genotype simulation on one hand, and deterministic and stochastic algebraic simulation on the other.

Deterministic algebraic simulation would provide only one answer; if both parents are heterozygous **Aa** the gamete ratios of each are 1 **A**:1 **a**, and the resulting family will appear in the zygotic ratio produced by forming the product of the two gametic ratios. That is, (**A**+**a**)(**A**+**a**) gives 1 **AA**+2 **Aa**+1 **aa**, and for a family of size n the numbers of individuals of each genotype would be given by n(**AA**+2 **Aa**+**aa**)/4, or their frequencies in any size of family by (**AA**+2 **Aa**+**aa**)/4. This is the only possible answer; it would of course be the actual answer in the corresponding natural system in only a minority of cases; hardly ever in fact where the family size is large and never where n is not a multiple of 4.

This deterministic algebraic model could easily be transformed to a stochastic one by making, for a family of n individuals, n random choices from four genotypes **AA Aa Aa** and **aa**. This done, division by n of the numbers so obtained in each of the three different genotype classes would give the genotype frequencies. If the family were now to be treated as a population, these frequencies (and not the deterministically calculated 1/4 **AA**, 1/2 **Aa**, 1/4 **aa**) would form the basis for the calculation of the next generation. It is important to realise that although this stochastic transformation is apparently made (in this example) by random choice of individuals, the choice is in fact made from abstract genotypes occurring in frequencies determined by calculation and these are never treated as individuals participating in reproduction. The chosen genotypes are used only as the basis for the next frequency calculation.

This is in direct contrast to the genotype simulation method which uses no algebraic expressions (except for the random choice procedures which will be further referred to at the end of the chapter), involves the model organisms individually in reproduction, and during the simulation of reproduction takes no account of gene or genotype frequencies; indeed, generally speaking these are only calculated when the model system has frequency dependent variables, or when they are required for output showing the progress or result of an experiment.

The elements of reproduction which require algebraic simulation in the algebraic model, where they are only implicit, are performed explicitly in the genotype simulation model by operations involving the simulated organisms individually. Putting it another way, we can say that the operations corresponding to the mathematics and statistics of the algebraic model are performed by the genotype simulation model as intrinsic elements of its structure. A pair of *Drosophila* in a culture bottle can produce a family agreeing with statistical expectations without performing any mathematical or statistical calculations, or indeed without even knowing anything of mathematics or statistics. The analogy is not as remote as it might seem.

This is why we can say that the genotype simulation method is non-mathematical, that it indeed avoids mathematics. This means that we are no longer faced with doubts about the validity of mathematical and statistical procedures It will become clear that with the genotype simulation technique it is easy for the reader, with little mathematical knowledge, to see precisely how a model is constructed and how its structure relates to the biology of the system being simulated. Judgment of the biological validity of this kind of model is very much easier than with the algebraic model, since it depends primarily on an understanding of biology.

Electronic Computers and the Construction of Genetic Models

Electronic computers are very fast and accurate calculating machines, and the way in which they may be applied to the operation of algebraic simulation models is fairly obvious. It is less obvious how they may be applied to the genotype simulation technique.

In fact, electronic computers are very versatile and in addition to mere calculation can do many things, numerical and non-numerical. The exploitation of this versatility in the worlds of commerce and industry is well known. Computers are particularly well adapted to simulate the genotypes and genetical behaviour of organisms.

The basic operational unit of an electronic computer is known as the *word*, and words may be stored temporarily, for the duration of the program, or more or less permanently within the computer or its ancillary equipment. The words are also the basic operational units of genetic simulation. The form of the word within the computer, its size and the way in which it is stored vary from one computer to another, but we do not need to consider here more than the broad general principles. As it is stored and used within the computer, the word may be imagined to take the form of a linear series of points at each of which there may or may not be an electric pulse or one of two states of magnetization, depending on the method of storage. That is to say, at each point in the word there are two possible conditions, presence or non-presence of pulse or magnetization. This forms the simplest of all possible bases for a code for the retention or transmission of information. A familiar example which corresponds to a yes/no basis for a code is the dot/dash alternative of the morse code. Punched paper tape with its hole/no hole alternatives provides another example, and when read into a computer designed for this method of input its hole/no hole sequence is in fact directly converted into a yes/no sequence within the machine. The yes/no points in the word are referred to as *bits*, and a word may be conveniently treated as a string of bits. Word size varies from one computer to another. In the KDF9 it has 48 bits; in the Elliott 803 it has 39 bits; in some IBM machines the word size is variable and the word is made up of 'syllables' called bytes which each have eight bits. These variations need not concern us further at this stage.

If words are to be the basic units of genetic simulation, or if we are going to discuss any other kind of use for them, we must have some way of representing the word on paper. The basic conventional way of doing this is to represent each bit by **1** or **0**, according to whether it is in the yes or the no condition. A 32-bit word for example might be

00011010010101110001000010101100.

This could mean one of several things to a computer; how the computer interprets it and how it will deal with it will depend on the way in which it is instructed by a program.

The simplest interpretation of this coded information would be to treat it as an integral number on a binary scale. On such a scale, the only digits which may be used are **0** and **1**. In binary, one is **1**, two is **10**, three is **11**, four is **100** and eighty-seven is **1010111**.

In order to avoid confusion between binary and decimal scales, the type forms **0** and **1** will always be used for representation of binary numbers, and for bit representations of words whether these are to be interpreted numerically or not. Decimal numbers will always use the type forms 0 1 2 3, etc. (except where part of an instruction). Whenever there is any possible ambiguity, 10 and 11 will always be spelt out as ten and eleven. This obviates the need to clutter the text with symbols indicating the scale in use.

Interpreted numerically, the 32-bit binary word exemplified above is the same as the decimal number 441,913,516. The computer may properly subject this number to a variety of arithmetic operations (usually involving a second number)—addition, subtraction, multiplication and division.

Alternatively, the word may be interpreted simply as a pattern of bits with no numerical implications at all. These bits may be manipulated in various logically-defined ways, and the operations involved are referred to as logical operations to distinguish them from arithmetical operations. Logical operations may involve one word or two and include such things as transformation of the bit pattern, the extraction of sections of the word or deletion of parts of it, movements within the word of the whole bit pattern or of the remainder after partial deletion, and procedures which are analogous to arithmetical ones but operate under logical rules of their own. Such quasi-mathematical operations are quite simple to understand and use, and the reader should not allow himself to be put off when he finds that they are sometimes referred to as boolean operations because they involve procedures of boolean algebra. This term will not be used in this book and is only mentioned here because the reader may encounter it elsewhere.

Thirdly, the word may be interpreted as a coded instruction to the computer to perform a certain operation, and in meeting the word in the right context the computer will interpret it and obey the instruction. In one sense, this is a special use of the word as a bit pattern, but parts of the pattern may have numerical sense as well. The operational part of a computer program consists of one or more sequences of consecutive words of this kind, and the computer makes the program effective by proceeding sequentially through these words and obeying each in turn; it has the facility, under instruction, of leaving one sequence and entering another.

The computer can interpret and treat any kind of word in any kind of way, because it has no intelligence and is quite incapable by itself of recognizing differences in significance between words and in the uses to which the words are to be put. It will try to obey a number if it meets one at the end of a sequence of instructions, not having been told to stop or move to a new sequence; or it may try to do some arithmetic on an instruction if another instruction refers it to a wrong word. This sort of thing normally happens only as a programming error, but it is important to remember that the way in which a word is treated depends entirely (programming errors apart) on the way in which we decide it is to be treated, and not at all on how a computer thinks it should be.

In genetic simulation we will mainly be concerned with the use of words as bit patterns and their manipulation through logical operations. Sometimes the words will be no more than bit patterns with no special meaning or significance (for example, they may be random sequences of ones and zeros used in randomization processes). More often, a bit pattern will represent some individual or provide (in code form) a description of some property of it, or both.

The bit pattern may, again in coded form, supply information or act as a medium for the storage of information which may later be retrieved by some kind of logical operation (this sort of use has very important commercial applications). For instance, the exemplary 32-bit word on the preceding page was not produced by writing haphazardly a string of ones and zeros, but was designed to represent an item not without genetical interest. In fact, it is a coded form of a six-letter word, each letter being represented by five consecutive bits, the two most significant bits being unused (the mathematical expressions *most significant* and *least significant*, abbreviated to m.s. and l.s., will always be used throughout this book for the left-hand and right-hand ends respectively of a word, irrespective of whether the word represents a number or not). Each set of five consecutive bits is to be interpreted first as a binary number, and then as the letter occupying that position in the alphabet (for example, **10111** would be decoded as W). We may think of the word, and rewrite it, as **00 01101 00101 01110 00100 00101 01100**, whence the reader will find the interpretation to be a simple matter.

We will not always use the whole word, for quite often less bits may be required for a particular purpose than are available and so some bits in the word will be redundant; normally, they will be zeros. Where appropriate, a sequence of superfluous bits will be indicated by three full-stops, so that the whole word need not be written out in full. Thus **...011010** will represent a word of which we are only interested in the six bits at the l.s. end, and will mean that all bits to the left of those printed are either zeros, or if they are not zeros they are of no significance in the context, and do not for the time being require to be considered by the reader.

A. S. Fraser (1957) pointed out that the binary choice between **0** and **1** for any bit of a word provides an excellent analogy for the binary choice between **A** and **a**, for example, which takes place during meiosis and segregation in a heterozygote **Aa**.

Continuing to take a simplified view, and supposing that we are only considering genes with two alleles, it is not difficult to see how we may represent the genotype of an organism through the bits of a word by using **0** to represent one allele of a gene and **1** the other. In this book, where there is dominance, **0** will be used to represent the dominant allele and **1** to represent the recessive. This convention has not been followed by all workers in this field, and there are occasional situations when it would be more convenient to use **1** for the dominant, but the convention adopted here has an important advantage which has a logical basis. **0** is dominant to **1** arithmetically, since **0** $\times$ **1** $=$ **0**. This is also true of the logical analogue of multiplication, as will be shown in Chapter 4, so that if we logically multiply together the bits representing the genotype of a heterozygote **01** we obtain the answer **0**, which represents the phenotype in the same way that the phenotype of **Aa** is **A**. Since with logical multiplication **11** becomes **1** and **00** becomes **0**, the same conversion from genotype to phenotype holds for homozygotes as well, and we thus have a very convenient technique for this conversion.

It will not be clear to the reader here why ordinary arithmetical multiplication would not serve this purpose just as well; it would with a single gene locus involved, but as will be shown a little later it would not do so with more than one locus.

If we are considering only a single gene, then we can use a word to simulate a diploid organism by using two of its bits to represent the genotype. Any two bits may be chosen provided they are defined in the program; the choice will usually be dictated by programming considerations, convenience of manipulation being one and force of habit another. There is a great deal to be said for adopting conventions (personal or otherwise) in programming and using them consistently except where special circumstances indicate otherwise. Consistent use of conventions means less likelihood of error through temporary forgetfulness. It also eases error tracing and the revision of old half-remembered programs, since there will be less burden in remembering or working out from the program the details of procedures which were used; the conventional ones will be remembered automatically. The same is true of writing a book, and unless it is specifically stated otherwise the convention will be adopted here of using the l.s. bits of a word to represent the genotype of the individual which the word is simulating.

An individual **Aa** will thus be represented by the word **...01**. Just as we can simulate segregation by taking a random choice of **A** or **a** from **Aa**, so the computer can manipulate the appropriate bits in a random way to give a choice of **...0** or **...1**. How this is done will be described in Chapter 6.

We are not limited to one gene. An individual of genotype

AaBBcCDdEEffGg

may be simulated by the word **...01001001001101** and suitable (though obviously more complicated) randomized manipulation of the bits will simulate segregation. An alternative binary representation of the genotype might be **...00100101001011**, corresponding to an alternative alphabetic form **ABcDEfG/aBCdEfg**. This would be the arrangement we would use if we wished to indicate which alleles were contributed to the diploid genotype by one gamete and which by the other, the implication being that one set of consecutive alleles came in one gamete and the other set in the other. It also has several advantages from a computing point of view. For example, it is easy to transform the single word **...00100101001011** into two words **...0010010** and **...1001011**, corresponding of course to **ABcDEfG** and **aBCdEfg** respectively. In logical multiplication of these two words (which involves a single computer instruction), bits in equivalent positions (that is, the two bits representing alleles of the same gene) would be multiplied together, but there would be no operations between bits in different positions (as there would be in arithmetical multiplication). That is, the logical product of **...0010010** and **...1001011** is **0×1 0×0 1×0 0×1 0×0 1×1 0×1** which is **...0000010**, corresponding to **ABCDEfG**, the phenotype of our exemplary individual. It should now be clear why arithmetical multiplication will not serve.

One difficulty may have suggested itself. In the alphabetical representation of the genotype it was obvious to which gene each letter was referring. This is not true of the binary representation. In practice however the programmer will know because it will have been his decision and he will have made a note of it. The computer will 'know', because there will have been written into the program information and instructions which will ensure that any genotype bit will always be treated in a way appropriate to the gene which it represents.

For many purposes, it will not be necessary to consider genes with more than two alleles, but the technique can be extended to deal with cases where multiple allelism is involved by using more than one bit to represent an allele. Thus two consecutive bits would cover four possible alleles at a locus and three could represent eight different alleles. This is relevant, for example, to the simulation of multiple allele incompatibility systems in plants. A little thought will show that genotype/phenotype conversion can no longer be simply performed by logical multiplication when we are dealing with a multiple allele situation.

More detailed accounts of the procedures involved in the simulation of evolutionary systems based on individual genotype simulation will be given in later chapters. The purpose of the preceding pages has been to introduce the idea that electronic computers may be used to simulate individual organisms through the binary representations of their genotypes.

Some comment should be made on the speed of this technique. It is obviously a slow process as compared with deterministic algebraic simulation, because the reproduction of new organisms has to be treated individually and consecutively—an electronic population cannot reproduce simultaneously. This tends to limit the size of population which may be simulated, according to the speed of the computer in use and the amount of computer time available to the worker. To a lesser extent this also holds for those stochastic algebraic models where (as in most cases) stochastic transformation has to take place at the individual level.

If the system being simulated is a fairly simple one, there may not be a great deal of difference in speed between a genotype simulation model and a stochastic algebraic one. If the system is a complicated one, the stochastic algebraic model will certainly have an advantage in speed, because the complications are confined to the algebraic calculations which will have to be carried out only once for each generation, whereas in the genotype simulation method the complications will enter into each act of reproduction. But there is a limit to the degree of complication which can be dealt with in an algebraic model.

Another limit on population size in the genotype simulation method arises from the fact that the individuals of the population have to be stored, and so the larger the population the larger the store capacity required. Particularly with small computers this may impose a serious restriction on population size. The algebraic methods do not suffer from this disadvantage, since the individuals produced are simply counted and not stored.

The advantages of the genotype simulation method are that it can deal with systems much more complicated than can be dealt with in a valid and intelligible way algebraically, and it may often be a considerable advantage to have a model population composed of individuals which can be recognized and treated individually. This is certainly more realistic.

In any particular case, the programmer will have to decide for himself which technique is preferable, taking into account his aims in making the simulation model, its complexity, and the characteristics of the computer available to him, especially its speed and storage capacity.

The Simulation of Random Processes

One subject which has not yet been discussed is that of random choice. A more detailed account will appear in Chapter 13, but there are some general points which may appropriately be made here.

We have referred to random choice in a number of contexts. It is used in stochastic transformation in algebraic models and in all operations in genotype simulation models where variability can arise, such as the pairing for reproduction of individuals in a population, and genetic segregation during reproduction.

If we are using simple visual models there are several methods of randomization open to us—coin tossing, dice, packs of numbered cards and tables of random numbers. Coin tossing immediately suggests itself for simulation by computer, because like the bits of a computer word it presents us only with a binary choice. If a computer could be persuaded to produce random bits, then it could produce strings of ones and zeros which would be precisely analogous to sequences of heads and tails produced by tossing a coin at random.

Unfortunately, a computer cannot produce random bits, for the simple reason that every operation it performs on a given set of operands can have only one answer, and so is non-random.

There is electronic equipment which can translate random electronic events into random numbers. Such equipment can be incorporated on line into a computer, and can then be used by a program which requires random numbers. Unfortunately, there are two difficulties. One is that there would always be uncertainty about the reliability of the randomness while the random number generator was actually in use. The second is that very few computers actually have this facility available on line.

Instead, we resort to the use of pseudorandom numbers calculated by the computer. Obviously, no number calculated by a computer can be random, but generating equations have been developed which can be used for the calculation of huge sequences of numbers which may, with care, be treated as though they were random. In general, we may describe the process by saying that an efficient generating equation provides a method of calculating iteratively from an integer r_0 a succession of integers r_1 r_2 r_3... etc., all values of r lying within a range 0 to n and preferable (but not necessarily) including every integer within that range once and once only; the sequence in which the integers r_0 r_1 r_2... occur has no relevance to their numerical magnitude, and is assumed to form a good usually reliable substitute for a sequence of truly random numbers. The validity of this assumption is discussed in Chapter 13; computer simulation of genetic systems depends on it.

The integers r are called pseudorandom numbers and obviously are not truly random, not only because each occurs precisely once in a cycle but because after n numbers have been calculated and the cycle completed the sequence returns to r_0 and thence repeats itself with r_1 r_2 and so on. Provided we use a generating equation with a very large value for n, the latter difficulty need not trouble us. For example, the pseudorandom number procedure used by the author in his first simulation experiments had a value of n rather higher than 2×10^9, and there are generating equations with larger sequences. It would be a massive experiment that would require so many pseudorandom numbers as that and would complete the cycle and begin repeating the sequence. Indeed, the same generating equation may reasonably be used for many experiments, for these are very unlikely to use identical portions of the cycle. Before the beginning of each experimental run the worker using the program will choose at random an integer in the range 0 to n, and will write this integer into the program which will use it as r_0, the starting point for the sequence of pseudorandom numbers to be produced and used during that run of the program. Not only is the possibility of choosing the same starting value for r_0 on two different occasions quite negligible, but if n is high enough the chance of using on different occasions sequences which overlap even slightly is very small. If an experiment requires a hundred thousand pseudorandom numbers, then if $n = 2 \times 10^9$ there is only one chance in ten thousand of any overlap in pseudorandom number sequence between two experiments.

The fact that any value of r occurs once and once only during a cycle is not normally of importance, because only rarely will integers of the size generated be needed and actually used entire. Instead, sections of the generated numbers are used. We have so far regarded the generated pseudorandom numbers simply as numbers. Since they will be produced in binary form, we may equally well regard them as pseudorandom strings of bits; if the generated integer may be treated as random, then it would seem logical also to treat the bits of which it is composed as random (though there may sometimes be reservations about this which will be discussed in Chapter 13). By the same argument, we ought to be able to use groups of bits within the pseudorandom word as though they too were random numbers.

For example, suppose the pseudorandom number generated were

010110110010111010001011101101 01.

We would hardly ever require to use a number of this size, but we could quite often need one of a size which could be satisfied by considering, say, only six bits; these can be quite easily extracted from the word and used on their own. Thus the six m.s. bits from the foregoing pseudorandom string would give us the integer 22. If we generated many such pseudorandom numbers and extracted six bits each time, then if any bit can be **0** or **1** at random we would get a series of integers which could take any value from **000000** to **111111** at random, that is from 0 to 63 or, putting it another way, from 0 to (2^6-1). We can generalize this and say that for any string of v binary bits there are 2^v possible combinations of zeros or ones, and these will be all the binary numbers from v zeros (0) to v ones (2^v-1) inclusive.

Further, if the pseudorandom number generating procedure is a valid one, the 64 different 6-bit integers will not copy on a lesser scale the behaviour of the original full-length pseudorandom numbers by each occurring only once in a cycle of 64 calculations. Instead, in any sequence of 64 calculations some will occur not at all, some once, and some more than once, just as would be expected of truly random numbers; and the next sequence of 64 will be different, and so on.

A little thought will show that the easiest ranges in which to produce useful pseudorandom numbers are those which may be generalized as 0 to (2^v-1) where v is an integer, since the only operation required after the original calculation from the generating equation is the extraction of v consecutive bits from the result. The analogue of penny tossing is when $v = 1$, that is, the use of a single bit which may be **0** or **1** with equal probability. For this purpose a single pseudorandom number can provide us with as many binary choices as it has bits, since these can be extracted and used one at a time. Larger strings of bits can be used, for example, for making random choices of individuals from populations; thus if we wish to choose one individual at random from a population of size 256, we use an eight bit number which will lie in the range 0 to (2^8-1). It should be clear that there is an advantage, where this procedure is to be used, in having a population size which is an integral power of 2.

A more detailed discussion of the generation and validity of pseudorandom numbers will be given in Chapter 13. Except in that chapter, the prefix 'pseudo' will for simplicity henceforth be dropped and whenever the term 'random' is used it will mean 'pseudorandom'.

The use of random number techniques has a number of applications in computing, and they are often referred to collectively as 'Monte Carlo' methods.

Before we discuss any further the use of computers in simulating genetic and evolutionary systems, we need to consider the basic principles and procedures involved in the construction of models of such systems, and these are dealt with in the next chapter.

CHAPTER 3

Model Making and Programming

The simulation of a genetic system involves two quite distinct and largely independent stages, although the requirements of the second stage have to be borne in mind while carrying out the first.

The first stage involves the mental conception of a model of the population and of its behaviour, and the representation of this conception on paper. The second is the translation of this model into a computer program. To those unfamiliar with computers, it might appear that the second stage would be the more difficult. In fact, it is much the easier.

The production of an abstract model of a genetic system demands not only an accurate knowledge of the genetics of that system and its breeding behaviour. The model will be a series of analogies representing different properties and processes of the system, and we must be sure that these analogies have biological validity. We have to be clear what other relevant factors should be included in the model, and how they are to be applied. The information about a system which is to be incorporated into a model must be precise in the sense that sufficient detail must be given of every operation to be performed on the model. For example, if we are simulating a population which is 80 per cent outbreeding, the model must include precise instructions as to how both outbreeding and inbreeding are to be effected; if selection pressure is to be applied, we must decide precisely what form the selection is to take, at what stage (or stages) of the life cycle it is to act, and precisely how it is to be performed in the model.

The fundamental requirement of all is that the model should make biological sense (unless we deliberately choose to introduce nonsense), whether we are trying to simulate a real situation, or a purely abstract theoretical one.

The novice in genetic simulation will soon find himself faced with the realization that his knowledge or understanding of the system he is trying to simulate is less than he thought it was. The stringent discipline of the technique will compel him to consider his system more carefully and more thoughtfully. In constructing his model, he will gain a deeper understanding of the system he is interested in even before he begins to translate it into a computer program. This will be very good for him.

The first stage of genetic simulation may be illustrated by a simple example which will be considered in detail from the moment the idea arises.

The Conception of the Model

The idea is the investigation of the effect of the breeding system of a diploid organism on selection against a deleterious recessive—other things being equal, is it true that inbreeding tends to increase the intensity of selection?

We will decide in the first place that our model is to be as simple as possible, consistent with giving us the information we require and being biologically sensible.

The first thing to be considered is whether we shall try to relate the model to a real situation, or conduct a purely abstract experiment. As the idea is primarily of general relevance, it is probably better that the model should be conceived in general terms rather than with reference to a specific example; it also makes our job simpler.

We will consider one gene with two alleles, **A** and **a**, and we will take the simplest situation of complete dominance of **A** over **a**, with **a** at a selective disadvantage. We will assume that Mendel's first law applies.

Before we proceed any further and get down to details, we need to have a general idea of the broad structure of our model and the way we shall operate it in performing an experiment with it. In computing terms, we need to produce a flow diagram. Every computer program is based on a flow diagram even if this exists only in the programmer's head.

Our model is going to consist of a population of individuals, and the program will have to begin by establishing a starting population. The individuals are going to reproduce according to a specified breeding system, and be subject to selection which may be applied during the reproductive stage (as a lowered fertility) or during embryology and subsequent growth (via bility). The population will change as the new individuals replace the old, and we need to decide whether reproduction and replacement shall proceed simultaneously (more or less as in a human population or perennial plants, for example), or whether the population will complete its reproduction and then die and be replaced by its offspring (more or less as in annual plants). The latter is simpler to program, and we will take the simpler alternative as more suitable for the purposes of demonstration. At regular intervals (we will assume every generation, but it could be less frequently) we shall need to score the population, that is, determine the numbers of the various genotypes, and this may conveniently be done after reproduction and the application of selection, and before the new individuals replace the old.

We can produce a tentative and very broad flow diagram by writing down in a connected way the major steps involved in the reproduction of one generation, reserving for the time being a decision about the time of application of selection. This flow diagram is shown in Figure 1.

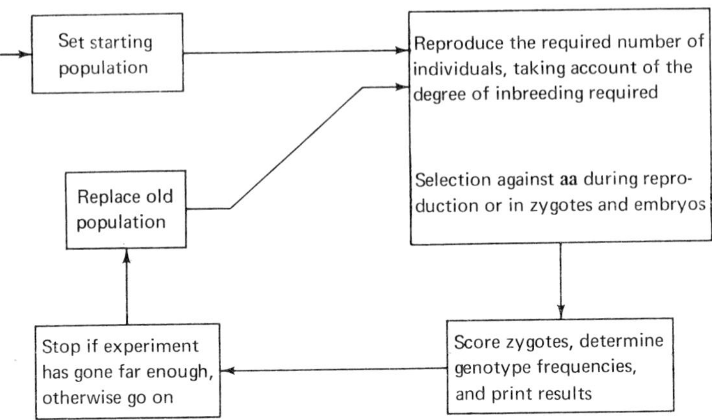

Figure 1. Flow diagram for the simple selection model, set out in broadest outline. It starts in the top left-hand corner. Many details of the program still have to be decided

General Plan of the Model

Having a sketch of the model in our minds, we can now begin to think in more detailed terms of how it is going to be realized. First of all, we need to decide on the population size, and this decision has to be made with the computer in mind. The relevant points here are the capacity of the store of the computer (which provides an absolute upper limit) and its speed. The significance of the latter is that we may have to make a compromise between what we consider to be the desirable size of the population and the amount of time we are prepared (or are allowed) to spend in running the program. Roughly speaking, there is a direct proportionality between the population size and the running time required per generation. An obvious further implication is that we have to take into account the number of generations for which we shall need to run the experiment; this may be difficult to estimate, for it will depend on the rate of genetic change shown by the experiment, and for the first run at any rate we may be able to do little more than make an intelligent guess.

The computer on which this program is to be run is yourself, the reader. You will probably have ample storage capacity, but you are very slow. The program is being designed as a demonstration for the purposes of this book, and we do not need to worry very much about the scientific adequacy of the results. A small population is therefore indicated, and it may run for as many generations as the reader feels he has time for (in these rather special circumstances, a decision which is normally the programmer's is left to the 'machine').

We ought, however, to keep electronic computers in mind, and here we have to consider the fact that, as pointed out at the end of Chapter 2, it is much simpler to produce a random number in the range from 0 to (2^v-1) inclusive where v is an integer, than in any other range. If any other range of random numbers were required, say 0 to b, then we would have to choose v so that b came between 2^v and $2^{(v-1)}$. Random numbers would be produced in the range 0 to (2^v-1); any larger than b would have to be discarded and the attempt to produce a number in the required range repeated. This would require extra time.

Any attempt to utilize every random number by scaling down and rounding will cause a departure from randomness, since all the relevant integers will not now appear with equal frequency, as the reader will discover if he takes a value for b of, say, 93 and scales down to the nearest integer all the integers from 0 to 127 by a factor 93/127. Also, little if any time would be saved; scaling would involve a multiplication which would add appreciably to the time taken in the calculation of each random number.

There will be occasions when we will have to use an inconvenient range for random numbers, and we should certainly then not bend the experiment for the sake of convenience; but where we have a choice which is not dictated by the experiment, simplicity and speed should decide.

Now if we wish to choose an individual at random (as we shall) from a population of n individuals, numbered from 0 to $(n-1)$ inclusive, we can do this by generating a random number in the range 0 to $(n-1)$ inclusive. This is obviously simpler if $n=2^v$, that is, if the population size is an integral power of 2. It also follows that it is simpler to keep the population size constant, since variation by powers of 2 would usually be biologically unrealistic though computationally simple; any other variation would add to the average time required to produce each random number.

Arbitrarily, we will fix the population size at 16.

Are we going to imagine our population to be composed of animals or of plants? Does it matter? In this particular case it does not matter very much, and we could well produce a good program applicable without change to either. In general, however, it is better to think in terms of one or the other, if for no other reason than that it reduces the risk of producing biological nonsense; this is particularly true when we have the breeding system as a special element in the model.

As the author is primarily a botanist, we will choose to simulate flowering plants, and this fits in well with our original decision that the population will complete its reproduction and then be replaced by its offspring. The plants will in fact be annuals, and we must recognize the further simplification which was implicit in the earlier decision, namely that all seeds will germinate in the year following their production; that is, there will be no dormancy beyond the first winter, and no generation overlap. We could (but will not in this case) treat this as a provisional assumption for the first runs of the model, and design that in such a way that it could easily be modified to produce a perennial situation.

It will be noted that by limiting dormancy of seeds we are already becoming unrealistic, but this is quite different from introducing nonsense, and so long as we remember what we have done in the interests of simplicity, no difficulties are likely to arise. In any event, it would be possible at a later stage to remove this restriction on dormancy in order to see if it did have any significant effect.

It is a good precept in this field of study that the first aim should be to get a program which works even if to some extent it may be unrealistic. Once a program is working, we can see what it is doing and check that its parts are behaving sensibly and as intended; it is then fairly easy to complicate it step by step while maintaining it in working condition. If we try to build up a complex program from the first, and it fails to make biological sense, it is much more difficult to see where and how the nonsense has originated. It might come from faulty biology or faulty programming, or both.

We now come to the question of reproduction. The first thing that may occur to us is that in a real situation many more seeds will be produced than will germinate and survive, and to a large extent this will usually be a matter of chance. But those that fail have no future and are of no interest to us—it would be a waste of time to produce them; we are only interested in, and apparently need only concern ourselves with, the 16 seeds which will germinate and grow to reproductive maturity to produce the following generation of our population of 16 plants (but this is a slight over-simplification as will be apparent shortly). Our method of simulating reproduction will be to consider each of these 16 seeds in turn. For each we retrospectively determine its parentage, simulate segregation and gametogenesis, and combine male and female gametes to produce a zygote and thus the genotype of the seed.

We next have to decide when selection is to be applied, and we have two alternatives. We could decide that **aa** plants have a lower fertility than **AA** or **Aa**, and arrange that they have a lower chance of being chosen as parents. Or we could decide that seeds with **aa** embryos have a lower chance of survival than those with **AA** or **Aa** embryos, applying a suitable test with a random basis on **aa** embryos and rejecting all those that fail it. The latter is somewhat simpler, because it only has to be applied once per relevant reproduction, whereas the former may have to be applied to either parent. The simpler choice would mean however that we might have to consider and produce the genotypes of rather more than 16 seeds per generation, depending on the number of viability failures, if we are always to have 16 seeds surviving to maintain the population size. With selection operating instead on fertility, we would need to produce only 16 seeds.

It would be possible to allow selection to operate on both fertility and viability and apply it at both stages, but for the purposes of this demonstration model we will choose the simplest, if perhaps the least realistic, procedure—selection immediately after seed formation.

We will decide that we would like to follow evolutionary change in the population by determining the numbers of the three genotypes at the end of each generation, and the obvious way of doing this is to score the genotypes of the viable seeds remaining after selection has been applied.

Finally, if we wish to pursue the experiment for a further generation, we will have to replace the old population by the new.

We can now revise the first flow diagram by rewriting it in more detail, and this has been done in Figure 2. There are still elements in it which are somewhat vague, but this does not matter. Indeed, one of the purposes of writing flow diagrams at this stage is that it helps to establish the broad

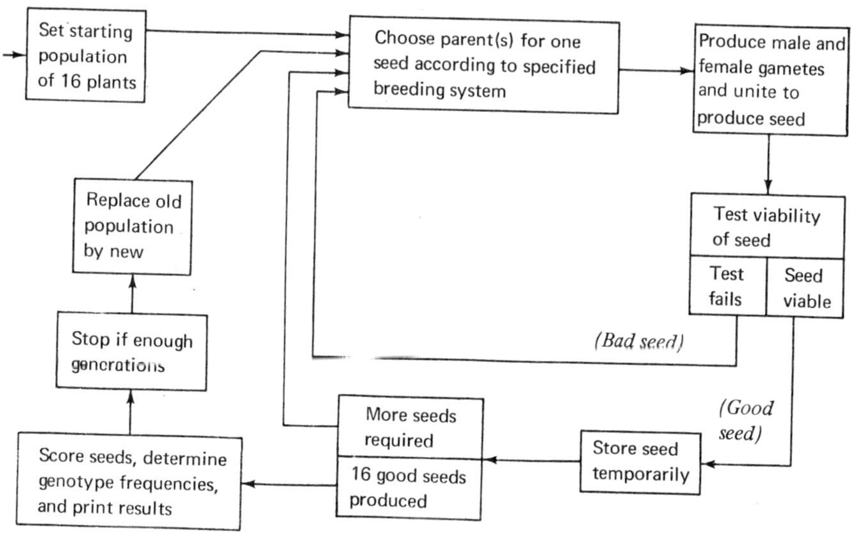

Figure 2. Flow diagram for the model program in greater detail. It has now been decided that selection shall take place after fertilization, at the seed or seedling stage

outlines which are fairly firmly determined and to focus attention on those parts where detailed decisions have yet to be made. It is preferable not to come down to details too early in the process of conceiving a simulation programme.

Detailed Construction of the Model

Having arrived at the flow diagram of Figure 2, we may now begin to think about it in more detail by considering how we are going to implement each of its sections.

Setting the Initial Population

Firstly, we have to consider the constitution of the population at the start. To some extent this may be arbitrary, and it is always worth writing the program so that it may be simply amended.

There is little point in this case in choosing a population constitution close to that which is expected to be the terminal one. As a beginning, and remembering that it can easily be altered for subsequent runs, we will begin with equal frequency of the alleles **A** and **a**. We now have to decide on the genetical structure of the population, that is on the proportion of individuals which are heterozygous. This should perhaps depend on the degree of inbreeding or outbreeding we are going to impose on the model, and which has not yet been decided. If we assume Hardy-Weinberg proportions of 1 **AA**:2 **Aa**:1 **aa**, this would conform with a high degree of outbreeding but would be inconsistent with a high degree of inbreeding if we choose that for the model; it might then be more realistic to begin with something like 7 **AA**:2 **Aa**:7 **aa**.

On the other hand, if our model were to be highly inbreeding but nevertheless started with Hardy-Weinberg proportions, we might expect it to show a rapid decline in the proportion of heterozygotes, and we could think of it as providing a demonstration (or confirmation) of this. This may add to the interest of the experiment, and since it is hoped that this book may interest as well as instruct, we will begin with a population consisting of 4 **AA**, 8 **Aa** and 4 **aa**. We may imagine these arranged in a row and numbered 0 to 15 (there is a computing advantage in numbering from 0 to 15 rather than 1 to 16, which is explained on p. 75).

Reproduction: Choice of Parents and the Breeding System

This brings us to reproduction and the breeding system, and these will be discussed together since implementation of the breeding system is to be effected through choice of parents, which is the initial operation in reproduction.

The object of the experiment is to see how selection varies with the degree of outbreeding, so we ought to design our program in such a way that we can do a series of runs with different degrees of outbreeding. It is a perfectly simple matter to produce a program which will amend itself to do this, and in practice that is what we would do. But in this chapter it would serve little useful purpose to introduce this refinement, and it would certainly make it rather less easy for the reader to follow. We will therefore write this program for one specified degree of outbreeding.

We have to decide how this is to be effected. The simplest method is to suppose that the plants are hermaphrodite, that inbreeding results from self-fertilization of a plant chosen at random from the population, and outbreeding from fertilization between two plants similarly chosen.

To make this demonstration model as simple as possible we will design it to simulate a population which tends more towards inbreeding than outbreeding and will suppose a degree of outbreeding which can be expressed as a fraction $1/p$, where p is an integer. This means that a fraction $1/p$ of the seeds produced will result from cross-fertilization at random, and a fraction $(p-1)/p$ from self-fertilization. Putting this another way, it means that for every p plants chosen at random to be seed parents, on average a second plant will have to be chosen to be pollen parent for one of them, while the other $p-1$ will be self-fertilized.

This can be implemented quite easily as follows. There are 16 plants in the population, imagined to be numbered from 0 to 15. A random number in the range 0 to 15 can therefore be used to choose one of them to be a seed parent. (During the production of the 16 seeds for each generation, some plants in the population will by chance be chosen as seed parents more than once and some not at all, which is what would be expected to happen in a natural population.) A random number in the range 0 to $(p-1)$ will be zero with an expected frequency of $1/p$, which is the frequency with which cross-fertilization is to occur; zero is a value that computers are designed to recognize readily. So, having chosen a seed parent at random, we produce a random number in the range 0 to $(p-1)$ and inspect it to see if it is zero. If it is zero, then we choose another plant for pollen parent by further production of a random number in the range 0 to 15; otherwise we take the originally chosen plant to be pollen parent as well as seed parent.

There is a point which needs to be considered here. If we choose a pollen parent entirely at random by producing a random number in the range 0 to 15, we might choose the first plant again (once in 16 times, of course), and this would be self-fertilization. This would mean that the actual degree of outbreeding would be less than intended. In a large population the difference would be negligible, and it would certainly be a waste of effort and computer time to introduce an elaboration into the program to avoid this contingency. At a population size of 16, the effect would be larger but still not very great, and hardly worth worrying about. In the special circumstances of a program to be performed by the reader of this book, it is better to remember that a nominal degree of outbreeding of $1/p$ represents an actual value of $15/16p$, than to risk confusing the reader by introducing an extra routine into the program. The reader may perhaps, eventually, care to consider how the appropriate amendment to the program could be made.

Since we need to produce a random number in the range 0 to $(p-1)$ inclusive, it is simplest to choose a degree of outbreeding such that p is an integral power of 2, for the same reasons as those which influenced our choice of population size. We will take a value of 1/4 for the degree of outbreeding.

In deciding to use for the degree of outbreeding a value of $1/p$, where p is an integral power of 2, we considerably restricted the values which could be used (0.5, 0.25, 0.125 etc.) and in particular seem to have left no possibility for the population to tend more towards outbreeding than inbreeding (except that a value for p of 1 would correspond to full outbreeding). The latter difficulty could easily have been dealt with by using $1/p$ as the degree of inbreeding and reversing the choice of action determined by zero or non-zero random number, selfing now after zero. We could ease the restriction on the values assignable for the degree of outbreeding (or inbreeding) by abandoning zero/non-zero as the determining criterion. Suppose for example that we wish to have about 35 per cent of outbreeding. This is approximately 11/32 (we must still keep the denominator at an integral power of 2), and the decision about self- or cross-fertilization is then made by producing random numbers in the range 0 to 31 — any value less than 11 indicating cross-fertilization, any of 11 or more indicating selfing. This would not take the reader any longer, but it would take more time on a computer.

Reproduction: Segregation, Gametogenesis and Fertilization

Having chosen two parents, or one if self-fertilization is to occur, we then have to produce two gametes by simulation of mendelian segregation. This is a simple enough process. Each parent will carry two alleles, which may be the same or different. Clearly, we do not need to simulate segregation if the parent is a homozygote, since only one kind of gamete could be produced. To take advantage of this involves prior recognition of the parental genotype and on a real computer it might be simpler (though not necessarily quicker) to simulate segregation even when the two alleles are alike. The reader, being more intelligent than a computer and well able to recognize **AA** or **aa** instantly, will prefer to short-circuit the segregation procedure in homozygotes, and the program will be written to suit him.

To produce a gamete from a heterozygote, segregation is simulated by making a random choice of one from the two alleles in the parental genotype.

If this genotype is written down as **Aa** or **aA** (the reader will soon find out that although these are of identical genetical significance and we usually write **Aa** for all heterozygotes, the computer will produce both forms, **Aa** and **aA**), then we can make a random choice by producing a random number in the range 0 to 1 (that is, producing 0 or 1 with equal probability) and choosing, say, the left-hand allele if we have produced a 0 and the right-hand allele if we have produced a 1.

A second gamete is produced in the same way, from the same or another parent as previously decided, and fertilization is simulated by combining the two alleles side by side, producing the seed. The subsequent fate of the seed is now decided by the next operation.

Selection

Turning to selection, we have already seen that there are basically two ways in which this could be applied. We have earlier decided that this should be in terms of the viability of the seed produced. We have now to decide on the intensity of selection which is to act against **aa**. **AA** and **Aa** seeds will have full and equal viability, in that they will all have the potentiality for germination and the attainment of maximum reproductive capacity. Their viability can be expressed as 1. For the viability of **aa** we will choose a value primarily on the basis of simplicity, as we did for the degree of outbreeding. Taking t to be an integer, we will suppose that a fraction $1/t$ of **aa** seeds will have the same ability to germinate and grow and the same potential reproductive capacity as **AA** or **Aa** seeds—that is, $1/t$ **aa** seeds will be just as 'fit' as **AA** or **Aa**. The remaining fraction of **aa** seeds, $(t-1)/t$, will either lack the ability to germinate or their seedlings will fail to grow sufficiently to reach reproductive maturity. Simply, the viability of **aa** genotypes will be $1/t$.

It will be necessary to distinguish **aa** seeds from **AA** and **Aa** as they are produced. **AA** and **Aa** seeds will go forward without further question. Each **aa** seed will be subjected to a viability test as soon as it has been produced; it will be rejected if it fails the test, and only those that are successful will be included among the 16 seeds that are going to produce the next generation. (This means that we are really considering a population which may vary slightly in excess of 16, but we confine our subsequent attention to the 16 plants capable of reproduction since the failures have no relevance to the evolutionary future of the population.)

The failure rate of **aa** seeds has to be $(t-1)/t$, and this is implemented by essentially the same procedure as was used for the breeding system. An **aa** seed having been produced and recognized, a random number is produced in the range 0 to $(t-1)$. If that number is not zero, the seed is rejected entirely; if zero it goes forward into the population for the next generation. The failure rate of **aa** seeds will thus be $(t-1)/t$ or, putting it another way, $1/t$ **aa** seeds will be successful.

By the usual argument, it is preferable that t should be an integral power of 2. As a purely arbitrary choice, we will take the viability of **aa** as 1/8.

Viabilities of more than 0.5, or values other than those expressible by the fraction $1/t$ where t is an integral power of 2, can be dealt with by amending the program in exactly the same way as suggested (in the small print section) for the breeding system.

The alternative way we could have treated selection would have been to assume that all seeds germinated to produce flowering plants, but that the reproductive capacity or fertility of **aa** plants was lower than that of **AA** or **Aa**, either because fewer flowers developed or because of bad pollen or ovules. If we express the reproductive capacity of **aa** as $1/t$, that of **AA** and **Aa** both being 1, we can then simulate selection by recognizing each **aa** plant every time we choose it as a parent and testing it by reference to a random number in the range 0 to $(t-1)$, using it as a parent only when the random number is zero, otherwise rejecting it and choosing another plant as a possible parent. From a programming point of view, this is exactly the same test applied at a different time.

In our example, the choice between viability and reproductive capacity as the vehicle for selection pressure has been made purely on the basis of simplicity, but it may often be dictated by the nature of the system which is being simulated or of the problem which is being theoretically investigated. Both can be combined, so that selection can be applied at both stages.

There are some consequential differences between the two methods. For instance, in populations in equivalent evolutionary states, those in which selection has been applied by way of reproductive capacity will contain a higher proportion of **aa** individuals since there is a delay in their elimination.

Temporary Storage of Seed, Scoring and Population Renewal

Each good seed immediately after it has been formed (and tested if necessary) is stored independently of the existing population, and we may imagine this storage to be in the form of a row, the seeds being numbered consecutively 0 to 15. Until the row has been filled, the program will go back and produce another seed. When the row is filled reproduction for that generation is complete, and we may then proceed to score the new generation of seeds, which can quite easily be done by counting the different genotypes.

A convenient form of output would be to give the numbers of **AA**, **Aa** (including **aA**) and **aa** individuals, and the corresponding number of **a** alleles; ordinarily we would probably prefer to give the result as frequencies rather than numbers, but with so small a population size numbers are at least as readily intelligible as frequencies would be and allow the calculation of the latter to be avoided.

After scoring and output, the next step is to decide whether the experiment has gone far enough, or whether another generation should be produced. The total number of generations may be determined beforehand and the computer simply counts, stopping when enough have been done. Or there may be no predetermination of the length of the experiment, a decision whether to stop or not being made perhaps on the basis of the evolutionary progress to date or possibly, in the case of the human computer, by factors external to the experiment such as boredom, meal-times, or matters relevant to his own genetical activities.

If the decision is to continue the experiment, then the final step in the generation cycle is the replacement of plants 0 to 15 by seeds 0 to 15 which 'germinate' and become the new population. Production of another generation can then begin.

The Final Flow Diagram

We are now in a position to draw up a final flow diagram which will be based on Figure 2 but will specify in greater detail the procedures by which the various operations are to be carried out. This flow diagram is shown in Figure 3. To distinguish between population and seed storage locations, the positions in the row of plants are referred to as **C0** to **C15**, and those in the row of seeds as **D0** to **D15**.

Writing the Program

The greater part of the work is now finished because the model has been conceived and constructed in detail, and the flow diagram of Figure 3 is sufficient specification of the model and of the procedures for carrying out this simulation experiment. But a computer cannot act on a flow diagram; it requires a program, and the final stage in the operation before execution is the translation of the flow diagram into a computer program.

The Reader as Computer

This program will be written in a 'language' which is basically an order code; that is, a series of short statements each of which indicates unambiguously that a certain operation is to be carried out. In the special case of this program which is designed specifically for this book, we will be using a computer (yourself) for which no suitable language exists. A simple language will therefore have to be designed before we can proceed further. We will offset this disadvantage by shamelessly taking advantage of the fact that you are more intelligent than a computer.

First, we must specify some simple equipment which will be part of you

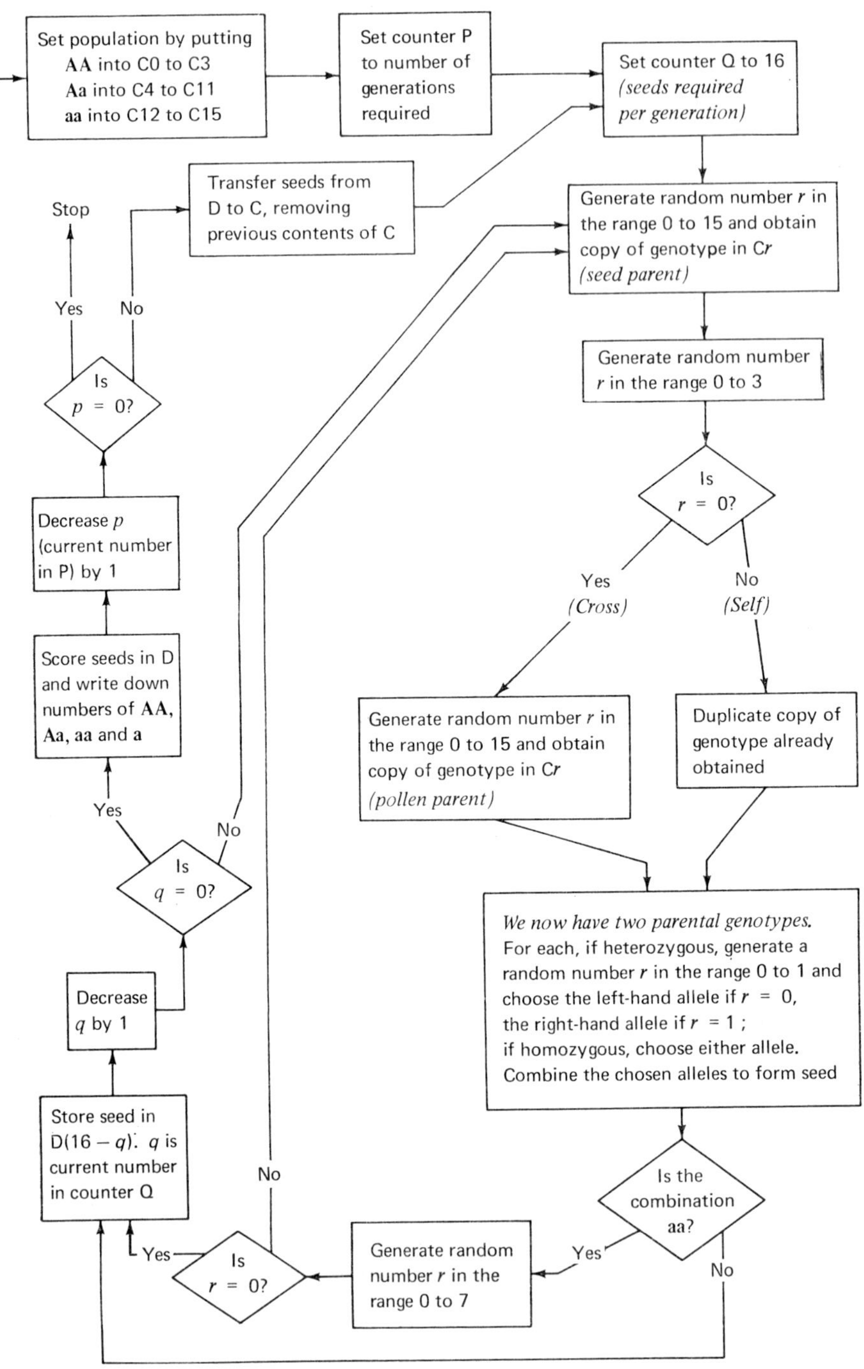

Figure 3. The final flow diagram for the selection model, given in detail. This now has to be translated into a program of written instructions

as a computer, and to which the order code will refer. The equipment is illustrated in Figure 4. You will need

1 A large sheet of paper or cardboard marked with two columns each of sixteen sections and labelled **C** and **D**, as in Figure 4.
2 Four small trays or saucers labelled **F, G, H** and **Q**.
3 Thirtytwo blank oblong cards slightly smaller than the sections of the columns, and four pairs of similar cards marked **AA, Aa, aA** or **aa** respectively for use as copies of parent genotypes.
4 Four boxes, labelled **RN1, RN2, RN3** and **RN4**. These boxes will contain blocks (or balls or cards or something equally suitable for making a

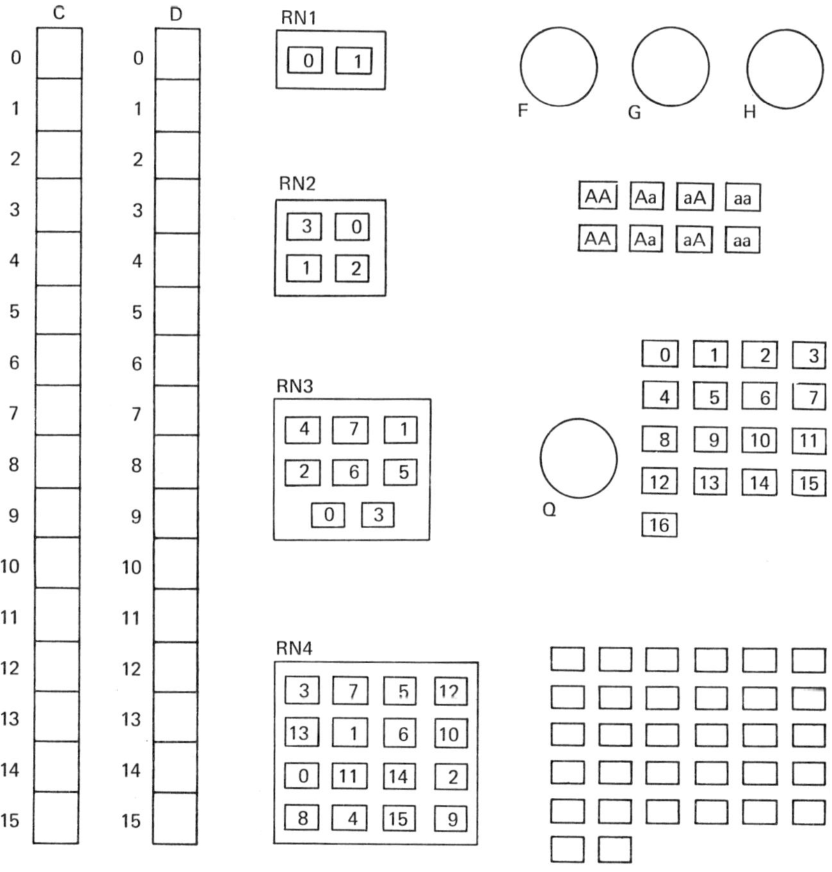

Figure 4. The equipment required to convert the reader into a human computer. See text

random choice) numbered respectively from 0 to 1, 0 to 3, 0 to 7 and 0 to 15, but otherwise identical.

5 Seventeen cards, numbered 0 to 16.

The Language

In the following exposition of the order code, **Xa** (or **Xb**) represents (and will appear in the written program as) **F**, **G**, **H** or any location in **C** or **D**. **Xb** will represent a different location from **Xa**. *j*, *m* and *n* similarly represent integers.

AA to Xa;	Write **AA** on a card and place this in **Xa** (similarly for **Aa** and **aa**).
from Xa to Xb;	Put a card bearing a copy of the contents of **Xa** into **Xb**, removing the previous contents of **Xb** but leaving **Xa** unaltered.
from LF to H;	Copy the allele on the left-hand side of the card in **F** on to a blank card and put this into **H**, removing any previous card in **H**.
from RF to H;	As above, but right-hand allele.
from LG add to H;	Copy the allele on the left-hand side of the card in **G** on to the right-hand side of the card already in **H**.
from RG add to H;	As above, but right-hand allele.
Q = *n*;	Stack numbered cards 0 to *n* sequentially, face upwards and with 0 at base, in pile **Q**; the top card at any time is referred to as **q**.
Q−1;	Remove the top card from pile **Q**.
J *j*;	Jump to instruction preceded by label (*j*).
J *j* **if ... ;**	Jump to instruction preceded by label (*j*) if the stated condition is true; otherwise, pass to next instruction in sequence.
RN*n*;	Choose at random a block from box **RN***n*, note its number (**r**) and return block to box; **r** always refers to the last number chosen, from whatever box; *n* = 1, 2, 3 or 4.
print AA;	Count the number of **AA** in column **D** and write this number down; (similarly for **Aa, aa** and **a—Aa** to include **aA**).

C($m-$**q**), or **D**($m-$**q**), means the position ($m-$**q**) in column **C**, or **D**, where m may be any integer and **q** is the number on the top card of **Q**.

Cr means the position in column **C** determined by the last chosen random number **r**; thus if **r** was 9, **Cr** would be interpreted by the computer as **C9**.

The Program

We can now translate the flow diagram into a program, but we will omit that part which counts the generations, leaving it entirely to the reader to decide when he stops. It may be noted here that the instruction **print AA;** takes advantage of the reader's intelligence in that he should be able to scan quickly through the cards in **D**, counting at the same time. A real computer program would have to be considerably more detailed.

To help the reader in following what the program is doing, comments have been added; these appear italicized in parenthesis and are not part of the program. The layout of the program is arranged entirely for convenience, and has no other significance; in particular, jump reference numbers appear only at the beginnings of lines. Instructions are to be obeyed sequentially as they would be read under the normal rules of reading a printed page, unless a jump is indicated.

The program now follows.

```
        Q = 4;
(1);    AA to C(4−q); Q−1; J1 if q ≠ 0; Q = 8;
(2);    Aa to C(12−q); Q−1; J2 if q ≠ 0; Q = 4;
(3);    aa to C(16−q); Q−1; J3 if q ≠ 0;
        (starting population is now set);
(4);    Q = 16;
(5);    RN4; from Cr to F; (F = seed parent); RN2;
        J6 if r = 0; from F to G; (parent duplicated in G to
        be pollen parent for selfing); J7;
(6);    RN4; from Cr to G; (G = pollen parent);
(7);    J8 if F is not Aa or aA; RN1; J8 if r = 0;
        from RF to H; J9;
(8);    from LF to H;
(9);    J10 if G is not Aa or aA; RN1; J10 if r = 0;
        from RG add to H; J11;
```

```
(10);  from LG add to H;
       (H now contains genotype of new seed);
(11);  J12 if card in H is not aa; (jump avoids viability test);
       RN3; J5 if r ≠ 0; (discard if test fails);
(12);  from H to D(16−q); Q−1; J5 if q ≠ 0; (repeat cycle
       if generation unfinished);
       print AA; print Aa; print aa; print a;
       J13 if another generation required; stop;
(13);  Q=16;
(14);  from D(16−q) to C(16−q); Q−1; J14 if q ≠ 0; J4;
       (seeds transferred from D to C for next generation);
```

Running the Program

When reading a book of this kind, sitting comfortably in a chair, the temptation simply to read rather than work at examples attacks even the best of us. It is particularly hoped that the reader has firmly resisted any such temptation in this case, and (if he has not already done so while studying the program) will now perform fully the operation which has been described above. Ease and efficiency in programming come only when the 'feel' of the process has been acquired, and if the author has been efficient in writing this chapter, the example will provide useful first steps towards this acquisition.

Amending the Breeding System

It was pointed out earlier that a program of this kind would often be written in such a way that it could amend itself to deal with different degrees of outbreeding. This would be done by supplying the program with a suitable parameter, and one of its first actions would be to execute a specially written routine which would amend the program in a manner appropriate to that parameter. The program which has been presented as an example has been kept less involved than that, but the reader could easily alter the program to allow other degrees of inbreeding. For complete outbreeding or complete inbreeding, the short sequence **RN2; J6 if r = 0;** would be eliminated anyway, and after **from Cr to F;** the program would either continue with **RN4; from Cr to G;** etc. for complete outbreeding, or with **from F to G; J8 if F not Aa or aA;** etc. for complete inbreeding (in either case the references **(6)** and **(7)** would be redundant). For a degree of outbreeding other than 1/4, one of the other random boxes could be used if suitable, or a new one made. If a value such as 11/32 for example were to be used, then a box would be required with 32 blocks numbered 0 to 31 and it would be referred to as **RN5**. The sequence **RN2; J6 if r = 0;** would be changed to **RN5; J6 if r<11;**

Some Fundamental Principles of Computer Programming

Simple though this exemplary program was, it illustrated some fundamental features of computer programming. Perhaps the most important of these is the ability of a computer to inspect the result of a calculation, or the state of the program, and on the basis of this inspection to make a decision on the future course of operations.

Decisions and Jumps

Our program showed two different applications of this ability. The first of these was in counting the number of times an operation was performed, repeating the operation until it had been performed the required number of times. It did this by setting a counter (the pile **Q**) to the desired number, decreasing this by one every time the operation was carried out, inspecting the counter to see if it was zero, and going back by means of a jump instruction to repeat the operation every time the counter was not zero. This kind of manoeuvre in a program is called a loop.

The second way in which a choice of a course of action was made was in choosing between two operations according to whether a particular number was zero or not. There were three examples of this—deciding on selfing or crossing, choosing an allele, and testing for viability or inviability. The first of these may be considered in detail.

After random choice of a seed parent which was placed in **F**, we had the sequence of instructions

RN2; J6 if r = 0; from F to G; J7;

(6); RN4; from Cr to G;

(7); J8 if F is not Aa or aA; etc.

If the random number produced by the first instruction **RN2** is zero, the computer jumps over two instructions to the one preceded by reference **(6)** and selects a second plant to be pollen parent, placing this in **G** and then proceeding sequentially to **(7)**. If the random number produced by the first instruction is not zero, then there is no immediate jump, a copy of the first chosen parent in **F** is made and placed in **G** to act as pollen parent as well; the program then jumps to **(7)**, avoiding the selection of a second plant. That is, according to whether the random number was zero or not, the program followed either the crossing sequence **RN2; J6 if r = 0; RN4; from Cr to G; J8 if F is not Aa or aA**; etc., or the selfing sequence **RN2; J6 if r = 0; from F to G; J8 if F is not Aa or aA**; etc.

A point of technique may be noted here. For outcrossing, one gamete each is selected from the genotypes in **F** and **G**. For selfing, we could have instructed the computer to select two gametes from the single genotype in **F**, but this would have involved having in the program two alternative versions of the reproduction routine. It was simpler to copy the genotype in **F** into **G**, and use the one reproduction routine for both cases.

Computers could operate perfectly well if zero versus non-zero were the only criterion of choice available, but this would often involve a little tortuous programming to ensure that the choice presented to the computer was between zero and non-zero.

In two sections of the program we cheated by assuming that the reader could recognize a genotype directly, during reproduction and in dealing with viability. For example, the latter case involved direct recognition of **aa**. In a computer, **aa** would be represented as a number and were only the zero/non-zero criterion available we would first have to subtract the number corresponding to **aa** from the number representing the genotype of the seed under consideration and then instead of the instruction to jump if not **aa** (to avoid the viability test) we would have had the instruction to jump if not zero.

But most computers have a variety of jump criteria which simplify programming and incidentally reduce the risk of mistakes by the programmer. These include not only such choices as zero/non-zero, positive/non-positive, negative/non-negative. We may for example have jumps according to whether two numbers (such as those representing seed genotype and **aa**) are equal, or according to some internal condition of the machine. A common example of the latter arises when we wish to test whether an arithmetic operation has led to the production of a number too large for the appropriate registers of the computer, a condition known as overflow.

It is the ability to choose between a course of action which has led to the fanciful analogy between a computer and a brain. But the choice of action is never really the computer's. It can only deal with a particular situation according to the precise instructions it has received from the programmer, and if he has failed adequately to consider all possibilities, then the computer may do something very silly indeed, as all experienced programmers well know.

Modification

A second important facility of a computer, which plays a large part in genetic simulation programs, is known as modification. This had a part in our example, but implicitly rather than explicitly.

In most computer programs there are operations which are performed many times. It would be hopelessly inefficient if the instructions for such operations had to be written out separately in the program for each time the operation was required. Instead, by suitable manipulation with jump instructions, often involving loops, the program may have only one set of instructions for the operation, and will run through these whenever it is required to perform the operation. But there is one problem which arises—the operation may be basically the same but will often involve the contents of different store locations (called *addresses* in computer programming terminology) each time it is used, but if the sequence of instructions is only written once, all instructions including those involving addresses will always appear the same to the computer.

This difficulty is overcome through the ability of the computer to modify its interpretation of an address in a special way. The instruction which contains the address to be modified remains permanently unchanged in the store of the computer. When it is to be obeyed, it is copied and the copy modified by the computer which adds to the address in the instruction some number contained in a special register, the *modifier*. The computer then obeys the modified copy of the instruction.

In the example program, we took advantage of your intelligence to take a short cut in this process. For instance, in making a random selection of a parent (a process repeated many times) you produced a random number **r**, and then extracted the plant from address **Cr**. A computer cannot do this quite so simply. It would first have to place the number **r** in a modifier which we can call **M**. When it comes to obey the instruction which is to be modified it would first add the contents of **M** to a base address specified in the instruction, in this case **C0**, and then obey the instruction in its modified form which would now have the address as **C(0+r)**, that is, **Cr**.

Inventing some new instructions, whose meaning should be clear enough, the section

RN4; from Cr to F;

would be rewritten as

RN4; r to M; from C0(M) to F;

The computer will then interpret **C0(M)** as the location in **C** equal to zero plus the number which happens at that time to be in **M**—that is, the address previously referred to as **Cr**. Since the number in **M** varies at random during successive performances of the routine, the address from which a plant is chosen will also vary at random, although the written form of the instruction does not alter.

Modification is particularly useful in operations involving loops, when we may wish to deal with consecutive addresses as we perform the repetitions of the loop. This is the typical use of modification.

The commonest situation is that in which each time we go round the loop we wish to refer to an address greater by one than the previous address. With some computers it is possible to use the counter directly as a modifier, and this is essentially what we did in our program. In setting up the starting population, for example, **AA** was put into locations written as **C(4−q)**, where **q** was the visible number in the counter pile **Q**. But we did this modification by subtraction, whereas a computer does it by addition. A simple amendment to the program would allow modification to take a more orthodox form. All that is necessary is to reverse the counting procedure, making the numbers in the counter pile negative; removing the top card from the pile is equivalent to adding one to the counter, instead of subtracting; modification then involves the addition of a negative number to the base address. If we let **(Q)** indicate modification by adding the visible number in **Q** to the base address, we can rewrite the beginning of the program as

Q = −4;
(1); AA to C4(Q); Q+1; J1 if q ≠ 0; etc.

As **q** changes from −4 to −1, the address to which an **AA** is sent changes from **C0** to **C3; q** then becomes zero and the program comes out of the loop.

As another example, the seed transfer section could be written as

(13); Q = −16;
(14); from D16(Q) to C16(Q); Q+1; J14 if q ≠ 0; etc.

Sometimes, we may require such modifications to be by steps other than one, and we may need to deal with modifier and counter separately. But even then, with some machines (e.g. KDF9) a single instruction may simultaneously alter the counter by one and amend the modifier by some other predetermined increment.

It is important to realize that it is the modifier which is changed regularly during the execution of a loop. The relevant instruction in the store of a computer remains unaltered.

An example of another way in which modification can be useful is in scoring the numbers of the different genotypes in a population, or in similar operations. In our program, at the scoring stage, the instruction **print AA** assumed that you could recognize and count the **AA** cards in a single operation. A real computer could do this, rather less simply, by running through the population, testing each plant to see if it was **AA**, and adding one to the count if it were. It would then have to repeat the process for **Aa**, **aA** and **aa**. A much neater method makes use of modification.

Suppose we have another section of store, **E**, and we decide to count the numbers of **AA**, **Aa**, **aA** and **aa** in locations **E0**, **E1**, **E2** and **E3** respectively.

(For the moment, the distinction between **Aa** and **aA** has programming importance, though it has no genetical significance.)

The genotypes will be represented in the computer as binary numbers of two digits, **0** standing for **A** and **1** for **a**. **AA** is therefore **00**, **Aa** is **01**, **aA** is **10** and **aa** is **11**, or in decimal notation 0, 1, 2 and 3 respectively. The method of scoring would simply be to run once through the population, using the genotype of each plant as it is inspected to modify the base address **E0** and adding one to the number in the modified address. The operation would start with all locations **E0** to **E3** at zero, and the number of **AA** would be counted in **E(0+0)**, of **Aa** in **E(0+1)**, of **aA** in **E(0+2)** and **aa** in **E(0+3)**. **Aa** and **aA** would be amalgamated by adding **E1** and **E2**.

Inventing still more new instructions, whose purpose should be clear, we can substitute the following for the line beginning **print AA**.

```
        Q = −4;
(15);   zero to E4(Q); Q+1; J15 if q ≠ 0; (E0 to E3 made zero);
        Q = −16;
(16);   from D16(Q) to M; add 1 to E0(M); Q+1; J16 if q ≠ 0;
```

and the program would then add **E1** to **E2** and print the contents of **E0**, **E2** and **E3**. **a** would be obtained by doubling **E3**, adding **E2** and printing the answer.

An even better method, which would save some time, would be to combine the scoring operation with the transfer of seeds from **D** to **C**, in the following way. All the original program from **print AA** onwards is deleted, and replaced by

```
        Q = −4;
(13);   zero to E4(Q); Q+1; J13 if q ≠ 0;
        Q = −16;
(14);   from D16(Q) to M; from M to C16(Q);
        add 1 to E0(M); Q+1; J14 if q ≠ 0;
```

followed by print-out and the decision to stop or go on.

Although this involves an unnecessary transfer in the final generation, this is outweighed by the saving of three instructions (**Q = −16**, **Q+1** and **J*j* if q ≠ 0**) per plant per generation.

In these particular examples, it would have been just as good to clear locations **E0** to **E3** by the sequence

```
zero to E0; zero to E1; zero to E2; zero to E3;
```

However, with more locations to be cleared, the use of a loop becomes more efficient in terms of program writing and space occupied by the program, though not in terms of running time. Here, the more generally applicable routine was preferred as an example.

The actual way in which the computer carries out modification, and the way in which it is indicated in the program, vary a great deal from one model of computer to another, but the basic principle remains the same. Modification is a process of great importance in the simulation of population genetics and evolutionary systems, and it is essential that it is clearly understood before we look more closely at the computing side of simulation procedures.

CHAPTER 4

Computers and Programming Languages

In the previous chapter a model was devised of a simple evolutionary system and translated into a program to be interpreted and put into effect by a human computer. This was used to introduce several important ideas which are involved in electronic computer programming. But electronic computers do not function quite like human computers, and before proceeding any further we must consider some aspects of the way in which electronic computers work and the languages which they can be made to understand.

Programming Languages

A more detailed account of the organization of computers is given later in this chapter. For the moment it is sufficient to say briefly and in general terms that a computer consists basically of a *store* which holds, permanently or otherwise and in a quasi-linear order, the words relevant to the program (instructions, numbers, information etc.), *registers* which hold words temporarily and which we may treat as though they were the site of the arithmetical and logical operations of the computer, and the *arithmetic and logical units* which carry out those operations. The elements of the store are also sometimes referred to as registers, but in order to avoid circumlocution and ambiguity the term 'register' will be taken to refer only to *accumulators*, *counters*, *modifiers* and special registers used as indicators. The location of a word in the store is referred to numerically by the *address* of that location, the addresses running consecutively from zero for the first word of the store.

In order that a computer may do something it must have some instructions which it can follow, and these instructions must, when stored in the computer, be absolutely unambiguous and in a form which the computer can translate into action. Each instruction will specify an action which has to be performed and, where appropriate, the location of the word or words (specified registers or store addresses) on which it is to be performed, whether modification is involved, and the location of the answer where there is any choice. In the case of a jump instruction it will specify the condition under which and the address of the instruction to which the jump is to be made.

Basically, there is a 1:1 relationship between instructions as a computer interprets them and those operations which are a built-in facility of the computer; these operations are usually referred to as *hardware* operations to distinguish them from *software* operations which involve a series of hardware operations and so require a series of instructions (a short routine) for their execution. For example, a number may be squared by a single hardware operation—multiplication—but the extraction of a square root is a software operation involving a series of instructions.

Since the instructions of the program in Chapter 3 were intended for a human computer, they were fairly easily and rapidly intelligible to the reader. In the form in which a computer requires them, instructions are not immediately intelligible to a human being since they are in a binary code, composed of the bits of the word holding the instruction (sometimes in machines with large enough words each word may hold two or even more consecutive instructions). We may consider an example from a specific computer, the Elliott 803, which has a 39-bit word holding two instructions, and only a single accumulator which is implicit and never specified.

The apparently meaningless string of bits

000101000010001000101000010000000110001

is interpreted by the computer as though it were in sections:

000 101 0000100010001 0 100 001 0000000110001

The central isolated bit has a special function as an indicator of whether modification is involved, but this is irrelevant for the present purpose. Each of the two groups of 3-, 3- and 13-bit sections provides the code for an instruction: the two smaller sections specify the action to be taken and the 13-bit section specifies the relevant store location. What this word means to the computer is 'subtract the contents of the word at store address 273 from the contents of the accumulator; if the contents of the accumulator are then negative jump to the first instruction in the word at address 49'.

Obviously, in writing the program, the programmer could not possibly be expected to write all the instructions in binary form, especially since he would in any case begin by thinking of the addresses in decimal. In fact, the word taken as an example is not as unintelligible even to a human being as it appears. If we replace each of its sections by its decimal equivalent and represent the central zero by a colon, the word becomes **05 273 : 41 49** (the 05 and 41 are octal and to be read as zero five and four one respectively, not as five and forty-one; 273 and 49 are decimal). This word is now in a language which is still readily intelligible to the computer (which can translate it into the required binary form by using a special program known as a *compiler*, supplied by the manufacturers of the computer) and to the programmer who will have learnt its limited octal vocabulary and simple grammar without too much difficulty. This basic programming language is often called by some name such as *machine code*, because it has a 1:1 relation between its instructions and the hardware operations of the computer, and can be directly translated on a 1:1 basis into the binary form required by the machine. What the programmer needs to learn is what the various hardware operations actually do, and what particular operation is referred to by any particular pair of 3-bit sections in an instruction. Thus 05 is the code for the operation 'subtract the contents of the specified location from the contents of the accumulator' and 41 is the code for the operation 'jump to the first instruction at the address specified if the contents of the accumulator interpreted as a number are negative'.

The order code of the Elliott 803 is not very large, and only a proportion of its instructions are used very frequently. These and their meanings are fairly easily memorized by use; the remainder one keeps on a readily accessible card and present little difficulty when they are needed for use in writing a program. Numerical codes of this kind do however have their disadvantages, apart from the fact that some effort is needed to remember them. A program written in a numerical code is not always immediately intelligible even to the experienced programmer when he tries to read it and interpret it, even with a crib by his side for the less familiar instructions. Further, numerical mistakes are fairly easy to make both in writing the program and in punching it onto paper tape or cards for input to the computer, not always readily noticed during checking, and sometimes hard to find even when it is known (because of program failure) that there is a mistake somewhere.

It would be much more satisfactory to have a language which is not simply a decimal (or octal) translation of the binary forms of the instructions. If letters and mathematical symbols could be used in the order code while still retaining a 1:1 relationship between coded instruction and hardware operation (which would of course require a more elaborate compiler for translation) it should be possible to produce coded forms of instructions which bear some obvious or easily remembered relationship to the operation which has to be performed by the computer. We might for example have a code in which the two Elliott 803 instructions already used as an example could be written **A−273:J49A<0**. There would be no difficulty in remembering that **A** referred to the accumulator, **J** meant 'jump' with 'to' and 'if' being understood, and the numbers were store addresses. Because they are more easily learnt and remembered, order codes or languages of this kind are called mnemonic codes; an excellent example is the KDF9 User Code. Such codes have greatly simplified machine order programming while retaining the 1:1 instruction: operation relationship. They have the advantage that their programs are not only easily written but are intelligible to read; indeed, rather like an ordinary language, translation from it may be easier than translating into it (the reverse tends to be true with numerical codes). With the KDF9 User Code an experienced programmer, when he has decided in detail what he wants the program to do, can write it almost as easily as if he were writing his own mother tongue, and can read it back at least as easily. This greatly reduces the possibility of fortuitous error (as distinct from a conceptual error in programming). When the elements of the code have an obvious meaning one is less likely to write down the wrong thing; for example, writing + for − is a less likely error than writing 04 instead of 05. The possibility of mistakes during punching is reduced because one is copying from something intelligible, and any which are made are more likely to be noticed because they will often produce obvious nonsense, for example if the code uses small words and one of these is accidentally misspelt during punching.

Once compilers have been produced to deal with mnemonic codes they may be developed to increase the versatility of such codes, to make them even easier to handle and reduce the risk of errors. As an example, we may consider jump instructions. In the Elliott 803, the jump instruction (both in the real order code and in our imaginary mnemonic form) is to a stated address. In the author's painful experience this was one of the most prolific sources of programming error with the 803, because revisions of the program (whether for improvement or correction) often involved change in the number of instructions involved with consequent changes in the addresses where instructions would eventually be stored. This would of course include addresses to which jumps would be made, and any such change of address would require an alteration of every jump instruction referring to it; it is only too easy to overlook one or two of these, with disastrous results when the program is run.

One way of minimizing this difficulty would be during the writing of the program to tag with a letter (or in some other easily recognizable way) each instruction to which a jump is to be made, and initially to write the jump instruction by referring to the tag and not the to actual address. Then, when the program is in its final form, the programmer simply goes through it and substitutes the final correct addresses for the letters; any which are overlooked will become obvious during punching.

There is no difficulty in making a compiler do something like this. With KDF9 User Code, the programmer writes a reference number before each instruction to which a jump is to be made, and in writing the actual jump instruction he refers only to that number (as we did in the program of Chapter 3). There is nothing further for him to do. During compilation, the compiler ascertains the actual address of any instruction preceded by a reference number, and as it compiles any jump instruction it substitutes the relevant address for the reference number, which disappears and is not part of the compiled program. For the programmer, nothing could be simpler. Alterations to the program involving changes in instruction addresses are irrelevant.

The quasi-programs given in this book (quasi because they cannot be compiled and implemented in their form as presented) will be written in a mnemonic language explained in detail later and specially designed for the purposes of this book. They refer to an imaginary idealized computer also specially designed. The primary purpose of this language is to allow where appropriate the combined use of flow diagrams and quasi-programs, and it is hoped that this will make it reasonably easy for the reader to follow the details of the procedures described and for him to be able to translate them into truly operational programs suitable for any machine to which he may have access. This mnemonic language, which will be called Mendol, will be essentially a machine order code in that it will maintain a 1:1 relation between instructions and operations, but some liberties will be taken by crediting our idealized computer (which will be described in detail later and will be named the XB1) with a few hardware facilities not normally possessed by computers. This will only involve simple operations for which the normally required software procedures would be obvious and equally simple, and has been done to shorten and simplify the programs where this can be done without loss of clarity.

This instruction code may look complicated at first, but this is deceptive and once a few routines have been followed through in detail it should be readily comprehensible. When, after using an Elliott 803, the author moved on to the more powerful KDF9, he was warned that he would find the KDF9 User Code difficult; the programming manual certainly looked rather fearsome. In fact, User Code proved easy to assimilate, was much easier to use than the Elliott code in spite of its larger repertoire of instructions, and the first program the author wrote in it (with no guidance other than that provided by the programming manual) was free from error, a hitherto unattained achievement.

In any case, the reader will be more concerned with reading Mendol than with writing it. A geneticist who has the type of mind that can grapple with the intricacies of population genetics and its application to the study of evolution should find little difficulty in learning to understand this code and in following the procedures described in this book. Once he has learnt to use a real computer, he should be able to translate and adapt these procedures for his own purpose.

What is particularly important is that he should then write his programs for himself, and not rely on the services of a programming expert. If the biologist doesn't understand the programming and the programmer doesn't completely understand the biology, their joint product is going to be of very doubtful value, for the latter may well fail to produce a valid computer analogy of the biology and the former will be in no position to assess the biological validity of the program. It is easier for a biologist to learn to use a computer than it is for a mathematician to understand all the facts of life. By writing his own programs, the geneticist will get into the habit of thinking of his populations in terms of computer models and procedures, and will through experience come to realize more fully the potential of the techniques of computer simulation and be able to deal with systems of increasing complexity in different fields of interest.

Autocodes

Before an account is given of XB1 and Mendol, something more may be said about programming languages. It has already been mentioned that XB1 will be credited with hardware facilities which a real computer would not possess but would need to perform through software operations. This leads logically to an idea which was actually developed in the fairly early days of computing when machine order codes were typically numerical, though we may here reverse matters and develop the idea by reference to mnemonic codes.

If a compiler can interpret an instruction which involves letters, symbols and numbers into a single binary instruction to carry out a single hardware operation, why could not one be produced which could translate a similar alpha-numeric instruction into a series of binary instructions to carry out what would then be a software operation? The answer is that it can. For example, if a compiler met a written instruction which required the transfer of the contents of locations 0 to 49 into locations 123 to 172, it could not translate this into a single binary instruction because the computer would not have the hardware facility to carry this out. Instead, the compiler could have as part of itself a short section of program which would be a generalised version of a routine for performing this operation. This routine would be copied into the appropriate part of the program under compilation, being adapted in the process by the insertion of the addresses 0 and 123 and a parameter 50 to count the number of items to be transferred.

It is not only simple operations like that which may be treated in this way. Mathematical procedures can appear in the written program as simple instructions and be translated by the compiler into routines; an obvious example would be a routine for the extraction of a square root which could perhaps be written by the programmer simply as **SQRT** plus the address of the number to be treated.

Languages of this kind which no longer have a direct relationship between instructions and hardware operations, but require translation of at least some of their instructions into software routines, are termed *autocodes*.

The early autocodes performed two functions. Firstly, the numerical order code with its instructions directly convertible into binary was replaced by a partly alphabetic notation which was more easily remembered by the programmer and more easily comprehensible, and programs written in autocode had fewer (often many fewer) instructions. For this reason, and also because the autocodes did not require a knowledge of store, accumulator, modifier and counter structure and manipulation, programming became much easier to learn and to carry out. Autocodes also allowed programmers to use mathematical procedures which they might find difficult to develop for themselves, and were particularly useful to people with a limited knowledge of mathematics who knew in broad mathematical terms what they wanted to do, but whose ability both in programming and mathematics did not allow them to program the appropriate mathematical procedures in detail.

An autocode instruction might correspond to quite a simple process involving only two or three hardware operations, or it might refer to a much more complex procedure requiring translation into many hardware instructions. We may regard an autocode program as being a set of instructions by reference to which a compiler composes a program in binary machine code. The compiler, not having any intelligence and therefore not being able to use any initiative, does not write programs from scratch. Instead, it uses procedures (algorithms) already written in machine orders and stored within it, and the process of compilation consists of the copying of those procedures as required with the addition of the appropriate parameters where necessary, and their assembly into a machine order program, as directed by the autocode program.

Although they performed a valuable service, autocode programs had a number of limitations in their early days, when computers had small store capacities. Since during compilation the compiler had to be in the store at the same time as the program it was compiling, there was a limit on its size and particularly on the number of algorithms it could contain (although this limitation largely disappeared later with the introduction of magnetic tape and disc backing store, capable of containing a large library of algorithms which needed to be called down by the compiler into the main store only when required). Compilers therefore only held those algorithms corresponding to procedures likely to be in fairly general use, and other procedures either had to be written in machine code and incorporated into the autocode program, or broken down into simpler and more generally used procedural steps which could be written in autocode.

Autocodes were thus best adapted for scientific, technical and mathematical programs using the more familiar mathematical procedures. No algorithms would be developed for example for such procedures as the bit manipulations involved in genetic simulation of the quasi-organism type, and if autocode programs were to be used for that purpose they would have to incorporate considerable sections written in machine code.

Another disadvantage of autocodes was that not only were they slow to compile, but the compiled programs were very inefficient in respect of speed when compared with machine code programs which could be written for the same purpose by a competent programmer. This is not surprising, since the compilers had to produce their programs in a stereotyped way from a limited number of elements, not always those most suitable for a particular program, whereas a programmer writing in machine orders would have no such restriction and could give full play to his ingenuity.

The time factor was not of great significance for short programs, especially in the early days when ample computer time was available if there happened to be a computer at all, but it was important for long-running programs. Taking all things into consideration, autocode programs were unsuitable for use in genetic simulation.

The early autocode programs very largely lacked what came to be a major advantage of the more elaborate autocodes which were later developed. Autocodes were originally designed for a particular model of computer, and to some extent at least with the hardware operations available in mind. Thus the same firm, Ferranti, had one autocode for its Pegasus and Sirius computers and another for the Mercury.

But it ought to be possible for an autocode instruction like **SQRT** to be interpreted by any compiler as 'calculate a square root' and thus to be translated into any machine order code. If the idea is abandoned that the autocode should be designed primarily for compilation into the machine code of a particular computer, then it ought to be possible to produce an autocode which, provided it was not too elaborate, could be interpreted into the machine code of any computer once a suitable compiler of that autocode had been written for that machine.

This has not been entirely practicable because storage and hardware limitations especially of some of the smaller computers make the writing of efficient compilers for autocodes with a large repertoire of procedures difficult or impossible, but autocodes do now exist which have a wide range of applicability and versatility, and these are commonly referred to as high level languages.

Some of the early stimulus to make autocodes more generally applicable came when institutions changed their model of computer but wished to continue using their old autocode programs without having to rewrite them; a new compiler for the old language but relevant to the new machine would allow this to be done. This gave pleasure both to those who enjoyed writing compilers and to those who did not enjoy rewriting programs. Another stimulus came from workers with access to one model of computer who wished to use without alteration programs developed by other workers for different models. Compilers were written, for example, by which Pegasus autocode and Mercury autocode could be used on a variety of machines including those of other manufacturers.

Three important high level languages for scientific purposes in use at present are FORTRAN, ALGOL and a relative newcomer PL/1. Autocodes of wide application have also been designed for other purposes; the languages and operations of industry and commerce are quite different from those of science and mathematics, and COBOL is a well-known example which serves those fields.

FORTRAN, which has a long history of development, was primarily designed to have relevance to IBM machines, but many of its features allowed it to be adapted so that compilers could be written through which it could be used on a wide variety of other computers. As a result, its current version, though still IBM based, has a general applicability.

ALGOL, unlike FORTRAN, was designed from the first as a machine-independent language and intended to be of universal application. If it has been less successful than FORTRAN this may be partly because its large repertoire of procedures makes the writing of efficient compilers for it complicated, and partly because of the vested interest of IBM in FORTRAN software.

PL/1 also comes from the IBM stable and, like ALGOL, has a large and comprehensive repertoire. Its early establishment as a universally applicable programming language has not been smooth, and its future seems to be uncertain; perhaps it tries to do too much.

The struggle for existence among these languages presents a fascinating evolutionary study for those who are fascinated by that sort of thing.

A great amount of time and effort has gone into the writing of compilers and other software for various high level languages, and there is a quite formidable literature about them. This situation has arisen because computers have largely been designed primarily from the point of view of the electronics, with various kinds of storage and accumulator arrangements etc., and hardware operations performed in quite different ways; this meant wide differences in machine order codes. It was perhaps inevitable that this should have happened, but it is a great pity that at some stage there was not international agreement to produce one machine order code and thence to base the electronics of subsequently designed computers on the execution of that code. Not only would this have meant that for each autocode a single compiler might have been sufficient for all computers, but that programs written in machine orders would have had universal applicability as well.

The big advantage of high level languages is that programs written in them may be used on a wide range of computers. This means that programs are easily interchangeable between scientists independently of the computers they are using, provided that the appropriate compilers have been written and are available.

They are said to be much easier to learn than machine code languages, and at the elementary level this is probably true, but it seems to the author that at the more advanced levels they become more involved and less easy for a non-mathematician to learn because the language implies a familiarity with mathematical procedures and modes of thought.

Given equal competence in the languages, there may certainly be greater speed and ease in writing programs in a high level language than in machine code, but for genetic simulation programs this advantage would not amount to very much since the actual writing of the program occupies only a relatively small part of the work. The greater part of the time involved is in the mental conception and construction of the model up to and including the stage of writing the flow diagrams; all this has to be done irrespective of the language which is to be used. Once the flow diagrams have been produced, their transformation into a written program is quickly done by a reasonably competent programmer, again largely irrespective of the language.

Although the author has little direct experience of high level languages, his observations suggest that they produce neither a lower tendency to programming error nor increased efficiency in tracing and rectifying any errors that occur. The greater ease which results from being able to program a procedure by means of an autocode instruction is offset by the fact that one often cannot be quite certain exactly how the relevant algorithm is actually executing the procedure, unless one understands machine orders and knows how to obtain a machine order transcript of the algorithm in its context.

In genetic simulation programming, program failure or an obviously wrong answer may broadly speaking be due to two causes, actual programming error (that is, error in translating a correctly conceived model into a written program, or faulty conception of the model perhaps through making biological assumptions which are invalid or using methods of simulation which do not accurately represent the biological system and which lead to the program producing biological nonsense.

Before looking for an error in conception, the possibility of an error in writing the program ought first to be eliminated, and this may occasionally be difficult unless the detailed hardware operations involved are accurately known, as they would be with a program written in machine code.

In the author's opinion, the usefulness of high level languages for genetic simulation programs differs as between algebraic simulation and genotype simulation. For the former, operating as it does through mathematical procedures, high level languages are quite suitable and may be satisfactorily used, as with any other kind of mathematical process.

For genotype simulation, high level languages are unsuitable. As far as the author knows, these languages do not include algorithms which could be used in such out of the way operations as those involving for example the bit manipulations of the simulation of segregation and reproduction, though doubtless they could be written and incorporated. Even if they were written and generally used, they would need to be specified in detail in terms of hardware operations, for it would be essential to the user of such an algorithm (unless perhaps he was working with a very simple system) that he should know precisely how the bit manipulations were being performed. It would certainly be possible to combine machine order and high level languages, using the latter for the more orthodox operations but writing the bit manipulations and similar processes in machine orders. But that is only possible if the programmer can write in machine orders, in which case he might just as well use them for the whole program.

PL/1 may permit bit manipulation procedures to be programmed on a 1:1 autocode instruction: hardware operation basis, but it is not clear that this has any advantage over direct programming by machine code. The big advantage of using machine orders (using the term broadly to include mnemonic codes) in genotype simulation is that the programmer is throughout thinking of the genetics of his quasi-organisms directly in terms of their bit structure, and this means that he will be at better grips mentally with his model, which will make it easier for him to use it with precision reliability, and understanding.

There is however one way in which the use of a high level language may be worth while, and that is in programming for the analysis and output of results and other information from simulation experiments. Output involves binary to decimal or alphabetic conversion, and if there is much information to be output awkward problems of layout may arise. This can sometimes require quite complicated programming with liability to error. It may often be preferable to use an output routine already written in a high level language by somebody else unless one is a very experienced programmer (in which case one can almost certainly do the job better oneself).

One of the main advantages of high level language programming, the general suitability of a program so written for a wide range of computers, is more apparent than real in genetic simulation. Few simulation programs will need to have a wide circulation; exceptions are those designed as teaching aids, and the author has to admit that his genetics teaching programs might have been more widely used if they had been written in FORTRAN and ALGOL.

Most simulation programs are designed to solve a specific problem or a series of problems in a fairly limited field corresponding to the interests of one worker or team of workers. They would rarely have a general applicability except perhaps where other people wished to repeat the same experiments with other parameters and under other easily modifiable experimental conditions, or perhaps where fairly simple programs could be incorporated into projects of greater complexity.

Many of the constituent routines of simulation programs are not of general applicability. Very few of the routines used by the author have appeared without substantial alteration in more than one distinct series of his own simulation experiments, so that even if his programs had been written in FORTRAN or ALGOL only quite small parts of them would be likely to be of direct use to anybody else.

It is true that if one has somebody else's program written in a language one can understand this might be very useful in showing one how particular problems of simulation and programming were tackled, and this might be of help in one's own programming; but unravelling someone else's program is not so simple as it might seem. (One's own programs written the year before are not always immediately comprehensible unless they have been well annotated; there are often several ways of doing something and one really needs to know what was going on in the programmer's mind when he was writing the program.) Copies of the flow diagrams would be much more useful because they can be comprehended more readily and provide a better explanation of the procedures involved in the program than would a copy of the program itself; but this of course depends on the programmer making intelligible flow diagrams and keeping them.

There seems to be a prejudice against machine order codes, fostering the illusion that they are difficult to learn, understand and apply. Difficulty in applying them depends largely on the inherent difficulty of the operation one is trying to perform. It is true that programming a complex mathematical operation in machine orders may be a tedious and difficult process which would be greatly simplified by the use of an autocode providing the relevant algorithms ready for incorporation, but computer manufacturers supply with their machines libraries of subroutines written in the appropriate machine order code, and it is almost as easy to incorporate these into one's machine code programs as it is to bring them into use by autocode instructions. Besides, one can sometimes improve on them.

Perhaps impatience has something to do with a preference for autocodes. Because a computer allows so much more to be done so very quickly, some people may feel that they ought to be able to learn to use it right away. But most complicated equipment needs expertise if it is to be operated efficiently and intelligently, and expertise is not always to be acquired rapidly. The facility to program in machine code may perhaps be acquired more slowly than that to program in an autocode, but it gives the programmer a much clearer idea of the operations which a computer can perform, of its versatility and of its potentialities for use in his own work, potentialities which he might well otherwise never realize.

The belief that machine codes must be difficult is a survival from the days when they were numerical and not readily intelligible, and when store and accumulator structures and relationships were complicated and not always easy to grasp. The author remembers the great difference in going from the Pegasus with its main store which was not immediately accessible, small computing store and accumulators which served as modifiers and counters as well, to the Elliott 803 with its single accumulator and a main store in which all words were immediately accessible and capable of being operated on without transfer. Change to KDF9 with its mnemonic order code made machine order programming still easier.

Biologists, and many others, were certainly rather scared of computers and, convinced that they would never understand them, failed to consider their potentialities. They were not encouraged by the apparently incomprehensible numerical order codes. The introduction of autocodes with obvious suggestions of intelligibility provided an important stimulus which attracted the less diffident to the use of computers, and was probably the major factor in the enormous expansion in the use of computers in the nineteen-sixties. But it does not follow that autocodes are therefore always to be preferred to machine codes.

A mnemonic machine code has been used in this book because the author believes that it provides the simplest and most readily intelligible way of expressing concisely the details of the operations involved in the various processes of genetic simulation through the use of quasi-organisms and the simulation of their genotypes.

The Computer

Although many features of computer design are widely applicable to different computers, there are sufficient differences of detail between computers to make it impossible to present an account of genetic simulation which would be immediately and directly applicable to all of them.

Two choices are open. One would be to consider one particular model of computer and to relate all the discussion in the book to that. This alternative was rejected. The other was to imagine an idealized computer, many of whose features would be broadly applicable to many different models and for which a suitable (but equally imaginary) language could be devised which would be fairly simple and easy to translate into languages with a more specific applicability. The imaginary design will pay close attention to the requirement of genotype simulation, and will have some common elements with the design of the foregoing human computer.

This imaginary computer is named the XB1 and its programming language is Mendol.

Words

We are going to suppose that our idealized computer has 32-bit words and, except where explicitly stated otherwise, all examples given in the remainder of this book are to be interpreted on that assumption.

Our earlier statement that one of the possible interpretations of a word was as the binary form of an integer, was an over-simplification. The numerical significance of a word to a computer, and its treatment during arithmetic operations, are of little consequence for the procedures involved in genotype simulation, and need not concern the reader for the time being. However, since he should at some time come to know this aspect of computer arithmetic, an account (which may well be skipped at first reading) is given later as part of the detailed description of the arithmetic operations which a computer can perform. Meanwhile, he will be perfectly safe in thinking of the word as a binary integer when it suits his convenience to do so.

There is, however, one important feature of the numerical interpretation of a word which must be pointed out here, though its detailed arithmetical implications can again be left until later. If we think of a word as a string of bits representing a binary number, there does not seem to be any obvious way in which it can be indicated whether that number is positive or negative. In fact, the m.s. bit of a word has a special significance in that it is used to indicate the sign. If the m.s. bit is **0** the number is positive; if **1**, the number is negative.

From our point of view, the important thing here is that when the computer executes a conditional jump instruction for which the criterion of whether to jump or not is the sign of a particular word considered as a number, the computer inspects only the m.s. bit of the word (the *sign bit*) and jumps or not according to whether that bit is **0** or **1**. The significance to the program of the other bits in the word is irrelevant; it makes no difference whether the word actually represents a number, or whether it is a piece of information, the genotype of an individual, the phenotype of an individual, or even a program instruction. This is of considerable value to us, since we can use the sign bit as a tag to indicate, for example, some particular characteristic of an individual which we wish to be the criterion for a choice of procedures in the program, the choice of course being implemented by jumping or not jumping.

Suppose we are dealing with a bisexual species and that we use two bits to represent the sex chromosomes (there is no reason why, in such a situation, a chromosome may not as well be represented by a single bit as a gene may be), **10** or **01** being **XY** and **11** being **XX**. It is not difficult, even when other bits in the word are being used to represent genes, to consider the two sex chromosome bits in isolation and use them directly as indicators of sex and so as a jump criterion. A neat way of doing this would be to have the two sex chromosome bits at the m.s. end of a word, with the one contributed by the sperm in the m.s. (sign bit) position. Males, **YX**, will then be **01...** and so positive; females, **XX**, will be **11...** and so negative. All that is then required is a simple reference to the sign of the word as part of the execution of a jump instruction.

The Store

The words of a computer are held in a *store*, and most computers have two kinds of store, *main store* (sometimes called *core store*) and *backing store*. Ignoring the latter for the moment, we may say that the main store holds the instructions of the program, parameters and other information, words which are to be operated on by the program (for example, words simulating the individuals of a population) and words which have been produced by the program (for example, words simulating the individuals of a new generation of the population, or containing the numerical results of population analysis). In some computers, some operations may be performed on words *in situ* in the main store; in others, the words always have to be transferred to accumulators (see next section) before they can be operated on. In either case, it is evident that access to words in the main store should be as fast as possible so that there is a minimum waste of time (even at the microsecond level). This requirement is well met in modern computers, and the main store is often referred to as the *fast store*. But fast storage tends to be expensive, and the amount available in any computer is limited, though it may be comparatively large in some of the more expensive machines. The IBM 360/67 owned jointly by the Universities of Newcastle and Durham has a fast store equivalent to a quarter of a million 32-bit words; the KDF9 at Newcastle had 16,384 48-bit words; the Elliott 803 at Durham had only 8,192 39-bit words, and there are smaller machines than that.

Some programs require much larger amounts of storage space for instructions, data, tables etc. than can be held in the available main store, but access to this material may not be required at all stages of the program. Many computers, and all the big ones, have further storage which is known as backing store, commonly taking the form of magnetic tapes or discs which have a very large capacity, millions of words in some cases. Material which is not currently required may be held in the backing store until it is needed, and then temporarily transferred to the main store—any displaced material in the latter having been previously transferred if necessary in the opposite direction. Access to backing store is relatively slow, especially with magnetic tape, but this difficulty can sometimes be minimized by anticipating transfer, since (subject to certain restrictions) this can take place simultaneously with the ordinary computational activities of the machine.

Partly because the type of backing store and the methods of programming for its use vary between computers, and partly because its use is not relevant to the programming techniques involved in genetic simulation, it will be supposed that our idealized computer XB1 has main store only, of adequate capacity. It will also be supposed that some operations, but not all, can be carried out directly on words in the main store, without the need for transfer to an accumulator.

However, since backing store has its uses in genetic simulation programs, a few further notes about it are added.

Store capacity is obviously a factor limiting the size of simulated populations but, since time is also a limiting factor, restriction of population size because of store capacity is not likely to be an embarrassment during the early stages of acquiring experience in programming for genetic simulation. There is one important use for backing store which arises from the fact that storage on magnetic tape or disc may be virtually permanent if required, remaining accessible indefinitely and not being lost at the end of the program run or overwritten by other programs as words in the main store would be. The study of some evolutionary systems may involve the simulation of very many generations, the number of which cannot be accurately forecast beforehand because it will depend on what happens to the population as the experiment proceeds. Obviously, the experiment should not be terminated before the critical stage has been reached, but one would also prefer not to waste computer time by continuing the run after it had ceased to provide useful information. To some extent this situation can be met by running the experiment for a predetermined time or number of generations, and then dumping the entire program (including of course the simulated population in its current state) into the backing store in such a way that it can be retrieved if necessary at a later time, replaced in the main store, and the run resumed as if it had never been interrupted. The decision whether or not to resume the run can be taken at leisure, after inspection and consideration of the results to date and the state of the population. Since the programmer may have a personal magnetic tape or small disc, which can be removed from the computer and held separately when not in use, resumption can be long delayed. For instance, it may sometimes happen that an experiment seems to have reached a satisfactory conclusion, but later work casts doubts on this and suggests that it might perhaps be worth while to extend the experiment for a further period. If the program has been dumped, this presents no difficulty.

Accumulators

The arithmetic and logical operations of a computer involve registers called *accumulators* whose word length is the same as that of words in the main store. There is a great deal of variety among computers in the number of accumulators, their organization and the way in which they are used.

XB1 is supposed to have eight accumulators referred to by the letters **A** to **H**. Except for operations in which a stated number is added to a specified location, all logical and arithmetic operations must involve at least one accumulator. That exception apart, if there is only one operand that must therefore be in an accumulator (being first transferred there if necessary), and the result of the operation will appear in that accumulator, replacing the previous contents. If there are two operands, one must be in an accumulator; for some operations, the second must also be in an accumulator, for others the second may be in an accumulator, main store location or (occasionally) in a counter or modifier (see below). The direct use of a main store location in this way is not common to all computers, but since it simplifies programming it has been allowed to the imaginary hardware of XB1. Where there are two operands the answer may replace either, leaving the other unchanged, as desired by the programmer; occasionally an answer occupies two words, in which case both original operands are replaced (if required for further use, copies of them will have been retained elsewhere).

Although each accumulator of XB1 (like each word of the store) has a capacity of 32 bits, longer words may be dealt with in certain operations by linking any two accumulators together in any order to produce a double length word of 64 bits.

In the model program of Chapter 3, **F G** and **H** were the accumulators.

Counters and Modifiers

Counting and modification vary from one computer to another. Sometimes an accumulator or other register may be used for both purposes (as **Q** was in the example program of the last chapter), but in order that counting and modification may be readily distinguished in our flow diagrams and quasi-programs, XB1 will use special and distinct registers for the two purposes.

There will be sixteen counters, designated by the letter **K** and numbered **K0, K1, K2** etc. The method of counting a procedure which has to be performed n times will be first to place (by a direct instruction) the integer n in a counter; at the end of each performance a count will be made which consists of two operations (usually but not necessarily consecutive)—decreasing by 1 the integer currently in the counter, followed by inspection of the latter to see if its contents are zero (which would indicate that the procedure has been performed the required number of times and that there should be no further repetition). In some computers these two steps in counting may be programmed as a single operation, or decreasing may be combined with and performed simultaneously with some other operation such as modifier incrementation, but they will be kept distinct in our quasi-programs. They are being treated separately here because in some computers decreasing is a separate operation and not automatic; in such a case translation into a real program of a procedure from a quasi-program which did not treat decreasing as a separate operation could lead to oversight of the need to decrease, with consequent program failure.

However, in order to save space in the flow diagrams and make them easier to follow, the double operation of decrease and inspection of the counter will usually be treated as a single step and be indicated simply by 'count **K***n*' where *n* is the number of the relevant counter. That is, 'count **K***n*' should be interpreted as 'decrease the integer in **K***n* by 1 and then inspect the contents of **K***n* to see if they are zero'. From each 'count **K***n*' there will be two exits, 'finished' indicating that **K***n* is zero, 'not finished' that it is still non-zero.

There will be sixteen modifiers, designated by the letter **M** and numbered **M0**, **M1**, **M2** etc. When a modifier is to be used in an operation or series of operations, a positive or negative integer or zero will be placed directly in it by a single instruction, either by specification of the integer in the instruction or by transfer from another register or store location. The specified integer may take the form of (that is, be written in the program as) a store address; the way in which addresses may be written in programming is discussed in the next section.

The contents of a modifier may be altered by addition or subtraction, either of a specified integer or of the contents of an accumulator. When the modifier is used as the essential element in the execution of a loop (its typical but by no means only use), alteration will usually occur regularly (that is, in phase with the cycles of the loop) and be constant in amount, the alteration then often being referred to as an increment. Some computers have a form of instruction by which this cyclical incrementation may be performed automatically immediately after the modifier has been used, but we will keep the two operations separate, not only in the quasi-programs as with counting, but also in the flow diagrams, so that it will be more obvious to the inexperienced reader when the increment is added and when it is not.

The basic principles of modification have been explained in the previous chapter. Combined use of **Q** as counter and modifier was made in the example program of that chapter in order to minimize the operations during loops and so increase the speed of the human computer. This was possible because the increment (or, more accurately, the decrement) required for modification was the same as that required for counting, and because the method of modification used there was deliberately chosen to make this combined use possible. In order that the procedures subsequently to be described in this book may be more readily followed, counting and modification will be treated as requite distinct operations.

Modification will always be by addition of the contents of the modifier to the address specified in the instruction (but remember that those contents may be negative) and will be indicated in the instruction by specifying the modifier in brackets after the address to be modified. Thus if **a15** is the way in which word 15 in the store is specified and **M3** contains the integer n, **a15(M3)** would specify word $(15+n)$. The brackets would probably be superfluous to a real compiler, but they are used here in order that instructions involving modification can be recognized by the reader at a glance.

For the operation of loops in which locations of the main store are to be addressed sequentially, the address to be modified will normally be the lowest address in the store section involved (not the highest plus one as in the previous chapter) and the modifier will begin with zero and its cyclical alteration will be by addition of an integer to it. In the previous chapter, for example, progress through the store from **C0** to **C15** was by subtraction from address **C16** of a number which began at 16 and decreased cyclically by 1; the method which will subsequently be used corresponds to the simpler one of addition to address **C0** of a number which begins at 0 and increases cyclically by 1. The principle is the same in either case.

Addresses—Absolute and Relative

Superficially, the specification of an address in the main store would appear to be a simple matter, since we may treat the locations as if they are arranged in a linear sequence and numbered sequentially from zero. All that has to be done to specify an address is to state its number in the sequence, and it is helpful if this number is preceded by a simple tag so that it may be recognized immediately and unambiguously as an address. Thus the addresses from the beginning of the store of XB1, written in Mendol, are **a0**, **a1**, **a2**, **a3** etc. For a reason which will be apparent shortly, these are known as *absolute addresses*.

Unfortunately it is hardly ever quite so simple as this, since it often happens during the writing of a program that we cannot specify the absolute address of a word because at that time we do not know precisely what it is.

For example, suppose we are writing a program which will use or place material in the store and to which it will therefore need to refer (parameters, working space, information, simulated organisms). Some at least of this material is likely to be stored after the program instructions. While the latter are being written the programmer will not know precisely (possibly not even approximately) how long the program will eventually be and hence at what address it will finish and where the storage of the remainder of the material will start. Even if all the material in question were to be stored before the program instructions, the programmer would not necessarily know initially how much storage space should be allotted for each particular purpose, and might in any case change his mind as programming proceeds; the same is true of course for material stored after the program and adds to the original difficulty.

All this means that frequently when the programmer wishes to refer in an instruction to a word in the main store he does not know the precise location in which it will be stored; that is, he does not know its absolute address and so cannot refer to it by that address. He could of course attempt to allow amply large gaps, after the instructions or elsewhere, but that would waste storage space; and if for example he badly misjudged the space needed by the program instructions and did not make enough allowance, he would have to change the arrangements for storage and alter all the relevant absolute addresses so far written in the program—a tiresome process pregnant with error.

This difficulty is overcome by a simple procedure known as *relative adressing* (which was in fact used in the example program of Chapter 3). Instead of referring to a word by its absolute address, the programmer works from a symbolic address which represents the first word in the relevant section of the store and is known as the *base address*. All words in that section of the store are addressed relatively to that base address.

The way in which the base address is referred to varies from one computer to another and from one programming language to another, but the principle remains the same. Relative addressing is a powerful programming facility. It may be used in the same program for several sections of the store, each with its own base address, and its use is not confined to the storage of information etc. It may be applied to sections of the written program; when writing one part of the program we may need to make reference to another part of it for which the absolute address is not known at the time; use of a relative address will overcome this difficulty. Relative addressing will be explained in terms of Mendol.

Suppose that our program, information, working space etc. will eventually be arranged in sections of the store which for convenience we may distinguish by the letters **s**, **t**, **u**, **v**. At the time of writing the program the absolute locations and possibly the extent of these sections will be unknown. Nevertheless we can symbolize the addresses of their first words as **s0**, **t0**, **u0**, **v0** without any implication as to absolute addresses, and these are the symbolic base addresses of each section respectively. We can then refer to the address of any word in a section by replacing the zero of the base address by the appropriate number and this will be the *relative address* of that word. For example, the fifteenth word in section **s** would be relatively addressed as **s14** —not **s15**, because counting begins with zero, not with one.

This last point may cause some confusion to the beginner, but he will quickly get used to the idea of counting from zero. The reason why we count from zero is mainly one of economy. If we begin counting with one, three binary bits can count only seven items, from one to seven—**001** to **111**, **000** being wasted. If we begin counting from zero, **000** is used and we can count eight, from zero to seven. There is a corresponding advantage when we are using random numbers. There are occasions when this economy is important.

In writing the program, the programmer simply uses the relative address, and does not need to commit himself as to the precise locations (absolute addresses) which the words referred to will actually occupy in the store. Indeed he may never even need to know them.

The relative addresses are never amended to the absolute form by the programmer—this is done by the computer which does require them in the absolute form. As pointed out earlier, when the program has been finally written, it is not in a form which is immediately intelligible to and usable by the computer, and has to be translated into binary by a special program known as a compiler. It is the compiler which transforms the relative to the absolute addresses.

If the compiler is a simple one, the written program will have to supply it with the absolute values of the base addresses, and these will have to be determined by the programmer when he has finished writing the program and knows how much space each section will require. The compiler will then by simple addition make the necessary amendments to the relative addresses as it compiles the program. For instance, if the absolute address of the base address **s0** is **a257**, then on reading the relative address **s14** in a program instruction the compiler will transform this and actually store it as 271 (the **a** is merely a tag for recognition purposes by programmer and compiler and is not part of the instruction as stored and obeyed in the computer since as obeyed all addresses are absolute and the tag would be redundant). If for any reason, perhaps further development or amendment of the program, the store requirements of the various sections are altered or new sections inserted, all the programmer has to do is to determine the new absolute values of the base addresses and amend the original values in the program; the compiler will do the rest when it reads the new version of the program. The relative addresses as written in the program will remain unaltered (unless of course amendment is required for some other reason). Thus, considering the previous example, if the base address **s0** becomes **a346**, **s14** remains unaltered in the written program but is now compiled as 360.

If the compiler is an elaborate one, it may be able to work out for itself the storage requirements of the various sections and the appropriate absolute values of the base addresses; the programmer need never know. This will be assumed to be true of XB1.

In the example program of Chapter 3, two sections of the store were relatively addressed by reference to the base addresses **C0** (for the population) and **D0** (for temporary storage of the seeds produced).

As will be described later, programs are usually written in sections called subroutines, and in addition to instructions these may contain words used for constants or other information. These may also be addressed relatively, the base address being the address of the first word of the subroutine; this allows easy cross reference between different parts of a program and is explained in detail in the next chapter, which is concerned with subroutines. In writing a program, modification of a relative address is indicated precisely as for an absolute address.

A Mnemonic Language—Mendol

Mendol is supposed to be a 1:1 instruction: hardware operation language. It is a quasi-language in the sense that it is not designed with a view to the possibility of its being compiled, but only as a language for describing the detailed steps of simulation operations and relevant only to an imaginary computer, XB1. In this section, the various hardware operations of XB1 will be described together with the form of the relevant instructions. Some of the latter contain more elements than a compiler would need for unambiguous interpretation, but this has been done to help the reader to interpret them more readily. For ease of reference, a summarized version of the order code is given in an appendix at the end of the book.

Some of the instructions will be used, for reasons of brevity, in the flow diagrams of subsequent chapters, either in their proper form or in an unambiguous and easily intelligible version. In quasi-programs only the proper forms, as they appear below and in the appendix, will be used.

When it is written in the program, each instruction is terminated by a semi-colon; such semi-colons have been omitted for isolated instructions and from the end of instruction sequences when these appear as parts of the text, in order to avoid confusion with punctuation.

In this account of the instruction code, *m* and *n* will be used to stand for suitable positive decimal integers (or zero); other letters used will be as they are actually written in the instructions. **A**, **B** will be used to represent any accumulators; **K***m*, **K***n* and **M***m*, **M***n* will be used to represent any counters or modifiers respectively; **s***m*, **s***n* will be used to represent any store address, whether absolute (**a***n*) or relative (**s***n*, **t***n*, **u***n*, **v***n*, **w***n*, **x***n*, **y***n*, **z***n* are permissible relative addresses, as well as the forms **p**n, **p**n**P**m which refer to subroutines). (Subroutines will be explained in the next chapter, they are considered in the current chapter where appropriate for the sake of completeness.) Any instruction containing **s**m or **s**n is valid with an address in the form **s**n**(M**m**)** indicating modification by the contents of **M**m.

Some of the sections in small print are intended to help readers to deal with situations where computers may lack particular hardware facilities possessed by XB1. They may refer to instructions which are not explained until later in the chapter, and are best skipped at first reading since they will not then be readily intelligible.

Transfers

A word may be transferred from one accumulator to another, one modifier to another and one counter to another, but not directly from one store location to another. It may also be transferred from any one of these four categories to any of the others. The previous contents of the receiving register or store location are lost, but those of the donating one remain unchanged. In effect, the process of transfer is one of copying into a register or store location from which the previous contents have been erased. Transfer to a store location is known as writing; transfer from a store location is known as reading or fetching. The instruction will use an arrow in the direction of transfer, which will always be from the first specified location. Thus **A→s**n means that the contents of accumulator **A** are copied into the store location **s**n, **A** being left unaltered. **s**n**→A** means that the contents of the store location are copied into accumulator **A**, **s**n being left unaltered. Precisely corresponding meanings are to be attached to the instructions **K**m**→s**n; **s**n**→K**m; **M**m**→s**n; **s**n**→M**m; **A→B**; **A→K**n; **K**n**→A**; **A→M**n; **M**n**→A**; **K**m**→K**n; **K**m**→M**n; **M**m**→K**n; **M**m**→M**n;.

In some computers, direct transfer between store on one hand and counters and modifiers on the other may not be possible, and would have to be through an accumulator. It has been allowed here to simplify programming. Direct store to store transfer, **s**m**→s**n, has not been allowed because it would simplify programming too much. It would affect the writing of some programming procedures, and it has seemed preferable that those procedures should be presented in a way corresponding more closely to the real thing.

There is a special kind of transfer by which an integer is placed directly by one program instruction in an accumulator, counter, modifier or store location (the original contents being lost); this is particularly useful for setting counters or modifiers. The integer may be positive, negative or zero, and the form of the instruction is **A**$=n$ or **A**$=-n$; **A** may be replaced by **K**m, **M**m or **s**m; the contents after the operation will be n or $-n$ respectively.

When $n = 0$, the instruction is said to clear the register or store location, by comparison with the corresponding operation on a desk calculating machine.

A variant of this instruction, which is sometimes particularly useful for setting modifiers and has a special use with subroutines, will place in any specified accumulator, counter, modifier or store location a positive integer which is the absolute address corresponding to any specified relative store address or jump instruction reference. The instruction is **A** = **(s***n***)**, where **A** may be replaced by **K***m*, **M***m* or **s***m*, and **s***n* may be any valid form of relative address modified or not, or may be replaced by any valid form of jump instruction reference (see later) when it will be written as in **A** = **(j***n***)** or **A** = **(j***n***P***m***)**. Note that if the relative address **s***n* is modified the instruction involves double brackets, thus **A** = **(s***n***(M***m***))**.

A simple operation which is related to the placing of an integer in a register or store location is the addition or subtraction of a positive integer to or from the contents of a register or store location. Strictly speaking, this is an arithmetic rather than a logical operation, but since it is most commonly used in a logical context it may appropriately be considered here. The form of the instructions is **A**+*n* or **A**−*n*, and **A** can be replaced by **K***m*, **M***m* or **s***m*. **K***m***−1** and **M***m***+1** are common instructions for decreasing a counter and incrementing a modifier respectively. Only integers, and not relative addresses, can be added in this way.

Logical Operations

Logical operations, sometimes termed boolean operations, treat words as collections of bits rather than as numbers. Some of them have obvious analogies with arithmetic operations, but they do not follow the rules of arithmetic and should be considered purely as bit manipulations which follow a few simple clearly defined rules.

They are being described before the arithmetic operations because bit manipulations are the typical operations of genetic simulation. In our simulation programs the function of arithmetic is largely confined to processing the results of population analysis.

Logical operations never involve rounding and never cause overflow, which are explained and discussed fully in the section on arithmetic operations and which need not for the time being concern us further.

Logical Multiplication (LM)

This is one of the most useful of all logical procedures because it provides a simple method of extracting a section of a word by a process sometimes known as *masking*, unwanted bits being delivered as zeros.

In an LM between two words, each bit of one word is multiplied by the bit in the corresponding position in the other. The bit multiplications are independent of one another, and result in **1** if both bits are **1** ($\mathbf{1} \times \mathbf{1} = \mathbf{1}$) and zero otherwise ($\mathbf{0} \times \mathbf{0} = \mathbf{0}$ and $\mathbf{0} \times \mathbf{1} = \mathbf{0}$). The result from each pair of bits appears in the corresponding position in the *logical product* (LP). As an example, we may represent an LM between two words with the resultant LP as follows.

```
        10110111000101110011011001000101
        11010110010110001101000111100100
        --------------------------------
LP  =   10010110000100000001000001000100
```

The LP will replace either of the two operands leaving the other unchanged. At least one of the operands must be in an accumulator; the other may be in a store location or an accumulator, but not in a counter or modifier. The instruction has the form **A & B** or **A & s***n*, followed by an arrow indicating where the answer is to appear, as **A & s***n*→**A** or **A & s***n*→**s***n*.

In a masking operation, one of the two operands (the *mask*) will usually consist of a sequence of **1**s, the remaining bits being zero. Thus if we wish to extract the eight l.s. bits of a word, the mask will be **...0011111111**. For example,

```
        10110111000101110011011001000101
mask    00000000000000000000000011111111
        --------------------------------
LP  =   00000000000000000000000001000101
                                 \_____/
                         the extracted bits
```

Where masking involves the m l.s. bits of a word, the required mask is numerically equal to $2^m - 1$. Since the corresponding numerical values quickly become stored in and are easily retrievable from a programmer's own memory, a convenient version of the LM instruction (restricted to accumulators) is introduced, **A &** *n*; the result of this is that **A** will contain the LP of its original contents and a binary word numerically equivalent to the positive integer *n*. For example, if the upper word in the preceding illustration were in accumulator **A**, the instruction **A & 255** would place the required LP in **A**.

Logical Addition (LA)

In the logical addition of two words, each bit of one word is added to the bit in the corresponding position in the other and any carry is ignored. The bit additions are independent of one another and result in zero if the two bits are the same ($\mathbf{0}+\mathbf{0} = \mathbf{0}$; $\mathbf{1}+\mathbf{1} = \mathbf{10}$, becoming **0** when the carried bit is dropped) and **1** if the two bits are different ($\mathbf{0}+\mathbf{1} = \mathbf{1}$). The result from each pair of bits appears in the corresponding position in the logical sum (LS) thus,

$$
\begin{array}{rl}
 & \mathbf{10110111000101110011011001000101} \\
 & \underline{\mathbf{11010110010110001101000111100100}} \\
\text{LS} = & \mathbf{01100001010011111110011110100001}
\end{array}
$$

The LS will replace one of the two operands leaving the other unchanged. As with LM, at least one of the two operands must be in an accumulator; the other may be in a store location or an accumulator, but not in a counter or modifier. The instruction has the form **A** $\not\equiv$ **B** or **A** $\not\equiv$ **s***n*, followed by an arrow indicating where the answer is to appear, as **A** $\not\equiv$ **s***n*→**A** or **A** $\not\equiv$ **s***n*→**s***n*.

Note that if we have two words in each of which only a certain section of bits is of any significance and all other bits are zero, then *provided these sections do not overlap* they may be combined into one word by either logical or arithmetic addition.

$$
\begin{array}{rl}
 & \mathbf{0000\overbrace{1011010111}00000000000000000000} \\
 & \underline{\mathbf{0000000000000\overbrace{1011011111010100101}}} \\
\text{LS} = & \mathbf{00001011010111011011111010100101}
\end{array}
$$

An arithmetic addition would have produced the same result. If each section is continuous and they do overlap they cannot be combined unless at least one of them is previously shifted. If the sections are discontinuous in such a way that they would interdigitate without any coincidence, then they can be combined directly as before. All this becomes of importance if we desire to *pack* several distinct pieces of information into one word. Unpacking may subsequently be achieved when desired by using LM with the appropriate masks.

There is no facility for performing an LA with a specified integer, as it would serve no particular purpose.

Some machines do not have the ability to perform logical addition as a hardware operation, but it can be done by a very short routine using arithmetic addition and subsequent subtraction of the carried bits. This routine may be described in Mendol as follows, assuming that the two words for which an LS is required are in accumulators **A** and **B**.

```
A→C; A+B→A; C&B→C; C up 1; A−C→A;
```

The LS is in **A**, **B** being unaltered. Overflow may be set during this routine (in distinction to a hardware LA) by either of the arithmetic operations, but this has no bearing on the result; if it is necessary that the overflow register is clear on completion of the routine, this may be concluded with **J***n***V; (***n***)**, otherwise clearing may wait until any primarily arithmetic procedure is about to occur.

Logical addition and logical multiplication play an important part in the simulation of segregation.

Bits

In genetic simulation, it is sometimes necessary to know how many **1**s there are in a word. There are several ways of doing this by means of a subroutine, but in some computers a single instruction will suffice, and it will be supposed that XB1 has this facility. The instruction **bits A** will leave in **A** a number equal to the number of bits which were **1** in the word originally in **A**.

If XB1 had not the '**bits**' facility, either of the two following routines would serve the purpose. The word is assumed to be in **A** (if not in an accumulator it must be transferred to one) and the answer will appear in **B**, the contents of **A** being lost. In the first method, the contents of **A** are shifted up one place at a time, and 1 added to another accumulator every time **A** is negative (that is, when the m.s. bit is a **1**). The procedure stops (as also in the second routine) when **A** becomes zero.

B = 0; (1); J2A ⩾ 0; B + 1; (2); A up 1; J1 A ≠ 0;

In the second method, bits are shifted off the m.s. end of **A** by using a double length shift with a zero accumulator, and added arithmetically to a third accumulator.

B = 0; (1); C = 0; CA up 1; B + C→B; J1 A ≠ 0;

These are clearly time-consuming procedures, but if it is known (as it may often be in genetic simulation) that a number of bits at the m.s. end must be zero, then an initial shift up by the relevant amount can save time.

Often, a quicker method would be to use table look-up, and a detailed account of this is given in Chapter 7 (page 201). By using a table of 256 entries, the number of **1**s could be determined by treating the word in four sections of eight bits, summing the values for the four sections.

Logical Shifts

A logical shift is simply the sideways movement of all the bits of a word, movements to the left being referred to as shifts up and those to the right as shifts down. Bits shifted off the end (except for circular shifts, see below) are permanently lost, and are replaced by zeros at the other end. Although superficially like multiplication or division by powers of two, logical shifts carry no arithmetical implications at all, and there is neither overflow nor rounding (see next section). For example,

01110101110101110001001011100 1101

logically shifted up eight places would become

10101110001001011100110100000000,

and logically shifted down eight places would become

00000000011101011101011100010010 1.

Shifts can only be carried out in accumulators.

It is sometimes necessary to preserve in a separate accumulator the bits which would be lost off the end of a word, and this may be done by performing a double length shift in which any two accumulators may be treated exactly as if they were a single accumulator accommodating a 64-bit word. Of the two accumulators specified in the relevant instruction, the left-hand one is the m.s. Thus if **AB** is specified, during a shift up the m.s. bits of **B** will become the l.s. bits of **A**, the m.s. bits of **A** being lost and zeros going into the l.s. end of **B**. In a double length shift down, the l.s. bits of **A** become the m.s. bits of **B** and the l.s. bits of **B** are lost, zeros going into the m.s. end of **A**.

In a circular shift, which can only be carried out single length, bits lost off one end of a word pass, in their original sequence, to the opposite end. In other words the accumulator is treated as if it were circular.

The instructions specify the accumulator(s), the direction of shift, and the number of places to be shifted either as an integer or by reference to a modifier whose numerical contents equal the desired number of places. For circular shifts, the direction of shift is preceded by **c/**. The various possible forms of the instruction are **A up** *n*; **A down** *n*; **Ac/up** *n*; **Ac/down** *n*; **AB up** *n*; **AB down** *n*. In any of these *n* may be replaced by **(M***m***)**, but note that if the contents of **M***m* are negative, the shift will be in the opposite direction from that indicated by the instruction. Thus if the number in **M14** is −7, the instruction **A up (M14)** will cause the contents of **A** to be shifted *down* seven places and **A down (M14)** would cause a shift *up* of seven places.

The combination of masking and shifting is a powerful one for the manipulation of blocks of consecutive bits in a word.

Arithmetic Operations—Numerical Interpretation of Words

Although arithmetic operations will be more familiar to the reader than the logical ones that have just been discussed, their proper understanding requires a much fuller account of the numerical interpretation of a word than has so far been given. Since, to begin with at least, the reader will be little concerned with arithmetic operations, it is suggested that this section might well be skipped at first reading and returned to when the reader is more familiar with computing procedures.

It must be pointed out that the account which follows is intended to refer specifically to the imaginary XB1, and although most of it will be of broad general applicability, there may be one or two points which are not universally valid.

So far, in our numerical interpretation of a word, we have treated it as a binary representation of an integer. But although this is a natural and in many circumstances a permissible interpretation it is in fact a considerable over – simplification, for the computer actually interprets the word not as an integer but as a fraction, with the point to the right of the m.s. bit. As we proceed right-handed from the point, each bit represents a value half that of the previous one. Thus the word **0101100...** has the decimal value 0.6875. There is however no difficulty in our regarding the word as an integer, whatever the computer may do about it; this is particularly simple when only addition, subtraction or multiplication by a power of 2 are concerned. The computer will treat the word **...0001** as the fraction 1×2^{-31}; any word which we wish to regard as an integer n will be treated by the computer as a fraction $n\times 2^{-31}$. If we have two integers m and n, their sum is $m+n$; to the computer the numbers are the fractions $m\times 2^{-31}$ and $n\times 2^{-31}$, their sum is $(m+n)\times 2^{-31}$, and the result will appear exactly as though it were the integer $(m+n)$ at the l.s. end of the word. Take a simple numerical example. $17+23=40$; to the computer this is $17\times 2^{-31}+23\times 2^{-31}=40\times 2^{-31}$. To both the computer and ourselves this will be

...0010001 + **...0010111** = **...0101000**.

No difficulty arises in our interpretation of **...0101000** as the integer 40. With subtraction, the argument is similar but a subtlety arises when the answer is negative, which will be dealt with shortly. Multiplication by a power of 2 also presents no difficulty. To the computer, the operation which we may choose to regard as 18×2^5 becomes $(18\times 2^{-31})\times 2^5=18\times 2^{-26}$, or in binary **...0010010** becomes **...001001000000**. This is in fact a shift up of 5 places exactly analogous with the way one would shift up a number on a desk calculating machine when multiplying by 10^5. We have no difficulty in interpreting **...001001000000** as the integer 576.

Division by a power of two (multiplication by a negative power of 2) proceeds similarly, with shifting down instead of up, but there is one additional point. In shifting down, bits are lost off the end of the word. This is similar to the operation in decimal arithmetic of discarding some l.s. decimal places; that involves rounding up when necessary, 41.3257 becoming for example 41.33 when the two l.s. digits are discarded. Similarly, when bits are lost off the end of a word as a result of an arithmetic shift down (division by a power of 2), rounding up must be applied when appropriate, which will be when the m.s. bit of those lost had the value **1**. For example, 18×2^{-2} is treated by the computer as $(18\times 2^{-31})\times 2^{-2}=18\times 2^{-33}$ and rounded to 5×2^{-31}, **...0010010** becoming **...00101**; in effect rounding may be considered as being dealt with by the addition of the m.s. bit of those lost to the l.s. end of the residual word. In decimal notation, $18\div 4=4.5$ which is rounded up to 5.

Rounding is confined to arithmetic operations, and is never applied to logical ones. There is thus a subtle but important difference between arithmetic and logical shifts down—the former does not necessarily preserve the original pattern of the remaining bits.

If we are working solely with integers and are performing only addition, subtraction and shifts, then so long as there is no possibility of the answer being too large (a contingency which will be dealt with later), we can treat the words exactly as though they represent integers and do not even need to know that the computer treats them as fractions.

It is however a different matter when we come to multiplication and division. $17 \times 23 = 391$, but $(17 \times 2^{-31}) \times (23 \times 2^{-31}) = 391 \times 2^{-62}$ and not 391×2^{-31}. In multiplication, the product always has more digits than either of the multiplicands (except sometimes when one of these has only one digit). That is why the product register of a desk calculating machine has to be larger than the other registers if full advantage is to be taken of their capacity. The same applies to a computer. If full advantage in multiplication is to be taken of the capacity of the accumulators, a double length accumulator will be required by the product and this may be achieved by treating two accumulators as though they were linked end to end. Thus the answer to the operation **A** × **B** will appear double length in **AB** as though this were a single accumulator, with the important proviso (for a reason which will appear later) that the m.s. bit of **B** does not form part of the product, the remaining 31 bits of **B** being considered as though they came directly after the l.s. bit of **A**.

The computer of course always treats this answer **AB** as a fraction. If we were treating the contents of **A** and **B** as fractions, then we might well decide that the 31 m.s. binary places in the product were enough and we would discard **B**. If however we were treating **A** and **B** as integers, then if the answer were less than 2^{31}, it would be wholly in **B**, **A** being zero. So we would discard **A** and treat **B** as the answer; that is to say, considering the earlier example, we multiply the computer's answer to $(17 \times 2^{-31}) \times (23 \times 2^{-31})$ by 2^{31}, producing the result which is for us the correct one, 391×2^{-31}. If we are multiplying very large integers together this operation will not do, because the answer may extend into **A**; this contingency is so unlikely to arise in the processing of results from simulation experiments that we will not consider it further.

Division presents different problems but before considering them, we must discuss the arithmetical interpretation of the m.s. bit of a word, to the left of the notional point. Although the computer may operate on this bit as though it had its usual binary meaning, it has in fact a special significance in that it indicates the sign of the number, a point to which reference has been made earlier.

If the m.s. bit of a word is zero, that word is to be interpreted in the obvious way as a positive number, **0101100...** as +0.6875; for integral interpretation **00...001** is +1.

If however the m.s. bit is **1**, the word is to be interpreted as a negative number, but *not* in the obvious way; **1101100...** represents not −0.6875 but 1.6875-2, which is −0.3125. Similarly, **10...001** is not to be interpreted integrally as −1, but as $-(2^{31}-1)$. The integer −1 would be a word in which each bit was **1**. This subtlety of how the negative binary number is to be interpreted will not normally concern us in simulation programming (but the curious reader may, among other possibilities, care to work out in binary 0.6875-0.3125, which may of course be done by adding **1101100...** to **0101100...**), but the interpretation of the m.s. bit as a sign bit is of considerable importance as has already been pointed out, since computers have a built-in ability to recognize negative numbers, and consequently the sign bit of a particular word may be used to determine a choice of procedures.

We can now see why, in double length arithmetic working, the m.s. bit of the right-hand accumulator is not part of the double length number. After multiplication, the sign bits of both accumulators holding the product will always be the same (so that if we multiply two integers and discard the m.s. accumulator, the answer in the l.s. accumulator will have the correct sign). In double length arithmetic shifts, the m.s. bit of the right-hand accumulator will always be skipped and remain unchanged; thus if **A** carries **...0101101** and **B 10110010...** a double length arithmetic shift up of **AB** of four places will give **...01011010110** for **A** and **1010...** for **B**. This is quite different from a double length logical shift, which for four places again would have given **...01011011011** and **0010...** respectively.

There is an important arithmetic implication arising from the use of the m.s. bit as a sign bit. If we add 0.6875 to 0.375, the answer is 1.0625; in binary this is **0101100...+0011000...** and the computer adding these together would produce the answer **1000100...** which is wrong because that actually represents −0.9375. A little thought will show that an answer equal to or larger than 1.0 cannot be correctly represented, nor can an answer less than −1.0 (−1.0 can be; it is **1000...00**). Except for −1.0, our computer can only treat numbers as though they were entirely fractional and any arithmetic procedure which produces an answer outside the stated limits will be wrong (subtraction from a negative fraction can do this just as easily as addition to a positive one). Such an answer is too large for the accumulator and occupies the sign bit, a phenomenon known as *overflow*. Except in circumstances foreseen by the programmer and deliberately ignored, overflow results from a mistake in the program (only very rarely by the computer), either directly from a programming error or indirectly through a failure to see a possible overflow-producing contingency. To deal with this the computer has a built-in automatic facility to detect when overflow occurs; in early machines its action then would be to stop the program; in modern machines it alters the state of a special register, the overflow register, which at the program's direction can subsequently be inspected and the appropriate action taken (if any is required) by means of a special conditional jump instruction.

Overflow can also occur as a result of arithmetic shifts up. Thus 0.375×2^2 would be a shift up two places of **0011000...** which gives **11000...** representing -0.5, which is obviously wrong; the real answer, 1.5, exceeds capacity and causes overflow. Shifting **0101000...** up two places arithmetically would also cause overflow, although the result does not alter the sign bit; it would give the answer **01000...** which is equivalent to 0.5 and is clearly not 0.375×4. This is equally detectable by the computer.

Overflow cannot occur during multiplication, because the product of two fractions is always a fraction. It can occur, only too easily, in division, even when we are treating this as an operation on two small integers (when overflow by addition is impossible). It will always happen when the numerical value (ignoring sign) of the divisor is equal to or less than that of the dividend, for the quotient must then be equal to or greater than 1.0.

There are various ways of getting round this difficulty. We can shift up the divisor n places so that it becomes larger than the dividend (or shift the latter down n places if that retains sufficient accuracy), and remember that the answer will be too small by a factor of 2^n. Or we may have recourse to *floating point* arithmetic (so called in contrast to *fixed point*, which is what we have been discussing), which is performed automatically by special instructions in modern computers. In floating point arithmetic, numbers are typically in the form $2^n \times m$ where m is a fraction not less than 0.5, the values m and n providing the stored form of the number. Not only does this greatly diminish the problems of overflow, but also increases considerably the range (large and small) of numbers which can be dealt with.

This is not an appropriate place to discuss floating point further. It presents no special difficulties, and programming manuals provide adequate instruction. Division will never be required for genotype simulation programs except in results processing. Its commonest use there will be in the calculation of gene and genotype frequencies; exceptionally, these may be 1.0, a contingency which can easily be recognised and dealt with; otherwise they will of course always be fractional and produce no difficulty.

Fixed Point Arithmetic Operations with XB1

For every operation, at least one of the operands must be in an accumulator.

The simplest, addition or subtraction of an integer, has been described earlier, as it is more likely to be met with in a logical context.

Addition and Subtraction

These are specified respectively by **A+B** and **A−B**, which mean precisely what they say. The answer will replace one of the operands, as indicated by an arrow, the other being left unchanged; thus **A+B→B** puts the sum in **B** but leaves **A** as it was. Both operands and the sum or difference must all be treated as integers or all as fractions—integers cannot be added to fractions.

One operand must be in an accumulator, the other may be in an accumulator, counter, modifier or store location and so may be the answer. Overflow may occur.

It is sometimes useful to change the sign of a number, and this may be done by the instruction **−A** which will change the sign of the contents of **A**, which must be an accumulator.

Another facility which may be useful is to obtain the absolute value of a number without regard to sign. The number must be in an accumulator, and the instruction **absA** will do nothing if the contents of **A** are already positive and change their sign if they are negative.

The two foregoing instructions cannot cause overflow except when the contents of **A** equal −1.0.

Multiplication

To the programmer, both operands may be integers, both fractions, or (so long as the programmer knows what he is doing) one may be an integer and the other a fraction. Both must be in accumulators. The instruction **A×B** will place a double length product in the linked accumulators **AB**. The sign bit of **B** will be same as that of **A** and will have no numerical significance; that is, only 31 bits of **B** have numerical relevance. If two large fractions are multiplied together, the bits in **B** will often be redundant; **B** may then be ignored, but it should be noted that the contents of **A** will be unrounded; this does not usually matter. If two integers, whose product is within the range $2^{31}-1$ to -2^{31}, are multiplied together the answer (correctly signed) will be wholly in **B** and **A** may be discarded; **B** may then properly be considered as the integral product of two integers.

Division

As far as the programmer is concerned both operands may be integers, both fractions, or one may be a fraction and one an integer, but the computer will treat both as fractions and it must appear to the computer that the absolute value of the divisor is larger than that of the dividend (that is, without regard for sign), for the answer must (to the computer) be less than 1.0. Otherwise there will be overflow and a wrong answer will result.

The divisor must always be in an accumulator. The dividend may be single length in an accumulator or store location, or it may be double length in two accumulators.

In single length division, **A/B** or **s***n***/B** will put the rounded quotient into **A** or **s***n* respectively, the divisor in **B** remaining unchanged.

In double length division, **CA/B** will put the unrounded quotient in **A** and the correctly signed remainder in **C**, the divisor in **B** remaining unchanged. This instruction allows an integer in **A** to be divided by a smaller integer in **B**; if **C** is zero (or all **1**s if the dividend is negative), the instruction sequence **CA/B ; C/B** will put the integral part of the answer in **A** and the fractional part in **C**.

Arithmetic Shifts

These are multiplications (up) or divisions (down) by powers of 2, but an arithmetic shift of a single accumulator produces a single length answer, not double length as in ordinary multiplication. They are similar in effect to logical shifts except that shifting up will cause overflow if capacity is exceeded and with shifting down rounding is applied if the m.s. bit of those lost off the l.s. end is a **1**, and replacement bits coming in at the m.s. end copy the previous sign bit, thus maintaining the sign. With double length arithmetic shifts the sign bit of the l.s. accumulator is ignored, the linked pair being treated as if the other 31 bits of that accumulator followed on directly from the l.s. bit of the m.s. accumulator, the shifted bits simply jumping over the sign bit; normally the sign bits of the two accumulators will be the same.

Only accumulators may be used for shifts. The instructions for single length arithmetic shifts are of the form **A×2/***n* and **A×2/**$-n$ and will arithmetically shift the contents of **A** up or down n places respectively (or multiply the contents of **A** by 2^n or 2^{-n} respectively, however one prefers to look at it).

AB×2/*n* and **AB×2/**$-n$ will do the same for a double length number in **AB**.

A×2(M*m***)** and **AB×2(M***m***)** will arithmetically shift the contents of **A** or **AB** up or down the number of places specified by the integer (positive or negative respectively) in the modifier **M***m*.

Floating Point Arithmetic

Since it has little relevance to genotype simulation, instructions for floating point arithmetic are not provided in Mendol.

Jump Instructions

In the execution of a program, orders are obeyed sequentially as written until one beginning with **J** is encountered, which indicates that the sequence may be broken with a jump to some instruction other than the next one.

In writing a program, instructions to which jumps may be made are preceded by a bracketed reference number and this number appears unbracketed after the **J** in the relevant jump instruction. Obviously, such reference numbers must not be ambiguous, and therefore within any section of a program none may appear more than once. As will be explained in the next chapter, programs are usually written as subroutines linked together by a main program. The restriction on repetition of a reference number applies only within the main program or within a subroutine; any reference number may appear in as many subroutines as desired as well as in the main program. There is no ambiguity; in a jump instruction a reference within the same subroutine is simply cited by itself, and for a reference within another subroutine the number of that subroutine is added to the citation. This is a form of relative addressing. Reference numbers may appear in any order, and it is not necessary that all numbers up to the highest in the subroutine should be used.

If no condition is specified by the jump instruction a jump will always be made, to the instruction specified (*unconditional jump*). An unconditional jump instruction is written **J**n which means jump to the instruction preceded by reference (n) in the current subroutine, or **J**n**P**m which means jump to the instruction in subroutine **P**m preceded by reference (n). For the purposes of jump instructions, the main program is treated as though it were subroutine **P0**. A jump may also be made to an instruction specified by its absolute address contained in a modifier, the instruction being **J(M**m**)**.

All three forms of instruction may be made *conditional*, by the statement of a condition at the end of the instruction. If the condition is true, a jump will be made; if it is not true, then there will be no jump and the program will pass sequentially to the next instruction. There are three types of condition.

Firstly, there is the relation between a specified accumulator or counter, and zero. There are six possibilities here, $= \neq < \leqslant \geqslant$ and $>$, and all six are available as conditions for jumps. The instructions are written, for example, as **J**n**A**$\leqslant$**0** which means jump to the instruction preceded by (n) in this subroutine if the contents of **A** are negative or zero.

Secondly, jumps may be made conditional on a comparison of the contents of two accumulators, or of one accumulator and a store location, depending on whether they are equal, unequal or which is the larger. **J**n**A**$<$**s**m requires a jump to be made if the contents of **A** considered numerically are less than those of store location **s**m.

Finally, jumps may be conditioned by the state of the overflow register. **J**n**V** will cause a jump if the overflow register is set, and will clear that register. It may also be cleared without a jump by the sequence **J**n**V;(**n**);** followed by the next instruction. **J**n**NV** requires a jump if the overflow register is not set, and also clears the register if set.

Jump specified as **J**n**P**m or **J (M**m**)** may also be conditional in the same ways as **J**n.

Finally, at the end of the program it will be required to stop. The instruction for this is simply **STOP**.

Parameters etc.

In addition to the instructions, the written program will usually need to contain other information such as parameters, constants, bit patterns etc. This information will be part of a subroutine (or the main program and the words concerned will be written immediately after the subroutine signal **P**m/n (see p. 96).

In any sequence of such words, zeros followed by non-zero words must be written in the program; zeros followed only by zeros need not be. Each parameter, bit pattern etc. which is written will be terminated by a semicolon, as with instructions.

Numbers will normally be written as decimal numbers. They must be integers or fractions, and may be negative or positive; if positive, the sign need not be written. They are written in the usual way thus, 427, −.623 etc. Integers will be stored as $n \times 2^{-31}$ and must be within capacity; that is n must be within the range $2^{31}-1$ to -2^{31} inclusive.

Bit patterns are essentially binary numbers. To write them down as binary numbers would be inconvenient. Instead, they are treated logically, the m.s. bit being considered as having the same significance as any other bit, and written as positive octal integers by breaking the binary pattern up into sections of three bits from the l.s. end and expressing each triplet as its decimal equivalent (which since it can never exceed seven is also its octal equivalent). The whole bit pattern so expressed is preceded by **8**/ and zeros at the m.s. end are ignored. Thus

00000010111010101011110000111101

becomes

00 000 010 111 010 101 011 110 000 111 101

which is written **8/272536075.**

When a programmer becomes really experienced, he will acquire a repertoire of tricks and devices. It is sometimes useful to be able to change an instruction in a program during the execution of a run, by an operation of the program itself. The simplest way of doing this is to have a stored copy of the new instruction, and transfer it when required. The receiving address must be known, and this can be arranged easily by giving it a reference number. Then if the instruction at, say, reference (**5**) is to be replaced by an instruction stored in **p3** of the same subroutine, and the replacement is to be effected by that subroutine itself, this can be achieved by an instruction sequence such as **M15 = (j5); p3→A; A→a0(M15)**. The instruction to be transferred is written exactly as it would be if written in the ordinary sequence of instructions, but if it is a jump instruction care needs to be taken with the reference which if unqualified by a subroutine number will be taken to refer to the subroutine in which the replacement instruction is stored and not to its final destination if these are different.

For convenience of reference, the instruction code of Mendol is set out in an appendix at the end of the book.

CHAPTER 5

Subroutines

Unless it is short, a computer program will not usually be written as though it were one continuous operation. Most programs will normally pass in a more or less regular sequence through a series of procedures which are largely well-defined and self-contained, and will be conceived and written as orderly assemblages of such procedures. The discrete sections of the program corresponding to such self-contained procedures are referred to as subroutines. They may be (and frequently are) written in isolation from the rest of the program, and will be brought into action (that is, entered by means of jump instructions) during the execution of the program by a special control section called the main program.

Subroutines fulfil several functions in computer programming, and their proper use is an important element in the art of programming, making it simpler, neater and less liable to error.

Broadly speaking, we can divide the use of subroutines into three categories. A subroutine may be concerned with a procedure which is used only at one point in a particular program; or it may be concerned with a procedure which is used at a number of different points in a program; or it may be concerned with a procedure (such as some widely used mathematical operation) which may be used without alteration in a number of quite different programs. These three categories and their uses will be considered in turn.

The usefulness of the first category is perhaps not immediately obvious but it is none the less real, and lies principally in the fact that it not only allows the programmer to think more readily about the broad outlines of his program without having to worry about details, but also allows him to deal with the detailed programming of a particular procedure without having to worry about the program as a whole. Further, if a program needs revision either for correction or improvement, this may be carried out without any need to touch those of its subroutines which do not themselves require revision.

The ability to consider subroutines and main program in isolation is particularly helpful to the inexperienced programmer, and corresponds to the way in which the demonstration program of Chapter 3 was developed, although as written that program was not actually divided into subroutines.

Had it been, the subroutines would individually have been concerned with the setting of the starting population, the production of one seed, the viability test, scoring the genotypes of the seeds, output of the results and replacement of the old population by the new, each of them being used in only one position in the program. At the end of this chapter, this demonstration simulation model will be reprogrammed in Mendol, and will be used to illustrate the way subroutines are incorporated into a program.

The use of subroutines does involve one disadvantage, in that a small waste of computer time is involved in jumping between main program and subroutine, but this disadvantage is outweighed by their great convenience in allowing a program to be written in self-contained sections.

Where a procedure occurs identically at more than one point in a program, subroutine treatment becomes even more useful because however many places there may be at which it is required in the program it need only be written out once, the main program entering it whenever it is required. That is, the procedure does not have to be written out at every point where it is needed. Even when the procedure involved is not always precisely the same, a single subroutine may still often be used, the main program supplying it with information enabling it to modify the procedure as required for that particular part of the program.

Even more valuable is the use of subroutines for procedures which may be applied to many different programs. These may be subroutines developed and written by the programmer himself, often having relevance primarily to the field in which he is working and therefore likely to be useful in a number of related programs. An example of this is the generalized subroutine for the simulation of segregation and fertilization with 15 independent loci, described in Chapter 6 (Figure 27). This subroutine could be applied without alteration to any simulation program for XB1 in which the simulation procedure required by the subroutine has been followed. It could be adapted for use with such programs on any computer, and so in that sense it is available to any other programmer who wishes to use such a procedure. Conversely, subroutines written by other people may also have a general applicability and so be of value to a programmer in supplying him with proven subroutines and relieving him of the work which would be involved in conceiving and writing them himself. Some of these will have been developed and written by people interested in the same sort of problems as the programmer, and therefore likely to be of relevance primarily to that field of study. Similar in fact to experimental techniques developed by research workers for their own purposes but usable by other workers in their experiments.

Other subroutines may have a much wider range of applicability, dealing for example with mathematical procedures, sometimes simple sometimes very complex. These are among the most useful of all subroutines and computer manufacturers supply many of these in libraries of subroutines suitable for use with their machines. The simpler ones will be required in many different programs; the more complex may have a more specialized application. Their particular value is that they allow the use of procedures outside the programmer's repertoire of mathematical knowledge and experience, or for which the development and writing of a program would be very difficult. Even where they are within the range of the programmer's ability they are still useful in saving him the trouble of writing them himself.

To non-mathematical biologists, the programming even of such relatively simple operations as square root extraction and pseudorandom number generation may be difficult. But through the use of generalized subroutines written by somebody else, these operations can in effect be treated as though they were hardware operations initiated by a single instruction—the jump instruction to a subroutine. As long as the programmer can be confident that the subroutine correctly performs the desired operation, he does not need to know how this is achieved either in programming or mathematical terms.

We have now gone one better than reducing to once per program the need to write down an often used procedure. We only need to construct a subroutine once for use in all appropriate programs. Provided it is in a language suitable to the machine we are using, we do not even need to write it down and punch it for each program in which it is used. Once it has been punched on to paper tape this can simply be copied mechanically or grafted into its appropriate position in the tape for the program; or if it has been punched on to cards, these can be used simply by putting them in the proper place in the stack of cards for the program. Or simpler still, if the equipment is available, the subroutine may be stored on magnetic tape or disc in a permanent library of subroutines and called in by the compiler when required and inserted into the program as it is being compiled. If the subroutine is written in a high-level language its use in this way is even less restricted.

It was pointed out previously that in the demonstration program of Chapter 3 there were six procedures, each used in one position only, which could have been treated as subroutines. There were also two procedures which were used at two different points in the program, and one which was used (though not always in identical form) at five different points.

The random choice of a parent from the population was so simple a process that it would not have been worth treating as a subroutine anyway. The production of a gamete from a parent was rather more involved, requiring five instructions, and might with some adjustment have been written as a subroutine, the jump instruction to the subroutine having the effect of an instruction meaning 'produce gamete'.

Rather different from these, and not requiring subroutine treatment in the demonstration program, was the production of random numbers within varying ranges. It did not require subroutine treatment there because the human computer had the hardware facility (four boxes of numbered cards or blocks) to produce a random number in a single operation in response to the single instruction **RN** followed by a number directing you to the appropriate box. But a real computer would not have such a hardware facility, and random number (strictly speaking, pseudorandom number) production would be by a subroutine, the main program on entry to this supplying the information specifying the range in random number required. Such a subroutine would be an example of a mathematical subroutine which could be used in any program for which pseudorandom numbers were required, and at several different points in any one program. The single instruction **RN3**, for example, would be replaced by specification of the number of bits required and a jump instruction to the subroutine. If we consider autocode programs, **RN3** would correspond to an autocode instruction calling for a procedure.

This reference to a pseudorandom number subroutine illustrates a further important point; if we write gamete production, for example, as a subroutine, then this would include the pseudorandom number subroutine within it. Subroutines may occur within subroutines, and in so doing are treated in precisely the same way as if they occurred directly within the main program. In fact if, as suggested earlier, production of one seed were written as a subroutine, gamete formation would be a subroutine occurring (twice) within that, and the pseudorandom number subroutine would be a subroutine within a subroutine within a subroutine, occurring there in fact four times.

Relative Addressing of Subroutines

That subroutines may be programmed in isolation is largely due to the fact that their words (instructions, constants, words used as working space etc.) may be relatively addressed as readily as may any other part of the program or relevant stored material.

How relative addressing operates for subroutines differs from one computer to another, but the method which will be adopted here conforms broadly to acceptable conventions. In the following account, subroutines are considered only in terms of Mendol.

The way in which a relative address of a word within a subroutine will be expressed will differ according as to whether the word is being referred to by the same subroutine, or by another or the main program.

For a reason which will be apparent later, any words which represent constants, parameters etc., or are to be used as working space will appear consecutively at the beginning of the subroutine and will be followed by the instructions; there is no intermingling of instructions and non-instruction words. When it is written, the subroutine will be preceded by a *signal* in the form **P**m/n where m and n represent integers. If the program were to be compiled, **P** would warn the compiler to expect a subroutine and to take any necessary action to deal with it; for example, subsequent relative addressing will refer to a new base address appropriate to that subroutine. m is a distinguishing number allotted to a subroutine by its programmer and used to refer to the subroutine or identify it. n is the number of non-instruction words in the subroutine before the first instruction.

The base address of the subroutine will be the address of its first word and will be referred to within the subroutine by the relative address **p0**, subsequent words being **p1**, **p2** etc., these addresses being modifiable in the usual way like any other form of address. The relative address of the first instruction will therefore be **p**n—since n non-instruction words will occupy locations **p0** to **p**$(n-1)$. But instructions, unlike constants etc., will not normally be referred to by their relative addresses; they are usually only addressed in jump instructions, and the relevant addressing will be by reference numbers in the usual way. These numbers may occur in any order in the subroutine, as with the main program, with the proviso that the reference for the first instruction must be **(0)**. Since the compiler will know that reference **(0)** will have the relative address **p**n, zero words at the end of the non-instruction section of the subroutine need neither be written down nor punched. For example, if $n = 15$ and eight constants are written in the subroutine followed immediately by the reference **(0)**, then after the compiler has dealt with the constants by putting them into locations **p0** to **p7** it will meet that reference and will then put zeros into locations **p8** to **p14** before it deals with the first instruction which will go into **p15**. This saves a little work by the programmer if the subroutine is to contain a number of initially zero words which it will later use for example as working space or storage, provided such words immediately precede the instructions; zeros interspersed among the constants would need to be written down and punched.

It should now be clear why non-instruction words appear at the beginning of a subroutine. If the instructions appeared at the beginning, then the locations of the non-instruction words would not be known when the instructions are being written since the space required for these would not be known either. To guess at the space required for instructions and add a margin of error would waste space if the guess were an overestimate, and lead to chaos if it were an underestimate and the margin of error were too small, since it would involve changing the locations of the non-instruction words and amending all those instructions already written which referred to them. Even if the first guess were right, subsequent revision of the program for correction or improvement might well increase the number of instructions and produce the same result. This sort of instruction amendment leads only too readily to error. With the instructions appearing at the end of the subroutine, changes in the number of non-instruction words do not matter, since changing the location of instructions does not affect the numbering of references.

The relative addresses **p0**, **p1** etc. and the references **(0)**, **(1)** etc. may occur in all subroutines, but no ambiguity will exist because instructions such as **A→p3** and **J4** refer only to location **p3** and reference **(4)** of the particular subroutine carrying those instructions. Where there is a subroutine within a subroutine, then the exemplified instructions appearing in the latter refer only to the latter's **p3** and **(4)**, and not to any location or reference in the internal subroutine; and vice-versa. Cross references in either direction require to be dealt with as described below.

The main program may require to address words in a subroutine, and one subroutine may need to address words in another (which may be internal or external to itself or quite separate). In those circumstances, ambiguity is removed by specifying the appropriate subroutine by its number. Thus while the instructions **A→p3** and **J4** appearing in the main program refer to main program address **p3** and reference **(4)**, the instructions **A→p3P15** and **J4P15** wherever they appear will refer to location **p3** and reference **(4)** in subroutine **P15**. Addresses such as **p3P15** are modifiable in the usual way.

For addressing purposes, the main program is treated as a subroutine numbered **P0**, and any subroutine wishing to address the main program would do so in the same way that it would address another subroutine, the previously exemplified instructions becoming **A→p3P0** and **J4P0**.

In some ways, the main program is written as though it were a subroutine, with *n* non-instruction words preceding the instructions; the signal at the beginning of the program is **P0**/*n* and the first instruction has reference **(0)**. The words of the main program are relatively addressed by the main program as **p0**, **p1** etc. in the same way that a subroutine would address its own words.

It is usually convenient (especially for subroutines written for more than one program) for tables and similar lists used by a single subroutine to be stored within that subroutine (before the instructions), since this allows a copy of the whole subroutine, written or punched, to be kept in one piece. But tables etc. used by the main program or by more than one subroutine are often best stored independently in sections of the store beginning for example **s0**, **t0** etc. or in instructionless subroutines. In the former case the table is constructed by the program which places it in this proper section of the store, since in Mendol it is not permissible to fill store sections **s**, **t** etc. directly by program input. (Table-writing subroutines are discussed in Chapter 6, e.g. see Figure 19). The words in tables in such sections will be relatively addressed by subroutines in the same way as by the main program, that is simply as (for example) **s12**, **t27**, modifiable in the usual way. The number of words required for each of the store sections will have to be specified at the beginning of the program, since a compiler has no way of deducing this information and it must leave room for them.

Instructionless subroutines may be used both for tables constructed by the program and for those written out, punched and placed in position during input. In the former case, the table will be empty at the beginning of the program, and all that has to be punched is the subroutine signal which must of course specify the number of words required for the table. In the latter case, the table itself is written and punched, with its items in their proper sequence, immediately after the signal. Instructionless subroutines are addressed in exactly the same way as ordinary subroutines, except of course that there are no references.

Writing and Using Subroutines

The category of subroutine makes no difference to the way in which it is written with regards to the signal, sequence of non-instruction and instruction words, methods of relative addressing and the use of references. But it does make a difference to the way it is used and some of the things which it can do, and there are a number of restrictions which must be applied to subroutines which are used in more than one place in a program or in a number of different programs. There are a number of conventions which should be applied, since consistency is desirable in certain cases where alternative ways of programming are available. It is usually worth while applying these conventions where appropriate even to subroutines used at one point only in one program.

Almost all subroutines will use accumulators, and may use counters and modifiers as well. One of the minor irritations in machine order programming is having to remember which of these are in use at any particular time, for those that are will not be available for use by a subroutine unless special (and time-wasting) steps are taken for temporary storage of their contents. If one is writing a subroutine which is to be used once only, it is not too difficult to remember or determine what the main program still has in use at the time of entry to the subroutine. But if it is to be used at more than one point this is obviously more awkward, especially if the main program is not yet written or if alterations requiring additional accumulators, counters or modifiers may have to be made to the main program in the relevant areas. Since a subroutine is only written down once, however many different points it is used at in the program, it must have identical requirements for accumulators etc. on each occasion that it is used. It should be obvious that it is the main program which has to conform to the requirements of the subroutine, and not vice-versa.

A good conventional way of minimizing this difficulty is for the main program to use accumulators from the **ABC** end and counters and modifiers from the low number end, and for a subroutine to use accumulators from the **HGF** end and counters and modifiers from the high number end. Where there are subroutines within subroutines, the innermost ones will have priority in the use of the highest numbered counters and modifiers, and accumulators from **H** downwards.

Where a subroutine (including others nesting within it) requires a lot of accumulators, the main program may have to release some by dumping their contents and picking these up again after the subroutine has finished; alternatively, the subroutine can do this itself, restoring the original contents to the accumulators before exit, but this may waste time (though it simplifies programming) when the main program has few accumulators in use.

It is good practice, even if particularly careful programming should be needed to do it, to keep the number of accumulators, counters and modifiers required by a subroutine to a minimum, since this simplifies writing the main program. It should also be apparent that even though the outline of the main program may have been conceived at the beginning of writing the program, the subroutines should be written in detail before the main program is written in order that the subroutine requirements for accumulators etc. may be fully known during the latter operation.

When exit is made from a subroutine, it must have finished entirely with the accumulators, counters and modifiers it was using, and these are available immediately for use by the main program or another subroutine. In other words, a subroutine cannot retain use of these registers between exit from it and the next entry to it. It may sometimes happen that a subroutine needs to retain information so held (acquired or produced by itself during the current use) between one use and the next; if that is the case the information must be transferred temporarily to a storage location within the subroutine, the register which contained it thus being released.

Addressing store locations presents no problems to a subroutine used only in one place in one program, and this may be done in the same way that it would be in the main program. But when a subroutine is used in several places in the same program or in different programs the same set of instructions may be required to operate on different store locations on each occasion, and then the subroutine cannot be written to refer directly to a specific location. The simplest way round this difficulty is for the subroutine, on each occasion that it is entered, to be provided by the main program with the relevant address which it subsequently uses as a modifier. For example, suppose the subroutine has to deal with a series of words, beginning at address **s13** on one occasion and **t27** on another. Immediately before entry, the main program will put the absolute value of the appropriate address, **s13** or **t27** as the case may be, either into a specified accumulator for transference to a modifier by the subroutine, or directly into a specified modifier (say **M15**). The subroutine will then use the modified address **a0(M15)**; since **a0** is the absolute address (zero) of the first word of the store, **a0(M15)** will of course refer to whichever address has been supplied to the subroutine; **M15** can be incremented in the usual way.

Where a program-specific subroutine has to refer to independently stored information such as tables, it will of course address these directly in the usual way, unless it has to refer to different tables on different occasions.

A subroutine which can be used for different programs cannot sensibly be written to address directly a store location external to itself, since such addresses are likely to be allocated for different purposes in different programs. As distinct from locations on which it is required to operate, all constants, tables, working space etc. which such a subroutine uses should normally be stored within itself and so be capable of being referred to by an address relative to that of its first word, **p0**, or that of an internal subroutine. This is the only permissible form of direct addressing in a subroutine designed for general use.

One thing will have become clear about subroutines—they will almost always have specific requirements of one kind or another, and the programmer cannot simply incorporate them in his program without knowing and satisfying those requirements. It is therefore not sufficient to supply just the written program of a subroutine; there must also be provided a specification for it, not for use by the computer (which does not need it), but for the programmer (who does).

Even if the subroutine will be used in one program and only by its author, a full specification should be provided. Details are easily forgotten (especially if a program is revised some time after it was written) and as it is a tiresome job to dissect the information from the written program, mistakes can easily be made.

If, as is usually the case, a subroutine has requirements for information at entry, the specification must state what this information is and the registers in which it is to be placed before entry. This information may include such things as the words (numerical or non-numerical) on which the subroutine is to operate (or the addresses at which they may be found), parameters where these may vary from one use of the subroutine to another, the number of times an operation is to be performed, and in the case of versatile subroutines coded details defining the particular version of the operation which is to be performed. The specification must include information about any additional registers used by the subroutine and any other subroutine nested within it. If the subroutine produces information (results of calculations, of operations on words, of data analysis and many other things) the specification must state what this is and name the registers or store locations in which the main program will find it.

Entry to and Exit from Subroutines

One important topic which still has to be discussed is that of entering and leaving subroutines. Entry presents little difficulty, and is by a jump instruction to the appropriate reference of the subroutine. This will usually be reference **(0)**, but can be to any reference. Where a subroutine has a certain versatility of action, it is often simplest to arrange that the precise action is determined by the point of entry; the action-determining information from the main program is the jump instruction itself, and no steps have to be taken actually to transmit this information in accumulators etc. from the main program to the subroutine.

As a simple example of a versatile subroutine, we can once again consider the program of Chapter 3. It would be possible to combine choice of one parent and production of a gamete from it into one subroutine, itself internal to (and used twice in) the seed production subroutine. Then for the first gamete the internal subroutine would be entered at its beginning, and would choose a parent and then produce a gamete from it, delivering a copy of this to the principal subroutine. For the second gamete, according to the result of the random choice of cross- or self-fertilization, the subroutine would be entered respectively either at the beginning again or would be supplied with a copy of the first parent and entered at a point subsequent to choice of parent but prior to gametogenesis. The direct action of the breeding choice procedure would be to determine which jump instruction to the subroutine is used.

Exit from a subroutine presents quite different problems. If the subroutine is program specific and used only at one point, exit is simple enough by a jump to the appropriate reference in the main program, and this will generally follow immediately after the jump instruction for entry. But where a program specific subroutine is used at more than one point in the program, then there are obviously at least two different points to which the program has to return at different times, and it cannot know which of these is the appropriate one unless it has been provided with the necessary information on entry or knows from what point in the main program it was entered and can determine the corresponding point of return. Such a subroutine cannot therefore be written with an exit jump instruction specifying a particular main program reference. This is still more so with a general subroutine, for that cannot even know by itself what program it is being used in, let alone where it has to exit to.

These difficulties are overcome by supplying the subroutine on entry with a *link*, and its exit jump is determined by use of that link. How the link is supplied is yet another of those things which differ from one computer to another (and about which autocode programmers do not have to bother). In the Ferranti Pegasus the subroutine had usually to be supplied with a full copy of the instruction used for return to the main program. In the Elliott 803, the subroutine is supplied (by a special instruction) with the main program address from which entry is made to it, and uses this as a modifier in its exit instruction. In the KDF9 special link registers are used and are set automatically by a special form of jump instruction for entry to subroutines, and no thought or action by the programmer is required. This last is simplicity itself, and could easily have been adapted for our quasi computer, but this was not done because it was felt that some readers will be using machines where links will have to be set and it is best that they should be allowed to become familiar with the principles of link setting and use. We will imagine that the link is set simply by placing into the subroutine immediately before entry the absolute address of the main program instruction to which the subroutine has to return; this is usually but not necessarily the instruction immediately after the jump instruction to enter the subroutine. The subroutine uses this absolute address in a modifier to direct the jump on exit.

Since all subroutines other than program specific ones used at only one point must be supplied with a link, it is convenient to place the link in identical locations in all subroutines which require one. This avoids the need for the programmer to remember where he stored the link when he comes to write the exit jump instruction, and like any other good convention it minimizes the possibility of error. It is also the only thing that every one of such subroutines must have, and the obvious place for the link is the first word **p0** of the subroutine. The link will be set by the instruction **p0P**m = **(j**n**)**, where m is the number of the subroutine which is about to be entered, and n is the reference of the main program instruction to which the exit jump from the subroutine is to be made. The instruction puts the absolute address of the main program word whose reference is (n) into the first word **p0** of subroutine **P**m.

Before exit, the subroutine will transfer the contents of its first word **p0** to a modifier; since by that time the subroutine is unlikely to have any further use for modifiers, **M15** will almost always be available for that purpose and we follow the convention of using the modifier with the highest number. The two instructions **p0→M15; J(M15)** will cause an unconditional jump to be made to the word whose absolute address is stored in **p0**. It will be noticed that these two instructions have no direct written reference to any location external to the subroutine.

We can exemplify link setting and entry to a subroutine by imagining a short sequence of instructions from a program, the first and last of these being arbitrarily composed and not directly relevant to the jump. The subroutine number is imagined to be 36. Note that it is useful in writing a program to place any referenced instruction at the beginning of a line, with the reference number projecting, as this makes it easier to follow jumps when reading or checking the program.

The sequence

s14→H ; p0P36 = (j7) ; J0P36 ;

(7) ; H→p3 ; etc.

causes the absolute address of the word carrying the instruction **H→p3**—that is, the word referenced by **(7)**—to be put into the first location of subroutine **P36**, and then jumps to reference **(0)** of **P36**. At the end of **P36** the instructions **p0→M15 ; J (M15)** will put the absolute address of the instruction **H→p3** into **M15** and the program will jump to that address and proceed with the main program by executing that instruction. (Note the difference in significance of the zeros in **p0** and **J0**—store location and reference respectively.)

In discussing links, we have referred only to cases where subroutines are entered from the main program. Exactly the same procedure is used when an internal subroutine is entered from another subroutine of which it forms part, and although for simplicity this account will be written in terms of entry from and return to the main program, it is to be interpreted in the more general sense.

This exit procedure may be adapted to simplify programming when using a subroutine which has a number of possible outcomes (depending on the results of its operations) which call for different subsequent action by the main program. The latter could examine the outcome from the subroutine and on the basis of this direct the program to the relevant one of several jump instructions and thence to the procedure appropriate to the subroutine outcome. It would often save effort in program writing if the examination of the outcome could be carried out by the subroutine itself which could then use one of a selection of exit instructions to re-enter the main program at the instruction required for passing to the procedure relevant to the subroutine outcome.

As an example of such a subroutine we can return once again to the program of Chapter 3 and consider the procedure for testing the viability of the seed. There were two possibilities when **aa** was tested—viability or nonviability of the seed as indicated by the random production of zero or a non-zero number. In the Mendol version of that program given later in this chapter, the viability testing subroutine is supposed to be a general subroutine (**P100**) and must therefore have a link. It is not entered directly from the main program, since it is actually part of a subroutine (**P2**) which produces one viable seed, and after performing the viability test on a seed sent to it by **P2** it must cause the program to return to that subroutine. If the seed is viable, **P2** will then exit to the main program, delivering the seed. If the seed is inviable, the program will not leave **P2** but will return to the beginning of **P2** to produce a new seed, the inviable one being rejected. That is, **P2** has to take one of two actions, according to the result of the viability test.

The appropriate course of action could be determined by **P2** after inspection of the random number (zero or non-zero) produced by **P100**. It is neater and more convenient for it to be determined by **P100** itself through manipulation of its link, **P100** returning to **P2** either at a jump instruction leading to exit from **P2** to the main program (seed viable) or at a jump instruction causing a return to the start of **P2** (seed inviable).

After **P2** has produced a seed in accumulator **F** (where **P100** expects to find it) it prepares to enter **P100** for the viability test by setting the link. The last four instructions of **P2** are

```
      p0P100 = (j4); J0P100;
(4); J0; J1P0;
```

The first of these four instructions sets the link, the second is the jump to enter **P100**. **J0**, referenced by **(4)**, causes the program to return to the beginning of **P2** and is obviously the instruction in **P2** to which return from **P100** should be made when the seed fails the viability test; it is also the instruction whose address has been set as the link. **J1P0** causes a return to the main program, and is the instruction to which return from **P100** should be made when the seed is viable; it is also the instruction whose address is greater by one than that which has been set as the link. (Note that **P2**, which is used in only one place in the program, was written without a link, return from **P2** to the main program being by a direct jump instruction, **J1P0**.)

The appropriate exit from **P100** to **P2** is achieved quite simply. If the random number produced for the viability test is non-zero (seed inviable), then **P100** uses the link as originally set and exits to reference **(4); J0** as required. If the random number is zero (seed viable), then the address in the link is increased by one before it is used and exit from **P100** to **P2** will be to the instruction one word later, that is to **J1P0**, again as required.

We may now look at the instructions at the end of **P100** (which has the link in the conventional position, **p0**). The testing random number has been produced in accumulator **H**, and **P100** ends with

```
p0→M15; J(M15) H≠0; M15+1; J(M15);
```

This technique is a very useful one because, for example, in writing **P2** the programmer did not need to know and so did not need to bother himself with the location of the test result of **P100**, nor even with the test criterion used. This naturally simplified programming. All that was necessary was to make sure that the instructions following the entry instruction to **P100** were in the proper sequence as specified for the use of **P100**.

The sequence used here is generally appropriate for subroutines with success/failure outcomes (although in this particular case it would apparently not matter, but see later). Success usually means proceeding directly with the course of the program and will often not involve an immediate jump; failure usually requires a return to some previous point by a jump instruction. It is therefore logical for the latter to come first since, as a little thought will show, of a pair of consecutive return instructions the first one has to be a jump instruction. If the success return instruction came first it would therefore have to be a jump instruction, which might otherwise have been superfluous.

In the particular example we have been considering, the success return instruction did happen to be a jump, **J1 P0**, and the order of the two instructions would appear to be of no consequence. But this is not so, for it is **P100** we have to consider, not **P2**. **P100** is a general subroutine and must be written for general applicability. It may be used in different contexts in different programs, and it may not always happen that the success instruction to which it will return will be a jump. In the interests of programming efficiency, **P100** was written with the specified requirement that in the main program or subroutine using it, the failure return instruction should precede the success one; **P2** had to follow this requirement.

It is important to note that it is the absolute address which is increased when one is added to the link, not the reference number which does not of course appear in the compiled program. Thus suppose that in the foregoing example the instruction **J0**, referenced by **(4)**, is in a word whose absolute address is **a167**. Then with the link unaltered in **M15** the instruction **J(M15)** would be equivalent to **J4 P2** and would direct the program to the instruction in **a167**. When one has been added to **M15**, **J(M15)** directs the program to the instruction in **a168** and is not equivalent to **J5 P2**.

In the way in which it has been used here, this method of manipulating the link to determine exit to different instructions depends on the 1:1 relationship of words and instructions which we have imagined for XB1, but it can be adapted for other circumstances.

Where there are more than two possible courses of action by the main program after activity by a subroutine, it is even more advantageous to have these determined and directed by the subroutine, which will add nothing, one, two, three etc. to the link in the jump instruction modifier before exit. Such a subroutine must of course be provided with a specification relating its various outcomes to the sequence of return instructions in the main program.

Subroutine Numbering

There is a point about the numbering of subroutines which may be mentioned here. The number allotted to a manufacturer's (library) subroutine must be permanent and unique, and not applied to any other subroutine by any programmer, otherwise there would always be the danger of an ambiguity arising in a program; it is obviously convenient for such unique numbers to fall within a specified range, so that all a programmer has to do when numbering his own subroutines is to avoid that range. Subroutines which we will suppose to be included in the XB1 library will use numbers from 200 upwards.

General subroutines personal to the programmer must also be permanently and uniquely numbered so far as his own programs are concerned, but may have the same numbers as other programmers' subroutines. If such a subroutine were to be used by somebody else, it might have to be renumbered. The subroutines which we shall imagine to be private general subroutines will use numbers from 100 to 199.

Finally, subroutines used only in one program (including subsequent revisions of that program) need to be numbered uniquely only so far as that program is concerned. That is, the same number can be applied to different subroutines in different programs. For such subroutines, the numbers 1 to 99 will be used (0 is always the number of the main program).

In the examples of this book, all subroutine numbers from 100 upwards will be applied uniquely; that is, a particular number in that range will always apply to one particular subroutine in all programs in which it is used. Numbers below 100 will be applied haphazardly and will have no such unique significance.

Writing a Program with Subroutines

As an illustration of the use of Mendol and of subroutines, the program of Chapter 3 is going to be recast in a form suitable for XB1 and written in Mendol.

The recasting of the program is partly because some operations which could readily be carried out in one way by a human computer either cannot be performed in that way at all by an electronic one, or not so satisfactorily. It has also been recast with a view primarily to illustrating certain points about programming and the use of subroutines, rather than with a view to producing the most efficient program in terms of running time, although where appropriate that is an important consideration.

Before we come to deal with the program itself, we are going to consider four general subroutines which may be used in its construction. Since they are general subroutines, we must suppose that they have been written without reference to any particular program, and it is appropriate that they should be dealt with in isolation from this program. When the latter is being written, we shall only need to consider their specifications.

Two of these subroutines are supposed to be XB1 library subroutines, **P200** producing pseudorandom numbers, and **P201** which is an output subroutine responsible for translating numbers in the computer into printed integers on paper and which will be used in output of the results of the program.

The other two general subroutines will be private ones by the programmer, designed to be applicable where relevant to any of his own programs. **P100** will provide a viability test on a seed, **P101** will produce one gamete from a specified parent where only one gene locus is involved.

The General Subroutines

P100 and **P101** use random processes and will use **P200** for the production of random numbers. The specifications of **P200** must be known before **P100** and **P101** are written; **P200** will therefore be dealt with first, but its detailed program will not be written out here. Pseudorandom number subroutines are considered more fully in Chapter 13, where a subroutine fitting the description of **P200** is given on page 453. Only the specification for **P200** will be given now.

P200. Pseudorandom number generator. Specification.

Uses **G**, **H**, **M15**. Requires a link in **p0**. At the beginning of any program using **P200**, a randomly chosen positive integer less than $2^{31}-1$ must be placed in **p1** by the main program. At entry, **M15** contains a positive integer (maximum value 31) specifying the number of random bits required. At exit, **H** contains a positive pseudorandom integer of the specified size at its l.s. end.

(For example, if a pseudorandom number in the range 0 to 255 is required, entry to **P200** must be preceded by the instruction **M15** = **8**, or one having the same effect. If a positive pseudorandom fraction is required, this could be achieved by setting **M15** at 31, but it would be better to use a different subroutine.)

The other library subroutine, **P201**, will also not be written out. Output methods vary so much from one computer to another that no useful purpose would be served in this book by giving the program for one, and **P201** is in effect imaginary. In any case, it would have no relevance to genetics and the programmer will almost always have access to a manufacturer's library subroutine or be able to incorporate an autocode procedure without having to bother about how it works. **P201** will convert from binary to decimal and print out equally spaced in one line the decimal integer equivalents (with sign if negative) of the binary words in a specified number of consecutive locations. The total length required per item of output (maximum number of decimal digits expected plus number of preceding spaces plus sign) must be specified; a positive sign will not be printed but will be replaced by a space; zeros at the m.s. end of the decimal number (i.e. when that number has fewer digits than the maximum expected) will appear as spaces. If the item length and number of items per line remain unaltered over a number of lines of output, the latter will therefore appear in regular columns.

P201. Binary to decimal integer output. Specification.

Uses **G, H, M15, K15**. Requires link in **p0**. At entry, **M15** must contain absolute address of first integer to be printed, **K15** must contain number of items to be printed (which must be in separate consecutive addresses) and **H** must contain an integer expressing the printed length of each item (decimal digits plus spaces plus sign). The product of the integers in **K15** and **H** must not exceed the maximum length of line for the printer in use. Each line begins with carriage-return line-feed.

Turning now to the private general subroutines, we will first consider **P100**, the viability test, which will be described and written out in detail. **P100** is perhaps rather too naive to be really useful as a general subroutine, but it will serve its present purpose which is primarily that of illustration. It is designed to deal with a situation in which all genotypes with which it is presented are fully viable, with one exception which has a viability (that is, a chance of surviving to reproductive maturity) of $1/2^v$ where v is a positive integer (this viability cannot therefore exceed 0.5, but if a higher viability were desired it would be easy enough to re-write the subroutine using $1/2^v$ as a degree of inviability).

The subroutine will be written on the assumption that in any program in which it is used the low viability genotype and its viability will remain unchanged throughout the program; this has the advantage of saving time, since the parameters will then not need to be specified at each entry to the subroutine. But if **P100** is to be of general use, it should be versatile enough to be able to deal with different genotypes and viabilities in different programs, and therefore these parameters will have to be specified (in a parameter list at the beginning of the main program) for each program in which **P100** is used, and placed in that subroutine by main program red tape. They can be changed for different runs of the same program, since such parameter lists are easily amended.

The operation of **P100** is so simple that it does not really need a flow diagram. At entry it will be presented with a seed genotype, which it will test against a copy of the relevant low viability genotype kept in one of its **p** stores. If the seed genotype differs from this no test is necessary and the subroutine will immediately exit to one address later than that specified in the link—the way in which the link is used to direct the appropriate point of return has been described earlier in this chapter. If the seed is found to have the low viability genotype, a random integer of v bits will be generated by using **P200**; if this is zero the seed survives and exit will be as before to one address later than the link address; if the random integer is not zero, the seed fails the viability test and exit will be to the link address. The chance of a random number of v bits being zero is $1/2^v$, which is the required viability.

The integer v will be in **p1**, the low viability genotype in **p2**. These do not need to be written down in the program since **p1** and **p2** will be zero until main program red tape inserts the parameters. The genotype may be expressed in any form, since the only operation in which it is involved is a comparison with another word representing a genotype.

In the subroutine as written down here, comments intended to help the reader appear italicized in brackets—they are not part of the subroutine.

P100. Viability test. Specification.

Uses **P200, F, G, H, M15**. Requires link in **p0**. At entry, **F** contains the genotype to be tested. Viability parameter v (where viability $= 1/2^v$) and copy of low viability genotype must be set in **p1** and **p2** respectively by the main program. If genotype inviable, exit is to the instruction at address specified in link. If genotype survives, exit is to an instruction one address later. At either exit, **F** still contains the tested genotype.

```
P100/3;
  (p1 = viability parameter; p2 = low viability genotype);
  (0); J1F=p2; p0→M15; M15+1; J(M15); (exit, no test required);
  (1); p1→M15; p0P200=(j2); J0P200; (H = random number);
  (2); p0→M15; J(M15)H≠0; M15+1; J(M15);
```

The other general subroutine is **P101**, which produces a gamete from one parent where only one gene locus is involved. It also will be written out but will not be described in detail since the simulation of segregation is discussed extensively in the next chapter. For **P101** a routine which is quite simple to follow has been chosen, and the reader may work out for himself the method used or take it for granted, as he pleases.

P101. Gametogenesis, single locus. Specification.

Uses **P200, F, G, H, M15**. Requires link in **p0**. At entry, **F** requires parental genotype in two l.s. bits. At exit, **F** contains a single allele in l.s. bit.

```
P101/1;
  (0); M15=1; pOP200=(j1); JOP200; (H = random number);
  (1); pO→M15; J2H≠0; F&1; J(M15);
  (2); F down 1; J(M15);
```

(Note that the link is put into **M15** three instructions previous to the exit jump. This saves writing the instruction twice. However, duplication in writing could have been entirely avoided by the sequence **(1); J2H = 0; F down 1; (2); F&1; pO→M15; J(M15)**, but this wastes running time since as often as not (when **H** ≠ 0) the instruction **F &1** will be superfluous; running time in a routine used so frequently in a programme as **P101** is more important than programme writing time.)

The Program

We may now come to the writing of the program itself. Although the program has been recast, the basic assumptions about the genetics of the system will remain as in Chapter 3, and the reader may refer back to that chapter for a description of the model. The parameters will be treated in a generalized way, and will be written in a parameter list at the head of the program, being placed where necessary by main program red tape into the actual locations (usually in subroutines) where they will be used by the program. The advantage of this is that it is then an easy matter to change some or all of the parameters from one run of the program to another simply by amending the parameter list. If the parameters were not all together but were written in scattered positions in the program their amendment might prove both awkward and irritating. This is even true of so simple a parameter as the number of generations for which the program is to run; this could easily be dealt with at the very beginning of the program by the instruction **K0 = 50** (supposing 50 generations to be required) but it is nevertheless better to have the generation number in the parameter list where it is more conveniently amendable.

The program will be written as though it were really going to be compiled. At the beginning it will need to provide for the computer a certain amount of information about itself, and we will suppose on this occasion that this is confined to a program title followed by a statement of the storage requirements for **s** and **t**, which will be used for the population and seed storage respectively (**C** and **D** of the program in Chapter 3). None of this information will be compiled into the program. Compilation will start when the compiler meets the signal for the main program **P0**.

The program proper will begin with this signal, which will be followed by the main program parameter list and any other non-instruction words that may be required. This will be followed by the program's red tape instructions, which will involve such operations as transferring parameters where necessary into their correct positions for use by the program, and setting any counters or modifiers which will not be reset during the course of the run.

It should be fairly obvious that we cannot begin the writing of the program with information for the compiler, parameter list and red tape, for the simple reason that much of this will not be known in detail until the program is in an advanced stage of development. Programming must start with the subroutines, and not until these have been produced can the main program be properly written. As the subroutines and any operational parts of the main program are written, a list must be kept of any of their parameters which will initially be stored in the main program parameter list and of the details of the relevant main program red tape operations which will be required. It is suggested that the reader should keep by him such a list and update it as he progresses through the remainder of this chapter. It will help him when we finally come to the writing of the main program. This would be following the normal practice of a programmer writing a program, and the author is doing precisely the same thing as this chapter is being written—the program and chapter are being written together; this is not an account of a program which has already been written but is more in the nature of a running commentary.

We cannot really begin to do anything until an outline flow diagram of the whole program has been produced. This can largely be written out in terms of subroutines, and Figure 5 shows the outline flow diagram from which we will work; it may help the reader to compare it with the flow diagram Figure 2 in Chapter 3.

Figure 5 is deceptively simple; for example, **P2** is quite a complex subroutine, containing within it four other subroutines, one used twice and including two of the others.

We may now proceed to translate Figure 5 into a program, and we begin by dealing with the various subroutines in turn. When these are all written, the main program will largely be a simple matter of stringing the subroutines together by a series of jump instructions.

The subroutines **P1**, **P2**, **P4** and **P5** shown in Figure 5 are each used in one position only in the program, and strictly speaking do not require links since for each there is only one point at which it will return to the main program. Return could therefore be by a direct jump to a specified reference which should preferably be known at the time the subroutine is written, that is, before the main program is written. This presents no difficulty, since jump reference numbers may be allocated in any order, and any main program reference number may be pre-empted for return from a subroutine provided a list of such pre-empted references is made and kept up-to-date as the subroutines are written. On the other hand, this is a bit of a bother and would increase the opportunity for error, so although using a link requires two extra instructions there is something to be said for deciding to use one (a sufficiently automatic mental procedure when writing the main program) and avoiding the need to keep a note of the relevant return reference.

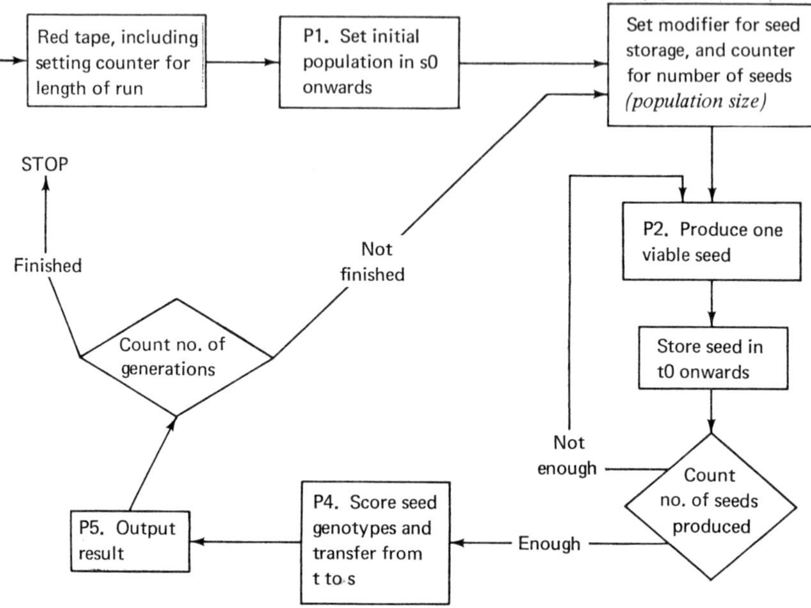

Figure 5. Outline flow diagram for simple selection model, the program for which is to be written in Mendol

P1 is used only once during any run of the program; **P4** and **P5** are used only once per generation; any time lost by using links for these three subroutines is therefore negligible and they will be written with links. **P2** on the other hand is used on average more than once for each viable seed produced, and a little time could be saved by dispensing with a link and using a directly referenced return to the main program; this course will be followed for **P2.**

In retrospect, the author thinks that this was perhaps a bad decision, being likely to confuse the reader, and that it would have been best to have used a link for all subroutines in this program. But to have changed this after the program and chapter were written would not only have involved some consequential alterations in the program and the related text—it would have required amendment to an earlier section in this chapter dealing with the manipulation of a link in directing return according to the outcome of a subroutine's activities, since the end of **P2** was involved in the example used. Even with great care, there is always the possibility in such a situation that a necessary amendment might be overlooked, to the greater confusion of the reader. When a program is working satisfactorily, it is as a general rule a mistake to alter it in the interests of efficiency if this involves a number of consequential amendments. The risk of error by oversight is a very real one, and is best avoided unless the increase in efficiency is substantial enough to be worth the risk. This is equally true when writing a book of this kind.

The first subroutine to consider is **P1**. This sets the initial population which will consist of three kinds of individuals, **AA, Aa, aa** in the ratio1:2:1 (decided in Chapter 3 and adhered to here). The binary equivalents of these three genotypes (with the decimal in brackets) are **00** (0), **01** or **10** (1 or 2) and **11** (3) respectively, and it is fairly obvious that the initial population can be set by filling the appropriate section of the store with equal numbers of the four integers 0, 1, 2 and 3. It does not in fact require a subroutine to do this, because the initial population could be written out and punched as an instructionless subroutine, signalled by **P**m/q where q is the population size, followed by 0; 1; 2; 3; 0; 1; 2; 3; 0; 1; etc. until the required number of words are filled. This may be all right when the population is as small as 16, but would be very tiresome (and mistakes might easily arise) if the population were, say, 2048. It is preferable (virtually essential if the population is large) to have the population set by a small subroutine, and in this case the starting ratio which has been chosen makes this particularly easy.

What is needed is a subroutine which will write 0 in **s0**, adds one and writes the answer in **s1**, adds one again and writes the answer in **s2**, adds one again and writes the answer in **s3**, reverts to zero and writes that in **s4**, adds one and writes the answer in **s5**, and so on. The problem is going from 3 back to zero, but this is simply solved.

If we begin with zero and increase in steps of one, then in binary we get the sequence **00 01 10 11 100 101 110 111 1000 1001 1010 1011 1100** and so on. If an LM with **...0011** is performed on each of these (that is, a masking operation which retains only the two l.s. bits), this sequence becomes **00 01 10 11 00 01 10 11 00 01 10 11 00** and so on, and this is obviously equivalent genetically to **AA Aa aA aa AA Aa aA aa AA Aa aA aa AA** and so on which is precisely what is required. So the subroutine will begin by setting a counter (for the population size) and a modifier (for storage in **s0** onwards), and with an accumulator at zero. At each cycle of the loop, after an LM with the mask **...0011** (equivalent to decimal 3) the contents of the accumulator will be copied into the next vacant **s** store and then increased by one.

This is such a simple procedure that a practised programmer would probably write it straight down with only a mental flow diagram, but perhaps we ought to show a written one here (Figure 6).

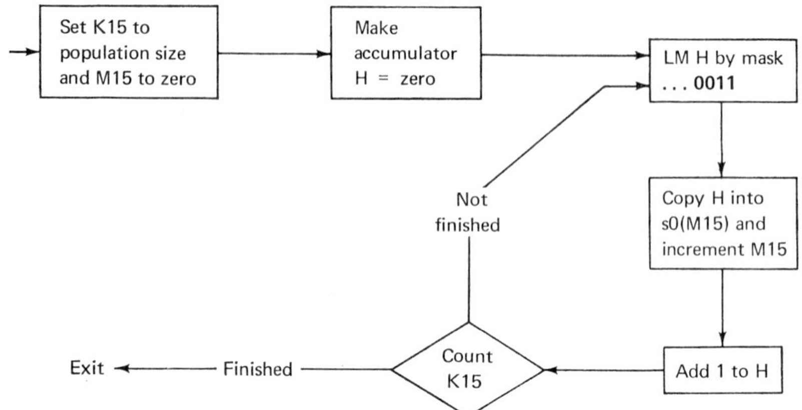

Figure 6. Flow diagram for subroutine **P1**, which sets the initial population

Main program red tape will have to provide the subroutine with the population size by placing it in one of the subroutine's **p** stores. A link is to be used for this subroutine and will be in **p0**, so **p1** will be used for the population size (and we make a note of this decision for reference when we come to write the main program).

In this case we can begin writing the subroutine with the complete signal since it is obvious from the flow diagram that no working space and no further parameters will be required. Neither of the **p** stores will be punched, since both will be zero at the start of the program—**p0** receiving the link prior to entry and **p1** being set with the population size by the main program red tape.

The subroutine can now be written down directly.

P1. Set starting population. Specification.

Uses **H, K15, M15**. Requires link in **p0**. Population size must be set in **p1** by main program.

```
P1/2;
  (p1 = population size);
  (0); p1→K15; M15=0; H=0;
  (1); H&3; H→s0(M15); M15+1; H+1; K15−1; J1K15≠0;
       p0→M15; J(M15);
```

If any other ratio of **AA**:**Aa**:**aa** had been required for the start, the subroutine would almost certainly have been less simple. It would probably have been necessary to write the subroutine in three sections, each filling the appropriate number of **s** stores with one of the genotypes (three sections only required because there would be no need to distinguish the heterozygotes **01** and **10**). It would not be very difficult to generalize the whole program in such a way that the starting population could be altered from one run to another by having the population specified by main program parameters and amending these as desired. But this is not the place to indulge in complications.

Subroutine **P2**, which produces one viable seed and is really the meat of the program, is less simply dealt with, because it includes two subroutines one of which is used twice and includes another, and all three include a fourth. Just as the whole program is written by dealing with its subroutines first, so here we begin with the internal subroutines.

But first we need a flow diagram for **P2** as a whole. The operations involved in this subroutine are successively the choice of a parent and the production of a gamete from it, a decision on selfing or crossing followed by the production of a second gamete from the same or another parent respectively, fertilization, and a viability test on the seed produced, with a return to the beginning of **P2** if the seed fails the test and exit to the main program if it is viable. The flow diagram is shown in Figure 7, and this may be compared with the relevant section of the flow diagram Figure 3 in Chapter 3. They do not coincide precisely. For instance, in Chapter 3 both parents were

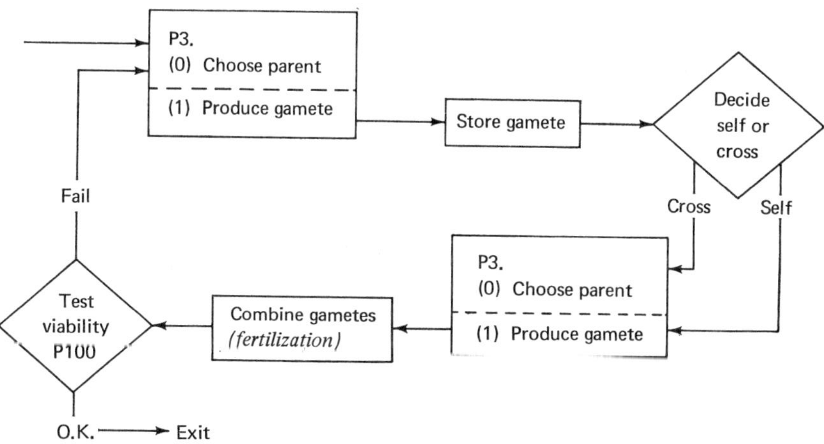

Figure 7. Flow diagram for subroutine **P2**, which produces one viable seed. This subroutine includes the internal subroutines **P3** which produces one gamete (Figure 8) and **P100** which tests viability, as well as the pseudorandom number subroutine **P200** which is used within **P3** and **P100**, and also for the self/cross decision. If the decision is to self, the parent chosen on the first entry to **P3** is used again for the second entry

chosen before any gametes were produced, whereas here choice of one parent and production of one gamete from it have been combined into a single subroutine. There is not much to choose between the two ways of ordering things, but the method used here is somewhat neater in the present context —this is by no means always the case, as will be shown in the next chapter.

One feature of Figure 7 which requires explanation is the two entry points at the second entry to the internal subroutine **P3**, which since it is the first internal subroutine in **P2** may suitably be dealt with first.

The action of **P3** is in two stages. First, it chooses a parent at random from the population, and then uses the already written general subroutine **P101** to produce a gamete. The first time **P3** is used during each passage through **P2** it is always required to choose a parent for gamete production, but at the second use it will only be required to choose a fresh parent if the test for selfing or outcrossing indicates that the parent first chosen is to be outcrossed. If selfing is indicated, then the parent chosen on the first use of **P3** must be presented again to **P101** for gametogenesis, and the random parent-choice stage of **P3** will need to be by-passed. This is easily arranged if the gametogenesis stage of **P3** is preceded by reference **(1)**, say, **(0)** being of course the reference to the first instruction of the subroutine. Then the first entry to **P3** will always be to reference **(0)**, and the second entry will either be to **(0)** for outcrossing or to **(1)** for selfing, as determined by the random test. This means that the parent chosen on the first use of **P3** must be preserved by **P3** or **P2**, or be capable of being readily made available again when **P3** is entered a second time.

P3 is quite simple to write, since **P200** (producing random numbers) and **P101** are already written. If the population size is 2^n, a parent is chosen by generating a random number of n bits (that is, in the range 0 to 2^n-1) and using it as a modifier of the address **s0** (that of the first plant in the population). **P101** is entered with the chosen parent in accumulator **F** as specified previously. At exit from **P101**, **F** will contain the gamete genotype and **P3** will then immediately exit to **P2** with the gamete still in **F**. A flow diagram is shown in Figure 8.

This flow diagram has failed to take account of the need to make the chosen parent available again if needed for selfing on a second entry. This could be done by causing **P3** to make a copy of the parent which **P2** would place in **F** before entry to **P3** at reference **(1)** for selfing. There is a quicker way of doing this which is really against the 'rules' of good programming, but an experienced programmer should not hesitate to break the rules when it is advantageous to do so and it can be done safely—but he must be careful. In this case, the second use of **P3** follows quickly upon the first, and **M14** is unaltered between the first choice of parent and the second entry to **P3**. At the second entry to **P3** therefore, **M14** still contains the random number used to choose the first parent, and the latter can be produced again for **P101** simply by by-passing the random number generation of **P3** and entering the latter at the instruction **s0(M14)→F**. It is therefore this instruction which will be referenced by **(1)** and not the entry to **P101**.

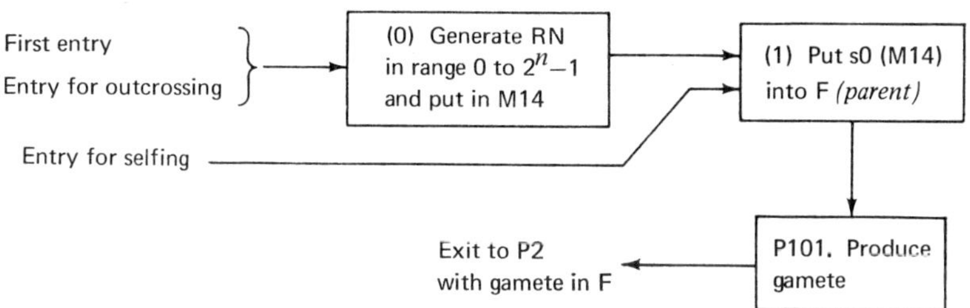

Figure 8. Flow diagram for subroutine **P3**, which chooses a parent and produces a gamete from it. See also Figure 7. During passage through **P2**, **M14** is unaltered between the first choice of parent and the second entry to **P3**; so if the latter is for selfing, **s0(M14)** gives the address of the parent chosen at the first entry

Since **P3** is used in two places, it requires a link. The only parameter needed is the population size, but as n (to specify the number of bits required for the random number) and not as 2^n. This can go into **p1**, and must be placed there by main program red tape.

P3. Choose parent and produce gamete. Specification.

Uses **P101**, **P200**, **F**, **G**, **H**, **M14**, **M15**. Requires link in **p0**. n, where population size is 2^n, must be set in **p1** by main program. If parent to be chosen, entry to reference **(0)**, choice being random from whole population. If parent not to be chosen, but same parent required as on previous use, entry to reference **(1)** but **M14** must have remained unchanged since previous use. Exit with gamete in **F**.

(Note that we do not need to specify the number of gene loci and the bits involved in the genotype. **P3** is program specific and must be written in such a way that it conforms to the requirements of the program. This has been done by using a gametogenesis routine **P101** which is suitable for the genotype simulation pattern used in the program.)

```
P3/2;
  (p1 = n);
  (0); p1→M15; p0P200 = (j2); J0P200; (H = random number);
  (2); H→M14;
```

(1) ; s0(M14)→F ; (*F* = *parent*) ; p0P101 = (j3) ; J0P101 ;
(*F* = *gamete*) ;
(3) ; p0→M15 ; J(M15) ;

(Note that as far as the programmer is concerned, the instruction **J0P101** has the effect of a single instruction 'produce gamete'. Jumps to subroutines may often be looked at in this way—thus the main program instruction **J0P2** has the effect of a single instruction 'produce one viable seed'.)

After the first use of **P3**, the gamete produced must be stored temporarily until it is needed for fertilization—it cannot be kept in **F** since **F** is required again in the production of the second gamete. The first gamete will be stored in **p1** of **P2**.)

There is no point in producing a separate subroutine to determine selfing or outcrossing, since this is such a simple operation and is best written as part of **P2**. If the degree of outbreeding is $1/2^m$ (m was 2 in the program of Chapter 3), then we generate a random number of m bits and outcross if this is zero, self if not zero, entries to **P3** being at references **(0)** or **(1)** respectively as already explained. It is convenient for the instruction testing the random number to be a conditional jump direct to **P3**, but this means that the link for **P3** must be set before the random number is tested. m must be placed in **P2** by main program red tape; since we have decided not to use a link with **P2**, **p0** is free and will be used for m.

After the second use of **P3**, fertilization is simply effected by shifting the allele of the second gamete (in **F**) up one place, and then adding to it the first gamete, whose allele occupies the l.s. bit of **p1 P2**, where it has been stored temporarily. The result is a zygote (which we may regard as a seed) occupying the two l.s. bits of **F**, where it is required by the viability testing subroutine, **P100**.

P100 is the only other subroutine in **P2**, and since it is an already written general subroutine we only need to comply with its specifications. It requires the seed under test to be in **F** (which we have just arranged), and the seed is still in **F** at exit. After viability failure, **P100** returns to **P2** at the link address and the relevant instruction must be a jump back to the beginning of **P2** in order to try again. **P100** returns to the following instruction if the test indicates viability, and this will be a jump to return to the main program, **F** carrying a seed of proven viability. A note must be made that the main program must place the viability and the low-viability genotype in **p1** and **p2** respectively of **P100**.

We may now write **P2**. We have earlier decided not to use a link, but to return to the main program by a jump instruction giving the reference directly. This will be reference **(1)** of **P0**, and we need to make a note that this has been pre-empted for this purpose.

P2. Produce one viable seed. Specification.

Uses **P3, P100, P101, P200, F, G, H, M14, M15**. No link required. At exit, **F** contains the genotype of one viable seed.

```
P2/2;
  (p0 = m, inbreeding parameter; p1 stores first gamete);
  (0); p0P3 = (j1); J0P3; (gamete in F);
  (1); F→p1; p0→M15; p0P200 = (j2); J0P200; (H = random
        number);
  (2); p0P3 = (j3); J1P3H ≠ 0; J0P3;
  (3); F up 1; F+p1→F; (fertilization); p0P100 = (j4); J0P100;
  (4); J0; (failure); J1P0; (O.K.);
```

The seed now requires storing in the next vacant word in **t**, which is quite simply done, and then a count is made to see if the necessary number of seeds have been produced. If so, the program then passes on to the next subroutine, which is **P4**, which scores the seeds and transfers them from **t** to **s**.

In Chapter 3, scoring and transferring were treated as two separate operations; they could quite easily have been combined by scoring the seeds as they were transferred from **D** to **C**. We shall adopt this procedure for the present program, since it saves time. In order to score a seed, it has to be fetched from store; it also has to be fetched from store if it is to be transferred to another section of the store. It is obviously convenient to make one fetch serve both purposes, transferring a copy of the seed immediately it is fetched and then dealing with the more complicated process of scoring.

It is true that seed transfer at the end of the last generation of a run is superfluous and wastes a little time, but this does not matter much, especially in a long run. In Chapter 3, the waste of time for the human computer would have been relatively greater, but the principal reason for not combining scoring and transfer there was that the validity of the method would have been less obvious than in the context of a program for an electronic computer, and the reader might have been confused to no good purpose.

The method of scoring will make use of modification in the way described at the end of Chapter 3, and does not require further description here. We have decided to use a link for **P4**. **M15** will be used as the modifier for fetching the seeds from **t** and transferring them to **s**; **K15** will be set at the population size and used to count the number of seeds scored and transferred; **M14** will be used as the modifier for scoring, the seed being fetched from store directly into **M14** (in some computers this would have to be done in two steps, by way of an accumulator). The subroutine will need to know the population size, and this will be set in **p1** by the main programme. **p2** to **p5** can be used for counting the numbers of **AA** (decimal 0), **Aa** (1), **aA** (2) and **aa** (3) respectively, and must be cleared initially by the subroutine each time it is used. The subroutine is extremely simple, and can be written down very easily.

P4. Score and transfer. Specification.

Uses **K15, M14, M15**. Requires link in **p0**. Population size must be set in **p1** by main program. At exit, **p2, p3, p4, p5** give respectively the number of seeds of genotypes **AA**, **Aa**, **aA**, **aa**, and the contents of store section **t** have been transferred to store section **s**.

```
P4/6;
  (p1 = population size; p2 to p5, working space for scoring);
  (0); p2=0; p3=0; p4=0; p5=0; (see comment below);
        P1→K15; M15=0;
  (1); t0(M15)→M14; M14→s0(M15); p2(M14)+1; M15+1;
        K15−1; J1K15≠0; p0→M15; J(M15);
```

With so few words to be cleared, piecemeal clearence of **p2** to **p5** is simpler than writing the instructions for a loop, which would be **K15 = 4; M15 = 0; (2); p2(M15) = 0; M15+1; K15−1; J2K15 ≠ 0; p1→K15;** etc.

Further treatment of the scores is not performed by **P4**, but by the output subroutine **P5**. The reason for this is that if the programmer changes his mind about the information required in the output, he will only need to amend **P5**, not **P4** as well.

P5 is the final subroutine to be dealt with and it will cause the desired results to be printed out at the end of each generation.

We first have to decide on the information we require from the output. Ordinarily, we would want the results expressed as frequencies of the genotypes and the recessive allele, and these to be preceded (purely as a matter of convenience) by the generation number. This would involve a mixed output of fractions and integers and some arithmetic which would be rather messy because it would have to guard against the possible elimination of **a** and a frequency of 1.0 for the **AA** genotype, which would have caused overflow during division; alternatively, we could use floating point arithmetic. As our immediate purpose is the exemplification of the use of Mendol and subroutines, **P5** has been kept simple and the output will be the generation number, numbers (rather than frequencies) of **AA**, heterozygotes and **aa**, and the number of **a** alleles, printed in that order and placed ready for printing in **p1** to **p5** respectively of **P5**.

At the beginning of each run, **p1** will be zero, and 1 will be added to it each time **P5** is entered. **p1** will therefore at the time of output contain the generation number. **P5** then has to convert the numbers of **AA, Aa, aA** and

aa held respectively in **p2** to **p5** of **P4** into the numbers of **AA**, (**Aa**+**aA**), **aa** and **a**, and place these in its own stores **p2** to **p5** respectively. This of course is quite simple and does not need detailed description—it should be easy enough to follow the operations in the written program of **P5**.

Having performed this operation, **P5** is then ready to enter **P201** for the actual output. At entry to **P201**, **M15** must contain the absolute address of the first word to be printed, which is in **p1 P5**; **K15** must contain the number of items (five) to be printed; **H** must contain an integer giving the total length including preceding spaces of each item as printed (all being the same). The last point still remains to be decided.

We are not likely to use a population size of more than four decimal digits, so we will take this as the maximum for any printed number; unused digits (that is, zeros at the m.s. end) will appear as extra spaces so the results over many generations will appear in regular columns. (Strictly speaking, for a population of 5000 or more, the number of **a** alleles could theoretically require five digits, but since **a** is under severe selection this is a very unlikely contingency which would in any event be met by occupation of one of the preceding spaces since **P201** is concerned only with the total length specified on entry.) Since the sign will always be positive, it will simply be represented by another space and we do not need to consider it. If a line printer is being used, the time taken in output is independent of the length of the line, and the number of spaces used between the columns has no effect on speed of output. A teleprinter on the other hand prints one character or space at a time, and output is therefore very much slower; it is then worth minimizing output time by minimizing the number of spaces. We will suppose that XB1 is served by a line printer and that we need not cramp our output. Five spaces (including the sign space) give adequate separation between columns. So the specification integer to be placed in **H** is nine.

We can now write down the program for **P5**, which illustrates rather well the convenience of library subroutines. The arithmetic at the beginning is long-winded, though what it does is trivial; the complication of binary to decimal conversion and printing out are dealt with by **P5** in four specification instructions (including link setting) and a jump instruction to the operative subroutine.

P5. Output results. Specification.

Uses **P201, G, H, K15, M15**. Requires link in **p0**. Expects to find numbers of **AA, Aa, aA** and **aa** in **p2P4** to **p5P4** respectively. **p1** must be zero at start of program.

P5/6;

(*p1* = *current generation number after first instruction*);

```
(0); p1+1; (increase generation count); p2P4→H; H→p2;
    p3P4→H; H+p4P4→H; (H = Aa+aA); H→p3; H→p5;
    p5P4→H; H→p4; H+p5→p5; H+p5→p5;
    H=9; K15=5; M15=(p1); p0P201=(j1); J0P201;
(1); p0→M15; J(M15);
```

(The first **H+p5→p5** could have been replaced by **H×2/1**.)

Having dealt with the subroutines, we now come to the main program. This consists of little more than dealing with the initial red tape and linking the subroutines properly together.

The program proper will be preceded by any information required by the compiler, and we will suppose this simply to consist of a short title to the program (which will be printed out by the compiler to label the output and allow it to be identified) and a statement of the storage capacity required for the **s** and **t** stores (the population size in each case). This information is not part of the program and will not be compiled—compilation will start when the compiler meets **P0/** at the beginning of the main program.

The author's list of red tape requirements and reference pre-emptions, which has been drawn up as this section of the chapter was being written, is as follows. g, m, n, q, r and v are positive integers. Main program storage locations for the parameters have not yet been allocated, and this will be done as the red tape requirements are listed.

- **p0** Starting random number r, less than $2^{31}-1$. To be placed in **p1 P200**
- **p1** Number of generations g for which the program is to run. To be placed in counter
- **p2** Population size q. To be placed in **p1 P1** and **p1 P4**
- **p3** n, where $2^n = q$. To be placed in **p1 P3**
- **p4** m, where $1/2^m$ is the degree of outbreeding. To be placed in **p0P2.**
- **p5** v, where $1/2^v$ is the viability of **aa**. To be placed in **p1 P100**
- **p6** 3, the decimal equivalent of **aa**. To be placed in **p2P100**

No other parameters or working space required.

Reference **(1)** pre-empted for return from **P2**.

There might well be some red tape operations required by the computer, but these will be entirely ignored as they would have no relevance for our purpose.

Since all the subroutines involved use only **F, G, H, K15, M14** and **M15,** there is no danger that the main program working from **A, K0** and **M0** will come into conflict with any subroutine.

We may now write the main program, representing the parameters by italicized symbols as above.

```
Selection under inbreeding;
  s/q; t/q;
P0/7;
        r; g; q; n; m; v; 3;
 (0); p0→A; A→p1P200; p2→A; A→p1P1; A→p1P4;
        p3→A; A→p1P3; p4→A; A→p0P2; p5→A; A→p1P100;
        p6→A; A→p2P100; (parameters transferred);
        p1→K0; (counter set, red tape completed);
        p0P1 = (j2); J0P1; (sets population);
 (2); M0 = 0; p2→K1; (modifier and counter for one generation);
 (3); J0P2; (one viable seed, in F);
 (1); F→t0(M0); M0+1; K1−1; J3K1 ≠ 0; (stores seed, counts,
        and returns if unfinished);
        p0P4 = (j4); J0P4; (scores and transfers);
 (4); p0P5 = (j5); J0P5; (prints result);
 (5); K0−1; J2K0 ≠ 0; STOP;
```

As the program has been written, it would have to be compiled afresh for each further run. This would normally be no hardship if any parameters were to be changed, but if the second run was to have the same parameters (with a different starting random number, of course), recompilation might be a waste of time and a direct restart would be an advantage. This would have to be at the instruction **p2→A** (since the original random number must not be reset), and a further instruction **p1P5 = 0** would be needed to reset the generation number.

It would be possible to replace the instruction **J3K1 ≠ 0** in the line beginning with **(1)** by **J0P2K1 ≠ 0**, going directly back to **P2** instead of via reference **(3)**, but this makes it less obvious that the program is actually returning during the execution of a loop and therefore the program may be less easily followed. Similarly, if **P4** and **P5** had been written without links, the exit instruction of **P4** could have been written **J0P5**, avoiding the intervening return to the main program before entry to **P5**. Short cuts of this kind are often possible, and an experienced programmer may sometimes use them; but they rarely save any significant time, and the benefit to the programmer usually consists of little more than the generation of self-satisfaction at his own cleverness. On the other hand, such short cuts make it less easy to take in the general shape of a program which may therefore perhaps be followed less easily by someone else reading it or even by the programmer himself if he needs to return to it after several months. There is more to efficiency in programming than simply minimizing the running time on a computer.

There is now written down, or available as library subroutines, the whole of the program, and if it were a real instead of a quasi program the next step would be to bring all the written material together and assemble it for punching onto cards or tape for input to the computer.

The main program must come first, but the order in which the subroutines are punched makes no difference to the compiler, since they may be stored in any order; all that is necessary is that the program should know where they are, and the compiler will see to that. But as a matter of general convenience, it is preferable to punch the subroutines in numerical order (which is not necessarily order of use) so that they may readily be located in the written program or any print-out of it—for the investigation of errors, perhaps. It is desirable when input is by punched tape to punch the program–specific subroutines before the library subroutines; punched versions of the latter will usually be available and a tape which has been partially punched may readily be completed by mechanical copying of the library tapes, or by grafting them on at the end.

The final program, then, would consist as written of the main program followed by **P1**, **P2**, **P3**, **P4** and **P5**, with **P100**, **P101**, **P200**, **P201** added by mechanical copying from private and XB1 library tapes or for card input simply by incorporation of the appropriate cards. At the end, **FINISH**, to tell the compiler when to stop reading (which is not the same as **STOP** which tells the computer to stop the program and will not usually be the last instruction in the program as written down, since it will be in the main program).

The punched program may then be input to the computer, which will read it by means of a suitable compiler which will convert it into a binary form stored in the computer. The jobs which the compiler has to do include the determination of the length of the main program, each subroutine and other sections of the store, allot them the appropriate amount of space, and determine the absolute address (base address) of the first word in each and the absolute address of any reference in each. Each instruction as written by the programmer is checked for legality (it might for example be an impermissible instruction such as **p3→t47**, simply an error in punching such as **p0P17=j3**, or might refer to a location in a section of the store beyond the number of words specified or allocated for that section), and if it is a good compiler the nature and position of the error will be output for the information of the programmer. If the instruction is legal (this is not necessarily the same as correct—the compiler cannot detect programming errors however idiotic if the instructions are legal—they will make their presence felt when the program is run), the compiler will translate it into binary, substituting the correct absolute addresses for all relative addresses and references.

When conversion is completed the compiler will (if that is the wish of the programmer) hand it over to the computer with an exit instruction which will effect a jump to reference **(0)** of the main program.

But so long as the programmer has followed the rules and conventions for writing the program as required by the compiler, he doesn't really need to know anything of how the compiler achieves this transformation of his program.

The reader has now been taken in detail through some of the more important operations in writing a computer program. Because this required a new way of looking at things, it may be one of the less easy chapters in the book, but if he has followed it patiently, preferably with pencil and paper, he should have a good grasp of the ideas and principles involved in programming.

It is suggested that as an exercise the reader should draw up a single complete and detailed flow diagram for the whole program, and take himself through it several times. If he can do this with fair fluency he should not find much difficulty in following the procedures of genetic simulation which are described in the remainder of this book. He will of course only need to read the programs, not to write them, so he will be dealing with the easier direction of translation and will not need to have the whole repertoire of instructions at his fingertips. But the author would stress that the best and most efficient way of learning from this book is to follow all the procedures carefully through the flow diagrams, and instruction by instruction where quasi programs are presented, using pencil and paper where appropriate and reconstructing flow diagrams from the quasi programs where this would help to make the latter clearer.

The big hurdle really is getting the 'feel' of computer programming, and it has to be admitted that this is a difficult, perhaps impossible, thing to acquire simply from a book. This 'feel' comes most readily with practice in programming, and the reader is encouraged to try his hand at something simple fairly soon. It is hoped that these opening chapters will have gone a fair way towards giving him confidence. Once a feel for programming has been achieved, it becomes quite a different sort of operation—no longer a fearful prospect but an exhilarating challenge to the ingenuity of the programmer, sometimes even a rewarding one.

CHAPTER 6

Segregation and Reproduction

The Simulation of Sexual Reproduction in a Population

In order to keep this account of the simulation of reproduction as simple as possible, questions of fitness and selective advantage will not be taken into account. It will be assumed that all genotypes are equally fit with equal reproductive capacities. The simulation of natural selection is dealt with in Chapter 7.

In general, organisms over-produce, often very considerably. That is to say, far more zygotes may be produced than will ever develop into adult individuals. For example, most plants produce abundant seed, but only a small proportion of the seed will germinate and grow into adult plants and so become part of the population. Similar considerations apply with animals.

It would therefore be a substantial waste of time to simulate the whole reproductive activity of a population, since most of the simulated progeny would play no further part in the history of the population. Ideally, we would wish to simulate only those acts of reproduction which lead to the establishment of an individual in the next generation, defining an act of reproduction as a process which ends with the fusion of one male with one female gamete.

What we do in effect is to imagine the total array of zygotes produced by the total reproductive activity of the population during the period under consideration (in the simplest case, a single generation), and take a sample from that array of sufficient size to give us the required number of individuals for the population in the next generation. What we actually do is to imagine the total array of reproductive acts, and perform a sufficient sample from that array. Each item in the sample is derived by simulating the formation of a gamete from each of two parents chosen at random (or according to any restrictions imposed by the breeding system or otherwise), or two gametes from one parent in the case of self-fertilization, followed by the combination of these gametes in an act of fertilization.

Another way of looking at this process is to suppose that we have a population of individuals initially of unknown genotypes, and we determine their genotypes retrospectively by simulating the acts of reproduction which might have produced them. The actual computing procedure would be the same in either case.

Basically, then, the simulation of reproduction in a population consists of the choice of one parent, the recognition of its genotype if necessary, the determination of a gamete genotype (segregation), the choice of a second parent (which may be quite independent of the first, or related to it in some way predetermined by the conditions of the experiment), production of a second gamete, and the combination of the two gamete genotypes (fertilization) to produce the genotype of a zygote, which will become an individual of the next generation.

Different ways of performing these operations will have different demands on time and storage space. For example, segregation procedures which involve recognition of parental genotypes will often save time, but only at the cost of increased requirements for storage space. Efficient programming will require careful consideration of the relative importance of time and space in order that the most efficient procedure may be chosen: most efficient, that is, in relationship to the particular circumstances of the program which is being written. The balance between the needs for economy in time or space may be reversed in going from one computer to another.

Choosing Parents

Constant Population Size

In its simplest form, this presents no difficulty, and can be dealt with quickly. If the population size is 2^n, where n is an integer, and the individuals are stored consecutively in separate locations, then it is only necessary to generate a random number in the range 0 to 2^n-1 and to use this as a modifier to choose a word representing an individual. This is illustrated in the flow diagram of Figure 9, and the relevant part of a program might read

M15 = *n*; **p0P200** = **(j1)**; **J0P200**; **(*H*** = *random number of n bits*);
(1); **H→M15**; **s0(M15)→F**; **(*F*** = *chosen parent*);

where in its first use **M15** specifies the number of bits n to be produced by the pseudorandom number subroutine **P200**, and the population is stored in **s0** onwards.

In using this individual as a parent, it must be left unaltered in its original location in the store, since removal would prevent it from being used again. In a population breeding at least partially at random, some individuals may not breed at all, while others may be used several times; the possibility of being chosen a second time must be retained for all members of the population. The individual is therefore used by having a copy made of it, using the copy to act as parent in reproduction.

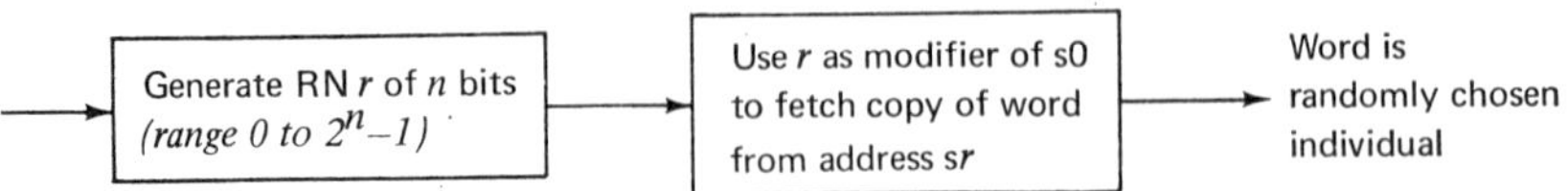

Figure 9. Flow diagram for random choice of one individual from a population of size 2^n of which the individuals are stored consecutively beginning with the location whose address is **s0**

Variable Population Size

Although it is obviously convenient to use a population size which is constant and a power of two, this is not always possible, since the conditions of an experiment may demand otherwise. For example, we may wish to simulate a population which is varying in size; only occasionally will this be exactly an integral power of two. If in any one generation the population size is d, and the individuals are stored consecutively from, say, **s0** to **s** $(d-1)$, random choice of an individual will involve production of a random number in the range 0 to $d-1$ and its use to modify the address **s0**. As explained in an earlier chapter, random numbers are initially generated in a range which is an integral power of two, and the problem is to convert a series of random numbers in the range 0 to 2^n-1 (where n is an integer) into a series in the range 0 to $d-1$, which should be the narrower of the two ranges.

We cannot do this by scaling down, which would be performed by multiplying each random number by $d/2^n$ and rounding the answer to an integer. This will certainly produce integers only in the range 0 to $d-1$, but some of these will appear twice and others only once. Clearly, this is no longer random. It is no use generating very large random numbers and scaling down more drastically—the integers then produced in the range 0 to $d-1$ will still not all appear with equal frequency.

Basically, what we have to do is to generate random numbers in a range 0 to 2^n-1 and reject all those which are larger than $d-1$. Clearly, this involves a loss of time unless $2^n-1=d-1$, which cannot often be the case in the example we are considering. Obviously, there will be 2^n-d rejected random numbers, and we must minimize the wastage by ensuring that this value is never greater than $d-1$. For example, if we want random numbers in the range 0 to 5, then the production of random numbers in the range 0 to 7 wastes only the two highest, whereas the range 0 to 15 would waste the ten highest. Wastage is minimized by ensuring that 2^n is the lowest power of two which is greater than or equal to d, that is the value of n must be such that $2^{(n-1)} < d \leqslant 2^n$.

For each generation (assuming that population size varies only between generations and not during one), the appropriate value of n is calculated before reproduction begins. It is the number of binary digits required to express $d-1$ (not d, because if d should happen to equal 2^n, then while the number of binary digits required to express $d-1$ is n, $n+1$ are now required to express d). Since n is also the number of the position, counting from the l.s. end, of the m.s. **1** in the binary representation of $d-1$, it may simply be determined by taking the binary number $d-1$ and shifting it down *logically* one bit at a time until it becomes zero. The number of shifts required to do this is n. For example, suppose $d = 154$; $d-1 = 153$ and the word representing this in binary is **...00010011001**. This requires to be shifted down eight places before it is zero, hence $n = 8$ and the random number range required is 0 to $2^8 - 1$, that is, 0 to 255.

A section of program determining the size of random number required might be as follows, **G** containing the population size.

G−1; H=0;
(1); G down 1; H+1; J1G ≠ 0; (*H* = *required number of bits for random number***);**

Clearly, difficulties arise if $d = 1$ or 0, but if a population gets as small as that there will be quite other, possibly catastrophic, difficulties, and if there is any possibility of this happening the program will always have to watch for it (for example, by an instruction causing a jump if **G** is not greater than zero after the instruction **G−1**), and take the appropriate emergency action when it does.

n having been determined, random numbers may now be generated in the range 0 to $2^n - 1$, and there are two ways in which numbers higher than $d-1$ may be rejected.

In the first method, we subtract $2^n - d$ from each random number as it is generated. The answers will be negative, zero, or in the range 1 to $d-1$. Negative numbers are rejected, and this leaves us with random numbers in the range 0 to $d-1$, which is what we require.

For this operation, 2^n has to be calculated from n, and this is done quite easily. If **H** contains n, then we transfer this number to a modifier and use a modified shift instruction to shift the integer 1 up n places. 2^n is produced in **G** by the sequence of instructions **G = 1; H→M15; G×2(M15)**.

n and 2^n are not of course calculated each time a random number is required, but only after each change of population size, the values of n and $2^n - d$ being stored by the operative subroutine. A random number in the required range, 0 to $d-1$, may then be produced as follows, supposing **p1** to contain n and **p2** to contain $2^n - d$.

> **(1); p1→M15;** (*specifying number of bits*)**; p0P200 = (j2);**
> **J0P200; (*H*** = *random number of n bits*)**;**
> **(2); H−p2→H; J1H<0;**
> **(*H*** = *random number in range* 0 *to* $d-1$)**;**

There is an alternative method which is initially more complicated but is equally effective. The binary representation of a breeding individual may of course be treated by the computer as if it were a number. If it can be arranged that all the individuals in the population are positive when considered as numbers, then we can extend the population of d individuals to a size of 2^n by adding consecutively 'dummy' words carrying negative numbers. Any random number greater than $d-1$, if used as a modifier to choose a parent from the population, will cause a dummy to be chosen, and this can easily be recognized by its negative sign and rejected. If, for some reason, it is desirable that the individuals of the population should numerically be negative, then the dummies can be given a positive sign.

It may not always be possible to use this second method. Use of positive or negative sign is a valuable way of allowing rapid recognition of critical phenotypes, and it will often happen that distinctions may be needed among the breeding individuals within the temporary population; if sign bits are used for this, they will not be available to identify dummy words. If breeding

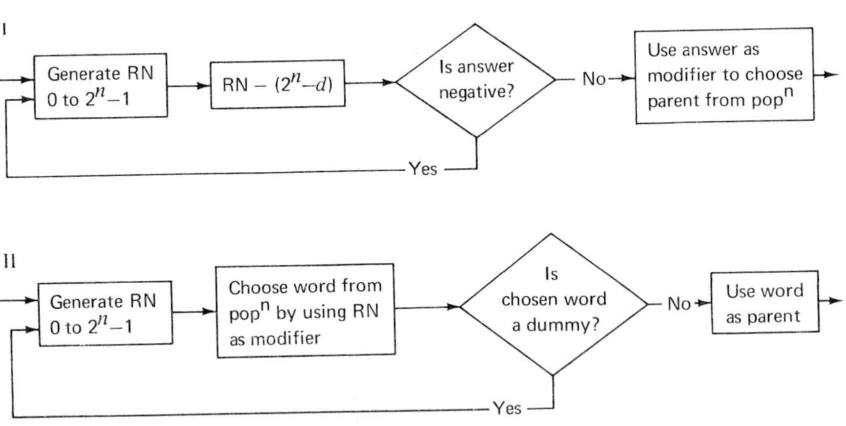

Figure 10. Flow diagram for the two methods described for random choice from a population whose size d is not an integral power of 2. Method I reduces generated random numbers by subtraction of 2^n-d, and rejects all which are then negative. Method II adds dummies to increase the population size to 2^n and rejects any dummy which is chosen. RN = random number

individuals are numerically never zero, then zeros could be used for the dummies. The computer can readily recognize positive, negative or zero, as the case may be, in a single operation. Any other kind of tag would usually require at least one additional instruction in order to effect a comparison, and we might just as well use the subtraction procedure.

Flow diagrams of the two methods of choosing from a population which is not an integral power of two are shown together for comparison in Figure 10. They may not be a great deal in terms of time to choose between them. Much will depend on the computer, especially on the speed of fetching from store. This will be slower than subtraction, and certainly the second method will be slower when the random number chooses a dummy; but breeding individuals have to be fetched in any case, and the second method will be quicker when they are chosen because there is no subtraction and fetching is the only operation involved (apart from testing, which is needed equally in both methods).

Choice of Second Parent

If the population is breeding entirely at random, choice of a second parent will proceed exactly as with the first. If however the breeding system is such that the choice of a second parent is not random with respect to the first, then a more complicated version of the procedure used for the first choice will be required.

Generally speaking, where we have non-random relationship between the two parents, the genotype of the first chosen limits the possible genotypes of the second. If, as will usually be the case, the genotypes of the individuals in a population have no relevance to their positions in the store (although if it would improve the efficiency of a program, suitable rearrangement of the population at the beginning of a generation might often be possible to produce such a relevance), choice of a valid second parent cannot be made in a single operation by restricting random choice to an appropriate section of the population. Instead, a potential second parent has to be chosen at random, and rejected if it fails to meet requirement. For example, in the simple case of sexual dimorphism, if the first parent chosen is a male, any male produced by the second random choice is rejected and random choice repeated until a female is found. This subject is also discussed in the section on breeding systems in Chapter 12, but it is worth pointing out here that with very small populations it may be desirable to check at the beginning of a generation that more than one mating type is in fact present in the population; if it is not, the program may go on trying in vain indefinitely.

One way of lessening the time-consuming waste of random number generation in the choice of unsuitable mates, where mating types are present in approximately equal numbers, would be to retain the last unsuitable mate and use it as the first parent for the following zygote. This is easy enough to arrange; if a chosen mate is unsuitable it is put into one accumulator and another set in such a way that in due course a jump instruction referring to the latter subsequently directs the program to use the former instead of randomly choosing a first parent. If all unsuitable mates are put into the first accumulator, the last one (which will have obliterated any before it) will be the one which is used for the next zygote. It would be possible, with more intricate programming, to economize further by utilizing more than one member of a 'losing sequence'. But if that degree of economy in random number generation were required, and if ample store space were available, a much better method would be to use the following procedure to choose all the parents for one generation before simulating any reproduction.

Supposing that we are dealing with two mating types only, say male and female, we would choose parents at random and store females consecutively in one section of store and males consecutively in another. Each section would of course need to be the same size as the population store (which is why the method is practicable only if ample store space is available), and choice would continue until both sections were full; for the first section to be completed, care would have to be taken to see that any further individuals of that type chosen were rejected. These would be the only individuals on which random number generation would have been wasted.

The two sections established, reproduction would proceed by pairing in the proper way individuals taken sequentially from them.

This procedure for parent choice would best be dealt with by a separate subroutine. No flow diagram for this is presented—it would be a good exercise for the reader, should he feel so inclined, to construct one from the program which follows.

A population size of 1024 will be assumed, stored in **s0** onwards. Females are to be stored in **t0** onwards and males, tagged with a negative sign bit, are to be stored in **u0** onwards. After the signal, the subroutine would proceed

```
(0); M14 = 0; M13 = 0; K14 = 1024; K13 = 1024;
(1); M15 = 10; p0P200 = (j2); J0P200; (H = random number 0 to 1023);
(2); H→M15; s0(M15)→H; (H = parent); J3H<0;
     (female chosen); J1K14 = 0; H→t0(M14); M14+1;
     K14−1; J1K14≠0; J1K13≠0; [link and exit];
(3); (male chosen); J1K13 = 0; H→u0(M13); M13+1;
     K13−1; J1K13≠0; J1K14≠0; [link and exit];
```

At exit, **t0** to **t1023** contain females, **u0** to **u1023** males, and the program can then proceed to reproduction.

Superficially, the method seems to resemble that of preliminary sorting and rearrangement of the population, but its practical implications are quite different, especially where the population size is an integral power of two. Unless the two mating types were equal in numbers in the population (which will rarely be the case), rearrangement would not produce sections which were integral powers of two, and random choice from either section would for that reason involve wastage of random number generation, considerable in the case of the larger section. With the method just described very few random numbers are wasted in this way if the population size is as stated, and the two equal sized sections are dealt with sequentially and not at random.

So far, we have only considered the situation where a second parent may come with equal chance from anywhere within the population—in other words, where spatial position and distance apart are entirely ignored. If we wish to consider position and distance, and restrict the breeding range of an individual (for example, if a plant may only be fertilized by pollen from one of its near neighbours), then we have to adopt much more complicated procedures. These will not be discussed now—an account of how this may be done is given in Chapter 11, where a program involving such a situation is described in detail.

However a parent is chosen, the next operation performed on it (in the absence of selection) will be the production of a gamete, and this will involve the simulation of segregation.

The Simulation of Segregation. Unlinked Genes

Segregation is the fundamental process in genetic simulation; above all others, therefore, it must be biologically accurate. Simplifications of the process which involve mathematical or statistical approximations should be rigorously avoided. Since it is performed many times in each generation, it must be programmed efficiently in terms of computer time.

Basically, there are two methods which may be employed.

We can imitate closely the actual process of segregation by making a choice from the alleles at each locus involved. If the genes are unlinked, this will mean a random choice independently at each locus. If the genes are linked, choice will still basically be random, but the choices at the different loci will be interdependent. The simulation of segregation with linked genes raises a number of special difficulties, which will be considered in a later chapter. In this chapter, only segregation of unlinked genes will be considered.

A second method involves a knowledge of the expected gametic ratios. We set up within the computer for each possible parental genotype a permanent population of gametes in which the possible gamete genotypes occur precisely in the expected frequencies. Simulation of gamete formation involves copying the genotype of a gamete chosen at random from that population corresponding to the genotype of the segregating parent.

The difference between these two methods may be illustrated by a simple example, in which we consider a heterozygote **AaBb** from which we wish to produce a gamete.

We could imitate segregation by selecting one allele at random from **A** and **a** and a second allele at random from **B** and **b**, combining the two selected alleles to produce the genotype of a gamete. This would be a relatively slow process, involving the production of two random numbers (but see p. 149) and some fiddling bit manipulation.

A much neater and quicker method would be to make use of the fact that the four possible gamete genotypes from **AaBb**, namely **AB**, **Ab**, **aB** and **ab**, occur with equal frequency. If the binary representations of these are stored in four consecutive locations in a table, we may produce the genotype of a gamete by choosing one of these locations at random ('random table look-up'), using a random number in the range 0 to 3 as a modifier.

It might seem that an even quicker method was available. In binary, the four gamete genotypes are **00**, **01**, **10** and **11**, which are the integers from 0 to 3. The generation of random numbers in that range would be a simple and accurate process for producing gametes from a parent **AaBb**. It could be generalised to cover any number of independent loci; for example, the integers 0 to 15 would represent all possible gametes from **AaBbCcDd**. But its use is severely limited because it is only applicable to situations in which there is heterozygosity at all loci concerned. It is useless as a general method in population simulation, which will almost always involve a number of different parental genotypes. This objection does not apply to random table look-up; for example, to form a gamete from a parent **AABb**, we would refer to a table in which the four locations were occupied by **AB**, **AB**, **Ab** and **Ab**. (Obviously in this case reference to a 2-location table, with **AB** and **Ab**, would be sufficient; but from a programming point of view it is much simpler to keep all tables—or rather all sections of one table, which is the way matters will be arranged in practice—the same size, for reasons which will be clear later.)

Genotype heterogeneity within a population raises a problem which is unavoidable with the table look-up method, namely recognition of the genotype of the parent from which a gamete is to be produced. Each different parental genotype will require its own array of gamete genotypes, and the program will need to identify the parental genotype in order that reference may be made to the correct array. There is scope for programming skill here, and the efficiency (in terms of speed) of a reproduction routine may depend to a considerable extent on skilful programming of the identification process.

Genotype recognition is unnecessary with the method in which each locus is treated separately, though it may sometimes be an advantage. To produce a gamete from **AABb**, a random choice may still be made at the **A** locus, even though it is really no choice at all. No preliminary recognition of the genotype is then necessary, but there is a waste of time in making a superfluous random selection. The programmer needs to decide, in the light of the particular circumstances, whether it is better to waste time making a random choice or to spend time in genotype recognition which would allow a random choice to be made only at heterozygous loci.

Before we proceed further to discuss the simulation of segregation and gametogenesis in detail, there is one point which needs clarification. With animals, 'gametogenesis' and 'gametic ratio' are unambiguous terms, since meiosis produces gametes directly. With higher plants (and many lower ones) meiosis produces spores, not gametes, and a generation of many or very few cell divisions may intervene before gamete formation. With flowering plants, no real difficulty arises, since a functional spore (pollen grain, or megaspore producing an embryo sac) produces a single effective gamete of the same genotype as itself, so that basically genotype ratios among the gametes of a flowering plant are the same as those among its spores. In fact, of course, many people loosely equate pollen grains with male gametes and ovules (which have one functional megaspore) with female gametes. To avoid unnecessary words, we will therefore use the terms 'gametogenesis' and 'gametic ratio' to refer both to those processes in animals and to sporogenesis and spore ratios in flowering plants. For the time being at least we will ignore the possibility of differential selection among pollen grains and ovules before gamete formation and fertilization; this would be a special genetic situation requiring special treatment, and might well be a problem for research by simulation techniques. In lower plants, such as ferns and mosses with their more prominent gametophytes, the question of selection prior to gamete formation assumes much larger proportions; it will not be discussed in this book.

The following account of the simulation of segregation will deal separately with single locus segregation, segregation at two independent loci, and segregation at three or more independent loci. It will discuss a variety of methods with varying emphasis on minimizing time, storage requirements, and programming intricacy.

Single Gene Segregation

Here, only three possible parental genotypes are involved—**AA**(**00**), **Aa**(**01** or **10**) and **aa**(**11**). We may dispense with genotype recognition (as in the demonstration program of Chapter 3 and its Mendol version in Chapter 5) and treat all genotypes in the same way by making a random choice of the l.s. or the m.s. of the two gene-simulating bits. If these two bits are at the l.s. end of the word which represents the parent, with the rest of the word all zeros, the easiest and most convenient way of making the random choice is to generate a single-bit random number (that is, zero or one with equal probability) and then to shift the word logically down one if, say, this is one, or if it is zero to leave the word unshifted and execute an LM using **1** as the mask, which will eliminate the unwanted m.s. allele. In either case, the l.s. bit of the word at the end of the operation will be the randomly chosen allele, with the rest of the word zeros; the word will now be the gamete.

For example, if the genotype of the selected parent is **aA**, the word simulating the parent will be **...00010**. Taking the action suggested above after random number generation, if this is a one the word is shifted down one and becomes **...00001**; the new l.s. bit is the chosen allele, in this case **1**, that is **a**. If the random number is zero there is no shift and the word remains unaltered for the moment as **...00010**; the chosen allele is the l.s. bit which is **0**, that is **A**, but we are left with an unwanted **1** which must be eliminated and this is done by performing an LM with the mask **...00001** which now produces the result **...00000**, which is what we require. Of course, if the unwanted allele were **0**, the LM would be superfluous; in fact this operation would always be carried out, since it is quicker to perform it than to find out whether it is necessary. When the random number is one, the unwanted allele is eliminated automatically by the shift down (which, for that reason, *must* be a logical and not an arithmetic shift which would give a rounded answer).

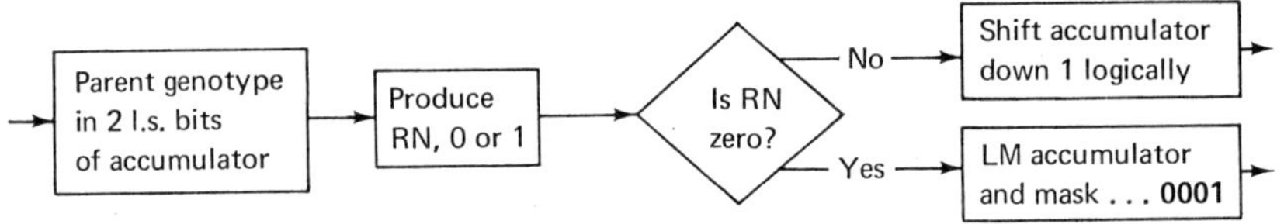

Figure 11. Flow diagram for a simple method of simulating segretation at a single locus. This corresponds to subroutine **P101** which has been written out without explanation in Chapter 5

The flow diagram of Figure 11 illustrates the process, and is in fact the flow diagram of subroutine **P101** which was written out in full but without explanation in Chapter 5. The parent genotype occupies the two l.s. bits of **F**. After a 1-bit random number has been produced in **H** and the link placed in **M15**—**J(M15)** being the exit jump from the subroutine—the operative instructions in **P101** are

```
     J2H ≠ 0; F&1; J(M15);
(2); F down 1; J(M15);
```

after which the gamete genotype occupies the l.s. bit of **F**.

An alternative and neater method is to use the random number as a modifier to specify the number of places (zero or one) by which the accumulator containing the parental genotype is to be shifted down. The flow diagram, Figure 12, illustrates the process, and the operative instructions of a subroutine would be as follows, **H** containing the 1-bit random number and **F** the parental genotype.

H→M15; F down (M15); F&1; etc.

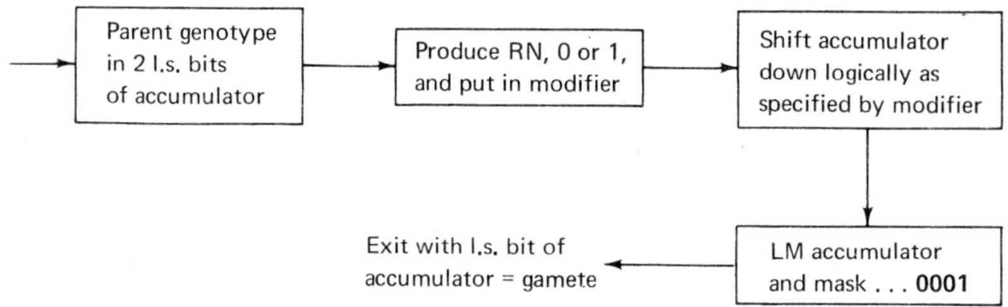

Figure 12. Flow diagram for an alternative method of simulating segregation at a single locus, using the generated random number (0 or 1) to specify directly the shift down (0 or 1 place)

With this method, the masking operation has to be performed every time, even when the parent genotype is shifted down and masking is apparently superfluous—the insertion of a jump instruction to avoid the latter situation would be pointless and would decrease the value of the method by lengthening it, the essence of this method being the avoidance of jump instructions. But the execution of a masking operation every time is not always a disadvantage—sometimes the word carrying the parental genotype will contain other information about the parent as well, a possibility which is discussed more fully in a later chapter. Such information will usually have to be deleted whether the accumulator is shifted down or not, and this deletion can be achieved simultaneously with that of any superfluous allele by the single masking operation.

If deletion of extra information were necessary in the previous method using a random number directed jump, the subroutine would need to be amended so that the masking operation was always carried out, by adding a second **F&1** after the shift in the last line.

If in either of these methods it is more convenient to place the genotype at the m.s. end of the word, essentially the same operations are performed, shifting up instead of down and using **1000...** as the mask (unless the sign bit is required for some special purpose and is not used as an allele bit, in which case the mask will be **01000...**).

When a population is being reproduced, the processes of gamete formation which have just been described are not necessarily the quickest. Unless there are many heterozygotes in the population, there will be too much time wasted in producing random numbers in order to make a superfluous choice between identical alleles in homozygotes. It may then be more efficient to have a means of identifying genotypes. Only when a heterozygote appears is a random number generated, and if this is 0 or 1 it may be used directly for the gamete without further manipulation. For homozygotes, the gamete is made **...001** or **...000** directly according to whether the homozygote is **aa(11)** or **AA(00)** respectively.

The flow diagram in Figure 13 illustrates one way of achieving this. At the beginning, the chosen parent is in an accumulator as before; in this case, if the word representing the parent contains any information other than the genotype, that information must be deleted at the beginning, since the numerical value of the genotype is to be tested. The flow diagram assumes this to have been done. Also, the genotype must now always be at the l.s. end.

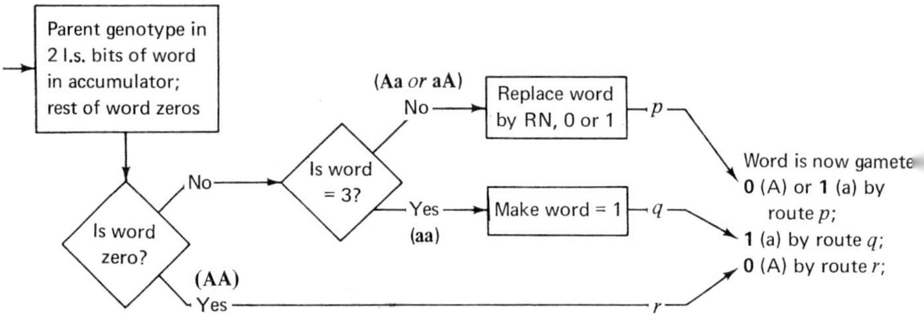

Figure 13. Flow diagram for a method of simulating segregation at a single locus which saves time by identifying genotypes and restricts random choice of allele to heterozygotes

This flow diagram is somewhat more complex than the previous ones, but in the situation where **a** has a low frequency in the population gamete formation will usually follow the very fast route *r* which involves only a single operation (the required gamete must be zero, and that is what the word is, so no further action is required). The essential elements of the procedure may be written down as follows, the parent being in accumulator **F** and **p1** containing **...0011**.

(0); **J1 F = 0**; **J2F = p1**;
  M15 = 1; **p0P200 = (j3)**; **J0P200**; (*H* = *random number*, 0 *or* 1);
(3); **H→F**;
(1); [link and exit];
(2); **F = 1**; [link and exit];

At exit, the gamete is in **F**.

Although less obvious a simulation of the process of segregation, random table look-up is both fast and simple and provides an equally satisfactory method of producing a gamete. The table consists of eight words, 0, 0, 0, 1,

1, 0, 1, 1, *in that order*. It will be seen that the consecutive pairs represent the genotypes, and so the expected segregations, of the four possible parents **00**, **01**, **10** and **11**. To produce a gamete, we have to make a random choice from the appropriate pair of words, and the appropriate pair is found by using twice the numerical value of the parent genotype as a modifier. The addition of a random number zero or one to the modifier then determines the choice within the pair. The process is illustrated by the flow diagram of Figure 14. Once again, all superfluous material must first have been deleted

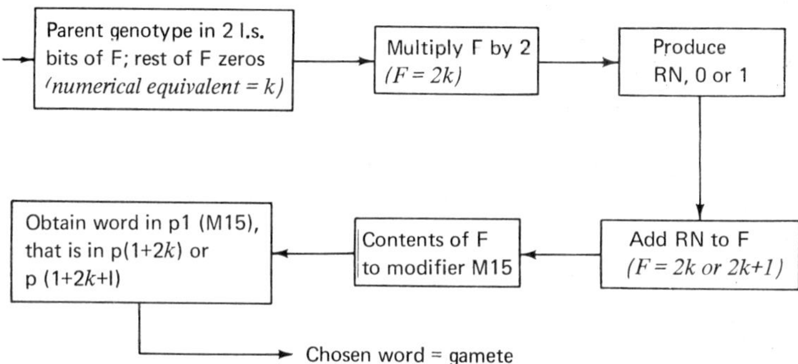

Figure 14. Flow diagram of procedure for simulating segregation at a single locus by random table look-up. The table begins in **p1**

from the parent word, leaving only the genotype which must be at the l.s. end. The flow diagram assumes the parent to be in accumulator **F** and the gamete table to be in **p1** to **p8** of the operative subroutine, which after the signal might read as follows.

0; (*for link*); **0**; **0**; **0**; **1**; **1**; **0**; **1**; **1**;
(0); **F×2/1**; **M15=1**; **p0P200=(j1)**; **J0P200**; (***H*** = *random number* 0 *or* 1);
(1); **F+H→F**; **F→M15**; **p1(M15)→F**; [link and exit];

At exit, the gamete is in **F**.

For example, suppose the parent chosen is **01**. This is decimal 1 and on doubling becomes 2. Addition of a random number, 0 or 1, makes this 2 or 3. The gamete table 0, 0, 0, 1, 1, 0, 1, 1 begins in **p1** and the use of the answer as a modifier of **p1** allows choice of **p3** or **p4** with equal probability; **p3** and **p4** are 0 and 1 respectively, so the gamete is **0** or **1** with equal probability, as required.

It should be pointed out that in this simple case with only one gene, time is once again wasted by unnecessary random number generation unless the proportion of heterozygotes in the population is high.

A more detailed account of the table look-up method follows shortly, and a more effective use of it is described.

Whatever method of gamete formation has been used, the next stage in the simulation of reproduction is the production of a second gamete using the same process, either following the choice of a second parent or, if self-fertilization is required, by using the first parent a second time. Fertilization is simulated by combining (adding) the words representing the two gametes after one of them (it does not matter which) has been shifted up so that its allele is in the second l.s. position.

Precisely the same result would be obtained whether the addition were arithmetic or logical, but since fertilization is conceived as a logical process it is preferable to simulate it by logical operation. As a generalization one should adhere to the rule that nonarithmetical processes should be simulated by logical and not by arithmetic operations unless there are special reasons to the contrary. Although it will usually make no difference in practice, there may be occasions when the two kinds of operation produce different results. The stronger the habit of using logical operations to simulate non-arithmetic processes the less likely will be disaster due to careless use of an arithmetic instruction. Of course, with a computer which has no instruction for logical addition, fertilization will be effected simply by arithmetic addition.

There is a still quicker but equally valid method of simulating reproduction in the case we are considering. Instead of treating the parents independently and carrying out gamete formation twice, adding to simulate fertilization, we can begin by choosing two parents and then perform the rest of reproduction in a single operation using the table look-up method.

For any combination of parental genotypes we know the expected ratios of the genotypes among the offspring. How we may take advantage of this may be illustrated by reference to Table 1, which shows for each possible cross the possible genotypes of the offspring in the ratios to be expected in a family of four. The fact that the table distinguishes between **Aa** and **aA** will be commented on later, as will the fact that the lines of the table are numbered from 0, not from 1.

Suppose that the first parent chosen is **AA** and the second **aA**. Then all we have to do is to refer to line 2 in the table, which begins **AA** × **aA**, and make a random choice from one of the four progeny in that line by using a random number in the range 0 to 3. This clearly gives equal chances of choosing **Aa** or **AA**, which corresponds to the correct ratio from the cross **AA** × **aA**.

There are three other rows from which a random selection would have the same effect—1, 4 and 8, beginning **AA** × **Aa**, **Aa** × **AA** and **aA** × **AA** respectively, since from the point of view of their genetical significance they are all

TABLE 1

The progeny genotypes to be expected in a family of four from each of the sixteen possible parental combinations from the genotypes **AA, Aa, aA** and **aa**. The table distinguishes the genetically identical **Aa** and **aA**.

Number of line in table	Parents	Progeny			
0	**AA** × **AA**	**AA**	**AA**	**AA**	**AA**
1	**AA** × **Aa**	**AA**	**Aa**	**AA**	**Aa**
2	**AA** × **aA**	**Aa**	**AA**	**Aa**	**AA**
3	**AA** × **aa**	**Aa**	**Aa**	**Aa**	**Aa**
4	**Aa** × **AA**	**AA**	**AA**	**aA**	**aA**
5	**Aa** × **Aa**	**AA**	**Aa**	**aA**	**aa**
6	**Aa** × **aA**	**Aa**	**AA**	**aa**	**aA**
7	**Aa** × **aa**	**Aa**	**Aa**	**aa**	**aa**
8	**aA** × **AA**	**aA**	**aA**	**AA**	**AA**
9	**aA** × **Aa**	**aA**	**aa**	**AA**	**Aa**
10	**aA** × **aA**	**aa**	**aA**	**Aa**	**AA**
11	**aA** × **aa**	**aa**	**aa**	**Aa**	**Aa**
12	**aa** × **AA**	**aA**	**aA**	**aA**	**aA**
13	**aa** × **Aa**	**aA**	**aa**	**aA**	**aa**
14	**aa** × **aA**	**aa**	**aA**	**aa**	**aA**
15	**aa** × **aa**	**aa**	**aa**	**aa**	**aa**

identical with the example we considered, **AA** × **aA**. In fact, the whole range of population segregation could be covered by a table of six rows corresponding to rows 0, 1, 3, 5, 7, and 15 of Table 1, and if we were using direct visual reference we would simplify it in this way since the mental rearrangement of any parental combination into the equivalent combination at the beginning of the appropriate line of the table (for example, **aA** × **AA** into **AA** × **Aa**) is quick and simple when compared with the process of random selection which would follow. We could make it even quicker and simpler by altering the **aA** in the progeny of line 5 into **Aa**; heterozygotes would always then be expressed as **Aa**, and reversal of parent position would be the only mental adjustment required.

With a computer, however, it would be relatively slow to test whether rearrangement was required and to perform it if it were, even if heterozygotes were always represented as **Aa**. It is much quicker for the computer to take the parental genotypes as it finds them, and since the object of using a table look-up method is to save time it would be wrong to economise on space by minimizing the size of the table when this would involve loss of time. Some saving of space without loss of time is possible, but further discussion of this point will be clearer after the table look-up procedure for reproduction has been considered in terms appropriate to computing.

To translate Table 1 into a form relevant to computer operation simply involves translating the literal representation of the genotypes into their binary equivalents, omitting the multiplication sign. With the addition of an extra column, whose purpose will be apparent later, Table 1 becomes Table 2.

TABLE 2

The binary translation of Table 1, showing the progeny genotypes to be expected in a family of four from each of the sixteen possible parental combinations from the genotypes **00, 01, 10** and **11.** The table distinguishes the genetically identical **01** and **10.** The address column supposes that the table will start at address **p1** of its subroutine

Number of line in table (k)	Parents	Address of first individual in family p(1+4k)	Progeny			
0	0000	p(1+0)	00	00	00	00
1	0001	p(1+4)	00	01	00	01
2	0010	p(1+8)	01	00	01	00
3	0011	p(1+12)	01	01	01	01
4	0100	p(1+16)	00	00	10	10
5	0101	p(1+20)	00	01	10	11
6	0110	p(1+24)	01	00	11	10
7	0111	p(1+28)	01	01	11	11
8	1000	p(1+32)	10	10	00	00
9	1001	p(1+36)	10	11	00	01
10	1010	p(1+40)	11	10	01	00
11	1011	p(1+44)	11	11	01	01
12	1100	p(1+48)	10	10	10	10
13	1101	p(1+52)	10	11	10	11
14	1110	p(1+56)	11	10	11	10
15	1111	p(1+60)	11	11	11	11

The first thing which should be noticed about Table 2 is that the binary number which represents the combined parents is in fact the number of the appropriate line in the table. In other words, the combined genotypes of the parents provide a direct reference to the appropriate line.

Only the last four columns, those representing the progeny, are stored in the computer, and they are stored in 64 consecutive locations taking the progeny in order as read naturally from the table, that is from left to right along the lines, beginning with line 0.

Supposing that this progeny table within the computer begins in location **p1** of the reproduction subroutine (if the subroutine is to be a general one, it is highly desirable that the table should be contained within it, and since **p0** will conventionally be required for the link, the table will start in **p1**). Then each entry in the third column in Table 2 shows the store address of the left-hand progeny in the corresponding line; proceeding right along this line, the store addresses will increase by steps of one. It should also be noticed that if for any line k = line number = numerical equivalent of the combined parental genotypes, then the entry in the third column equals **p(1+4k)**. The addition to this value of a random number in the range 0 to 3 allows random reference to one of the four store addresses containing the progeny genotypes in line k and so random choice of one of those four genotypes.

The whole process of the simulation of reproduction by table look-up can now be described quite simply. We will assume that the words representing the parents carry nothing other than the alleles; that is, all bits other than the genotype are zero (otherwise the extra material would first have to be deleted from each parent).

One parent is chosen and shifted up two places; a second is chosen and added to the first, the two parents now occupying the four l.s. bits and having a numerical value of k. This is multiplied by four by shifting the whole up a further two places. A random number r is produced in the range 0 to 3 and added to the result of the previous operation, giving a word having the numerical value $4k+r$. This is used as a modifier of **p1**, the base address of the table, to select the progeny represented by the word at address **p**$(1+4k+r)$.

This may be illustrated by taking the example previously given of the cross **AA** × **aA**. The binary equivalent of **AAaA** is **0010**, which is decimal 2. Four times this is 8; the addition to this value of a random number in the range 0 to 3, and the use of the sum to modify the address **p1**, will lead to the selection with equal probability of the word in one of **p9**, **p10**, **p11** and **p12** (**01**, **00**, **01** and **00** respectively), which is what is required.

The flow diagram for this process is very simple, with no branching, and is shown in Figure 15, which assumes that the words representing the parents carry no information other than the genotype.

A subroutine in Mendol for this operation is equally simple. It will not include choice of parents (as the flow diagram does) because if it were designed as a general subroutine it would then need to have considerable flexibility to deal with different breeding systems and population sizes. It is better to have these things dealt with by program specific subroutines or by separate subroutines written for specific breeding system requirements, keep-

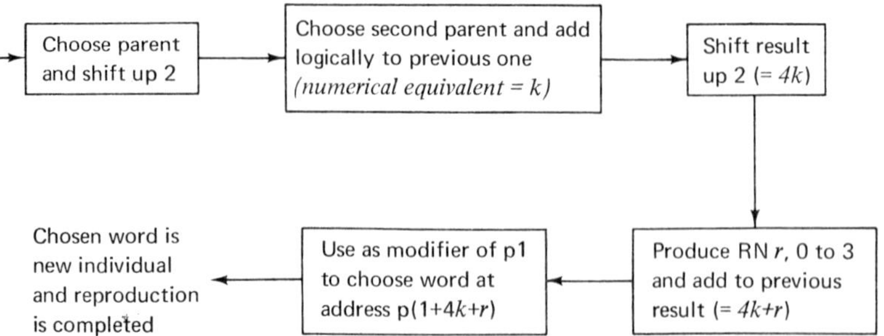

Figure 15. Flow diagram for production of zygote in a single operation by simultaneous simulation of gametogenesis and fertilization, using random table look-up. Single locus. All bits in parent words other than the genotype bits must be zeros. Table begins in **p1**.
Note that provided it has been described elsewhere, an operation involving several instructions may be prescribed in a single box. Thus 'choose parent and shift up 2' may now be treated as a single operation since 'choose parent' has been previously described (Figure 9)

ing this reproduction subroutine simple. We will suppose that the main program delivers to this subroutine the two chosen parents (or the same parent twice for self-fertilization) side by side at the l.s. end of accumulator **F**, and with any other material that may have been in the parent words eliminated. The subroutine thus begins at the third block of Figure 15. The progeny table begins in **p1** of this subroutine after the signal and a zero (**p0** for the link) and will be written as the decimal equivalents of the binary words in the same sequence as the latter appear in Table 2. The instructions will proceed

(0); F×2/2; M15 = 2; p0P200 = (j1); J0P200; (*H* = *random number* 0 *to* 3**);**
(1); F+H→F; F→M15; p1(M15)→F; [link and exit]**;**

At exit, the required progeny genotype is in **F**.

It should be clear from this example why it is simplest for the computer to take the parental genotypes as it finds them, simply treating the binary representation of the parental genotype combination as an integer, even though it may involve the use of a rather large progeny table. However, if it is imperative to economize on store space, this can to some extent be achieved without loss of time. If the progeny section of Table 2 is amended so that heterozygotes are always represented by **01**, then the parental combinations 2, 6, 8, 9, 10, 11 and 14 will not occur, and the corresponding lines in the table would become superfluous. The other lines would have to occupy their

TABLE 3

Economy version of Table 2, which has been amended by re-writing all **10** genotypes as the genetically equivalent **01**. Unused words available for other use are indicated by *. Only the address and progeny columns are given here.

Address of first individual in family	Progeny			
p1	**00**	**00**	**00**	**00**
p5	**00**	**00**	**01**	**01**
p9	*	*	*	*
p13	**01**	**01**	**01**	**01**
p17	**00**	**00**	**01**	**01**
p21	**00**	**01**	**01**	**11**
p25	*	*	*	*
p29	**01**	**01**	**11**	**11**
p33	*	*	*	*
p37	*	*	*	*
p41	*	*	*	*
p45	*	*	*	*
p49	**01**	**01**	**01**	**01**
p53	**01**	**11**	**01**	**11**
p57	*	*	*	*
p61	**11**	**11**	**11**	**11**

original locations as shown in the table, otherwise the parental genotype combinations could not be used as references to them; but within the body of the table there would be a block of 16 successive locations and three blocks of four which could be used for other purposes.

The amendments are shown in Table 3, an asterisk indicating the words which are free for other use. The main objection to this device is that it is the sort of complication which leads to programming error, and it is therefore not to be recommended unless economy of store is essential. With the large store capacities of modern fast computers, the saving of a few words of store will usually be of little or no consequence, but there may be occasions with smaller machines and more complex tables than the one we have been considering when it is worth saving storage space in this way.

This is a suitable place to illustrate a further small point about saving time. We may consider the situation where the words representing the parents do carry information other than the genotype, a common and useful practice known as *packing* and which has already been referred to in passing. For instance, as will be described in the next chaper, when different genotypes have different fitnesses it may sometimes be convenient to store a factor representing the fitness in the same word as the genotype, occupying some of the bit positions unused by the genotype. Suppose we decide that the relative fitness of homozygous recessives is to be 0.5625. In binary, this is **0.1001**, and it can be packed into the same word as the genotype, at any convenient place and not necessarily at the m.s. end which might seem the obvious place for a fraction. If we decide to have the point between the eighth and ninth bits from the l.s. end, then a homozygous recessive with this fitness, which could be expressed as – 0.5626 – **aa**, would in binary be represented by the word **...00010010011**. Before the genotype can be used as a modifier to refer to a progeny table, all the **1**s left of the genotype have to be eliminated and this of course can be done, whatever the genotype, by performing an LM with **...00000000011**. The obvious procedure would seem to be to perform the LM on each parent as soon as it is chosen, but time could be saved if the LM had to be carried out only once, after the two parents have been added together. This is possible provided that at least as many bits immediately left of the genotype are zero as there are bits in the genotype, which in the case we are considering is two; that is, there must be a gap of the appropriate size of unused bits between the fitness and the genotype. The sequence of operations would then be: choose parent and shift up two places; choose second parent, add to first and do LM with **...0000001111**.

At the time of addition, the gene positions of the two parents will be such that the gene bits of both will be added to zero, that is they will be unaltered. For example, if the words for the two parents are **...0011000010** and **...0010010011**, the former after shifting becomes **...110001000** and the result of the logical addition is **...1110011011**. LM with **...0000001111**gives **...0000001011**, which is the correct combination of the genotypes **10** and **11**. The fact that the fitnesses have been added together and produced rubbish does not matter; they are not required any more (or if they are, previous steps will have had to be taken) and the rubbish is removed by the LM.

The time saved by the elimination of one LM may be slight (two instructions at most), but in an operation performed very many times, as the simulation of reproduction will be, the overall saving may be worth making, especially since it is done by simplifying the program. It is always a great temptation for those of us who enjoy programming to spend time refining programs in the pursuit of elegance and efficiency. Sometimes this is worth doing, sometimes it is not, and unless the pleasure of achievement is regarded as sufficient reward for the labour, each case should be considered on its merits before a process of program refinement is embarked upon. It is not worth rewriting a section of a program in order to save a few milliseconds on an operation which is performed only once or a few times during the running of a program. Even smaller amounts of time can be worth saving if the operation is performed many thousands of times. It was worth doing in the case we have been considering, especially since it could be done so easily; indeed, in situations of this kind an experienced programmer will see the efficient way almost automatically. It was simple because no difficulties were involved in leaving the necessary unused bits to the left of the genotype; if, however, sufficient unused bits could not be left without causing difficulties in other sections of the program, as might easily be the case where more genes are involved and not very much room is available in the word for other information, then it might well be preferable to have maximum utilization of the bits in a word, and to accept the need to perform the LM separately on each parent.

In case the author should seem to be too preoccupied with saving time, it should be pointed out that programs simulating evolution are liable to have long running times, especially if the populations are large and many generations are involved; this is simply because reproduction can only be simulated consecutively and not concurrently as in populations of real organisms. Increase in demand for computer time continually outstrips increases in computer speeds and in numbers of computers available. Where computer time is in short supply, the programmer needs to be able to make the best use of the time available to him, but he must always use his judgment carefully in deciding where it is profitable to spend his own time in streamlining a program and where it is not.

The case we have just been considering also provides an example of a point referred to a little earlier, that is the importance of using logical operations to simulate non-arithmetic processes. If the additional information in the words representing the parents is packed at the m.s. end, both arithmetic addition and arithmetic shifting up would be liable to cause overflow. This could lead to trouble in a program in which there are arithmetic operations and the occurrence of overflow during their execution has to be recognized, unless extra tests for overflow are included in the program which may be both a nuisance and a waste of time. Logical addition cannot produce overflow; overflow occurring as a result of a logical shift is always ignored by the computer. If the computer in use is one which does not have an instruction for logical addition, arithmetic addition may as well be used, since the substitute short routine described in the section on logical addition in Chapter 4 may cause overflow.

A situation where an actual error may result if an arithmetic operation is used occurs when a shift down is used to bring bits representing genes to the l.s. end, since an arithmetic shift down is in fact a division by a power of two and with most computers will include a rounding operation where appropriate. Consider the gamete formation routine previously described, in which a shift down is used to bring the required allele to the l.s. position. If the parental genetype is **01**, represented by the word **...00001**, a logical shift down of one place will give the correct answer, **...0000**; since the bit shifted off the word is in this case a **1**, becoming equivalent to decimal 0.5 when shifted down, an arthmetic shift down will round the answer up to **...0001**, which is wrong in this context since the allele in the l.s. position should have been **0**. That is, while the logical operation simply shifts bits and sheds bits, the arithmetic operation in this case divides 1 by 2 and rounds the answer 0.5 up to 1. Similarly, an arithmetic shift down one place of **...000011** (**aa**) gives the answer **...00010**, and the allele in the l.s. position is **A**, which is absurd; $3/2 = 1.5$ which rounds up to 2.

The simple case with only one gene will probably not be met with very frequently in genetic simulation, but it has been dealt with at some length and in some detail as it provides a useful context in which some points of programming technique could be discussed.

Two Unlinked Genes

This is essentially a more complicated version of the situation with a single gene, and is best dealt with by a table look-up method. Other methods which are less direct but which operate in a way more closely analogous to real segregation are at best inelegant and slower. They may however have their uses when there is not a great deal of store space available (although it may then be preferable to use the general method of the next section, which can equally well be applied here), and they will be used for choice in programs which are used for genetics teaching at an elementary level where it is desired that the students shall be able to see how the program imitates the process of segregation. A short account of this more precise simulation will be given. For the most part it is essentially an extension of the corresponding process described in the preceding section, but has the complication that the arrangement of genes and alleles in the zygote and the diploid organism is not immediately compatible with what would seem to be the natural way of arranging them in a gamete.

Consider a double heterozygote, **AaBb**. If a gamete is produced from it, say **AB**, and combined in the obvious way with a second gamete, say **ab**, by placing them side by side, we will get another double heterozygote which will now be represented by **ABab**, which is a different way of symbolizing the same genotype as we started with. We can see fairly easily that **ABab** and **AaBb** are the same thing, but this is not true for their binary representations, **0011** and **0101**. The gene locus equivalence of any two bit positions corresponding to a pair of alleles must remain the same, permanently, for we have no other sensible way of knowing to which gene a particular bit refers. For example, in the two binary representations given above, the first and third bits of **0011** refer to the same gene as the first and second bits of **0101**, and it would be ridiculous to complicate the program so that track could be kept of such alterations in significance of the bits.

Looking at it in another way, **0101** could mean either of the genetically different **AaBb** or **AbAb**, since without specification of bit equivalence we would not know whether the bit pair representing the two alleles at a locus was composed of consecutive or alternate bits unless we had been laboriously logging the alternating bit significance.

Ambiguity can easily be removed by deciding, for instance, that the genotype of a zygote should always be simulated in such a way that the two alleles of each gene are represented by a pair of adjacent bits, with the pairs corresponding to the different genes arranged consecutively; in the formation of a zygote, one gamete at fertilization will contribute the m.s. allele of each pair, the other the l.s. alleles.

Using * to represent an unused bit (which will always be zero, but needs for the moment to be distinguished from a zero with genetic significance) and considering the double heterozygote **AaBb** of the foregoing example, this will have been formed by the combination of gametes **A*B*** and ***a*b**, as can be seen by superimposing these with elimination of the asterisks. Or, in binary, the combination of **0*0*** with ***1*1** produces **0101**, which is now unambiguous since we have specified that the m.s. pair of bits will always represent the alleles of the **A**/**a** locus and the l.s. pair those of the **B**/**b** locus.

Similarly, if we have two gametes **Ab** and **aB**, arranged **A*b*** and ***a*B**, these would also produce a heterozygote, this time **0110** interpreted unambiguously as **AabB**. It is true that the only other sensible interpretation, **AbaB**, is genetically the same thing, but the order of the recessive alleles would need to be known during any subsequent gametogenesis.

If the foregoing discussion be kept in mind, it will be found that the segregation of two independent genes presents no great difficulty, and no detailed explanation should be needed in order to follow the description and flow diagrams. It makes no difference whether the word carrying the genotype is otherwise empty or not. It will be assumed that the gene bits are at the l.s. end of the word representing the parent, and that the pair of bits representing the two alleles of one gene are as before consecutive, an individual of genotype **aaBB** for example being represented by the word **...1100**.

We may deal with the two genes separately or simultaneously. Considering separate segregation first, we will begin with the l.s. gene. A parent having been chosen, a copy is made, since production of an allele at one locus will destroy the rest of the genotype. A 1-bit random number is produced and used as a modifier to specify a shift down of the parental word one place or none, and an LM with **...0001** performed on the result. A second 1-bit random number is produced and used as a modifier to specify a shift down of the copy one place or none, and an LM with **...0100** performed on the result. The two results are added together to give the gamete which may need to be shifted up one place according to whether it is the first or second gamete.

Alternatively, a randomly determined jump method can be used as described for a single gene, but in the present case this does not save a masking operation since now an LM will always have to be performed for each gene whether there is a shift or not, since there are always liable to be superfluous bits to be removed, namely recessive alleles of the other gene. Figure 16 shows flow diagrams for both methods.

It may be pointed out that whichever method is used it is not necessary actually to generate two random numbers, even though two are required. If one is generated and two bits extracted from it, one bit may be used to determine segregation of the first gene and the other that of the second. Since this gametogenesis subroutine will then twice have to cut the delivered random number down to one bit, there is no point in using a pseudorandom number subroutine (**P200**) which delivers a specified number of bits, since the initial cutting down by **P200** to two bits (which is presumably what would be specified) would be superfluous and a waste of time. Instead, we may use a pseudorandom number subroutine simply delivering 31 bits and which we will suppose to be numbered **P202** (31 bits rather than 32, the sign bit not being used). In the random shift method, this 31-bit number is first used unshifted and masked by **...0001**, and for its second use is shifted

I. Random shift

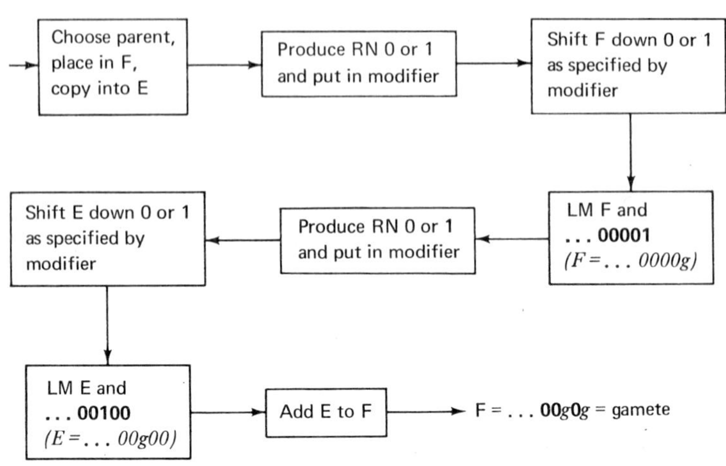

II. Random jump

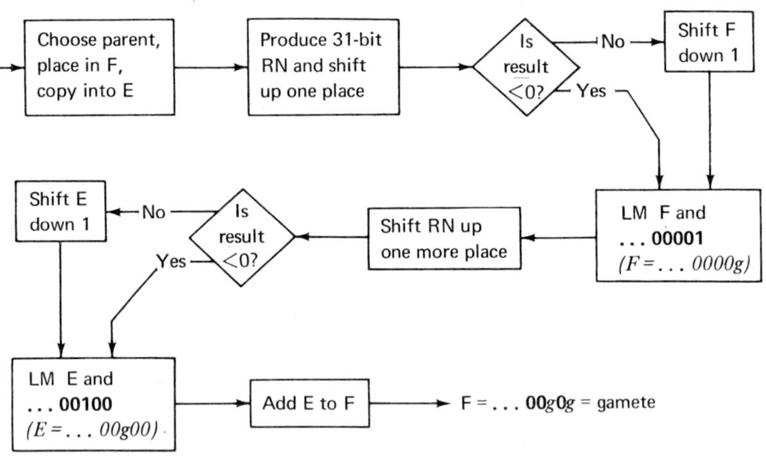

Figure 16. Flow diagrams for two variants of one method of simulating segregation at two independent loci. In the upper diagram (random shift) a random number (0 or 1) is used as a modifier to specify a shift directly; in the lower (random jump) it is used as a criterion for jumping to a shift or non-shift sequence. In the notes, *g* represents an allele which has been chosen at random

down one place and again masked with **...0001**. For the random jump method, the simplest way of using the 31-bit random number is to shift it up one place (putting the m.s. random bit in the sign position) and using positive or negative (equally likely) as the jump criterion. This avoids having to keep a copy of the random number for the second test, which would be necessary if the test involved the extraction of a bit by masking.

Both methods of gametogenesis are given below in Mendol, it being assumed for each that the parent is at the l.s. end of **F** at the start, and the gamete is in **F** at exit. The random shift method would be

(0); F→E; p0P202 = (j1); J0P202; (*H* = 31-*bit random number*)**;**
(1); H→G; H&1; (H = 1 *or* 0)**; H→M15; F down (M15);**
F&1; (*F* = *one allele*)**;**
G down 1; G&1; (*G* = 1 *or* 0)**; G→M15; E down (M15);**
E&4; (*E* = *allele of other gene*)**; E ≢ F→F; (*F*** = *gamete*)**;**
[link and exit];

The randomly directed jump method would be

(0); F→E; p0P202 = (j1); J0P202;
(1); H up 1; J2H<0; F down 1;
(2); F&1; H up 1; J3H<0; E down 1;
(3); E&4; E ≢ F→F; [link and exit];

A quicker alternative method of simulating the independent segregation of two genes is to deal with both at once by making use of the fact that, considering allele positions, there are four equally possible outcomes of segregation. Using g to represent any allele and numbering the allele positions, we can represent the parent by **...00**$g_4 g_3 g_2 g_1$. Then the four possible outcomes of segregation are the combinations of alleles in positions 1 and 3, 1 and 4, 2 and 3, 2 and 4. These could be achieved respectively by carrying out LMs with the masks **0101**, **1001**, **0110** and **1010**. Randomness of the four possibilities of segregation would be obtained by random reference to a table of four words containing those masks. We will suppose such a table to be in words **p1** to **p4** of a gametogenesis subroutine.

This procedure however does not necessarily leave the alleles in their proper positions for fertilization, which we have already decided shall be $*g*g$ or $g*g*$. For example, if the parent genotype is **aAbb**, which is **1011**, and the randomly selected mask is **1001**, then this produces a gamete **1001** in which the allele arrangement is $g**g$ which is not their proper position. This result, **1001**, needs to be transformed either into **0101** or into **1010**, according to whether we have decided on the $*g*g$ or the $g*g*$ arrangement. One of these arrangements will be required for one gamete and one for the other; it is simplest to produce all gametes in the same arrangement in the

TABLE 4

Table for transformation of gamete as originally produced into form as required with allele occupying l.s. bit of each pair. Assumed to begin at address **p5** of its subroutine. Diploid gene arrangement, for example, **aaBB** = **1100**.

Gamete as produced	Decimal value	Address in table	Gamete as transformed to $*g*g$	Decimal equivalent
0000	0	**p5**	**0000**	0
0001	1	**p6**	**0001**	1
0010	2	**p7**	**0001**	1
not possible		**p8**		0
0100	4	**p9**	**0100**	4
0101	5	**p10**	**0101**	5
0110	6	**p11**	**0101**	5
not possible		**p12**		0
1000	8	**p13**	**0100**	4
1001	9	**p14**	**0101**	5
1010	10	**p15**	**0101**	5

first place and to shift one of each pair of gametes up one place prior to fertilization. We will arbitrarily decide to use the $*g*g$ arrangement, and so **1001** would need to be transformed to **0101**. The easiest way of doing this is by using the numerical value of the gamete as originally produced to refer to a transformation table. If the right-hand column of Table 4 is stored in consecutive locations of the gametogenesis subroutine from **p5** onwards (that is, after the masks), then the word at address **p**$(5+n)$ contains the transformation required for the gamete whose original binary form has the numerical value n. The transformation is then carried out quite simply by using the gamete in its original form as a modifier of **p5** to extract the appropriate transformed gamete genotype. It will be noticed that four of the gametes in Table 4 do not require transformation; the process will still be carried out on them (with no change, of course) since once again it is quicker to carry it out for all gametes than to test beforehand to find out if it is necessary (not a simple job) and carry it out only if it is. It will also be noticed that the words in **p8** and **p12** in the table are zero. This is because there are no corresponding gametes; both alleles of the same gene cannot be chosen, and so the bits of a pair representing a gene cannot both be ones, as they would be in **0011**, **0111** and any 4-bit word of higher value than ten, since a one always represents an allele; this is not true for zeros, since zero can represent either an allele or nothing, an ambiguity which is entirely without consequence.

The whole operation of gamete formation is then quite simple. Superfluous information does not require removal from the chosen parent, since it will automatically be eliminated during the gametogenesis masking operation. After the parent has been chosen, a random number in the range 0 to 3 is used as a modifier of **p1** to choose a mask from the stored table of masks. An LM between parent and mask produces the original form of the gamete and this is then used as a modifier of **p5** to produce the transformed gamete from the transformation table. The flow diagram is shown in Figure 17. This may be written in program form as follows, the chosen parent being delivered to the subroutine in accumulator **F**.

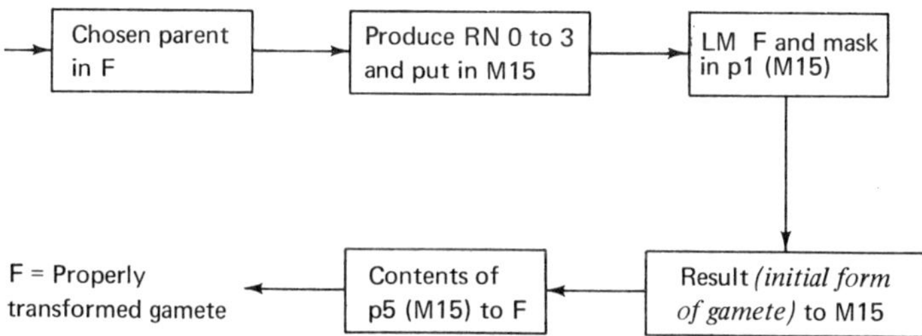

Figure 17. Flow diagram for a method of simulating segregation at two independent loci simultaneously, using a randomly chosen mask followed by a transformation procedure to place the chosen alleles in their correct bit positions. Table of masks begins in **p1**, transformation table in **p5**

After the signal, the subroutine will proceed

```
     0; (for link); 5; 6; 9; 10; (four masks); 0; 1; 1; 0; 4; 5;
     5; 0; 4; 5; 5; (transformed gametes);
(0); M15 = 2; p0P200 = (j1); J0P200; (H = random number 0 to 3);
(1); H→M15; F&p1 (M15)→F; F→M15; p5 (M15)→F;
     [link and exit];
```

At exit, the gamete is in **F**.

This particular method of simulating segregation lends itself readily to the production of a fertilized zygote in a single operation from two parents. This gives a considerable advantage of speed at some cost in store space; the transformation table will require 171 words. If the two parents are chosen and brought together in one word, so that one occupies the four l.s. bits and the other the next four bits, then we can produce a gamete from each simultaneously by performing a single LM with a duplicate mask formed by combining two randomly and independently chosen masks (**1010**, **1001**, **0110** or **0101** as before), one in the four l.s. bits and the other in the next four bits. There are obviously 16 equally likely combinations for the duplicate mask, so there will be a table of sixteen words from which a choice will be made by using a random number in the range 0 to 15.

The result of the masking operation will however not only produce gametes which may not have their alleles in the proper positions, but the gametes will be side by side and not interleaved as they must be when the zygote is finally delivered by the subroutine. For example, suppose we choose two parents, **1101** and **0110**. We put these into a single word, **1101 0110** (leaving a space between to help the reader), and do an LM with a randomly chosen mask which we will suppose to be **1001 1010**; we then get $\bar{1}00\bar{1}\ \bar{0}0\bar{1}0$ (which is decimal 146), bars indicating the bits which are alleles. If we decide that the gamete from the l.s. parent shall occupy the relatively l.s. position in the zygote (that is, $*g*g$), then $\bar{1}00\bar{1}\ \bar{0}0\bar{1}0$ has first to be transformed into $\bar{1}0\bar{1}0\ 0\bar{0}0\bar{1}$ and the two sets of four bits (the transformed gametes) added together to give $\bar{1}\bar{0}\bar{1}\bar{1}$, which is the proper representation of the zygote. It would obviously be very much simpler to perform this transformation by reference to a table beginning at address **p17** (the masks being in **p1** to **p16**) and in which the word at address **p(17+146)** will be **...1011**.

So the whole routine for the reproduction of one individual can be quite simply described in a flow diagram (Figure 18) which is a straightforward modification of that in Figure 17, with one important proviso. The existence of additional information in the parent which is shifted up is of no conse-

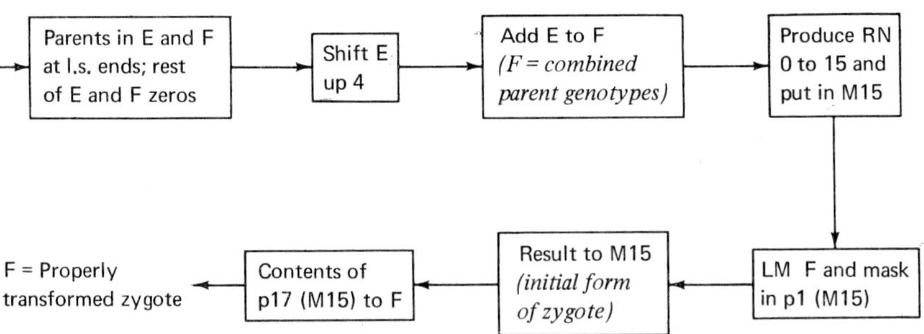

Figure 18. Flow diagram of Figure 17 adapted to allow production of a zygote in a single operation from two parents by simultaneous gametogenesis and fertilization, using a randomly chosen mask followed by a transformation procedure. Two independent loci. Table of masks begins in **p1**, transformation table in **p17**. (This subroutine is referred to in Figure 19 as **P102**.)

quence, but the other parent must now be entirely zero in the four bits immediately adjacent to the genotype. If it can be arranged that those four bits are never used for information, no action is necessary; otherwise a masking operation with **...001111** will have to be carried out before the parental words are combined.

The program is very much like the previous one. Omitting the **p** stores (which now occupy a lot of space) but supposing the gametogenesis masks to be in **p1** to **p16** and the zygote transformation table to be in **p17** onwards, and assuming the parents to be in **E** and **F** with extra information deleted if necessary, we would have

(0); E up 4; E≢F→F; M15=4; p0P200−(j1); J0P200;
    (*H* = *random number* 0 *to* 15)**;**
(1); H→M15; F&p1 (M15)→F; F→M15; p17 (M15)→F;
    [link and exit]**;**

At exit the zygote is in **F**.

The sixteen masks required would have the decimal values 85, 86, 89, 90, 101, 102, 105, 106, 149, 150, 153, 154, 165, 166, 169, 170, as the reader may care to verify for himself.

From the programmer's point of view, the only real labour involved is in the construction of the transformation table. This requires a great deal of care, not only in the writing of it but also in punching it for input to the computer, since absolute accuracy is essential. Most errors in writing or punching make their presence felt when the program is run, but errors of the kind likely to occur in this table can easily remain unsuspected. As an

TABLE 5

Exemplary portion of table converting zygotes as originally produced with gametes side by side, into form as required with gametes interleaved. Table assumed to begin at **p17** of its subroutine. The impossible configurations are **10010011** and **10010111**. Diploid gene arrangement, for example, **aaBB** = **1100**

Address	Zygote as produced	Zygote as transformed	Decimal equivalent
p(17+146)	**10010010**	**1011**	11
p(17+147)	not possible		0
p(17+148)	**10010100**	**1110**	14
p(17+149)	**10010101**	**1111**	15
p(17+150)	**10010110**	**1111**	15
p(17+151)	not possible		0

example, Table 5 shows a section of the transformation table, of which the right-hand column is stored at the address indicated. Actually, only 81 words of the table have to be determined, since the remaining 90 contain at least one impossible gamete and will be entered as zeros.

There is however a better alternative for the programmer than writing the table himself. This is to write a short subroutine by which the program itself writes the table as one of its first operations. This presents no difficulty, and has the advantage that accidental errors cannot occur in the table if the routine is correct.

Such a subroutine would write the zygote transformation table by making use of the gamete transformation table used in the previous gametogenesis subroutine and shown in Table 4, but that (for a reason which should be clear later) will need to be extended by the five impossible gametes **1011** to **1111** (11 to 15).

The procedure is fairly straightforward. The addresses of the items in the required zygote transformation table will correspond of course to the numerical values of the original forms of the zygotes (correspond, not equal, because the first address is to be **p17**, not **p0**). Each of these is equal to 16 times that of the original form of the m.s. gamete plus that of the original form of the l.s. gamete, the factor being 16 for the former because the m.s. gamete is four places up in the word. Expressed in this way, the sequence of addresses corresponds to zero plus the numbers 0 to 15 in turn, then 16 plus 0 to 15, 32 plus 0 to 15, 48 plus 0 to 15, and so on. The last sensible item in the sequence will be at 160 plus 10, corresponding to the original zygote **1010 1010**, since any higher value must have at least one impossible gamete. But since in practice it would be awkward to stop the last 0 to 15 addition short of 15, the transformation table will finish with five impossible zygotes and occupy 176 words.

Each item in the zygote transformation table will be the corresponding transformed m.s. gamete one place up ($g{*}g{*}$), plus the transformed l.s. gamete (${*}g{*}g$), as in fertilization. The numerical value will therefore be that of the transformed l.s. gamete plus twice that of the transformed m.s. gamete.

The sequence of values for transformed gametes, corresponding to a sequence of original values 0 to 15, is 0, 1, 1, 0, 4, 5, 5, 0, 4, 5, 5, 0, 0, 0, 0, 0, as can be seen from Table 4. All zeros except the first correspond to impossible gametes. Clearly, the items in the zygote transformation table will be zero plus each item in turn of this sequence, followed by ten repetitions of the sequence added in turn to 2, 2, 0, 8, 10, 10, 0, 8, 10, 10, that is to twice the value of the items in the sequence in the same order but in this case not proceeding beyond the last possible gamete. The last sensible item will be 10+5, the binary equivalent of which is **1010**+**0101**, that is **1111**, which is the required transformation of **1010 1010**.

Many items in the table will be superfluous, corresponding to impossible zygotes; indeed, two whole sequences of 16, the fourth and the eighth, will be superfluous. But it is quicker and simpler to let the subroutine write them than to make it identify the items which do not require writing, The fact that some items will be nonsense does not matter—they will never be referred to.

The subroutine will operate in eleven loops each of 16 operations involving in turn the items of the gamete transformation table, each loop adding in turn twice the value of the items in that table. Three modifiers will be required, one to direct the writing of the zygote transformation table, one to run at intervals of one loop through the first eleven items of the gamete table, one to run through all 16 items of the gamete table during each execution of a loop; the first two will be set, once only, at the beginning of the subroutine; the third will be set and reset at the beginning of each loop. Two counters will be required, one to count 16 items and to be reset for each loop, the other to count eleven loops and set only once, at the beginning.

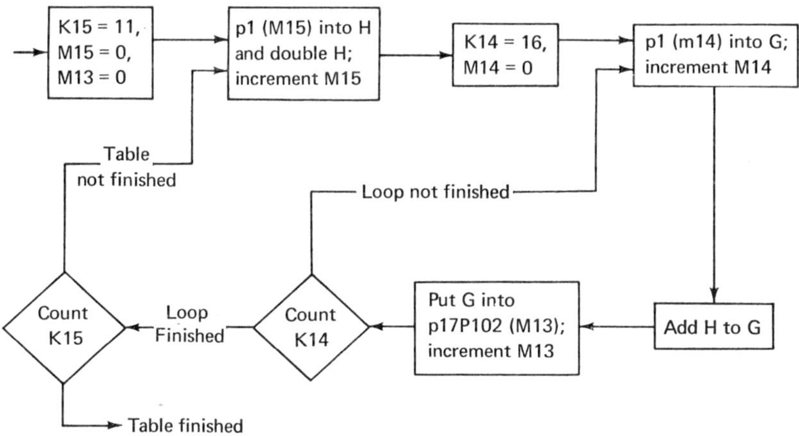

Figure 19. Flow diagram of a subroutine which will, from a gamete transformation table beginning in **p1**, write a zygote transformation table for the reproduction subroutine of Figure 18, which will be called **P102**. The zygote transformation table will begin in **p17** of **P102**

It should now be fairly easy to construct a flow diagram, which is shown in Figure 19. We will suppose that the subroutine writing the zygote transformation table carries the gamete transformation table in its own stores **p1** to **p16**, and that the zygote transformation table will be written into **p17** onwards of the last written reproduction subroutine (p. 155), which is where it will be used and which we may for the sake of argument call **P102**.

After the signal, which must indicate 17 **p** stores, the subroutine would read

```
      0; (for link); 0; 1; 1; 0; 4; 5; 5; 0; 4; 5; 5;
      (0; 0; 0; 0; 0; need not be written);
(0);  K15=11; M15=0; M13=0;
(1);  p1 (M15)→H; M15+1; H up 1; K14=16; M14=0;
(2);  p1 (M14)→G; M14+1; H+G→G; G→p17P102 (M13);
      M13+1; K14−1; J2K14≠0; K15−1; J1K15≠0;
      [link and exit];
```

The technique of using the computer to set large tables is a valuable one; not only may it save the programmer labour, but it considerably reduces the chance of error since it entirely eliminates errors by the programmer in writing and punching the table, errors which are not only surprisingly easy to overlook in checking the print-out of a punched program but which (unlike most programming errors) may not make their presence obvious during the running of the program. A single such undiscovered error may lead to unjustifiable conclusions being drawn from spurious results. An error during the writing of the table setting routine will, if the latter still succeeds in producing a table, almost invariably lead to multiple errors in the table, and these are much less likely to remain undetected; in any case, a small routine is much easier to check for accuracy than a large table.

Table setting by program is only practicable when the table contents follow a simple pattern or (as in the case just described) a combination of simple patterns. From our point of view, the most frequent use of table-setting routines will be in setting the starting populations of evolutionary experiments, and this is usually quite a simple matter—an example was given in the previous chapter. An example of a more complex table is described at the end of this section.

Generally speaking, the routines for simulating reproduction so far described, except perhaps the last one (simultaneous random masking of two parents), are not likely to find much application in research programs. Their usefulness is really limited to situations where it is required to demonstrate realistic simulation in programs used in genetics teaching. However, during the description of these routines a number of programming devices have been introduced which have a much wider application and will be found useful in many different contexts. They should become part of an experienced programmer's repertoire of techniques.

The method of simulating reproduction by random masking which has just been described combines two table look-up operations—a randomized one simulating segregation and producing gamete or zygote, the other a straightforward one rearranging gene bits into an acceptable form. A logical improvement would be to short-circuit the process by cutting out the gametogenesis simulation and, with the appropriate element of randomness, going directly from the parental genotype or genotypes to a table of gametes or zygotes, as we did on a simpler scale in the previous section.

This is much the neatest and fastest method of simulating reproduction, but it is practicable only when very few gene loci are involved, because of demands on store space. This direct method of table look-up takes no more time for two genes than it did for one. But it does require a very much greater store space, especially if the reproduction is performed in a single operation by taking the two parents simultaneously. If store space is limited, it may be necessary to form the two gametes separately; this requires a table of 64 words as against one of 4096 if the single operation procedure is used. However, if the optimum combination of speed with economy of store space is desired, the already described procedure using random masks on two parents simultaneously is to be preferred. Nevertheless, in order to allow the reader to see the options available to him, the description of direct table look-up which follows will take no further account of that possibility; the reader, though, should not forget it.

Reduction in table size may be achieved by packing, which will be discussed at the end of this section. We may also make sections of the table redundant by representing all heterozygotes identically, either as **01** or as **10**; the extent of the table will remain the same, but there will be extensive unused sections within it. Thus, in the 4096-word table, only 1296 words would be required, and redundant space which could be used for other purposes would be comprised of one block of 1024 consecutive words, three of 256, nine of 64 and 27 of 16.

Except in one important respect, the smaller table, for gamete production only, is identical with that of Table 2 (if 'gamete' replaces 'progeny'). This is because the binary form used for reference to the table can apply equally well to one gene and two parents or to two genes and one parent. For example, **1011** can represent two parents **aA** and **aa**, or one parent **aAbb**. The binary representation of the progeny outcome from the former is identical with that of the gamete outcome from the latter, with the important exception that for reasons explained earlier in this section the two alleles in the latter case have to be separated by a zero (to give $*g*g$). The progeny section of Table 2 is easily modified to meet this point, and becomes the gamete section of Table 6, which is used in essentially the same way as before except that only one parent is chosen for reference to it. This is illustrated by the flow diagram of Figure 20. A second gamete will then have to be produced in the same way, one of them will be shifted up one place, and they will be combined by addition to simulate fertilization and give a new individual.

Again, it would obviously be quicker to deal with two parents simultaneously, as in the case with a single gene, but this requires a huge table. Dis-

TABLE 6

Gametogenesis in a single parent, with two loci, by direct table look-up. Each gamete has its two alleles properly spaced (separated by a zero) as required for fertilization. The table gives for each of the sixteen possible parental genotypes the four gamete genotypes to be expected from a single meiosis, and is assumed to start in **p1** of its subroutine. Diploid gene arrangement, for example, **aaBB** = **1100**

Number of line in table (k)	Parent	Address of first gamete in line **p**(**1**+**4**k)	Gametes			
0	0000	p1	000	000	000	000
1	0001	p5	000	001	000	001
2	0010	p9	001	000	001	000
3	0011	p13	001	001	001	001
4	0100	p17	000	000	100	100
5	0101	p21	000	001	100	101
6	0110	p25	001	000	101	100
7	0111	p29	001	001	101	101
8	1000	p33	100	100	000	000
9	1001	p37	100	101	000	001
10	1010	p41	101	100	001	000
11	1011	p45	101	101	001	001
12	1100	p49	100	100	100	100
13	1101	p53	100	101	100	101
14	1110	p57	101	100	101	100
15	1111	p61	101	101	101	101

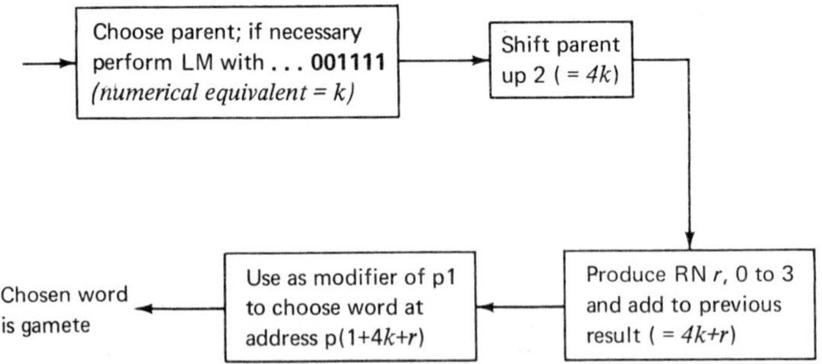

Figure 20. Flow diagram for simulation of gametogenesis with two independent loci, using random table look-up. The table begins in **p1**. Compare with Figure 15

tinguishing **AaBb**, **AabB**, **aABb** and **aAbB**, there are 16 possible parental genotypes and therefore 256 possible combinations of parents. Each of these would require a line of 16 words for progeny, giving a total requirement of 4096. It is not proposed to illustrate this by a complete table (space is as important in books as it is in computers), but Table 7 shows what a section of it might look like. As pointed out earlier, whole sections can be made redundant if we do not, for example, distinguish between **Aa** and **aA**, **Bb** and **bB**, but arrange that for the two genes the heterozygotes are always treated as **Aa** and **Bb** respectively. In Table 7, line 78 would then be redundant (one parent is **aabB** and the line for **AaBB** × **aaBb** would be equivalent to line 78), and alteration would be needed to the progeny shown in italics in lines 80 and 81, any pair of alleles appearing as **10** being reversed to **01**.

The use of Table 7 is essentially the same as that of Table 2; the shifts now have to be four places, and random choice has to be from 16 progeny instead of four. The flow diagram of Figure 15 now becomes Figure 21.

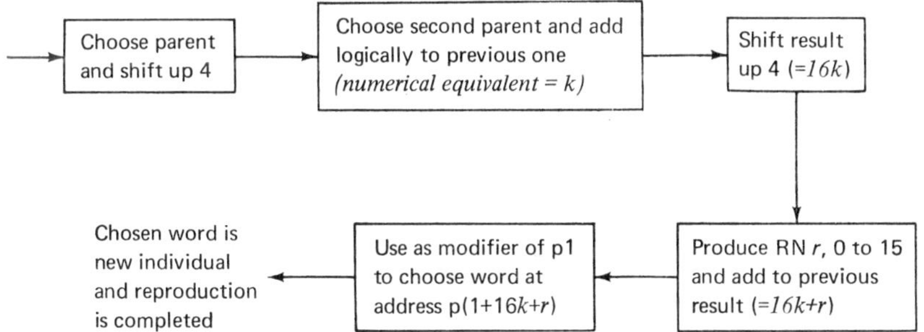

Figure 21. Flow diagram for production of zygote in a single operation from two parents by simultaneous simulation of gametogenesis and fertilization, using random table look-up. Two independent loci. Table begins in **p1**.
[Figure assumes no extra information in parental word; if there is, LM with ...**001111** will have to be performed on each parent as it is chosen; or with ...**0011111111** on the combined parents provided the four bits left of the genotype are always zeros in the parental word]

The reproduction subroutine is quite simple. We will assume that the main program supplies the subroutine with the two parents side by side at the l.s. end of **F** and all other bits in **F** zero (the subroutine beginning at the third block of Figure 21), and that the progeny table begins in **p1** of this subroutine.

The last assumption may not always be practicable. Some computers limit the area of the store within which instructions may appear, and the storage of

TABLE 7

Zygote production by two parents, with two loci, by direct table look-up. The full table would give for each of the possible 256 combinations of two parents the progeny to be expected in a family of sixteen, but only a small section is shown here, as an example. The table is supposed to start in **p1** of the reproduction subroutine.

If we convert the progeny in line 81 to literal representation of the genotypes, not distinguishing between the order of the alleles in any pair, we get a family of **4AABb**: **4AaBb**: **2AABB**: **2AAbb**: **2Aabb**: **2AaBB**, which is the ratio we expect from the cross **AaBb** × **AABb**.

The table distinguishes, for each gene, the arrangements **01** and **10**; if in each zygote in which it occurred (for example those in italics in the table) the latter were amended to the former, the table could be produced in an economy form, and a large number of lines (of which line 78 is an example) would be redundant and the corresponding store space could be made available for other use.

Line number (k)	Parents	Parents in binary	Address of first individual in family **p(1+16k)**	Progeny
78	**AaBB** × **aabB**	01001110	p(1+1248)	0101 0100 0101 0100 0101 0100
79	**AaBB** × **aabb**	01001111	p(1+1264)	0101 0101 0101 0101 0101 0101
80	**AaBb** × **AABB**	01010000	p(1+1280)	0000 0000 0000 0000 *0010 0010*
81	**AaBb** × **AABb**	01010001	p(1+1296)	0000 0000 0001 0001 *0010 0010*

		Progeny
(78)	. . .	0101 0100 1101 1100 1101 1100 1101 1100 1101 1100
(79)	. . .	0101 0101 1101 1101 1101 1101 1101 1101 1101 1101
(80)	. . .	*0010 0010 1000 1000 1000 1000 1010 1010 1010 1010*
(81)	. . .	0011 0011 *1000 1000 1001 1001 1010 1010 1011 1011*

large tables within subroutines may make the overall area of the store spanned by instructions larger than permissible. In this case the table will have to be stored elsewhere and steps taken in each program to ensure that the subroutine knows where the table is. This can easily be done by causing the main program red tape to supply the parameter list of the subroutine with the absolute address of the first word of the table and adding this to the modifier before the table is referred to.

Suppose this address is stored in **p1** of the following subroutine. Then the last line of this would read **(1); F+H→F; F+p1→F; F→M15; a0(M15)→F;** etc. Note that the address to be modified is **a0, M15** in fact carrying the absolute address of the word required.

The instruction sequence of the reproduction subroutine, following the progeny table beginning in **p1**, will be

(0); F×2/4; M15=4; p0P200=(j1); J0P200; (*H* = *random number* 0 *to* 15)**;**
(1); F+H→F; F→M15; p1 (M15)→F; [link and exit]**;**

The required progeny genotype is in **F**. This is almost identical with the routine used with the two-parent single gene table look-up method.

This is a very fast method of simulating reproduction, and is obviously to be preferred if store space is available for the table, but it does raise one serious problem—that of constructing the table if this is to be done during the writing of the program. The individual items in the table (even the economy version has 1296) would have to be accurately determined and accurately punched onto the program tape or cards—a considerable task very liable to error. Once again, this problem can be satisfactorily solved by making the computer produce the progeny table. A relatively simple example of this has already been described.

In the present example, there is brought into action at the beginning of the program a subroutine which uses the gamete section of Table 6 to produce in the correct sequence the progeny for each possible cross.

Let us consider the progeny line of 16 individuals from a cross I×J, where I and J represent the parents. If i and j are the numerical values of the binary representations of the genotypes, then the line number in the progeny table is $16i+j$. Suppose that in the gamete table the four gametes (of I) in line i are $\mathrm{i}_0\ \mathrm{i}_1\ \mathrm{i}_2\ \mathrm{i}_3$ and the four gametes (of J) in line j are $\mathrm{j}_0\ \mathrm{j}_1\ \mathrm{j}_2\ \mathrm{j}_3$. Then if the i gametes have been shifted up one place for fertilization, the progeny line numbered $16i+j$ should contain the 16 zygotes $\mathrm{i}_0+\mathrm{j}_0\ \mathrm{i}_0+\mathrm{j}_1\ \mathrm{i}_0+\mathrm{j}_2\ \mathrm{i}_0+\mathrm{j}_3\ \mathrm{i}_1+\mathrm{j}_0\ \mathrm{i}_1+\mathrm{j}_1\ \mathrm{i}_1+\mathrm{j}_2\ \mathrm{i}_1+\mathrm{j}_3\ \mathrm{i}_2+\mathrm{j}_0\ \mathrm{i}_2+\mathrm{j}_1\ \mathrm{i}_2+\mathrm{j}_2\ \mathrm{i}_2+\mathrm{j}_3\ \mathrm{i}_3+\mathrm{j}_0\ \mathrm{i}_3+\mathrm{j}_1\ \mathrm{i}_3+\mathrm{j}_2\ \mathrm{i}_3+\mathrm{j}_3$ which we may abbreviate to

$$\mathrm{i}_0+[\mathrm{j}_0\cdot\mathrm{j}_1\cdot\mathrm{j}_2\cdot\mathrm{j}_3],\ \mathrm{i}_1+[\mathrm{j}_0\cdot\mathrm{j}_1\cdot\mathrm{j}_2\cdot\mathrm{j}_3],\ \mathrm{i}_2+[\mathrm{j}_0\cdot\mathrm{j}_1\cdot\mathrm{j}_2\cdot\mathrm{j}_3],\ \mathrm{i}_3+[\mathrm{j}_0\cdot\mathrm{j}_1\cdot\mathrm{j}_2\cdot\mathrm{j}_3],$$

which though unconventional should be clear enough in interpretation especially if reference is made to Table 7. If the progeny table begins at address **p1** of the reproduction subroutine, then this line will begin at **p**$\{1+16(16i+j)\}$ of that subroutine.

The full progeny table is composed of 256 such lines, made up in the same way by taking each possible m.s. parent in turn and pairing it with all possible l.s. parents in the proper sequence. Table 8 shows a symbolized version of the gametic table, Table 6, and we will suppose this now to be stored in the table writing subroutine. Table 9 shows, in abbreviated form and in the unconventional symbolism used a few lines back, fragments of the progeny table which should be sufficient to make clear the structure of the whole.

TABLE 8

Symbolic version of gamete table, Table 6, to clarify text description of table writing subroutine. (O and P have been excluded from parent column, to avoid possible ambiguity.)

Address of first gamete	Parent		Gametes
p1	A	0000	a_0 a_1 a_2 a_3
p5	B	0001	b_0 b_1 b_2 b_3
p9	C	0010	c_0 c_1 c_2 c_3
p13	D	0011	d_0 d_1 d_2 d_3
p17	E	0100	e_0 e_1 e_2 e_3
p21	F	0101	f_0 f_1 f_2 f_3
p25	G	0110	g_0 g_1 g_2 g_3
p29	H	0111	h_0 h_1 h_2 h_3
p33	I	1000	i_0 i_1 i_2 i_3
p37	J	1001	j_0 j_1 j_2 j_3
p41	K	1010	k_0 k_1 k_2 k_3
p45	L	1011	l_0 l_1 l_2 l_3
p49	M	1100	m_0 m_1 m_2 m_3
p53	N	1101	n_0 n_1 n_2 n_3
p57	Q	1110	q_0 q_1 q_2 q_3
p61	R	1111	r_0 r_1 r_2 r_3

The problem of writing the table then becomes one of combining the gamete lines for the m.s. parents with those for the l.s. parents (both taken of course from Table 6 but with the former shifted up one place) in their proper combinations in the proper sequence. This is not too difficult if the programmer keeps a clear head; it is mainly a matter of organization.

There are two ways of doing this. The simpler but long-winded way is to deal with the l.s. and m.s. parents separately, first filling the progeny table

TABLE 9

rtions of symbolic version of progeny table, of which Table 7 shows a section, to clarify .t description of table writing subroutine. Addresses in first column are in reproduction subroutine

Address of first ndividual n family	Symbolic formulation of progeny
p1	$a_0+[a_0.a_1.a_2.a_3]$, $a_1+[a_0.a_1.a_2.a_3]$, $a_2+[a_0.a_1.a_2.a_3]$, $a_3+[a_0.a_1.a_2.a_3]$
p17	$a_0+[b_0.b_1.b_2.b_3]$, $a_1+[b_0.b_1.b_2.b_3]$, $a_2+[b_0.b_1.b_2.b_3]$, $a_3+[b_0.b_1.b_2.b_3]$
⋮	
p241	$a_0+[r_0.r_1.r_2.r_3]$, $a_1+[r_0.r_1.r_2.r_3]$, $a_2+[r_0.r_1.r_2.r_3]$, $a_3+[r_0.r_1.r_2.r_3]$
p257	$b_0+[a_0.a_1.a_2.a_3]$, $b_1+[a_0.a_1.a_2.a_3]$, $b_2+[a_0.a_1.a_2.a_3]$, $b_3+[a_0.a_1.a_2.a_3]$
⋮	
p497	$b_0+[r_0.r_1.r_2.r_3]$, $b_1+[r_0.r_1.r_2.r_3]$, $b_2+[r_0.r_1.r_2.r_3]$, $b_3+[r_0.r_1.r_2.r_3]$
p513	$c_0+[a_0.a_1.a_2.a_3]$, $c_1+[a_0.a_1.a_2.a_3]$, $c_2+[a_0.a_1.a_2.a_3]$, $c_3+[a_0.a_1.a_2.a_3]$
⋮	
p1282	$f_0+[b_0.b_1.b_2.b_3]$, $f_1+[b_0.b_1.b_2.b_3]$, $f_2+[b_0.b_1.b_2.b_3]$,$f_3+[b_0.b_1.b_2.b_3]$
⋮	
p4081	$r_0+[r_0.r_1.r_2.r_3]$, $r_1+[r_0.r_1.r_2.r_3]$, $r_2+[r_0.r_1.r_2.r_3]$, $r_3+[r_0.r_1.r_2.r_3]$

with the gametes of the l.s. parents in their correct sequence, then shifting all the gametes in the gamete table up one place in their words, and finally adding in to the progeny table the shifted gametes of the m.s. parents in their correct (and different) sequence.

Dealing with the l.s. parents first, we begin the table by writing the four words a_0, a_1, a_2 and a_3, and then repeating this to a total of four times; then we write the four words b_0, b_1, b_2 and b_3, and repeat this to a total of four times; and so on down to r_0, r_1, r_2 and r_3 (o and p have been excluded). We repeat the whole process to a total of 16 times.

For the m.s. parents, after performing the 1-place shifts on the words of the gamete table, we go back to the start of the progeny table and begin again by adding a_0 to the first four words, a_1 to the next four, a_2 to the next four and a_3 to the next four; this process is then repeated to a total of 16 times. We then continue the table by repeating this whole process with b_0, b_1, b_2 and b_3, and then with c_0, c_1, c_2 and c_3, and so on down to r_0, r_1, r_2 and r_3.

The whole operation of writing the table may be symbolically represented as follows.

1 For the l.s. parents:
$\{(a_0 . a_1 . a_2 . a_3) \times 4;\ (b_0 . b_1 . b_2 . b_3) \times 4;\ \ldots\ (r_0 . r_1 . r_2 . r_3) \times 4\} \times 16.$

2 The contents of all words in the gamete table are then shifted up one place.

3 For the m.s. parents we add to the gametes already in the progeny table: $(a_0 \times 4;\ a_1 \times 4;\ a_2 \times 4;\ a_3 \times 4) \times 16;\ (b_0 \times 4;\ b_1 \times 4;\ b_2 \times 4;\ b_3 \times 4) \times 16;\ \ldots\ (r_0 \times 4;\ r_1 \times 4;\ r_2 \times 4;\ r_3 \times 4) \times 16.$

The flow diagram for this procedure is shown in Figure 22. It is supposed for the sake of argument that the reproduction subroutine in which the progeny table is to be written is numbered **P103**, so that the address of the basic gametic table and the progeny table may be differentiated, beginning in **p1** of the writing subroutine and **p1 P103** respectively; the former does not need the subroutine number to be specified here, since it is only referred to within the same subroutine. The flow diagram is given largely in order form, since this requires less space and should make the diagram less difficult to follow. A detailed description of this flow diagram is not given, since it will be much better for the reader to work through it himself with the aid of Tables 8 and 9 and the symbolized procedure given in the text.

The subroutine, after the signal and the gamete table beginning in **p1** would read

```
(0); M13=0; K15=16;
(1); K14=16; G=-4;
(2); G+4; K13=4;
(3); G→M14; K12=4;
(4); p1(M14)→F; M14+1; F→p1P103(M13); M13+1;
     K12-1; J4K12≠0; K13-1; J3K13≠0;
     K14-1; J2K14≠0; K15-1; J1K15≠0;
     K15=64; M15=0;
(5); p1(M15)→H; H up 1; H→p1(M15); M15+1; K15-1;
     J5K15≠0; M13=0; K15=16; H=-4;
(6); H+4; K14=16;
(7); H→M15; K13=4;
(8); p1(M15)→E; M15+1; K12=4;
(9); E≢p1P103(M13)→p1P103(M13); M13+1;
     K12-1; J9K12≠0; K13-1; J8K13≠0;
     K14-1; J7K14≠0; K15-1; J6K15≠0; [link and exit];
```

A more intricate but neater and more satisfying way of writing this subroutine would be to deal with both parents simultaneously. This requires a very clear head. The appropriate flow diagram is shown in Figure 23. The reader may care to note that, with suitable spatial rearrangement, it could

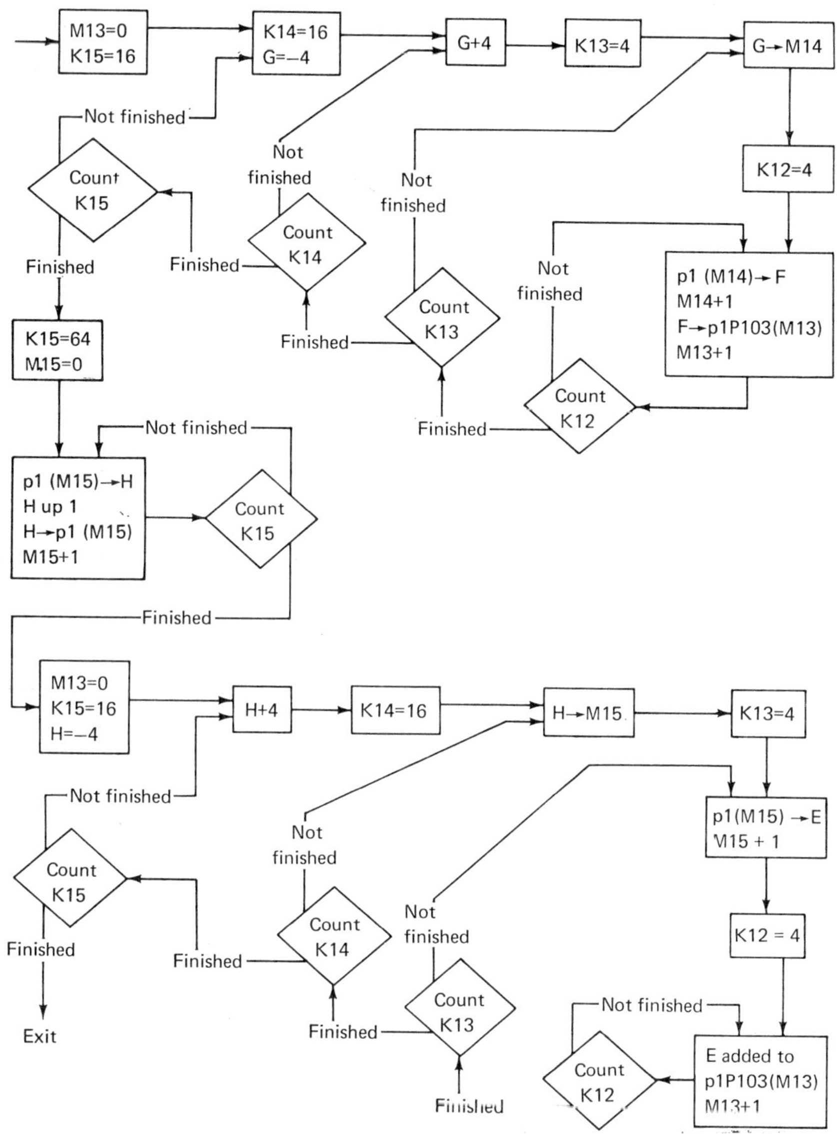

Figure 22. Flow diagram of subroutine for writing progeny table for all possible combinations of two parents, with two independent loci, for use in the simulation of reproduction as in Figure 21. The table is written by dealing with the m.s. and l.s. parents separately, and uses a gamete table (single parent) beginning in **p1**. It begins in **p1P103**. For explanation refer to text. (The apparent lack of economy is use of accumulators and modifiers is to help the reader with the next figure, 23, each accumulator, modifier and counter serving identical purposes in the two subroutines, as listed in the legend to Figure 23.)

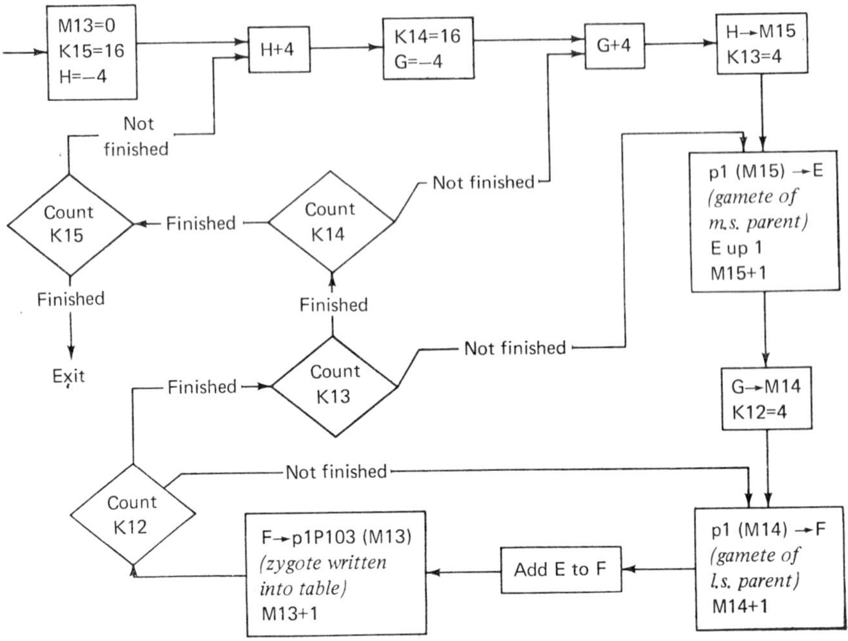

Figure 23. Flow diagram of subroutine for writing progeny table for all possible combinations of two parents, with two independent loci, for use in the simulation of reproduction as in Figure 21. The table is written by dealing with the m.s. and l.s. parents together, and the flow diagram combines into one the two principal operations of the flow diagram of Figure 22. The table is derived from a gamete table (single parent) beginning in **p1**, and itself begins in **p1P103.**
K15 and **K14** count m.s. and l.s. parents; **K13** and **K12** count gametes of m.s. and l.s. parents; **M15** and **M14** deal with gametes of m.s. and l.s. parents; **M13** stores progeny; **H** holds address of first gamete of current m.s. parent, to re-set **M15** when necessary; **G** similarly holds that of l.s. parent, to re-set **M14**; **H** and **G** initially set at −4, since the first increment of 4 is added before the first setting of the relevant modifiers, which have to begin at zero.

almost (but not quite), be formed by superimposing the two major sections of Figure 22.

The subroutine, after the signal and gamete table beginning in **p1**, would read, with deceptive simplicity,

(0); M13 = 0; K15 = 16; H = −4;
(1); H+4; K14 = 16; G = −4;
(2); H→M15; G+4; K13 = 4;
(3); G→M14; p1(M15)→E; M15+1; E up 1; K12 = 4;

(4); p1(M14)→F; M14+1; E≢F→F; F→p1P103(M13);
M13+1;
K12−1; J4K12≠0; K13−1; J3K13≠0;
K14−1; J2K14≠0; K15−1; J1K15≠0; [link and exit];

Neither of these versions of the table writing subroutine has taken account of the possibility that many lines in the progeny table could be made redundant if heterozygotes were always represented as **01**. This is because, as pointed out before, it is easier to let a subroutine write superfluous lines than to program it to avoid them.

If it is desired in the interests of store economy to utilize redundant lines for some other purpose, the progeny table would be better stored independently of the reproduction subroutine. If the latter is written as a general subroutine it will then need to be supplied by the main program red tape with the absolute address of the first word of the progeny table; the way in which this would operate has been described earlier (p. 163). Since all heterozygotes will now have to be represented as **01**, an amended form of the table writing subroutine will have to be used which will transform the zygotes **0010**, **0110**, **1000**, **1001**, **1010**, **1011**, and **1110** into **0001**, **0101**, **0100**, **0101**, **0101**, **0111** and **1101** respectively. This is easily accomplished if the table writing subroutine carries after its gamete table a transformation table of 16 words (it will have to include those which do not need transforming) and each zygote as it is produced is referred to this table and transformed as appropriate. This 16-word table will begin in **p65**; then in the shorter version of the table writing subroutine, in the line beginning with **(4)**, the two instructions **F→M12; p65(M12)→F** will be inserted after **E≢F→F**.

The amount of storage space which would be made available for other use is considerable and has the additional advantage that it is mostly concentrated in large continuous blocks of words. Thus there is one sequence of 1024 consecutive spare words (corresponding to m.s. parents beginning with **aA**) and three sequences of 256, together with some smaller and thus generally less useful sequences. But there is one very important proviso—the redundant space in the table cannot normally be utilized until after the table has been written, since the act of writing would automatically delete any other material already stored there. The fact that the redundant words will no longer be zero after the table is written is of no consequence—they will be deleted by any material which is later written there, or they can if necessary be made zero by the program.

If, for any special reason, it were desired to fill the spare space before the table is written, it would be possible to do this by causing the subroutine when it comes to write the table to by-pass writing in those regions, though it would have to go through most of the other motions in order to ensure that the modifiers would be in the correct state to resume writing at the proper point in the sequence—otherwise this would involve unnecessary complications. Saving only the major blocks, it would write the first 512 progeny, skip 256, write 768, skip 256, write 256, skip 1024, write 512, skip 256 write 256. This could be achieved quite easily in the shorter subroutine by amending the innermost loop (**K12**). A counter would be set at 512 at the start of the subroutine and would be tested at each passage through the innermost loop. The numbers 256, 768, 256, 256, 1024, 512, 256 and 256 stored in a small table after the transformation table would be extracted in turn by a modifier when the counter reaches zero and used to reset that counter. An accumulator would be set initially with a positive number and its sign changed each time the counter reaches zero and is reset. Writing would be by-passed whenever the accumulator is negative.

The amendments to the subroutine would be as follows. The numbers for the counter would be stored in **p81** onwards. Using **K11** as the new counter, **M11** as the modifier to extract the numbers for **K11**, and **D** to carry the by-pass determining integer, the additional instructions **K11 = 512; M11 = 0; D = 1;** would appear at the start of the subroutine, which would then be as before up to reference **(4)**. From then, the subroutine would read

```
(4); J5D<0; p1(M14)→F; E≢F→F; F→M12; p65(M12)→F;
    F→p1 P103(M13);
(5); M14+1; M13+1; K11−1; J6K11≠0; −D; p81(M11)→K11; M11+1;
(6); K12−1; J4K12≠0; etc. as in original version.
```

It would even be possible to use the spare storage space for sections of the program, but this would lead us to deep involvement in programming techniques rather remote from the simulation of reproduction. But with small computers and the need for economy in the use of space, use of such techniques may well be worth while, although they will not be considered any further here.

Because of the importance of minimizing the conflict between speed and storage space with small computers, we will continue this small print section to give an account of quite a different way of economizing in storage space. This is by using a technique known as *packing*, which has many applications in programming and is therefore worth considering in some detail.

The words of XB1 are of 32 bits. Therefore (remembering that we are still within the 2-gene section of this chapter) if we store only the genotype of one individual in one word we use only one-eighth of that word; 28 bits are wasted. We could make maximum use of the word by storing the genotypes of eight individuals within it, in groups of four consecutive bits. Thus for example the eight individuals **AaBB**, **AABB**, **aABb**, **AabB**, **aaBB**, **aabB**, **Aabb** and **AAbb** could be stored as

01000000100101101100111001110011.

This obviously requires more complicated programming and will require more computer time, both in setting the table and in extracting progeny from it, but the table size will be cut to 512 words. Whether the loss of speed is such that it would no longer be worth while using a progeny table look-up method, and would be better to revert to the gamete table look-up, will depend to some extent on the various instruction speeds of the particular computer in use, and will be a matter for the judgment of the programmer. It will be the speed of the look-up operation which is important, since this process will be performed very many times; the speed of the once-performed table setting procedure is of little importance.

Table setting will be considered with reference to the original version of the shorter subroutine (corresponding to Figure 23), and the question of redundancy will be ignored since it is now of much less importance. We will suppose that the reproduction subroutine, which will be somewhat different from the one we have called **P103**, is numbered **P104**. The only part of the table writing subroutine requiring amendment is that relating to the operation of writing into the progeny table. This will no longer be done directly into **p1P104(M13)**, but into an accumulator **D** which has previously been logically shifted up four places. When eight such additions have been made, **D** will contain eight genotypes and will be put into **p1P104(M13)** and **M13** incremented by one. The only other thing needed is a counter (**K11**) which will need to be set at 8 at the beginning of the subroutine and reset after every transfer of the contents of **D** to the progeny table. **D** need never be cleared, since by the time eight items have been placed in it, all previous contents will have gone (this would not be true if less than eight 4-bit words were being packed into **D**).

The amended table writing subroutine will have **K11** = **8** at the start, and will proceed as follows from reference **(4)**.

(4); p1(M14)→F; M14+1; E≢F→F; D up 4; F≢D→D;
K11−1; J5K11≠0; D→p1P104(M13); M13+1; K11=8;
(5); K12−1; J4K12≠0; etc. as in original version.

Reference to the progeny table by the reproduction subroutine is less simple since it involves not only fetching a word from the table but also extracting the required sequence of four bits from that word.

Thinking for the moment of the progeny table in printed form as in Table 7, each line will now consist of two words instread of 16, each word containing eight 4-bit genotypes. As before, the line number k will be the numerical equivalent of the binary representation of the combined parental genotypes, and for the basic reference to the progeny table this will now have to be shifted up only one place (that is, $\times 2$) instead of four ($\times 16$) (see Figure 21). $2k$ having been determined, we choose at random one of the two words in line k by adding to $2k$ a 1-bit random number (0 or 1) and using the sum as a modifier. This is essentially the same operation as before, using a 1-bit random number instead of a 4-bit one, but this time the process does not stop there—we have now to extract at random from the word one of the 4-bit progeny genotypes. This is done by obtaining a 3-bit random number (0 to7), multiplying it by four, and using the product as a modifier to shift the word down 0, 4, 8, 12, 16, 20, 24 or 28 places. The four l.s. bits after the shift (which must of course be logical) are then extracted by performing an LM with the mask ...**001111**, and are the required progeny genotype.

We do not need to generate two random numbers for this operation. If we generate a random number with at least five bits, an LM against the mask ...**0001** will give a 1-bit random number which determines the choice between the two words in a progeny line, and an LM against the mask ...**0011100** will give a random number in the range 0 to 7 already multiplied by four as required for the shift. Since the reproduction subroutine will now itself extract the required number of bits from the generated random number, the latter does not need to be produced to a specified size and we can use the faster **P202** (producing 31 random bits) instead of **P200**.

The flow diagram for the whole process is shown in Figure 24. The subroutine is quite simple. We will suppose (as we have assumed in the table setting subroutine) that the progeny table begins in **p1**. We will also suppose that the main program supplies the subroutine with the two parents side by side at the l.s. end of **F** (all other bits in **F** being zero), the subroutine beginning with the third block of Figure 24. The relevant instruction sequence for the subroutine will then be

(0); F × 2/1 ; p0P202 = (j1); J0P202; (*H* = 31-*bit random number*)**;**
(1); H→G; H &1 ; G &28; F+H→F; (*F* =$2k+r_1$**); F→M15;**
p1 (M15)→F; (*F* = *word with eight genotypes*)**;**
G→M15; F down (M15); F &15; (*F* = *single genotype*)**;**
[link and exit];

The technique of packing is an important one, and may be valuable in a number of different programming contexts. It is hoped that the foregoing account may have been a useful introduction to the basic idea of the technique.

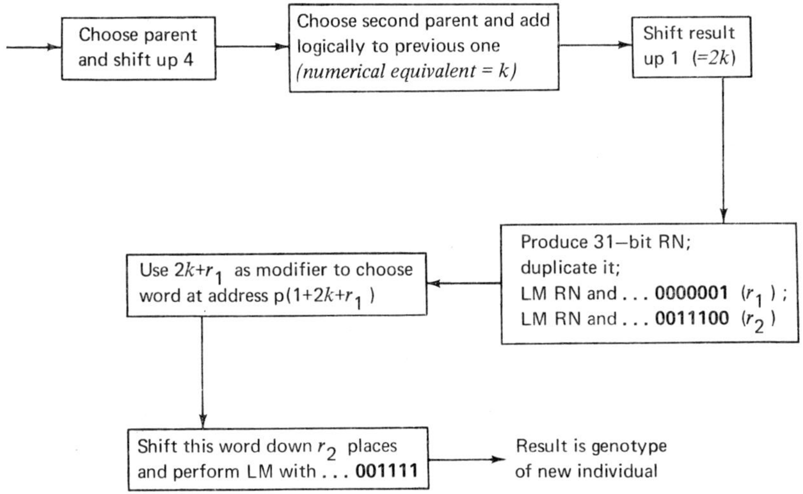

Figure 24. Flow diagram for production of zygote in a single operation from two parents by simultaneous simulation of gametogenesis and fertilization, using random look-up in a table with progeny packed at eight genotypes to a word. Two independent loci. Table begins in **p1**. Compare with Figure 21

Three or More Independent Genes

As the number of genes to be dealt with increases, all the methods so far described involve greatly increased demands on time or space. Realistic simulation of segregation along the lines explained in the early part of the preceding section becomes more complex and inelegant, and would really only be used where it was desired to demonstrate step by step simulation of segregation. Even then, the technique about to be described is preferable, though perhaps not so immediately comprehensible.

Table look-up, taking two parents simultaneously, is now impracticable even with only three genes; the full progeny table would consist of more than a quarter of a million items and not more than five progeny genotypes could be packed into a 32-bit word. The gamete table with three genes requires (unpacked) 512 words, and so table look-up taking parents individually does remain within the field of practicability there, but for each additional gene, the size of the table is increased eightfold. So long as store space is available, the speed of table look-up will always make it an attractive method, but four genes would appear to be the practicable maximum, with a gamete table of 4096 items.

There is however a quite different and elegant technique (Fraser, 1960) for simulating gametogenesis with several unlinked genes. It provides a realistic simulation of segregation simultaneously for all loci involved and, within the limits of the number of genes which can be accomodated within a single word, the time required is independent of the number of genes—it can deal with thirty as quickly and easily as it can with three, and it is fast. As an example we will consider a case with eight independent loci, and take an organism of genotype **AaBBCcdDeeFFgGhh**, from which it is required to produce a gamete.

The way of representing the genotype will now be changed from the traditional one given above, and the diploid genotype will be rewritten with the genotypes of its parental gametes side by side instead of interleaved. This is not essential for the technique, which as shown later will work equally well with the traditional arrangement, but is preferred for the moment because it will make the account easier to follow. The genotype under consideration becomes **ABCdeFghaBcDeFGh**. This will all go into a single word, which would be the normal way of storing the genotype of an individual organism. If the number of loci were more than half the number of bits in a word, two words would be used for the diploid genotype, one parental gamete in each (in this case, the traditional interleaved arrangement of the parental gametes would not work efficiently). This would in fact simplify the gametogenesis procedure since the first requirement of the method is that the two sets of genes should be brought into identical positions in two different words if they are not so arranged already. When this is achieved, the diploid genotype can be rewritten as $\frac{\mathbf{ABCdeFgh}}{\mathbf{aBcDeFGh}}$. It can now be seen at a glance that segregation involves in this example a choice of alleles at only four loci, since there is no choice at the homozygous loci **B e F h**. If we translate the diploid genotype into two binary words, $\frac{00011011}{10101001}$, we can paraphrase the previous sentence by saying that a choice is available where we have **1** and **0** in the same bit position (that is, where the gene is heterozygous), but not where we have **1** and **1**, or **0** and **0**. Consider the consequences of two logical operations, LM and LA, on these two words, indicating with italics in the results those positions where there is a choice of allele.

1) LM		2) LA	
	00011011		**00011011**
	10101001		**10101001**
LP =	***00001001***	LS =	***10110010***

It will be seen that in the LP all homozygous loci appear as the obligatory allele, **0** or **1** as the case may be, while all heterozygous loci appear as **0**. In the LS on the other hand, all homozygous loci (whether **00** or **11**) appear as **0** while heterozygous loci appear as **1**. That is, in the LS ones mark the loci at which a choice of alleles has to be made; in other words, segregation involves transforming the ones in the LS into zeros or ones at random. These zeros or ones, when added into the LP in the appropriate (italicized) positions will produce a properly generated gamete.

The main problem would then appear to be that of transforming the ones of the LS into randomly chosen ones and zeros, and this can be done quite easily by doing an LM between the ones of the LS and randomly produced bits which will be **0** or **1** with equal probability. If the random bit is **0**, the **1** of the LS will become **0**; if the random bit is **1**, the **1** of the LS will remain a **1**. All that needs to be done therefore is to produce a random number with at least as many bits as there are loci, do an LM with this and the original LS (all the random bits in the homozygous positions will become **0**, since the LS has **0** in each of those positions) and add the result to the original LM (arithmetically or logically, but the latter is to be preferred as a matter of principle for a non-arithmetic operation; in this case both give the right answer because the only possible additions are **0** to **0** or **0** to **1** and there cannot be any carry). The answer is the required gamete.

Continuing with the same example, suppose the random number generated is **11010110**. Then the operation continues

3) LM		4) add	
original LS	**10110010**	original LP	**00001001**
random number	**11010110**	answer from 3	**10010010**
	10010010		***10011011***

The result is **10011011** which represents a gamete **aBCdeFgh**. The whole is a very simple operation, complicated only if no LA instruction is available, in which case the short routine described on p. 80 will have to be used.

If in the population store two (adjacent) words are used for each individual, the genes from the two parental gametes being in different words, gamete formation can begin as soon as the parent has been chosen; to choose a parent in that case, if the population size is N, a random number r in the range 0 to $N-1$ is generated, doubled and the result used as a modifier to select the words in positions $2r$ and $2r+1$ in the population store.

If an individual is represented by one word carrying the genes from both parental gametes, as will normally be the case if the number of loci permits, then there has to be some rearrangement of the gene sets so that they come to be in identical positions in different words. This is easily done, after the parent has been chosen in the usual way (assuming for the moment that the word carries no information other than the genotype), by making a copy of the word and shifting it down logically n places, where n is the number of loci involved. In the example we have been considering, the parent word **ABCdeFghaBcDeFGh** will become the two words **ABCdeFghaBcDeFGh** (unshifted) and **ABCdeFgh** (shifted). The retention of the left-hand set of alleles in the unshifted word does not matter, because everything that goes on to the left of the eight l.s. positions is quite irrelevant and all irrelevant bits will be deleted, the end product being a word in which all bits except those representing the genes required for the gamete will be zero. This deletion is automatic if the random number used has only the same number of bits as there are loci, as would be the case using **P200**, since then the final LM operation will eliminate all remaining redundant bits. If a random number subroutine (which we have previously called **P202**) is used which produces a wordful (or rather 31) as distinct from a specified number of bits, then the process will have to finish with a further LM with a mask 2^n-1 which will retain only the bits required for the gamete genotype, all superfluous material again being eliminated; this might be somewhat quicker than using a subroutine such as **P200**. Whichever method is used, any additional coded information about the parent which may be stored in the same word if n is small will also be eliminated without any need for special action, and can be ignored.

Figure 25 shows the flow diagram of a subroutine using this technique of gametogenesis. It assumes that the parent occupies a single word and is delivered to it in accumulator **F** with the genotype at the l.s. end, that there are n loci, and that the random number subroutine used is **P200** which will deliver the specified number n of random bits at the l.s. end.

Where the number of loci is such that the parent genotype is stored in two words (at the l.s. end of each) and delivered in two accumulators, say **F** and **G**, then the first two operations of Figure 25 are omitted.

If the subroutine is to be a general one, variability in the number of loci must be possible from program to program, and n must be supplied to the subroutine preferably by main program red tape; alternatively, it could be made a specification requirement of the subroutine that n should be set in a modifier immediately preceding each entry to it, but generally speaking where such a parameter is invariable throughout a program (as this one almost always would be, unless more than one species was involved in the system being simulated) it is better dealt with entirely within the subroutine so that the programmer does not have to bother about it when writing the operative part of the program.

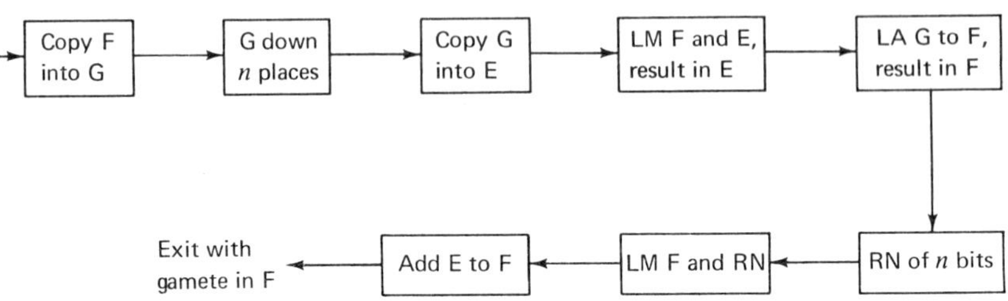

Figure 25. Flow diagram for simulation of gametogenesis with n independent loci. At entry, **F** contains the parent genotype at its l.s. end. For description, see text

In the following written version of the subroutine, we will suppose that at the beginning of the program n has been placed in **p1**. After the signal (no parameters need to be written) the subroutine will proceed

(0); F→G; p1→M15; (*this also sets **M15** for **P200** later*)**;**
G down (M15); G→E; F&E→E; F≢G→F; p0P200=(j1);
J0P200; (*H* = *random number of n bits, see previous note; also note that **G** is finished with before **P200** which uses it is entered*)**;**
(1); F&H→F; E≢F→F; [link and exit]**;**

The gamete is in **F**.

In a version requiring a final masking operation with 2^n-1, this would also need to be set as a parameter by main program red tape.

The reader will note that this is a simple and compact subroutine for the simulation of what is genetically quite a complicated process. Being written as a generalized subroutine it could be used without alteration in many different kinds of program (provided that the genotype of the parent is always simulated in a way which conforms to the requirement of the subroutine), the programmer merely having to treat entry to the subroutine as though it were a single instruction having the meaning 'produce gamete in accumulator **F**'. A better example could hardly have been found of the power of a generalized subroutine than this one, which deals so neatly with the fundamental process of all genetic systems.

A similar and equally effective method of simulating segregation at n independent loci is given, without description, in the following procedure. The reader should have little difficulty in seeing how it works. **p1** contains n; **p2** is the mask 2^n-1, used not in the usual way but to produce by LA the complementary bit pattern to the n-bit random number. As before, the parental genotype is supplied to the subroutine at the l.s. end of **F** with its parental gamete genotypes side by side, and the new gamete is delivered in **F**.

```
(0); F→G; p1→M15; G down (M15); p0P200 = (j1); J0P200;
(1); H→E; E≢p2→E; G&H→G; F&E→F; F≢G→F; [link and exit];
```

There is no need to remove the superfluous alleles from **F**, since they will disappear when the LM is performed.

There is no particular reason to prefer one of these methods to the other. The one described first and in detail is the one the author has always used and, for no better reason than that, it is the one which will be assumed throughout the rest of this chapter and elsewhere appropriate in this book. But this second method may be adapted to deal with the difficult problem of linkage, discussed in Chapter 8.

An alternative and in some ways preferable method of generalizing the gametogenesis subroutine would be to standardize it to a constant value of n, no parameter insertion by the main program then being required. But there would be a requirement for one specific genotype arrangement which might not always be convenient, as will be pointed out later.

A good value to choose for the standardized value of n would be the largest which allows the diploid number of genes ($2n$) to be carried within a word without using the m.s. bit (the usefulness of the sign bit as a quick indicator of some action-directing information about the individual is not lightly to be discarded, as has been pointed out earlier). For the 32-bit word of XB1, 15 would be a good value to take for n, and we will discuss the subroutine on that basis. This method means that unless the actual haploid number of genes is 15, the two gametic sets of genes in the diploid parent will no longer be adjacent, but will be separated by irrelevant bits. Thus the parent in the example we used in the early part of this section ($n=8$) would be represented by the word

$$000000000\overline{00011011}0000000\overline{10101001}.$$

The bits under the bars are used for the alleles, the others are spare and available for other information.

In manipulating the bits to align the alleles in the required way, the word is copied as before, and the copy shifted down 15 places. This produces the two words

$$\mathbf{000000000000110110000000\overline{10101001}}$$
$$\mathbf{00000000000000000000000000011011}$$

and the sections under the bar are exactly as on p. 173, everything to the left of the bar being irrelevant and having no effect on the final outcome.

The random number will now always need to be of at least 15 bits. The generalized operation of gamete formation will then follow the flow diagram of Figure 25 with 15 being substituted for n. The only alteration to the written version would be the substitution of **M15** = **15** for **p1→M15**, and an amendment to the signal since **p1** would no longer be required.

This method of generalizing the gametogenesis subroutine is less convenient if, n being small, the programmer wishes to utilize spare space in the word by storing within it extra information about the organism, such as fitness, age or location, in addition to the genotype. Not only would it be less convenient to have the spare space in two sections of $17-n$ and $15-n$ bits than in one section of $32-2n$ bits, but unless the random number were of n bits instead of 15 (which would make pointless this method of generalization of the subroutine) there could be superfluous bits of nonsense in the word containing the newly formed gamete, and these would have to be removed by a masking operation (with 2^n-1) by the main program after exit from the subroutine, unless the extra information had been removed from the parent with a more complicated mask by the main program before entry to the subroutine.

Since when n approaches 15 there isn't going to be much room for extra information anyway, a compromise might be to have two versions of the subroutine, one with $n=15$, and one with $n=8$ for smaller numbers of loci which would provide a continuous section of at least 16 spare bits. (Alternatively, as explained later, a version using the **AaBb**... arrangement of the genes could be used.)

Whichever form of the gametogenesis subroutine is used, reproduction would be completed by the production of a second gamete. If the diploid genotype is to be contained in one word, then one of the two gametes is shifted up n or 15 places and the two are combined by addition.

But, as with the case of table look-up, it is possible to produce in a single operation one diploid offspring from two parents, the only condition being that n is not more than half word size. There is a clear advantage in doing this, not only because one random number only is then required for the whole operation but also because the sequence of logical instructions involved in gametogenesis has only to be performed once.

We will consider the normal case in which we have the whole parental genotype in a single word, and we will produce a generalized subroutine with *n* standardized at 15, since the advantages of standardization are now greater than they were with the simple gametogenesis operation.

Considering only the thirty bits involved with the genotypes, let us place the two parents one above the other and represent them as

*rrrrrrrrrrrrrrr*rrrrrrrrrrrrrrr
*sssssssssssssss*sssssssssssssss,

the letters serving to distinguish the genes of the two parents and not individual genes, and italics distinguishing in each parent one gametic set from the other. Reproduction then consists of simulating segregation by choosing simultaneously one allele from each locus from *rr*...*r*/rr...r, giving say a gamete such as rrrrrrrrrrrrrrr, and then doing the same thing for *ss*...*s*/ss...s, giving say a gamete such as sssssssssssssss. Fertilization would combine the two gametes to give a zygote

sssssssssssssssrrrrrrrrrrrrrrr.

It would be an obvious advantage if the *rr*...*r*/rr...r segregation could be performed simultaneously with the *ss*...*s*/ss...s segregation. This can be achieved quite simply if the four gene sets from the parental words are rearranged into two words

sssssssssssssssrrrrrrrrrrrrrrr
sssssssssssssssrrrrrrrrrrrrrrr.

It can be seen from this juxtaposition that, considering the two words together, each bit position has two homologous alleles from one parent, and in segregation a choice from these has to be made at each of the 30 bit positions. We can therefore treat the two rearranged words exactly as if they were the two homologous sets of alleles from a single parent with 30 loci, and simulate segregation in the way which has already been described; although in fact the outcome of this will not be a gamete with a 30-bit genotype, but a zygote composed of two gametes with 15-bit genotypes.

Other rearrangements than the one given above, such as *ss*...rr.../ss...*rr* or *rr*...*ss*.../rr...ss... etc. would work equally well.

There are several ways of performing the rearrangement, variously involving masks and logical shifts; in making a choice, ease of programming and the relative speeds of the different operations must be taken into account; generally speaking, masking operations are quicker than shifts. One method which uses only shifts will be described in detail, and will assume a word size of 32 bits and a value for *n* of 15, the sign bit and its neighbour being unoccupied.

Continuing to represent the genotype as before, but now including unused bits, the two parental words are

00rrrrrrrrrrrrrrrrrrrrrrrrrrrrrr

and

00ssssssssssssssssssssssssssssss.

These are placed in accumulators **E** and **F** respectively (**G** and **H** will be required for random number production) prior to entry to the subroutine. Accumulator **D** is made zero and a double length logical shift down of 15 performed on **ED**. This gives the result

E = **00000000000000000**rrrrrrrrrrrrrrr

and

D = rrrrrrrrrrrrrrr**00000000000000000**.

A double length shift down of 15 is now performed on **FD** and **D** shifted down a further two places, giving

F = **00000000000000000**sssssssssssssss

and

D = **00**sssssssssssssssrrrrrrrrrrrrrrr.

F is now shifted up 15, and added to **E**, giving

E = **00**sssssssssssssssrrrrrrrrrrrrrrr.

A flow diagram for this rearrangement is shown in the upper half of Figure 26.

The lower half of Figure 26 shows an alternative method, substituting a copy and an LM for each of two shifts, and an LM for a third small shift. In machines where shifts are rather slow, this may well be the quicker and more efficient method of making the rearrangement. The masking operation after the shift up of **C** perhaps requires some explanation. When **C** is shifted up, the left-hand gamete is not entirely eliminated—its two l.s. bits remain as the two m.s. bits of **C** after the shift. Although these two bits will not affect the gametogenesis operation which follows they could persist and appear in the resultant zygote unless a random number of exactly 30 bits is used in gametogenesis, which as explained below may not be convenient. Although they do not affect the current gametogenesis, they would interfere with reproduction when the zygote in its turn comes to reproduce, and they must be eliminated before the zygote is put into the population. If the number of gene loci is few, and spare space is used for other information, this also will have to be eliminated eventually even though it does not interfere with gametogenesis (the information bits will behave exactly as though they were gene bits). The reproduction subroutine we are considering is a general one, and such elimination will best be done by the main program after exit from

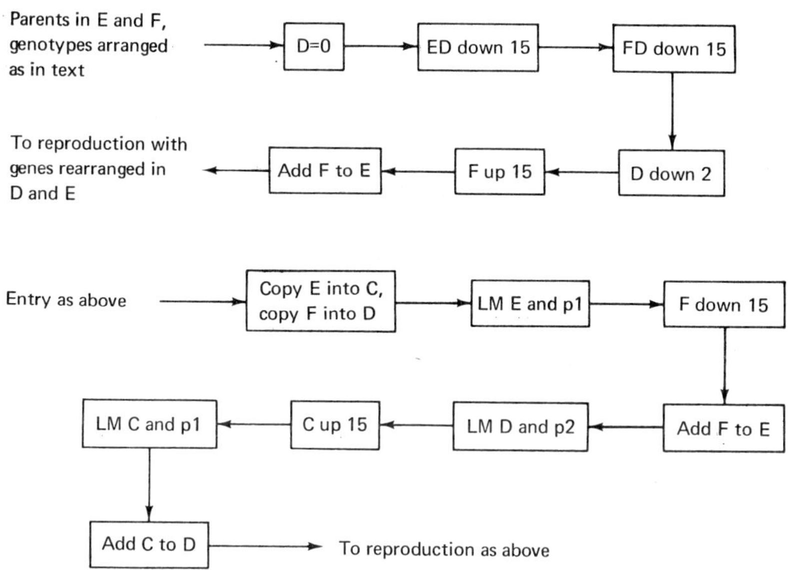

Figure 26. Flow diagrams showing two methods of rearranging gametic sets of two parents, so that the method of Figure 25 may then be used for the production of a zygote in a single operation by simultaneous simulation of gametogenesis and fertilization. The n of Figure 25 is here standardized at 15. Masks: **p1** contains **001111111111111110000000000000000** (2^{30}-2^{15}) and
p2 contains **000000000000000001111111111111111** (2^{15}-1)

the subroutine since the mask required—$(2^n-1)(2^{15}+1)$ if the l.s. bits of each segment of 15 are used for the genes—will be programme specific. The two unwanted m.s. bits could then be removed by the main program in the same operation. However, since the subroutine is a general one, it should also be able to deal with the situation when no masking operation by the main program is performed; for this reason, it is preferable for the subroutine to eliminate the two m.s. bits of **C** and this is best done immediately after the shift.

Whichever method we use for rearranging the genotypes, the two operative accumulators (**D** and **E** in Figure 26) will come to contain the parent genotypes arranged in such a way that homologous alleles from the same parent occupy identical bit positions. We can then proceed directly to a gametogenesis procedure which treats the two words as homologous sets of alleles of one parent.

All we need to do is to enter a subroutine, slightly modified from that of Figure 25, at the third block in the figure, but different accumulators will now apply. Apart from differences in the allocation of accumulators, the only other change will be that the random number will need to be not of n bits, but of $2n$—that is of 30 bits. Since both of the rearrangement procedures already described leave the two m.s. bits of the 32-bit words at zero, it would not matter if the random number had more than 30 bits, and it would be pointless to use a subroutine such as **P200** which delivers a specified number of bits, since time would be spent in meeting a needless specification.

For our present purpose, it would be preferable to use **P202**, or a similar generator producing at least 30 bits, as the pseudorandom number subroutine. However, care must be taken in the choice of generator; this subject is discussed in greater detail in Chapter 13, but it should be pointed out here that with some generators not all the bits produced may reliably be treated as random; it is essential for our present purpose that all 30 bits used should provide a reliable simulation of randomness.

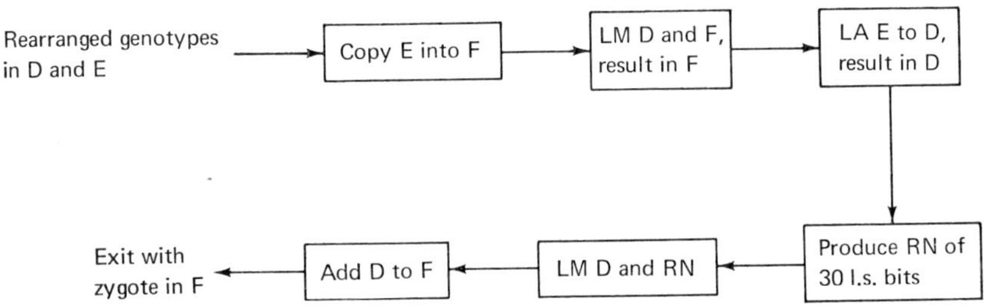

Figure 27. The flow diagram of Figure 25 modified for use after either rearrangement procedures of Figure 26, for production of zygote from two parents by simultaneous simulation of gametogenesis and fertilization

Figure 27 shows the flow diagram for gametogenesis, and this follows on directly from either of the rearrangement flow diagrams of Figure 26. The whole reproduction subroutine is easy enough to write. We will use the pseudorandom number subroutine **P202**, which requires a link but no bits specification. At entry, the two parents will be in **E** and **F**. Using the rearrangement process corresponding to the upper half of Figure 26, the subroutine proceeds after the signal

(0); D = 0; ED down 15; FD down 15; D down 2; F up 15;
F ≢ E→E; E→F; D & F→F; D ≢ E→D; p0P202 = (j1);
J0P202; (*H* = *random number***);**
(1); D & H→D; D ≢ F→F; [link and exit]**;**

Using instead the rearrangement process of the bottom half of Figure 26, we would have after the signal

> **0; (*for link*); 8/7777700000; 8/77777; (*masks*);**
> **(0); E→C; F→D; E&p1→E; F down 15; F≢E→E;**
> **D&p2→D; C up 15; C&p1→C; C≢D→D;**
> **E→F; D&F→F;** etc. as above.

Either of these reproduction subroutines is now of general use for any number of independent loci up to a maximum of 15. Application is very simple, demanding only that the words representing the parents should be in accumulators **E** and **F** on entry and should have their genotypes represented in the specified way.

Once a subroutine of this kind has been developed and is working properly, it would be used in many programs which will be conceived, developed and finally produced on the basis throughout that the method of genotype representation used will be appropriate for this subroutine. The programmer does not need to think about what goes on inside the subroutine, which will come to be used almost as though it were an instruction for a single operation, so that amid all the complexities of his program he will with hardly a thought deal with reproduction simply as 'choose parent; choose another parent; reproduce one offspring'. Unless of course the evolutionary situation he is trying to simulate involves some complexities in the first two elements of this chain of three.

Although this account of the simulation of reproduction has been based on a diploid genotype arrangement which has the gamete genotypes side by side rather than interleaved in the familiar way, **AaBbCc** etc., it will work perfectly well with the latter arrangement which may sometimes be more convenient—for example where different genes are concerned with different phenotypic effects, including fitness, it may be preferable to have the bits of alleles dealing with one aspect of phenotypic expression in one continuous group. It also has an advantage when few loci are involved in that the spare bits available for storing additional information are in one continuous section, not two separated ones.

Using *r* r, *s* s as before to distinguish the original gametic genotypes of the two parents respectively, the latter may now be expressed as

*r*r*r*r*r*r*r*r*r*r*r*r*r*r*r*r*r*r*r*r*r*r*r*r*r*r*r*r*r*r
*s*s*s*s*s*s*s*s*s*s*s*s*s*s*s*s*s*s*s*s*s*s*s*s*s*s*s*s*s*s

and to perform gametogenesis and fertilization simultaneously with these we will need to rearrange them in such a way as

rsrsrsrsrsrsrsrsrsrsrsrsrsrsrs
rsrsrsrsrsrsrsrsrsrsrsrsrsrsrs

and precisely the same gametogenesis operation is performed as before, producing a 30-bit zygote with the genotype in the required arrangement. The rearrangement presents no difficulties.

Two masks are required. We will suppose **p1** to contain the mask

001010101010101010101010101010

and **p2** the mask

000101010101010101010101010101.

As before, the two parents will be supplied to the subroutine in **E** and **F**, and the rearranged genotypes will be in **D** and **E**.

After the signal, the subroutine will proceed

0; (*for link***); 8/05252525252; 8/02525252525; (***masks***);**
(0); E→C; F→D; E&p1→E; F down 1; F&p2→F; (*does not work like previous subroutine where shift down eliminated one set***);**
E ≢ F→E; D&p2→D; C up 1; C&p1→C; C ≢ D→D;
E→F; D& F→F; etc. as in previous subroutine.

Where the number of loci is such that the diploid zygote requires more bits than there are in a word, the **AaBb...** arrangement is virtually impracticable, and an individual will be represented with its constituent gametes in different words, the gene bits consecutive. Since two parental genotypes cannot then be accommodated within two words, two separate gametogenesis operations will have to be performed, and it is not possible to deal with both parents simultaneously.

CHAPTER 7

Fitness, Selection and the Expression of the Phenotype

The application of selection is an essential part of almost any experiment simulating evolutionary processes. It was discussed superficially in Chapter 3, and now needs to be dealt with in greater detail.

Occasionally, as with some situations involving the breeding system (Crosby, 1960), selection may be an intrinsic part of the system and not require explicit formulation or programming treatment. More usually, selection will occur through differences in viability and reproductive capacity, and this is the context in which it will be considered. Orthodox population genetics has its own methods of quantifying and manipulating selective advantages and disadvantages, and it would be possible to approach selection in simulation experiments in the same sort of way. But those methods have been devised as a convenient means of describing natural systems in terms amenable to mathematical treatment, or of trying to deduce the selective situation in a natural system.

With the genotype simulation technique (to which this chapter will be confined), we are in effect back among the individual organisms, and we have no need to apply mathematical formulations to our experiments, though they may prove useful when we come to describe those experiments and their results.

The simplest way of dealing with selection would appear to be to suppose that the fitnesses of the individuals in a population, that is their relative abilities to leave descendants, depended on their genotypes, and to allot or calculate an appropriate value for fitness to each particular genotype, translating this into some sort of action during the execution of the program. A convenient way of allotting a parameter for fitness would be to consider the fittest genotype as having a fitness of 1.0, and to express those of all other genotypes as the appropriate fractions.

But it is not quite as easy as that, because we have to decide in what way differences in fitness are going to express themselves, and at what stage or stages of an organism's life history the selection pressures are to be applied.

Viability

There are a number of words which geneticists tend to use rather loosely, perhaps because of disinclination or inability to be more specific. 'Viability' is one such word, and has been used as a synonym for fitness, but strictly speaking it should have a more specific meaning, which nevertheless is rather difficult to define and if it were defined it would not be entirely sensible biologically. It could simply mean an ability to live, and an organism could be considered to be viable if it reached the stage of birth, hatching or germination. On the other hand, by itself that is not enough from an evolutionary viewpoint. Even subsequent substantial growth is not enough unless the organism develops sufficiently to be capable of reproduction. It could be said that an organism which fails to attain reproductive maturity might as well not have lived, and has zero fitness; it would play no part in the genetics of the population, and could reasonably be treated in a simulation program as being inviable. So that for practical purposes the meaning of the term viability could well be restricted to the ability to grow and reproduce, any organism falling short of this to be considered inviable. This is the view which will be adopted.

There is a subtlety here. Most organisms over-reproduce, often considerably; plants with high seed production and insects which lay large numbers of eggs provide obvious examples. The majority of their zygotes fail to develop, or die before reaching reproductive maturity, and chance must play a large part in determining which survive and which do not. An individual may grow to maturity and produce zygotes none of which themselves succeed in growing to maturity, and in a sense it might then be said to have just as well not existed.

The extent to which an organism contributes genetically to future generations is thus determined both by chance and its genotype, and we should at this stage distinguish mentally between reproductive failure due to chance and that due to an inferior genotype. Chance is taken care of by the stochastic processes of the simulation program; genotype determines a fitness for which we have to assign (arbitrarily or otherwise) a parameter and construct a course of action for applying this parameter in simulation of natural selection.

We will suppose for the moment that fitness will be considered in terms of viability only. If the viability of a particular genotype is f, then ignoring the elimination of zygotes consequent on over-reproduction, what we are saying is that on average a fraction f of all zygotes with that genotype will grow and attain the ability to reproduce, and that the remainder will not. In considering fitness only in terms of viability, we are also saying that all viable (that is, surviving) genotypes, of whatever kind, have equal capacities for reproduction—a dubious assumption to which we will return later.

It is necessary to remind ourselves, as pointed out in Chapter 6, that we do not simulate the entire reproductive activity of a population. The logic of this was obvious when we were taking no account of selection—where there is overproduction of zygotes and many (by chance in the absence of selection) fail to develop, or die before reaching reproductive maturity, it would be a waste of time to simulate their production. If in fact we did simulate the entire reproduction, the logic involved in the application of selection pressure would be obvious. We could simulate reproduction of the whole population, producing a large number of zygotes, and then simulate selection by eliminating for each genotype a proportion $1-f$ where f was the viability of that particular genotype. That completed for the whole zygote output, a random choice would be made from that output to produce the number required for the breeding population of the next generation.

Where we do not waste time in simulating over-reproduction, the logic is less obvious. When selection has to be applied in terms of viability, we will have to produce some zygotes which have no future, namely those which are eliminated by selection, but this is no longer a waste of time since it has now become an essential part of the selection process. While avoiding the production of excess zygotes whose elimination in a natural population would be entirely a matter of chance, we need at the same time to retain the production of those whose elimination is a selective process.

What we do is to produce that number of zygotes which will, when reduced by selection, provide sufficient individuals for the next generation. At the beginning of reproduction for each generation we cannot know the number to be produced initially, since we do not then know the frequencies of the different (and differently viable) genotypes which will be produced, and therefor we do not know how many of the zygotes produced can be expected to be eliminated by selection, quite apart from additional uncertainties of stochastic origin.

This docs not however raise any difficulties in practice because selection elimination is carried out as reproduction of the next generation proceeds, and this continues until the required number of surviving zygotes has been produced. Elimination of the various fractions $1-f$ for the various disadvantageous genotypes can be carried out in two ways. Wc may count the number of each genotype as it is produced and eliminate regularly so that the correct proportion f of viable zygotes is retained. This has the advantage of speed, since no random number generation is required, but can be awkward to carry out in practice unless f or $1-f=1/n$ where n is an integer, when selection may be simulated by the retention or elimination respectively of every nth zygote having the genotype under consideration, beginning with number $n/2$. The objection to this is that selection is then not subject to stochastic variability.

To apply selection stochastically, each zygote is considered as it is produced, and eliminated or not with a probability of $1-f$ that it will be eliminated. This was essentially the method used in a very simple form to simulate selection against **aa** in Chapter 3, our f being equivalent to $1/t$ in that chapter. Simplification was there achieved, with a view to the 'computer' in use, by making the viability of **aa** equal to 1/8 and generating a random number in the range 0 to 7, the probability of an **aa** zygote being eliminated being the same as that of producing a non-zero random number, namely 7/8.

This would be extremely simple with a real computer, which can distinguish between zero and non-zero very easily, but we cannot restrict ourselves in simulation experiments to viabilities or inviabilities which so neatly correspond to reciprocals of powers of two. At best, this would tend to be unrealistic in a simple situation. Where several genotypes are involved, with additive effects or interactions, it would be virtually impossible without loss of biological sense.

Selection is applied to a zygote of viability f by first generating a positive random fraction. If this fraction exceeds f the zygote will be rejected; if not, the zygote will survive. Clearly, the chance of survival is f if the fraction is random over the whole possible range from zero upwards.

There is one subtlety here. The fraction f can never equal 1.0, which would exceed capacity and is therefore impermissible, so a viability of 1.0 cannot be so expressed. Instead, we use the largest possible fraction, $1-2^{-31}$ (all **1**s except for the sign bit) in the case of a 32-bit word; this obviously can never be exceeded by the random fraction, For a viability of zero, a random fraction of zero would allow survival; the chance of such a contingency is so small that it may be neglected, and in fact in some pseudorandom number routines the production of zero is impossible. Alternatively, the criterion $\geqslant$ instead of $>$ could be used, when zero viability would never survive, and full viability would fail to survive with an entirely negligible frequency.

If a table look-up method is used to determine viabilities in a system where a large number of genotypes are possible and the table would therefore be very large, it may be desirable to reduce table size by restricting the number of bits used to express the viability and so allowing the viabilities of two or more genotypes to be packed into a single word. If the number of bits used for the viability is small this does raise some problems, though not very serious ones.

If for example eight bits are used for the viability (there is no need to include the sign bit, which must always be zero), then the maximum expressible value for this would be $1-2^{-8}$; if all 31 bits generated are used for the random fraction, this will have a maximum value of $1-2^{-31}$ and exceed that for the maximum viability (and so reject fully viable genotypes) with a frequency of $1/2^8$. This could be prevented by using only the eight m.s. bits of the random fraction (which then could not exceed $1-2^{-8}$) but this would then have a zero value (and with $>$ as the criterion fail to eliminate lethal genotypes) with a frequency of $1/2^8$, quite irrespective of whether the subroutine could or could not generate zero. It matters less that a fully viable genotype may occasionally be rejected than that a lethal genotype may occasionally survive. Generally, the best procedure is simply to use all 31 bits of the generated random fraction and accept the fact that fully viable genotypes will occasionally be rejected.

The way in which comparison between viability and random fraction is effected depends on the computer. With a computer liberally endowed with jump instructions, a jump based directly on a comparison of two numbers may be available, as we have supposed for XB1. Otherwise it may be necessary to subtract one from the other and use the result to provide the criterion of whether to jump or not.

The operation is very simple, and a procedure in Mendol might be as follows. We will imagine that the viability has been determined and is in **F**, and that **P202** is used to generate a positive random fraction. We will suppose that if the viability test fails a jump is to be made to reference *n*, otherwise the program will continue in sequence. Then the viability test will be performed by the sequence of operations

p0P202 = **(j***m***)** ; **J0P202** ; **(***random fraction in* ***H*****)** ;
(*m***)** ; **J***n***H** > **F** ; etc.

The higher the viability in **F**, the less likely the jump to *n*. Since, in the context in which we are considering the viability test, failure means rejection of the zygote just produced, the jump to reference *n* will usually take the program back to initiate the production of a new zygote to replace the one rejected.

Reproductive Capacity

The interpretation of fitness as viability and its implementation at or shortly after zygote formation is very convenient, since it means that the test has to be applied to each individual once only, and eliminated individuals never form part of the population and do not have to be stored. But it is not biologically accurate. In practice, a low fitness is not likely to take the form of a low survival rate coupled with full reproductive capacity of the survivors. It would be more realistic (especially for plants) to assume that all genotypes had equal survival values and that differences in fitness were expressed as differences in reproductive capacity. This is fairly obvious in flowering plants where apparent differences in vigour among individuals of the same species are often matched by differences in the numbers of flowers produced and of seeds set. To what extent this holds for animal species will depend on the group of animals or the species concerned. It may well be that in birds or mammals fitness is more concerned with survival to sexual maturity, with relatively small differences between surviving genotypes in the numbers of offspring produced.

But it is not as simple as that; even if all genotypes produced the same number of offspring per act of reproduction, decrease in life length (which might well be a way in which lower fitness is expressed) would lead to fewer acts of reproduction and thus to a lower reproductive capacity. This is as true for perennial plants as for animals. Another complication is that lower fitness may be due to lower fertility in the sense of the quality rather than the quantity of gametes produced, a proportion of these being faulty. This is a familiar situation where hybrids and their descendants are involved, and also occurs for example with structural heterozygotes, aneuploids and polyploids; in some of these cases the *viability* of individuals with low fitness resulting from poor fertility may be higher than that of individuals of maximum fitness.

This discussion underlines the need for a thorough understanding of the relevant biology of a system if it is to be sensibly simulated.

In reality, fitness will usually be compounded both of viability and reproductive capacity, to different extents in different systems. To try to take both into consideration in simulating fitness would probably be over-elaborate in many cases, and it would certainly increase the time required for an experiment. Although there are definite exceptions, it will in practice often make very little difference whether fitness is treated as viability or reproductive capacity; the most obvious quantitative difference concerns the gene and genotype frequencies in the population in any generation, since their estimation will exclude those that have failed to survive in the first case, but include all zygotes produced in the second; but this will not make any qualitative difference to the ultimate outcome. There may also be some difference in the genetic variance in the two cases. How fitness is to be considered and applied in any simulation experiment will depend on the circumstances and must rest with the judgment of the experimenter. But it would seem to be wrong, however little practical difference it would make, to use viability as the medium for expression of fitness in a situation where fertility or otherwise of gametes was of primary interest.

There is at least one kind of situation where a distinction between viability and reproductive capacity is important, and that is in experiments where spatial relationships of the organisms are being taken into consideration. That is, where the breeding range of the individual and the dispersal range of its zygotes are smaller than the extent of the population (Chapter 11). This may be illustrated by taking a rather extreme example of a population in which there are produced ten genotypically identical individuals of fitness 0.1. With a viability of 0.1 and reproductive capacity of 1.0, we would expect nine of these to be eliminated and only one remain, its genes being available for reproduction only within its own breeding range. But with a viability of 1.0 and a reproductive capacity of 0.1, we would expect to have ten individuals at least moderately dispersed, and although the same number of gametes would be produced from that genotype in the two cases, they would be available for reproduction over a wider area (and thus to a wider selection of potential mates) in the second case.

With reproductive capacity as the criterion of fitness, the fitness test is applied in exactly the same way as for viability, but at a different stage in the life cycle. The programming techniques are the same and the discussion of the principles involved in viability testing is applicable to testing on the basis of reproductive capacity.

The argument is fairly simple. If the reproductive capacity of an individual is f, then the chance of its being a parent, as compared with that of an individual of reproductive capacity 1.0, is also f. So when a potential parent has been chosen it is subjected to a fitness test in which the value representing its fitness is compared with a random fraction in such a way that the chance of its being retained for reproduction on that occasion is f. If it fails the test, then it is rejected and a further choice of a potential parent is made and that subjected to a fitness test, and so on until a test is successfully passed and the identity of one parent determined. The second parent is determined in the same way, and normally the two determinations are independent of one another.

It is not necessary, of course, that the reproductive capacities of the two sexes should be the same for otherwise identical genotypes, nor for example in the case of hermaphrodite plants of low fertility that the goodness of pollen and ovules should be the same; in practice they are usually not. In the case of hermaphrodite flowering plants where self and cross fertilization are both possible, a subtlety arises. If we have a system which is partially inbreeding, this may be effected by making a choice of a plant to be seed parent, and then a second choice of whether this same plant is also to be used as the pollen parent or whether the pollen parent is to be different. In the latter case, the second chosen parent will of course be subject to a fitness test. If selfing is to be performed, the question then arises quite logically as to whether the plant chosen in the first place as seed parent ought to undergo a second test to see if it should in fact be used also as a pollen parent on that occasion. Failure would of course mean rejecting it as seed parent (since selfing allows no choice of pollen parent), for which it has already passed the fitness test.

The question is more complex than it might appear to be at first sight, and a simple general answer cannot be given. It is a genetical problem and not a computing one, and will usually only arise in situations where the breeding system of a model population is one of the matters under investigation. It will be assumed for the time being that an adequate treatment of the situation under discussion would be, when selfing has been decided on, to use the same plant as pollen parent immediately without testing a second time. There are certainly real situations for which this would be a realistic action, and it is a biologically sensible one.

One obvious disadvantage of interpreting fitness in terms of reproductive capacity is that it doubles the amount of fitness testing which has to be carried out for each generation, since each single reproductive act (except self-fertilization) will require at least two tests instead of the one viability test performed on the resultant zygote, and although in general it may be more realistic to use reproductive capacity than viability, the question has to be decided as to whether the gain in realism makes a difference which is sufficiently significant to justify the extra time required. The achievement of additional realism by having both viability and reproductive capacity as components of fitness is even more doubtfully worth while (unless of course there are reasons dictated by the objects of the experiment), since tests would have to be applied both to zygotes and potential parents.

The Expression and Determination of Fitness

Before an individual can be tested for fitness, its fitness must be determined. Fundamentally, this determination must be based on its genotype, both for the obvious theoretical reason that the genotype determines the phenotype and fitness is one expression of the phenotype, and for the practical reason that the individual is simulated and stored in terms of its genotype and initially the only genetical information we have about it is its genotype and it is that that we have to work from.

We may determine the fitness of an individual directly from its genotype or indirectly from the phenotype after the former has been converted to the latter. Where there is no dominance, there is no practical distinction between phenotype and genotype and this alternative does not arise; for example, plants of *Senecio vulgaris* with radiate, intermediate and normal forms of the capitulum are represented respectively as **RR**, **Rr** and **rr** whether we are thinking of their phenotypes of their genotypes. Where there is dominance there are fewer phenotypes than genotypes and the former require only half the number of bits to represent them and would therefore be expected to form a simpler basis for fitness determination. To what extent this is of practical importance will depend not only on how much simpler the determination becomes, but also on how readily the conversion from genotype to phenotype may be effected.

Broadly speaking, there are two ways in which a relationship between genotype and fitness may be established—by calculation and by arbitrary assignment. One thing which is not practicable is to have a direct relationship between the fitness and the numerical equivalent of the genotype, since **Aa** and **aA** are genetically equal, but not numerically (**01** and **10**). But where there is dominance, it would be possible to have a simple direct relationship between fitness and phenotype (since **01** and **10** have identical phenotypes, **0**).

Consider two loci with dominance; the four phenotypes **AB**, **Ab**, **aB** and **ab** might be assigned fitnesses of 1.0, 0.875, 0.75 and 0.625 respectively. So far, we have considered numbers in the computer either as integers at the l.s. end of a word, or as fractions with the point after the m.s. bit, but there is no reason why we should not treat them as fractions with the point anywhere we choose, however the computer may consider them. For example, if we have the phenotype at the l.s. end of a word, and we choose to put the point before the third l.s. bit, then the numerical equivalents of the phenotypes **AB**, **Ab**, **aB** and **ab** would in binary be **...00.000**, **...00.001**, **...00.010** and **...00.011**, or in decimal 0.0, 0.125, 0.25 and 0.375. If we subtract these from **...01.000** we get **...01.000**, **...00.111**, **...00.110** and **...00.101**, or in decimal 1.0, 0.875, 0.75 and 0.625, which are respectively the required fitnesses. The generation of a 3-bit random number will give us numbers which we may treat as fractions in the range zero to 0.875 in steps of 0.125; the criterion for rejection will be that the random number will equal or exceed the fitness, when the chances of success for the four phenotypes will be 1.0, 0.875, 0.75 and 0.625.

It should be noted that where we imagine the point to be elsewhere than after the m.s. bit, 1.0 is permissible for the representation of a fitness. **1000...** is not 1.0, but **...01000** is 1.0×2^{-28}.

We do not in fact need to think in terms of fractions at all. We can equally well regard the preceding operation as being based on the integral values of the phenotypes, 0, 1, 2 and 3, subtracted from 8 to give 8, 7, 6 and 5, and compared with a 3-bit random integer (range 0 to 7); rejection if the integer equals or exceeds the value of 8 minus phenotype will give respective chances of survival of 1, 7/8, 3/4 and 5/8, as required. If the repertoire of jump instructions does not permit the 'greater than or equal to' criterion, then subtraction of the genotype from 7 and use of 'greater than' would produce exactly the same result.

But although it might occasionally be possible in dealing with a very hypothetical model to arrange fitnesses so nearly related to the phenotypes, it will generally not be so, and the experimenter should certainly not force his model into unrealism simply for the sake of programming convenience.

If fitness parameters have been allotted to the alleles at each locus, and if all the desired interactions are capable of mathematical formulation, then given the genotype of an individual it would be possible to calculate its fitness.

This may be a fairly short operation, or a lengthy one, even when the presence of dominance allows the calculation to be simplified by basing it on the phenotype. Unless it is very short, it would be a considerable waste of time to carry the calculation out whenever a fitness is tested, since for each genotype identical calculations would then have to be performed many times in each generation and over many generations.

It would obviously be much better to perform the calculation once for each possible genotype or phenotype, before any reproduction takes place, and to combine the results in a table from which the fitness of any individual could be ascertained as required simply by table look-up, using as a modifier the numerical value of its genotype or phenotype (as appropriate) in the way explained in an earlier chapter.

Where fitness is arbitrarily assigned to a genotype or phenotype in such a way that it could not be determined by calculation from the bit pattern or its numerical equivalent, then the preliminary construction of a genotype/fitness or phenotype/fitness table is the only method.

But whether it is essential or not, the determination of fitness by table look-up has one advantage, even where the relationship between genotype and fitness is a simple one. If it is desired to repeat an experiment with different fitnesses, it is a simple matter to substitute an amended fitness table, whereas an alteration to a routine may be awkward and there is always the possibility of introducing programming error. Also, a table of fitnesses is a good form of permanent record, and it is easy to remind oneself later of the fitness values used in a previous experiment should the need arise.

Where, as with dominance, there is a practical difference between genotypes and phenotypes, the question arises of whether it is better to use a genotype/fitness table or a phenotype/fitness one. From one point of view, the more direct use of the genotype in referring to a fitness table is to be preferred. At the time of fitness determination it will usually be the genotype which is available, and use of a phenotype/fitness table would involve the extra step of converting genotype to phenotype.

As an illustration, suppose we are dealing with two loci each showing dominance and have decided that the fitnesses of the phenotypes **AB**, **Ab**, **aB** and **ab** should be 1.0, 0.96, 0.91 and 0.66 respectively (but as explained earlier, 1.0 is impermissible if we suppose the point to be after the m.s. bit, so it will have to be represented by $1-2^{-31}$, which we can loosely write here, as 0.9999). A four-word table with those fractions in that order and using the numerical values of the phenotypes (0, 1, 2 and 3 respectively) for look-up, would adequately serve the purpose but would require genotype to phenotype conversion. It would be quicker (in terms of computing time, but the original production of the table would be slower) to use a genotype/fitness table and refer to it directly by use of the genotype without conversion. This table would have 16 words. Assuming that the genotype is stored with the original gametes side by side (for example, **AbAB**), then the following sequence of fractions would constitute the appropriate table (the reader should confirm this for himself): **.9999; .9999; .9999; .9999; .9999; .96; .9999; .96; .9999; .9999; .91; .91; .9999; .96; .91; .66**. If these are stored in a fitness testing subroutine sequentially from **p1**, and the zygote which is to be tested is in accumulator **F** with the genes at the l.s. end and the rest of the word zeros, then the instruction sequence **F→M15; p1 (M15)→E;** will put the appropriate fitness into accumulator **E**. If the genotype were **abAb**, this would be 0.96.

But a little reflection will show that the genotype/fitness table has one disadvantage, especially when more than a few genes are involved. If the number of gene loci (with complete dominance at each) is n, then the phenotype/fitness table has 2^n entries and the genotype/fitness table has the square of this, 4^n (it must be remembered for purposes of table look-up **Aa** and **aA** are different, having different numerical values **01** and **10**). Even with only four loci, the genotype/fitness table would have 256 entries, and the labour of calculating and writing out the table with the program and subsequently punching it would be considerable, as would be the possibility of error at one stage or the other—careful checking would be essential.

This difficulty can be mitigated if the fitness is derived by calculation from either the numerical equivalent or the bit pattern, since this can be done quite easily as part of the program itself, at the beginning. If there are n loci, there are 4^n genotypes and these will take numerical values from 0 to 4^n-1 inclusive. All that has to be done is to execute a loop 4^n times, beginning with a genotype zero, calculating its fitness, storing the latter using the genotype as modifier, and then increasing the numerical value of the genotype by one at the end of each cycle. This will produce the required genotype/fitness table of 4^n words.

Suppose we have four loci, and that the table is to be constructed in **P99** from **p1** onwards. Basically, the table writing subroutine would be

```
(0); K15 = 256; M15 = 0; (M15 = genotype);
(1); [instructions operating on the word in M15 to determine its fitness,
     producing the answer in F, M15 being unchanged];
     F→p1 P99(M15); M15+1; K15−1; J1K15≠0;
     [link and exit];
```

This is only as complicated as the determination of the fitness.

If the assignment of fitness to genotypes is in any degree arbitrary, in the sense that there is no clear numerical or bit relationship, then the fitnesses cannot in general be computed but have to be decided individually during the conception of the program and the fitness table written and subsequently punched as part of the written program. However, if complete dominance is involved at all the loci concerned, then the labour of constructing a genotype/fitness table can be considerably reduced by doing it in two stages. First, the appropriate phenotype/fitness table is written and punched with the program. At the beginning of the latter there will be a short routine which will produce a genotype/fitness table by considering all possible genotypes in the sequence of their numerical equivalents, determining their phenotypes and thence by reference to the phenotype/fitness table their fitnesses, and writing these elsewhere in the same sequence.

The writing of this routine is quite simple. Suppose for example we are considering a system involving four loci, each showing complete dominance, and we require a genotype fitness table. A phenotype fitness table would have only 16 items, and can easily be written with the program once it has been decided what fitnesses are to be assigned to each phenotype; the fitnesses in the table must of course be in the order of the numerical equivalents of the phenotypes. We will suppose that this phenotype/fitness table is to be stored in **p1** onwards of table writing subroutine **P98** and that the desired genotype/fitness table of 256 items is to be stored in **p1** onwards of fitness testing subroutine **P99**.

All 256 genotypes occur in a numerical sequence from 0 to 255 (that is, expressed as genes, from **ABCDABCD** to **abcdabcd**), so that in the same way as before we begin with the genotype which is numerically zero and add one each time round the loop until we have reached and dealt with number 255. To produce the phenotype from the genotype is simple; we duplicate the current genotype, shift one copy down four places (in this case), and carry out an LM. Since the dominant alleles are represented by zero (indeed, ready phenotype determination is the principal reason for representing them by zeros), the LP will represent the phenotype, each heterozygote **...0...1** becoming **...0**. For example, suppose we have a genotype **abcDAbCD**; this is **...11100100** (decimal equivalent, 228). Shifted down four places it becomes **...00001110** and we can represent the LM operation as

$$\begin{array}{r} \ldots 11100100 \\ \ldots 00001110 \\ \hline \text{LP} = \ldots 00000100 \end{array}$$

The phenotype is in the four l.s. bits of the LP, which represent **AbCD.** This LP (decimal 4) is then put into a modifier and used to select the appropriate value of the fitness from the phenotype/fitness table (that is, the value in **p5** of **P98**) and this is then put into the appropriate position in the genotype/fitness table (that is, into **p229** of **P99**, as determined by adding the numerical value of the genotype to **p1**).

The whole routine can be written down quite simply. A flow diagram is really superfluous and the reader should have no difficulty in following the routine; if he does, then it would be a good exercise for him to draw up a flow diagram for himself. After the phenotype/fitness table in **p1** onwards, the subroutine would proceed

(0); K15 = 256; M15 = 0; (*M15* = *genotype***);**
(1); M15→H; M15→G; G down 4; H&G→H; H→M14;
p1(M14)→H; H→p1P99(M15); M15+1; K15−1;
J1K15 ≠ 0; [link and exit]**;**

For n loci, the numbers 256 and 4 would be replaced by 4^n and n.

If there is no dominance, then with an arbitrary series of fitness/genotype relationships there is no alternative to determining and writing out the table with the program, unless the arbitrariness is only partial and some degree of calculation would be possible and could be carried out by the program. But this is getting involved. If it seems to the reader that once simple genetic situations have been left behind, fitness becomes a complicated and tiresome matter to deal with, he should reflect that if he wishes to investigate complex genetical systems he must expect that he will often be involved in complicated procedures requiring a lot of work on his part. It is, however, one of the curiosities of genetic simulation that there is not always an obvious relationship between genetic complexity and the degree of intricacy in the program; some quite complicated situations may lend themselves to simple programming (either intrinsically or through the skill of the programmer) and some quite simple genetic processes may be quite difficult to deal with. There are two dangers; we may choose to investigate systems which are easy to program and neglect others of more fundamental interest because they are difficult; or we may try to manipulate the genetic system in a way which allows substantial simplification in the programming, and this of course must be done with care and a clear understanding of the system if the danger of introducing biological nonsense is to be avoided. After all, the computer is allowing us to investigate evolutionary situations which would involve far too much work for us to tackle without its aid, and we ought not to be grudging if it has to leave us a little hard work to do ourselves, in addition to a lot of hard thinking. If we want to consider a complex situation, we must expect difficulties and hard work. The only alternative is not to consider complex situations, but these are the interesting ones, and computers have brought them within our grasp.

More serious than the work involved in producing a genotype/fitness table are the storage problems involved, because to these there is no simple solution. The 256 item table required with four loci will not usually present any difficulty, but six loci would require a table of over four thousand entries, which would not leave much (if any) room for the population in many smaller computers, and eight loci would require a genotype/fitness table with over 65 thousand items. It is true that these requirements could be cut (at the cost of look-up time) by packing, but even packing four viabilities into one word of the table would only allow one more locus to be considered for the same storage space.

It is important to realize that table look-up requires immediate access. A very large table could of course be held in a backing store, especially on disc or better still on drum, but the random access time to such a table would be too slow (it would be random access, since the genotypes are produced at random), and it would be quicker to calculate the fitness separately for each individual, if that were possible. To some extent this difficulty could be overcome if all the zygotes for any one generation were produced before their fitnesses were dealt with; consecutive sections of the fitness table could be brought one at a time into the immediate access store and the relevant genotypes dealt with either by running through all the genotypes each time and operating on the ones appropriate to that section of the table in use, or by preliminary sorting of the genotypes into sections corresponding to the sections of the table. Where fitness is expressed as reproductive capacity, this would require the fitness to be packed with the genotype as described later in the chapter.

Of course, where the genetics of the situation are such that a phenotype/fitness table could be used, we can simply abandon the ideal method of referring to the table by use of the genotype and use the phenotype instead. This makes a considerable difference, since a phenotype/fitness table for 8 loci would have only 256 entries; but the problem is clearly becoming difficult again with many computers by the time more than ten loci are involved.

But where we wish to investigate a situation where there are as many phenotypes as genotypes, then the number of loci that can be considered is severely limited unless it is possible to abandon the table look-up method and calculate the fitness of each individual as it is required, or possible to specify the genetics of the situation in such a manner that by the exercise of ingenuity a way can be found round the difficulties.

For example, suppose we wish to investigate a system involving twelve gene loci. If there were no interactions between the genes, and the fitness of the whole genotype were the product of the individual fitnesses attributable to each locus, then we could use a compromise between table look-up and calculation. We could consider the twelve loci in three sections of four; each of these would have 256 possible sub-genotypes, and we could have three genotype/fitness tables each of 256 items from which three contributions to the overall fitness could be ascertained by using the three appropriate sections of the genotype; the overall fitness would then be the product of the three partial fitnesses. This device could be used even where there were interactions, so long as the genotype can be divided into sections between which there are no interactions, whatever may be the situation within each section.

A little thought, however, will show that the determination of the fitness of each zygote will now be rather lengthy process, and if awkward manipulations are to be avoided it will be necessary to use the gene arrangement of the form **AaBbCc...Ll** and not **ABCD...Labc...l**, since with the latter the extractions of the genes relevant to four loci would leave them not as eight consecutive bits but as two groups of four bits with eight zeros in between, having a maximum value when shifted down as far as possible of $15(2^{12}+1)$. The size of a genotype/fitness table is actually determined by the maximum numerical value among the genotypes and not by the number of genotypes; for the sections we are considering the former will always greatly exceed the latter unless all the genes concerned are in consecutive bits. It would therefore be necessary with the **ABC...Labc...l** type of arrangement to manipulate the two blocks in each section after they have been extracted, to make them contiguous, and this would waste time.

Even with the **AaBbCc...Ll** arrangement, fitness determination in the case we are considering requires 15 instructions, and it is worth writing out a routine to illustrate this point. Using a complete heterozygote solely for purpose of illustration, the genotype **AaBbCcDdEeFfGgHhIiJjKkLl** would be stored at the l.s. end of accumulator **F**. The three sections would go from **A** to **d**, **E** to **h**, **I** to **l**, and we will suppose that the first entries in the relevant genotype/fitness tables are stored in locations **p1**, **p257** and **p513** respectively of the fitness testing subroutine. The procedure is to move (if necessary) each section of eight bits in turn to the l.s. end and to extract them (if necessary), using each of the three results as a modifier to obtain in turn the relevant partial fitness from its appropriate table. The partial fitnesses in the tables are expressed as fractions, so problems of scaling do not arise and the overall fitness will be the product of the three partial fitnesses and will be delivered as a fraction in **F**. After the tables, the fitness testing subroutine proceeds as follows (N.B. After each multiplication only the m.s. half of the result will be required and accumulator **G** can be used again immediately.)

```
(0); F→G; G&255; G→M15;
     F down 8; F→G; G&255; G→M14;
     F down 8; F→M13;
     p1(M13)→F; p257(M14)→G; F×G; p513(M15)→G;
     F×G;
```

The subroutine then proceeds to test the fitness. The time taken by fitness determination in this way would be of the same order as that required for the test (including random number generation).

Various other devices may be used, depending on the genetics of the situation. It is not proposed to discuss this point any further, because it is felt that by the time the reader comes to deal with complex genetical situations he should have enough programming experience to be left to his own devices.

One point is clear. Situations in which there are as many phenotypes as genotypes may present severe difficulties if the number of loci involved is high, and it is important that this should be realized at an early stage by someone wishing to investigate such a situation so that he may either change his mind and go for something simpler (and who shall blame him? Computer time is not unlimited, and it is no use producing a program for which one is never going to get adequate time to run) or take early steps to ameliorate the difficulties.

So far, the matter of genotypes and phenotypes has been written of as though it was entirely bound up with the question of dominance. This will often be the case, but it is not always so. If we consider a polygenic system in which the gene loci make equal contributions to fitness, then even in the absence of dominance the number of phenotypes is quite small. Suppose for example we have a number of loci each with two alleles, **A**/**a**, **B**/**b**, **C**/**c**, etc., and that the fitness depends solely on the number of lower case alleles present and not at all on which. Thus **ABCdEFgHAbcdEFGh** would have the same fitness as **aBCdEFGHaBcdeFGH**. The relationship might be one of direct proportionality, in which case a fitness table would not be required; or it might be less simple or even arbitrary, in which case there would have to be a table. But it would be a very small table with only $2n+1$ entries where n is the number of loci.

The procedure for table look-up would be very simple, provided that the computer had an instruction equivalent to the **bits** instruction of XB1, since when the genotype is represented in binary the fitness will be determined by reference to the number of **1**s in the genotype. If the genotype has been put in **F**, the instruction **bits F** delivers this number in **F**, and this is then transferred to a modifier which is used to refer to the table to extract the appropriate fitness. For example, the two genotypes given just previously would in binary be **0001001001110001** and **1001000010111000** respectively and the **bits** instruction would deliver the answer 6. All genotypes with six **1**s would have the same fitness.

This technique was used by the author (Crosby, 1970, described later in Chapter 11) in an investigation of the population genetics of interbreeding subspecies, where hybrids had a low fertility. Eight genes were used to define the hybridity status of individual plants, the genotype of one subspecies being represented by sixteen **1**s and that of the other by sixteen **0**s; the F_1 hybrids had eight **1**s, and F_2 and backcross plants various intermediate numbers. Values for the fitness (fertility in this case) were assigned arbitrarily, with sixteen **1**s or sixteen **0**s having the maximum value, and eight **1**s having the minimum in the main series of experiments.

It would not be difficult to make the fitness relationship more complex by supposing that the effects on fitness were not the same for all loci. Thus in the example on p. 200, we might suppose that the effect on the viability of the alleles **e f g h** was twice that of **a b c d**. This can be dealt with by extracting the two sets of genes separately with the appropriate masks (**...0000111100001111** and **...1111000011110000** respectively), performing the **bits** operation on both, doubling the answer for the first and then adding the two together. This would take seven instructions instead of one, so that this idea cannot be taken too far if time is an important consideration.

When a **bits** instruction is not available, the quickest alternative is to use a table look-up procedure. Storage space will limit table size, so that the word will have to be dealt with in sections. 8-bit sections would be convenient, and the table would then have 256 items corresponding to all possible 8-bit combinations, and would be referred to in the usual way by use of a modifier. A 32-bit word would be dealt with in four sections, each in turn being shifted to the l.s. end and extracted by an LM with 255, the numbers of **1**s for the sections being totalled to give the value for the whole word. The procedure is quite simple; a subroutine which would execute it might be as follows. The table would run from **p1** to **p256**, the entries in sequence giving the numbers of **1**s in the binary equivalents of 0, 1, 2, 3 ..... 255. After this table, the subroutine would proceed as below, it being supposed that the word for which the number of **1**s is required is supplied to the subroutine in **H** and the answer is delivered in **F**.

```
(0); H→G; G&255; G→M15; p1(M15)→F;
     H down 8; H→G; G&255; G→M15; F+p1(M15)→F;
     H down 8; H→G; G&255; G→M15; F+p1(M15)→F;
     H down 8; H→M15; F+p1(M15)→F; [link and exit];
```

It would look neater if this were written as a loop executed four times, but this would involve the performance of thirteen more instructions and so take almost twice as long.

```
(0); K15=4; F=0;
(1); H→G; G&255; G→M15; F+p1(M15)→F; H down 8;
     K15−1; J1K15≠0; [link and exit];
```

Once again it would be better to use a subroutine to write the table, and this can be done by taking each possible 8-bit combination in sequence (beginning with zero and increasing by steps of one) and actually counting the number of **1**s, entering the answer at the appropriate address in the table. Counting may be done quite easily by having the eight bits at the m.s. end of an accumulator, shifting up logically one place at a time, and counting the number of times the word is negative (that is, when the m.s. bit is **1**). We do not need to set a counter for the shifts, since when all the **1**s have been counted and shifted off the end the accumulator will be zero, and that can be used to indicate that the count is finished—there would be no point in inspecting the remaining bits when these are all zero.

If we suppose that the table is to be stored in **p1** to **p256** of a bit counting subroutine **P105**, then the instruction sequence of the table writing subroutine would be as follows.

```
(0); M15 = 0; (for the 8-bit combinations); K15 = 256;
(1); M15→H; H up 24; G = 0;
(2); J3H ⩾ 0; (H negative if m.s. bit now 1); G+1;
(3); H up 1; J2H ≠ 0; G→p1P105(M15);
     M15+1; K15−1; J1K15 ≠ 0; [link and exit];
```

This procedure for counting the number of **1**s in eight consecutive bits could of course be used for counting the number in a whole word, as described in Chapter 4, but would require three or four instructions for each bit inspected and so would be hopelessly extravagant of time if the operation were to be performed more than a few times in each program.

Returning to a more general consideration of fitness determination, there is a further point to be discussed. If the fitness is being treated in terms of viability, then the obvious time to test a zygote is immediately on its formation by determining its fitness and applying the test at once.

But if fitness is being treated in terms of reproductive capacity, the test will be applied whenever the individual is chosen as a possible parent, which will on average be at least twice in an outbreeding population (and considerably more than twice if the average reproductive capacity is low). Two possibilities now arise. The fitness could be determined (as with viability) immediately before the test, being determined as many times for each individual as it is chosen to be a parent. Or it could be determined once for every individual at some stage prior to reproduction (for example, immediately after zygote formation, population scoring, or transfer of zygotes from temporary store to population store) and stored either by being packed in the same word as the genotype (if space there is available) or by being placed in a word whose address is readily determined from that of the genotype; in either case it is then available almost immediately whenever required for testing. Where separate words are used, the genotypes could for example be stored in locations **s0 s2 s4 s6...** and their fitnesses one location later in **s1 s3 s5 s7...**; or in a population of size n the genotypes could be in successive words from **s0** onwards and the corresponding fitnesses in the same sequence from **s**n onwards, the location of a fitness having an address greater by n than that of the corresponding genotype; generally speaking, the latter is preferable since it is easier to make a random choice from consecutive locations than from alternate ones, which would require the random number to be doubled before use.

Whether the fitness should be determined immediately prior to every test, or predetermined and stored, will depend on circumstances with time once again the predominating consideration.

If the determination of fitness is not very quick (for example, if it is not simply a matter of single table look-up using the genotype directly as modifier), then it will almost always be better to predetermine the fitness once for each zygote, especially if the genotype is not too large and the fitness can be stored with sufficient precision in the normal position for a fraction at the m.s. end of a word. Thus if the genotype occupies, say, the 16 l.s. bits of a word, 15 bits are available for the fitness which could then be expressed to an accuracy of about 0.000025—more than adequate for most purposes. Moreover, the addition to the value of the fitness which would result from non-elimination of the genotype bits would be negligible (except for zero fitness), and for the fitness test the whole word could be used directly without extracting the fitness or removing the genotype, which is both rapid and convenient. It must be remembered however that for a successful genotype an extra instruction may be required later to remove the fitness bits before the genotype is used for reproduction.

It would be somewhat less rapid if the fitness had to be stored in a separate word; but in this case the choice of a possible parent would first be made by fetching the fitness, the genotype only being fetched if the fitness test was passed, so not much more time would on average be involved.

It would also be less rapid if for any reason it were desirable that the genotype should be at the m.s. end of a word, with the fitness at the l.s. end and treated either as an integer or as a fraction with the point elsewhere than after the m.s. bit—possibilities discussed briefly near the beginning of this section. The fitness would then have to be extracted at each test. But it would usually still be quicker on average for each individual to determine its fitness once and extract it n times, than to determine it n times, unless determination were a very simple and quick operation.

Selection by Population Truncation

It will by now have become clear that the application of selection can be a complicated and time-consuming process. Except in special cases it is not something which can be avoided, and it is natural that attempts should be made to simplify and shorten it. Such attempts should always be made with great care, otherwise the balance of selective forces may be upset and misleading results may be produced. The danger is particularly great where selection pressures are small, for example where second-order selection effects are being considered. There is one part of the process for which the time required is independent of genetical complexity; that is the actual testing once the fitness has been determined, and most of the time required for this is used in the production of a random number. The simpler the genetics, the greater is the proportion of the time involved in the various operations of selection which is taken up by testing, and perhaps the temptation to economize on testing may be greatest in the simpler situations.

As an example of the dangers involved in simplification, we may quote a method used by Fraser (1957) and by Young (1966) which avoids the fitness test by arranging the individuals of a population in order of fitness, and then establishing by truncation a 'parent pool' composed only of the fittest individuals, a random choice from this pool being made for each reproduction. The desired intensity of selection was applied to the population through the degree of truncation. With intense selection the population would be heavily truncated and only a small proportion of it would form the parent pool; with weak selection, truncation would be light and relatively few members of the population would be excluded from the parent pool.

This method is open to two objections—it fails to differentiate between individuals of different fitnesses within the parent pool, and by eliminating the least fit altogether it transforms the improbable into the impossible. This compares with the sort of approximation which sometimes makes algebraic simulation objectionable.

The curious thing about the use of this technique by Fraser and by Young is that the time saved by the elimination of individual fitness testing was not particularly large in comparison with the time required in their programs for the other operations involved in selection, and one would guess that only a relatively small amount of time, compared with the total running time of the program, was saved. The relationship between fitness and genotype was quite complicated, especially in Young's models where he superimposed an environmental variation on the calculated phenotypic fitness, and although programming details are not given it seems likely that the determination of the fitness of any genotype will have been a fairly lengthy operation, probably longer than that which would have been required for a fitness test. Moreover, a table look-up method was apparently not used, although this point is not absolutely clear from the text, in which case fitness determination must have been by a separate calculation for each individual.

The operation of ordering individuals according to fitness is also a lengthy one, although it can be shortened by approximation; it would only be in the region of the truncation that the order would have to be accurate. Young gives no indication of how he carried this out.

Substantial advantage from the elimination of individual fitness testing would only be likely when there were many genotypes of low fitness and a high frequency of testing.

If time has to be saved by eliminating random fitness testing, a much less objectionable method would be to truncate each genotype class separately, after all reproduction for the generation is completed, by removing the correct proportion of that class (in principle the same as the non-stochastic method described in an earlier section in which every nth individual of a genotype is eliminated as soon as it is produced, but applied differently in practice). This is really only practicable where relatively few genotypes are involved, and raises obvious difficulties where some genotypes are represented by only one or a very few individuals. It would be possible to get round this by a compromise in which the common genotype classes are truncated and each individual of the rare ones subjected to a random fitness test.

Other Expressions of the Phenotype

There is another aspect of genotype/phenotype relationship which may be considered here, because although it is not directly a matter of fitness, its treatment has a number of features in common with the treatment of fitness. For example, we may be concerned with genes which affect the breeding relationships or behaviour of the organism, and whose phenotypic expression cannot be regarded directly in terms of fitness, although it may certainly have an indirect effect.

Simple examples would be those concerned with the breeding system, and these are quite easily dealt with as will be described in Chapter 12. A more complicated example may be cited from the author's own work (Crosby, 1970) on interbreeding subspecies of plants, already referred to briefly earlier in this chapter, and described in detail in Chapter 11.

The problem under investigation was the possibility of the evolution of genetic barriers to interbreeding, selection pressure arising from low hybrid fertility which gave hybridization a selective disadvantage. Time of flowering was chosen as a possible barrier to interbreeding, and two groups of genes controlled this. One group, with two loci involved, determined the length of time for which the plant was in flower in any one season; the other, with three loci, controlled the date of flowering. In each group there was no dominance, and the genes were of equal effect.

The total period available for flowering was eight weeks, with a minimum of two and a maximum of six for any individual plant, the corresponding genotypes being **0000** and **1111** respectively, with the number of weeks in excess of two being equal to the number of **1**s, that is from zero to four.

Reproduction of the population proceeded in weekly instalments, and the problem of translating genotype to phenotype was that of determining for each plant from its genotype the first week in which it would flower and the total number of consecutive weeks during which it would be in flower, so that during any week it would be possible to ascertain which plants were available for reproduction.

The problem therefore was two-fold: the determination of the phenotype from the genotype, and the expression of the phenotype in such a way that the determination of whether the plant was in flower or not could be carried out as efficiently as possible.

The relation between genotype and phenotype was not quite straightforward. For the date of flowering genes, **000000** gave the earliest flowering and **111111** the latest, with nominally a linear proportionality according to the number of **1**s, that is from zero to six. This proportionality worked satisfactorily for plants flowering for only two weeks, since the seven possible flowering time genotypes would then cause flowering to occur in weeks 0 and 1, 1 and 2, 2 and 3 ... 6 and 7 respectively (numbering from 0 for the first week). But at the other extreme, with plants flowering for six weeks, such a neat relationship was not possible because there were only three distinct flowering periods available—weeks 0 to 5, 1 to 6 and 2 to 7, so that not all plants flowering in, say, weeks 1 to 6 would be genetically identical. This difficulty could have been overcome by considering reproduction on a daily basis, so that in the case cited (1 to 6) for example some plants would start flowering at the beginning of week one, and others towards the end (running over into week 7) according to their genotypes. This would not have involved any great difficulty, but would have added to the running time of the program. Another method would have been to change the assumption that was in fact made that a plant flowered uniformly through its flowering period, and suppose instead that for plants flowering during, say, weeks 1 to 6 those with the earlier flowering genotypes would have their peak flowering period earlier during those six weeks than plants with later flowering genotypes. Again, this would have been time-consuming, and it would have involved some quite complicated programming.

In the light of the purpose for which the model was being used, such refinements were considered to be unnecessary. Instead, each possible combination of date and length of flowering values (that is, in terms of the numbers of **1**s) was considered and allocated a flowering period, care being taken to see that a proper balance was maintained over all genotypes and over all eight weeks of flowering. A table (see Table 14, Chapter 11) was therefore drawn up (an arbitrary table, to some extent, since many of its entries would not be readily calculable), to be referred to by a number derived by combining the number of **1**s in each of the two sections of the flowering period genotype. These were determined by extracting each section separately with the appropriate mask and performing the operation **bits** on each; the number of **1**s in the length of flowering section was multiplied by 8 and added to the number of **1**s in the date section, the sum being used as a modifier to refer to the table, each item in which specified the appropriate first week of flowering and the number of weeks. For example, in this model 13 loci were involved, eight being the sub-species characteristic genes referred to earlier in the chapter, the remaining five being the flowering period genes and stored at the l.s. end of each gamete. If we represent the subspecies characteristic genes by asterisks, we can imagine a plant of genotype ********00101********01100. Of the flowering period genes, the two length ones occupied the m.s. positions in the relevant parts of each gamete and the appropriate mask (considering only the genotype bit positions) was **00000000110000000000011000**; the date genes occupied the l.s. positions and the mask was

00000000001110000000000111.

In the example just given, the numbers of **1**s were one and three respectively, and so the number to go into the modifier for reference to the table was $8+3$, that is 11. The corresponding entry in the table was the *octal* number 23, indicating respectively that flowering commenced in the third week (counting in the computer begins with zero!) and that it lasted through three weeks.

This octal number, representing the flowering period characteristics of the phenotype, was determined shortly after the zygote was produced. It was stored with the genotype, occupying six bits (**010011**). Separate determination on each of the eight times it was required (once per week) would have wasted time. The actual position of the octal number in the tabulated word was the same as the position required for storage in the zygote, so having been extracted it was added in directly. The table occupied 39 words (zero to $8 \times 4+6$), and included zero entries corresponding to impossible values of 7 for the date bits.

The way in which the flowering period phenotype was used was quite intricate. Let us represent the octal number as *ab*, *a* being the first week and *b* the number of weeks. In order to find out which plants were in flower during any week, the population store was scanned and all plants examined; this operation was carried out each week.

For any plant, if *a* was zero, then that indicated that the plant was due to flower in that week and a copy of it was transferred to a temporary store containing the current flowering plants. If *a* was not zero it was decreased by one and the operation repeated with each week's scanning until it had become zero. As soon as the plant had come into flower, *b* was reduced by one each week and the plant was considered to be still in flower until *b* became zero, which indicated that flowering was finished.

As stored originally in the population store the plant was in effect positive, its sign bit being zero (the alert reader should have noticed that the m.s. bit could not have been used as a sign bit in this context with a 32-bit word, since the genotype plus flowering period phenotype would together use all available bits; in fact, the experiment being described was carried out on a machine with 48-bit words, so no problem arose). To speed determination of its flowering status, the sign bit was changed to **1** (so that the plant would be recognized as a negative number) as soon as it came into flower, and when flowering was finished the whole word representing the plant was made zero (the plants were supposed to be annuals, so once flowering was finished the genotype and phenotype were no longer required).

A flow diagram of the procedure for dealing with a single plant is given in Figure 28.

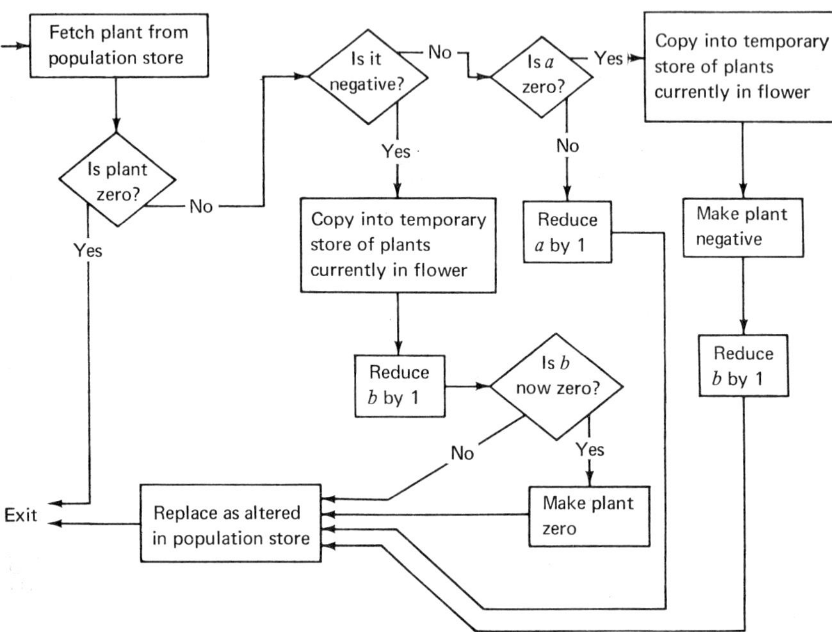

Figure 28. Flow diagram for procedure implementing flowering period phenotype. For detailed description see text; a fuller description of the model of which this was a part is given in Chapter 11. a = first week of flowering, counting from zero for current week; b = number of weeks of flowering remaining

This subroutine provides an excellent example of how even an experienced programmer can get himself involved in intricacies by overlooking the obvious. There was a much simpler method by which the operation of identifying the flowering plants in any week could have been carried out.

Instead of the entries in the flowering period phenotype table giving directly the first week of flowering and the number of weeks, they could have given the same information in a string of eight bits corresponding to the eight possible weeks of flowering, **0** indicating not flowering, **1** flowering.

Thus in the example given previously, instead of the octal number 23, the appropriate item in the table would have been the binary pattern **00111000**. Although this would have required two more bits, it would have presented no difficulty because the work was carried out on a KDF9 whose 48-bit word would have provided adequate room for this 8-bit pattern as well as for the genotype and the fitness which was also stored in the same word.

Testing for flowering would have been quite simply by fetching each plant in turn from the population store, and doing an LM with a mask containing a single **1** in a position corresponding to the relevant week (**...10000000** for the first week, **...01000000** for the second and so on, the flowering period bits being at the l.s. end). If the resulting LP were not zero, the corresponding bit in the pattern would have been **1**, the plant would be flowering, and the appropriate action taken; if zero, then it would not be flowering and no action would be required.

It is difficult to estimate how much time would have been saved by this method, but it seems likely that it would have been no more than a moderate amount. Four KDF9 instructions would have been required (in addition to the fetching) for the inspection of every individual; in the cumbersome method actually used, a plant which had finished flowering needed only two instructions for this to be established, but a plant still in flower required about twelve. The difference between the two methods in overall time taken by this operation per generation would depend on the number of times on which a plant being inspected was one which had finished flowering.

But quite apart from the question of time, the second method is much neater and the programming involved much simpler and therefore less liable to error. It was not used because the author never seriously considered it. Preliminary work on the problem was begun before the KDF9 was available, and a machine with a smaller word size was used in which there was room for six bits for the flowering period information, but not eight. With that word size, it was also necessary for another reason which is not relevant to the present discussion to carry in readily available form the number of weeks of flowering. If the use of an 8-bit pattern was considered at all (a point on which the author's memory is not now clear) it would have been rejected as impracticable, and the details of how it could have been operated would not have been considered and its simplicity not realized. When the program was adapted for the KDF9, the procedure originally used was simply translated without any thought being given as to whether the larger word size of the KDF9 might not allow the development of a more efficient procedure for this particular operation, although it was considered for other operations and improvements were effected.

The moral is clear. When a program, particularly an involved and time-consuming one, is transferred to another machine, it is always worth while looking at its routines, especially the longer ones, to see if the new machine presents opportunities for improvements in programming techniques.

But apart from the question of a change of machine, when the programming of a routine becomes (or threatens to become) intricate, there is much to be said for considering whether some entirely different approach might not be an improvement. The trouble is that whenever one is constructing a program and has already produced solutions for the technical problems involved, there tends to be a mental block against taking a fresh look at them. It was not until the example which has been discussed was considered as subject matter for this chapter (five years after the program was originally written) that it occurred to the author that binary representation of the eight possible weeks of flowering was the obvious way of doing it in the KDF9 program, and he now finds it surprising that he used any other way.

CHAPTER 8

Linkage and Crossing-over

One of the more difficult problems in genetic simulation is that of linkage, and except in cases where few loci are involved no really satisfactory solution which is generally applicable seems to have been produced; usually rather a lot of time or a great deal of storage space is required. There is no method quite so quick and simple as that described for three or more unlinked genes in Chapter 6. Linkage and crossing-over are important components of many problems in genetics, and naturally we would wish to be able to treat such problems by simulation methods.

Basically, there are two situations. We may have all the loci under consideration situated on one chromosome, that is in a single linkage group; or we may have several linkage groups with independent segregation of the chromosomes. In this chapter we will deal only with the former (of which the other is essentially no more than a multiple version) since it covers the essential features of linkage simulation.

In Chapter 6 we considered the genotype of a diploid organism as being represented by a string of bits corresponding to the genes contributed by one gamete, plus a second string corresponding to the other. If all genes are in one linkage group, then this conception of the genotype becomes modified so that the two strings of bits now specifically represent two chromosomes rather than simply the genes of its two constituent gametes.

A distinction needs to be drawn between the precise simulation of chiasma formation and the simulation of genetic crossing-over. If we are considering segregation in an ascus, then we need to produce all four chromosomes resulting from a meiosis, that is we need to simulate in detail all the consequences of chiasma formation, and it is a matter of importance which chromatid of each chromosome is involved in recombination at each point.

But we will rarely be dealing with such a situation. In the great majority of cases, not more than one gamete or spore nucleus from any one meiosis will take part in reproduction. This is obvious enough on the female side of flowering plants and many groups of animals where only one of the four nuclei from a meiosis has any future. For all practical purposes it is equally true on the male side; the quantity of sperm produced is usually so great, that the chance of two sperm from one meiosis contributing to the next generation is extremely small; the same thing is usually true of pollen grains, for although these are not produced in such prodigious numbers, we also have to take into account the frequently considerable overproduction of seed. In the method previously described for simulating reproduction, that is beginning with a zygote and determining its genotype by working backwards to its parents and thence to the single act of fertilization which produced it, it was implicit that all the gametes involved in the reproduction of a population are of independent meiotic origin.

In considering linkage and crossing-over, therefore, we only have to consider the production of one chromosome from a meiosis. Suppose we have an organism heterozygous for a series of linked genes, all the recessives **a b c...** being on one chromosome and **A B C...** on its homologue. If we refer to each chromosome by its first allele, then at the beginning of meiosis the two chromosomes **a A** become the four chromatids $\mathbf{a}_1$ $\mathbf{a}_2$ $\mathbf{A}_1$ $\mathbf{A}_2$. To produce one resultant chromosome from a meiosis, we can choose the end of one of the four chromatids at random and determine how crossing-over alters the sequence of recessive and dominant alleles. Our endpoint will be a string of alleles beginning with the first one on the chosen chromatid, and the constitution of this string can be described by proceeding sequentially from that first allele. Suppose the initial choice falls on chromatid $\mathbf{a}_2$. At the position of the crossover involving that chromatid nearest to the **a** end (which is not necessarily the chiasma nearest that end), the sequence changes to the alleles of the homologous chromosome and we proceed with those in the same direction until we reach the next point of crossing-over (if any). It makes no difference whatever which of the two chromatids $\mathbf{A}_1$ and $\mathbf{A}_2$ is involved in the first crossover, nor whether at the second crossover the sequence returns to the original chromated $\mathbf{a}_2$ or to $\mathbf{a}_1$. Nor have we any specific interest in what happens to $\mathbf{a}_2$ distal to the first crossover.

In other words, whereas in the precise simulation of meiosis we would have to treat chiasma formation as a 4-strand process, we can quite properly simulate genetical crossing-over by treating it as a 2-strand process. Determination of chiasma distribution plays no part in the determination of crossover positions for several reasons. At any one chiasma position, there is only a 50 percent chance of any particular chromatid being involved in crossing-over. Indeed, it will often happen that a chromatid will come through meiosis without crossing-over, whereas except in special circumstances such as male *Drosophila* it is not possible for a bivalent to come successfully through meiosis without at least one chiasma.

The non-randomness of chiasma formation which is due to end or centromere interference is irrelevant, since genetic maps are based on crossover frequencies and not on actual distances. Non-randomness due to chiasma interference does produce crossover interference; the extent to which this is taken into account is a matter for decision by the experimenter.

We can now express the problem more clearly. If for illustration we consider eight linked loci, and for the sake of clarity we suppose all the upper case alleles to be on one chromosome and the lower case alleles on the other (although in practice of course it will often be otherwise), we can represent the heterozygote conventionally and in binary form respectively as

(i) **ABCDEFGH** and (ii) **00000000**
a b c d e f g h **11111111**

supposing that in (ii) the two chromosomes are carried in identical positions in two words, all other bits in those words being ignored.

Gametogenesis now requires the production from (ii) of a string of eight bits which is no longer the product of independent random choice at each locus, as in Chapter 6, but a string of bits of which one will have been chosen at random and the other seven will depend on the linkage relationships, that is the map distances, of all the loci. Clearly, one of the first things that will have to be done for any program will be the specification of the genetic map. This will provide the parametric basis for the simulation of segregation in gametogenesis, and the problem can now be more specifically expressed as the translation of the genetic map into a procedure for the simulation of segregation.

Linkage Simulation by Table Look-up

The quickest method of simulating linkage and crossing-over is an adaptation of the second general method for any number of independent loci briefly described at the end of Chapter 6, combined with the use of table look-up. That method consisted of producing a random number with the same number of bits as there were loci, and performing an LM between it and one of the parental gamete genotypes, and between its complement and the other gamete genotype, and adding the LPs. The random number and its complement are in fact randomized complementary masks, one extracting alleles from some loci in one parental gamete, the other extracting alleles from the remaining loci in the other gamete. Random masks produce independent segregation. We could simulate linkage, which is a non-random process, if we could produce suitable non-random masks, and perform LMs between these and the two parental chromosomes. This is easy enough in principle, as may be shown by the following simple example.

Consider three linked genes, separated by map distances $100p$ cM and $100q$ cM, that is with crossover frequencies p and q. We will depart from the customary use of **0** and **1** to represent dominant and recessive alleles, and use **000** to represent the genes on one chromosome and **111** those on the other, irrespective of how the dominants and recessives are distributed. Then **000/111** will represent the parent genotype, **000** and **111** will be non-crossover gamete chromosomes, **011** and **100** will be one kind of single crossover, **001** and **110** will be the other, and **010** and **101** will be double crossovers.

If the genes had not been linked, these eight binary combinations (which are the primary masks required to operate segregation) would have been expected with equal frequency, and could be obtained by generating random numbers in the range 0 to 7, the complementary masks on each occasion being obtained by LA to **111**.

However, when the genes are on the same chromosome with crossover frequencies p and q, the eight binary combinations are not expected with equal frequency and cannot be produced so simply. If we ignore crossover interference for the moment, non-crossovers (**000**, **111**) are expected with a frequency $(1-p)(1-q)$, single crossovers (**011**, **100** and **001**, **110**) are expected with frequencies $p(1-q)$ and $q(1-p)$ respectively, and double crossovers (**010**, **101**) with a frequency of pq, the two masks in each class of course having frequencies half those. These eight crossover or non-crossover chromosomes which are the operative masks may be produced with the required expected frequencies by random choice from a table in which they occur with those frequencies. Such a random choice of a mask having been made, its complement is produced by LA to **111** and the two masks combined in LM with the two parent chromosomes to produce the required gamete chromosome.

Taking, for the sake of example, convenient round figures, suppose that $p=0.25$ and $q=0.125$. Then the values for $(1-p)(1-q)$, $p(1-q)$, $q(1-p)$ and pq are 21/32, 7/32, 3/32 and 1/32 respectively, and the required frequencies of the eight masks can be achieved in a table of 64 items, **000** and **111** each occurring 21 times, **011** and **100** seven times each, **001** and **110** three times each, and **010** and **101** once each. Random reference to the table using a 6-bit random number (range 0 to 63) will produce these masks with the appropriate frequencies.

Of course, as the reader will have realized, if the parent had been a heterozygote in full coupling, **ABC/abc**, the chromosome representation **000/111** would also be in more conventional usage its genotype, and random choice from the table would produce gamete chromosomes directly in the required frequencies. But the individuals of a population will have different genotypes with various coupling and repulsion arrangements, which is why we do not use the table entries directly but as masks. Thus suppose we have a parental genotype **Abc/aBC**, which reverting to allelic binary notation would be

011/100. If random reference to the table of masks produces **001** as the mask, LA to **111** produces the complement **110** and the gamete chromosome required is produced by adding the LP of chromosome **011** and the mask **001** to the LP of **100** and the complementary mask **110**. The two LPs are **001** and **100**, and addition gives **101** which is the binary representation of **aBc**, a single crossover between **b** and **c**—the position indicated by the chosen mask **001**.

It does not matter which mask is logically multipled to which chromosome, since for any crossover position or non-crossover the two complementary masks have equal probabilities of being chosen from the table. Thus in the example given, **110** was as likely to be chosen as **001** and would also have produced a crossover between **b** and **c**, but this time **AbC**. That is, the complementary genotypes **aBc** and **AbC** would be expected to appear with equal frequencies, which is as it should be.

A subroutine for this method of linkage simulation is very easy to produce, and a version will be given which is general for any number of loci up to 15, and for any size of crossover mask table; these two parameters must be stored with the subroutine. The parent genotype will be supplied to the subroutine in **F**, with its constituent chromosomes side by side at the l.s. end; the subroutine will separate these into two accumulators **E** and **F** (for a version allowing more than 15 loci, the parent chromosomes would have to be supplied already in different accumulators, **p1** would not be required, and the first line of the subroutine would be deleted). The gamete chromosome will be delivered in **F**.

p1 = m = the number of loci
p2 = $2^m - 1$, for production of the mask complementary to the chosen one
p3 = n, where 2^n is the table size; n is the number of bits required for the random number
p4 is the first address of the table.

After the parameters and table, the subroutine proceeds as follows.

(0); p1→M15; F→E; E down(M15); (*chromosomes separated*)**;**
p3→M15; p0P200 = (j1); J0P200; (***H*** = *n-bit random number*)**;**
(1); H→M15; p4(M15)→H; (***H*** = *mask*)**; H→G; G ≢ p2→G;**
(***G*** = *complementary mask*)**;**
E&G→E; F&H→F; E ≢ F→F; [link and exit]**;**

(Note that in separating the chromosomes, the bits of the superfluous m.s. chromosome do not need to be removed from **F**—they disappear when the LM is done later.)

As will appear later, application of this technique to large linkage groups may require very much larger tables of crossover masks, perhaps larger than the computer in use can accomodate. In those circumstances, table size can be halved by including only one of the two complementary masks for each kind of crossover or the non-crossover. Thus in the example we have been considering (although with so small a table such economy would rarely be necessary in practice), we could reduce the table size to 32 by having only the masks **000**, **011**, **001** and **010** occurring 21, seven, three and one times respectively. It would now matter how the chosen mask and its complement are applied to the parent chromosomes, since mask and complement are no longer randomly arranged. If the two parent chromosomes are in accumulators **E** and **F**, and the masks in **G** and **H**, then we need either **E & G** and **F & H**, or **E & H** and **F & G**, with equal probability, and this choice can be effected either by using a 1-bit random number (zero or one) or a random number which can be negative or positive with equal probability. Since this will require extra time, this procedure will only be used when it is essential to minimize the space occupied by the crossover mask table.

The following version of the previous subroutine uses the smaller table with only half the masks, only one form being included for each crossover type. Application of masks and chromosomes has thus to be randomized. This is easily arranged economically by generating a random number with one bit more ($n+1$) than required for the table, and placing the surplus bit in the sign position of another accumulator (which need not be previously clear) by a double length logical shift down one place. The second accumulator is thus positive or negative with equal probability, while the original accumulator contains the required n bits for reference to the table.

The **p** stores are as before, except that

p3 $= n+1$, where $2^n =$ the table size.

The instruction sequence proceeds

```
(0); p1→M15; F→E; E down (M15);
     p3→M15; p0P200 = (j1); J0P200;
(1); HD down 1; H→M15; p4(M15)→H; H→G; G≢p2→G;
     J2D<0; E&G→E; F&H→F; E≢F→F; [link and exit];
(2); F&G→F; E&H→E; E≢F→F; [link and exit];
```

It might be thought that randomnization of mask/chromosome combination in this subroutine would usually be unnecessary, since except in special cases the arrangement of the chromosomes in the parental genotype is random, and this should be sufficient. Unfortunately, it is not. Consider the first gene on the chromosome; homozygotes are irrelevant, but the heterozygotes should occur in the population with **A**/**a** and **a**/**A** equally frequent. Deviations from equality do not of course alter the gene frequency, but they will become transformed into changes in gene frequency if the association of masks and chromosomes is not randomized. Suppose the mask chosen is always combined with the first chromosome and its complement with the second. In the position corresponding to the first gene, the chosen mask will always have **0** and its complement will always have **1**, and so the allele on the second chromosome would always be chosen. Thus if more heterozygotes were **A**/**a** than **a**/**A**, this would lead to an excess of **a** alleles in the offspring of individuals heterozygous at this locus, and a spurious increase in frequency of **a**.

Table Size

The method is clearly very simple and quick. One difficulty of applying it generally lies in the size of table required, and this may become prohibitive unless a computer is in use with ample immediate access storage capacity. Immediate access store is essential for the table, otherwise far too much time is required for random reference to it. The example we took presented no difficulty, because the crossover frequencies were carefully chosen. But table size requirements would be increased if it were desired to introduce interference, have smaller and/or less neatly rounded crossover frequencies, or have more loci.

For instance, if we introduce interference into the example discussed by halving the frequency of double crossovers, a table of twice the size will be required in order that it may contain the minimum of one double crossover (assuming for the sake of argument that the table contains both masks of each complementary pair). But now another point arises—the new table cannot give precisely the stipulated recombination values. On doubling the table size, we have to remove one complementary pair of double crossover masks in halving their frequency, and this leaves two vacant words in the table, best filled with masks of the commonest type, in this case non-crossover. The vacant words need to be filled, because it is highly desirable that the table size should be maintained at an integral power of two, otherwise time will be wasted in testing each random number to make sure that it is within range, and numbers will be wasted when they are not—as has been pointed out in earlier chapters.

This leads to the question of the precision with which the required frequencies of the masks can be achieved in a table, the question arising because the number of occurrences of any mask in a table must always be integral.

Thus suppose, again with three loci, we wish to use map distances of 30 and 10 cM, the values for p and q being 0.3 and 0.1. With no interference, the expected frequency of doubles is 0.03, and this obviously cannot be obtained precisely with a table whose size is an integral power of two. With a table of size 256, two complementary sets of 81 non-crossovers, 34 and nine single crossovers, and four doubles would give actual values for p and q of 0.297 and 0.102, which should be good enough for most purposes. Indeed, if a lower degree of precision were tolerable, a 64-word table made up of two complementary sets of 20, nine, two and one would work very well, giving values for p and q of 0.313 and 0.094.

Clearly, if considerable latitude is permissible in the specification of a linkage map, as will very often be the case unless situations with special requirements are being simulated, it will usually be possible by thoughtful choice of linkage parameters to keep the table small, although the inclusion of low recombination frequencies will always raise difficulties because of the resultant very low frequencies of multiple crossovers. Values for p and q of 0.04 and 0.06 give an expected frequency for doubles with no interference of 0.0024, which could well be met by five entries in a table of 2048 (with only one mask type of each complementary pair now represented) and the smallest table size which could represent doubles at all with a frequency of not more than 0.0024 would be 512 with one double crossover giving a frequency of 0.0020. The introduction of realistic interference in this case would require a much larger table if doubles were to appear at all, but in fact at those map distances doubles would be so scarce that they could well be treated as impossible and omitted altogether. In which case, a table of 256 entries (one mask type only of each complementary pair) with 10 and 15 of the two kinds of singles would give actual values for p and q of 0.0391 and 0.0586. With four loci fairly close together, it would almost certainly be desirable to ignore the possibility of triple crossovers.

As the number of loci increases, so does the difficulty of keeping the table size small while retaining a satisfactory degree of precision. Again, it will often be possible to choose linkage parameters judiciously, but if the experiment requires small map distances, then a large table becomes inevitable.

By the time we get to eight loci, even if we impose a realistic maximum of three crossovers, we are likely to be comitted to using a table with only one mask type of each complementary pair. Even then, 64 different masks will be required (one non-crossover, seven singles, 21 doubles, 35 triples), and it is obvious that if a wide range of frequencies are to be accommodated and differentiated the table will have to be large.

Let us consider as an example an 8-locus linkage group with distances 14, 27, 19, 33, 11, 22 and 16 cM; none of these are particularly short. The rarest triple crossover would have a frequency of 0.00084 (the calculation is not as obvious as it looks), and would be rather imprecisely represented by one entry in a table of 1024. Four other triples with expected frequencies from 0.00103 to 0.00145 would also be represented once, and eight with expected frequencies from 0.00160 to 0.00235 would have two entries. Such imprecision and poor differentiation between rare crossovers might not matter very much, and it might even be that a table of half this size would be adequate.

But it will often happen that a linkage map under consideration will have a number of smaller distances than those in this example, of only a few cM, and the expected frequencies of the rarest crossovers will be much less than 0.001; the introduction of interference will have the same effect, even with the larger distances. Unless the rarest crossovers are to be considerably over-represented, or ignored altogether, a much bigger table than 1024 would be needed, and storage capacity for so large a table might simply not be available. It might well be that in that case the best solution would be to ignore the rarest crossovers, but it might be difficult to know where to draw the line; a simple decision to eliminate triples altogether would not do (quite apart from its artificiality) because the rarest doubles may well have a lower frequency than the commonest triples, as they do in the example given.

An alternative method would be to have two crossover mask tables to different 'scales', having the rarest crossovers in one table and the rest in the other, the latter table containing entries which are not masks but indicators that the former table should be referred to. For instance, in the example we have been discussing, with a table of size 1024, the twenty rarest crossovers require 36 entries, the maximum for one of these crossover types being three. For the remaining crossovers, the minimum number of entries in the 1024 table is four, and this could well be satisfied by one entry in a table of 256. In such a table, the 36 entries for the rarest chromosomes would become nine entries in the form of negative numbers. If random reference to the 256 table produced a negative number instead of a mask, then a second random reference would be made, to another table containing the twenty rarest crossovers in numbers re-calculated to bring the total number of entries there to 64. Thus the total storage space required would be reduced to less than a third, at the cost of some loss of precision for the crossovers in the 256 table and the occasional (9/256) need for use of an extra random number; but no rare crossovers would be excluded and there would be a slight overall gain in precision for them.

There seems little doubt that where few loci are involved, where latitude is permissible in fixing the linkage parameters for an experiment, where great precision is not required, or where ample immediate access store is available, the method of table look-up is the quickest and most satisfactory way of simulating linkage and crossing-over. One particular advantage which it has is that no special programming procedures are necessary in order to introduce interference, since this may readily be taken into account in calculating the frequencies with which the various crossover masks are to occur in the table. However, the calculation of mask frequencies may be an onerous job, especially when many loci are involved and when interference is introduced.

It will not be described in detail here—it is a matter of genetics rather than one of computer simulation and the reader who does not know how to do it ought not really to be indulging in the simulation of complex linkage systems. But an example will be described as a general illustration.

Suppose we have six loci, at map distances expressed as crossover frequencies $a\ b\ c\ d\ e$, and we choose to ignore interference and double crossovers within the same region, and to put the number of crossovers per gamete chromosome at a maximum of three. Then the frequency of single crossovers in region a is $a(1-b)(1-c)(1-d)(1-e)$, and similarly for the other four single crossovers. The frequency of double crossovers involving regions a and b is $ab(1-c)(1-d)(1-e)$, and similarly for the other nine doubles. The frequency of triple crossovers involving regions a, b and c is $abc(1-d)(1-e)$, and similarly for the other nine triples. If the total frequencies of singles, doubles and triples as calculated above are p, q and r respectively, then the mean crossover frequency per gamete chromosome is $p+2q+3r$. This will not add up to $a+b+c+d+e$, as it should, because of the absence of quadruple and quintuple crossovers, and so the calculated frequencies need scaling up before multiplying by the table size to give the actual numbers of the masks. The residual places in the table would go to non-crossovers. Introduction of interference considerably complicates the calculations—for example, the effect of interference is much stronger on the double crossover in a and b than on the one in a and e.

This calculation could be carried out, and the table set, by a special subroutine at the start of the program. The subroutine would be fairly involved, but should not present too great a difficulty if the programmer knows how to do the frequency calculations.

Perhaps the trickiest part would be producing the right crossover masks for each calculated frequency. The simplest way of doing this is to have a small table of single crossover masks and for each frequency calculation logically add the masks corresponding to the crossover positions involved, in the way described for a different method of crossing-over simulation later in this chapter.

The number required for each mask having been determined, it is used as a counter for placing copies of that mask in the table. Since the numbers of each type of mask must be integral, rounding of the calculations may mean that the total number of crossover masks may not correspond precisely to the total frequency. This does not matter—the correct total for the whole table will be obtained since the number of non-crossovers is determined by subtraction.

Even if a subroutine is not used to calculate the frequencies and numbers, there is certainly the usual advantage to be gained if the table is large in using a subroutine to set it from previously calculated numbers. This would be simple enough, being based on a table of the required numbers to be used as counters, running parallel to a table of the relevant masks.

Subtraction Method

What is basically the same method of simulating linkage and crossing-over may be used in a way which does not involve table look-up, and which therefore avoids the problem of excessive table size. It also allows crossover type frequencies to be implemented with full precision. It does however take longer in operation and appears to be more clumsy, but in fact it is not so badly time-consuming or clumsy as it appears to be at first glance.

As in the table look-up method just described, it requires calculation of the expected frequencies of all possible crossover types, but instead of having these types each represented the appropriate number of times in one large table, we have two smaller tables identical in size, one carrying the crossover masks each represented once, the other carrying in the same sequence the expected frequencies. In the latter table, it is important that the frequencies when *represented in binary* should total 1.0 precisely (remember that very few decimal frequencies can be exactly represented in binary).

The procedure is then to generate a random fraction, and subtract the frequencies from it one at a time in the sequence in which they occur in the table, until a negative answer is obtained. The mask indicated is that corresponding to the last subtracted fraction, and is readily obtained from the other table. Thus, taking a simple example dealt with previously, with three loci having p and q 0.3 and 0.1 respectively and no interference, we would have two tables of four words each, one containing the frequencies 0.63, 0.27, 0.07 and 0.03, and the other the masks **000**, **011**, **001** and **010**, both in those sequences. If we generate a random fraction 0.92314, subtraction of 0.63 leaves 0.29314; further subtraction of 0.27 leaves 0.02314; and now subtraction of 0.07 gives a negative answer and the mask indicated is **001** obtained from the table by using the same modifier as used for passing through the frequency table.

For this method to be efficient, the mean number of subtractions per gamete chromosome produced must be kept at a minimum. Hence (but see also later) only one mask of each complementary pair will be considered (as in the example above), but each frequency in the table must be that for the total frequency of the relevant crossover type. Also, the sequences in the table must be in descending order of frequency, so that the largest are subtracted first; this produces the minimum number of subtractions for any random fraction (had the frequencies in the example been taken in the reverse order, four subtractions would have been required).

There is, however, a subtlety. Since only one mask of each crossover type occurs in the table of masks, when its complement has been produced their application to the parental chromosomes must be randomized, as in similar circumstances described in the table look-up method. This randomization was slightly messy, but can now be made more neatly by doubling the size of the frequency and mask tables in the following way (they are both so small that doubling their size will rarely raise problems).

The frequency table now has each total frequency for the crossover type (*not* the frequency for each mask of the complementary pair) twice, in adjacent words; that is each word of the original table is duplicated. Each word of the original mask table now becomes two words, the original mask and its complement, also in adjacent words. Thus the two tables exemplified would now be 0.63, 0.63, 0.27, 0.27, 0.07, 0.07, 0.03, 0.03 and **000**, **111**, **011**, **100**, **001**, **110**, **010**, **101**. For running through the frequency table, the modifier is set not directly at zero but in the following way. A random fraction is generated and a double length arithmetic shift up of one place executed with an empty accumulator, which will then be zero or one with equal probability. This number is then transferred to the modifier, which will then similarly begin with a value of zero or one. The use of an arithmetic shift up means that the sign bit of the l.s. accumulator will remain unchanged, and we will still be left with a positive random fraction in that accumulator—the fact that the l.s. bit will always be zero is of no consequence whatever.

The modifier increment will now be two, so subtraction will proceed through the frequency table in steps of two and whatever the starting value of the modifier the frequencies 0.63, 0.27, 0.07 and 0.03 will be subtracted once in that sequence exactly as before. But now, when a negative answer is arrived at, a mask in the **000**, **011**, **001**, **010** series will be obtained if the modifier started at zero, and a mask in the **111**, **100**, **110**, **101** series if it started at one. That is, for each crossover type, either of the complementary masks will be chosen at random, and so when a mask has been chosen and its complement produced they can be applied to the parental chromosomes in an arrangement which is always the same, obviating the necessity for a further random test and awkward use of a jump instruction. Even with a large number of loci, doubling the table sizes to allow of this procedure will not usually raise any problems.

The following subroutine is written for eight loci, with no more than three crossovers per gamete chromosome produced giving one non-crossover and 63 possible crossover types. It uses a mask table giving both masks of each crossover type as explained previously, mask and frequency tables each having 128 entries. There is no need to count the subtractions provided the frequencies add accurately to 1.0; a negative answer must be reached.

p1 = 255 (**11111111** for complementation)
p2 = first address of frequency table
p130 = first address of mask table.

At entry, the parent is in **F**, its two chromosomes side by side at the l.s.

end, and separated by the subroutine in the usual way. The instruction sequence proceeds as follows.

(0); F→E; E down 8; p0P202 = (j1); J0P202; (*H* = *random fraction*)**;**
(1); G = 0; GH × 2/1; G→M15; (*M15* = 0 *or* 1)**;**
(2); H − p2(M15)→H; M15+2; J2H>0;
p128(M15)→H; H→G; G ≢ p1→G;
E&G→E; F&H→F; E ≢ F→*F*; [link and exit]**;**

Comment is required on the use of **p128** rather than **p130** in the instruction fetching the mask from the table. If the apparently natural **p130** were used, **M15** would need to be in the same state as it was when it fetched the relevant fraction for subtraction; but immediately after subtraction, before the mask-fetching instruction is reached, the modifier is incremented by two and is then too large by that amount; the easiest way of dealing with this is to modify the address **p128** instead of **p130**. This situation, incidentally, is one which by oversight often leads to programming errors.

It might be thought that with more than a very few loci this method would become impracticable because of the large number of possible subtractions required, with occupation of much time. That this is by no means so can be shown by reconsidering the specified 8-locus example of the previous section on table size in the context of this subroutine.

With a maximum of three crossovers per gamete chromosome there are 64 possible crossover types (including the non-crossover). This implies a possible maximum of 64 subtractions; but that number will only be required with a frequency of about 0.0008, that of the least frequent triple crossover. The need to arrange the masks in order of decreasing frequency should now be clear. In this example, non-crossovers have the highest frequency, at about 0.199, and that will be the first frequency to be subtracted from the random fraction; clearly, in about 20 per cent of cases this will be the only subtraction required. The sum of the first six frequencies in the table (non-crossover plus the five most frequent single crossovers) is about 0.51, so that half the gamete chromosomes produced will have required six or fewer subtractions. In fact, the average number of subtractions required per gamete chromosome produced is only about 10.8. With shorter map distances (and a consequent higher frequency of non-crossovers) the average would be less—the opposite of the situation with table look-up, where short distances make matters worse.

Clearly, although the subtraction method takes longer than table look-up, with eight loci the extra time is by no means prohibitive and it provides a perfectly acceptable alternative where table look-up would require too large a table or where a high degree of precision in representing crossover frequencies is required.

But it must be recognized that with more loci the time required may become increasingly inconvenient. It is therefore worth considering whether any different approaches to the simulation of linkage and crossing-over can provide practicable alternatives.

Crossing-over by Separate Determination of Crossover Positions

An effective method of simulating linkage and crossing-over which requires neither frequency calculation nor excessively large tables of masks is one which determines crossover positions one at a time and combines single crossover events to produce a gamete chromosome with varying numbers of crossovers, or none. The method is rather time-consuming and uneconomical in terms of random number requirements, but steps can be taken to minimize this.

The basic principles in the implementation of crossing-over by this technique are quite simple, though their application may not be. Let us again consider the example with eight loci separated by map distances 14, 27, 19, 33, 11, 22, 16 cM, totalling 142 cM for the whole chromosome. Random distribution of crossing-over, to a precision of 1 cM, can be simulated by generating a random number in the range 0 to 141 inclusive, that number indicating a crossover position on the chromosome. With no interference, further random numbers in the same range will indicate additional points of crossing-over. The implementation of these crossover position determinations is quite easy.

We will again use the binary digits **0** and **1** to distinguish chromosomes rather than alleles, and represent the parent by **00000000/11111111**. In this particular case we would have a table of 142 words, each word carrying a string of eight consecutive bits representing a chromosome after one crossover. Locations 0 to 13 would contain **01111111**, 14 to 40 would contain **00111111** and so on, ending with **00000001** in locations 126 to 141. These are obviously the masks which, together with their complements, would be required for implementation of single crossovers by application in LM with the two parental chromosomes. The random numbers would be generated as random integers in the range 0 to 141, and these would be used as modifiers to select a crossover mask from the table. Thus 117 would select **00000011**, which is the result of crossing-over between the sixth and seventh loci.

Surprisingly, additional crossovers present no problems of implementation. Suppose we have three crossover positions indicated by random numbers 95, 109 and 14. These will extract masks **00000111, 00000011** and **00111111** respectively. LA of these three (which would have to be carried out on the computer by adding two together, and then adding the third to their logical sum) gives the required mask which corresponds to the three crossovers, as can be seen below (remember that however many lines are added, there is no carry).

		00000111
		00000011
		00111111
LS	=	**00111011**

As in the earlier methods, the complement of this mask is obtained by LA to **11111111**, and the two masks are applied in one of the two possible ways at random to the two parental chromosomes; addition of the two resultant LPs gives the gamete chromosome in the usual way.

In this example, the complementary mask is **11000100**. Suppose the parent is the heterozygote **AbcDefgH/aBCdEFGh**, written in binary (allelic representation now) as **01101110/10010001**. Application of masks to parental chromosomes could be as follows.

chromosome	**01101110**	**10010001**
mask	**00111011**	**11000100**
LP	**00101010**	**10000000**

Addition of the two LPs will give **10101010**, or **aBcDeFgH**. If the alternative combination of masks and chromosomes is used, we have

chromosome	**01101110**	**10010001**
mask	**11000100**	**00111011**
LP	**01000100**	**00010001**

Addition of the LPs now gives **01010101**, or **AbCdEfGh** which is obviously the complementary crossover to the other (alternation of **0** and **1** in the final chromosomes here is entirely fortuitous—the original numbers and gene arrangements were chosen for the example without regard being given to the final outcome).

Which combination of masks and chromosomes is used, and thus which of the two possible chromosomes is produced may be determined by random choice with equal probability for either. If space for a larger table is possible, a simpler method which avoids a need for choice at this stage and allows the same combination of masks and chromosomes to be used every time, is to double the size of the table by including the complementary masks. Thus in the example we have been discussing, the table length would be 284 words, the first 28 alternating **01111111** and **10000000**, the next 54 alternating **00111111** and **11000000**, and so on. A random number of twice the range will now be required for extraction, and for three crossovers three random choices are made from anywhere in the table. If the reader thinks that this does not work, he can test it by considering the eight possible mask or complement combinations of the three masks exemplified previously.

The example chosen has considered map distances with no more precision than 1.0 cM. No difficulty arises if we wish to be more precise, provided adequate store capacity is available. Thus if we had wished for slightly different map distances with a precision of 0.1 cM, we would have needed a table of 1420 words (assuming a total length of 142.0) and random integers in the range 0 to 1419, each type of crossover mask having roughly ten times as many occurrences as before. If complementary masks are to be included, the table would of course need to be twice as big, and that might well raise problems.

As happens frequently in genetic simulation, the operation that one expects to be most difficult turns out to be easy, and one which appears at first glance to be easy turns out to be more difficult. In what has gone before, three crossovers were taken arbitrarily, for illustration. We did not consider at all the question of the determination of the numbers of crossovers per gamete chromosome. For a chromosome 142 cM long, we would expect on average 1.42 crossovers. The number will be variable—sometimes it will be zero. We need to consider variation in crossover numbers, and implement it in our procedure, bearing in mind that it is not the same thing as variation in chiasma number, which except in special cases is never zero.

How difficult this is depends on whether we decide to take crossover interference into account, and we will for the moment suppose that we do not.

There are two ways of effecting variability in crossover frequency. The simplest is to assume a maximum possible number of crossovers and choose that number of masks from the table every time, but to have in the table a number of non-crossover masks (**00000000**, and **11111111** if the full size table with complementary masks is used). This will give a range in number of crossovers per gamete chromosome from zero to the maximum, and the number of zero masks in the table should be such as to give the required mean number of crossovers (using 'zero masks' to include the complementary all ones mask where appropriate). The determination of the required number of zero masks however is not a simple one, since reduction in crossover number can also arise from the occurrence of more than one crossover between a given pair of adjacent loci; two such crossovers would appear as no crossover, and three would appear as one.

Suppose we have a linkage group 140 cM long with eight equidistant genes. The mean crossover frequency per gamete chromosome should be 1.4, and the table (without complements) will contain a total of 140 single crossover masks, twenty of each kind. If we decide on a maximum number of three crossovers, and produce the gamete chromosome by combining three masks randomly chosen from the table, the number of zero masks required in the table in addition to the 140 crossovers is not 160, but only 114, as may be shown in the following way.

Call the non-crossover section of the table P and the crossover section Q, and suppose that the former contains x zero masks. Then if three random choices are made from the table, three, two, one and no choices will fall in region P with frequencies which may be calculated from the expansion of $(xP+140Q)^3/(x+140)^3$. If all three fall in P, the outcome will be a gamete chromosome with no crossovers. If one falls in Q, the outcome will be a single crossover. If two fall in Q, we will get a chromosome with no crossovers or two, depending on whether or not they fall within the same intergene region; the former will happen with a frequency of 1/7. If all three fall in Q, we will get a triple crossover when they do so in three different intergene regions (30/49), and a single crossover when either two or three fall in the same intergene region (19/49). By combining the two sets of frequencies, it is possible to determine the mean number of crossovers in terms of x, and when this is equated to the required mean of 1.4, x is found to be 114 to the nearest integer. A table with 114 zero masks and 140 crossover masks will, with eight equidistant genes and with three random choices from it, produce triple, double, single crossovers and non-crossovers with frequencies of 0.102, 0.351, 0.398 and 0.149 respectively, giving a mean chiasma number of 1.406. The exact value of 1.4 is not obtained because the table is constructed to a precision of 1 cM, and the calculated value for x was not quite integral.

When the genes in the linkage group are not equidistant, the calculation of x becomes more difficult; the frequency of coincident double crossovers increases (reducing the number of realized crossovers) and the value required for x falls. In addition, the relative values of the linkage distances are changed, since coincident doubles are disproportionately more frequent in the longer sections and so disproportionately reduce their true realized crossover values. In other words, we really need to start from a working linkage map which differs from the one we wish to use in the experiment in that the longer distances will need to be exaggerated and the shorter ones diminished, and it is the working linkage map which will be used to establish the table of single crossover masks.

The calculations are not impossible, but require patience or a computer, and the programmer may well decide to take the easy way out. Unless the precise crossover frequencies within the linkage group are critical, a provisional map may be drawn up which fulfils sufficiently well the requirements of the experiment. An approximate value for x is calculated on the basis of equidistance, and a small program run using the crossover subroutine to produce a large family of gamete chromosomes from which the true linkage map may be determined, and this map rather than the provisional one is considered relevant to the experiment. Unless distances are critical, the difference between the provisional and the true map will not usually be of much significance. If it is, it is easy to see whether the value for x is too large or too small, adjust it with a little guesswork, and try again. The provisional map (or rather the table) may also be amended if the relative values of the crossover frequencies come to be too different from those intended.

This sort of approach to a situation of this kind is often better than the determination of parameters by involved calculation, even when the latter is within the ability of the programmer; it has the advantage in that one knows what the parameters are doing—in this case what the linkage map actually is—whereas an error in the calculation of parameters may well pass unnoticed unless some sort of test (such as running off a family of chromosomes) is made on them.

Before producing a subroutine which will carry out this procedure for simulating linkage and crossing-over, there are some other points which arise. The advantage has previously been stressed, when a random choice has to be made, of using tables whose size is an integral power of two. Usually, no great difficulty arises in amending the table size to achieve this. In the example we have been considering, the total table size at 254 was fortuitously close to 256; increase in the number of zero chromosomes to 116 would give a table of size 2^8 and would make no effective difference to the map distance which to the nearest cM would remain at 140. Usually the adjustment required would be greater, but this would not seriously affect the linkage map. The only effect would arise from the fact that the operational unit of crossing-over (one unit of the random number corresponding to one word of the table) would no longer even nominally be equivalent to one cM or a multiple of that, and table size adjustment could only be made by whole words of the table. This would alter slightly the relative values of the linkage distances.

As an example of how a table may be adjusted, suppose a table as originally determined has 136 zero masks and 17, 32, 23, 39, 4, 26 and 20 of each crossover mask, giving a total of 297 words. A table of 256 words could be obtained by amending these numbers to 112, 15, 29, 20, 35, 4, 24 and 17, while amendment to 224, 29, 59, 40, 71, 7, 48 and 34 would give a table of 512 words. Inspection of these last two tables shows that they cannot give identical linkage maps, but the difference is small and one would imagine that it would matter only rarely and in special circumstances.

Time can also be saved by economy in random number generation if each generated number can be split into independent sections each reliably random. Thus if three selections from the table are required, corresponding to a maximum of three crossovers, a 31-bit random number could give three independent number large enough to deal with a table size of 1024, and leave one bit over if required for determining at the end the way in which masks should be paired with parent chromosomes for the final operation.

In order to illustrate how a subroutine using this method for simulating linkage and crossing-over may be written, we will generalize it for the number of loci m up to a maximum of 15, and for crossover mask table size 2^n up to a maximum size of 2^{10}—the table being the smaller version without complementary masks and so requiring randomization of mask/chromosome association at the end. Different linkage maps can easily be simulated by amendment of this table. We will set a maximum for crossovers at three per gamete chromosome.

Choice of mask from the table will require an n-bit random number, and since n is not greater than ten three such numbers can be obtained in the following way from one generated 31-bit fraction using **P202**. The 31-bit fraction is shifted up logically one place, and then for each reference to the table an n place double length logical shift up into an empty accumulator will put n random bits in the right position for use in modification; after three such n-bit integers have been produced, the residual bits in the original accumulator will be a positive or negative number with equal probability.

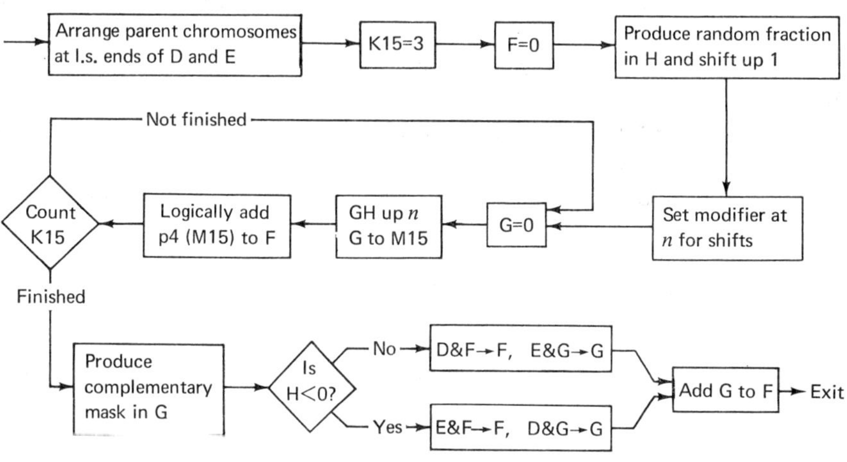

Figure 29. Flow diagram for simulation of crossing-over by logical addition of randomly chosen crossover masks. Maximum of three crossovers. Parent in **E** at entry. Table of crossover masks (without complements and including zero masks) begins in **p4**, and has 2^n entries

It will be supposed that the parent from which a gamete chromosome is to be produced is supplied to the subroutine in **E** with its chromosomes side by side at the l.s. end. The m-bit masks in the table and the m **1**s used to produce the complementary pattern of the final crossover mask are also at the l.s. ends of their words. The flow diagram is shown in Figure 29.

p1 = m, the number of loci
p2 = $2^m - 1$, for mask complementation
p3 = n, where 2^n = table size (maximum 2^{10})
p4 = first address of single crossover mask table

The instruction sequence will be

(0); p1→M15; E→D; D down(M15); (*parent chromosomes separated***);**
K15 = 3; F = 0; p0P202 = (j1); J0P202; (*H = random fraction***);**
(1); H up 1; p3→M14; (*for shifting up n places***);**
(2); G = 0; GH up(M14); (*G = n-bit random integer***);**
G→M15; F ≢ p4(M15)→F; K15 − 1; J2K15 ≠ 0;
p2→G; G ≢ F→G; J3H < 0;
D & F→F; E & G→G; F ≢ G→F; [link and exit]**;**
(3); E & F→F; D & G→G; F ≢ G→F; [link and exit]**;**

At exit, the required gamete chromosome is in **F**; the parent is unchanged in **E**.

(Note that the superfluous chromosome bits do not need to be removed from **E**—they are automatically dealt with by the final LMs.)

If a double length table with complementary masks were used the maximum permissible size for random number economy would still be 2^{10}; the instructions from **J3H < 0** to **(3)** inclusive would be omitted. If more than 15 loci are required, the parent chromosomes would be supplied to the subroutine in separate accumulators and the number of loci m would require no specification.

A different method of producing the required mean frequency of crossovers per gamete chromosome with variability in number would be to decide on the required frequencies of zero, one, two, three or more crossovers, and to have those numbers in the correct proportions in a table. For each gamete chromosome, random choice from the table will decide the number of crossovers, that number being put into a counter before the loop is entered for the first time, steps being taken to see that if zero is chosen the loop is not entered. There will now be no zero masks in the table; if the gamete chromosome is to be a non-crossover, a random choice is simply made from the two parental chromosomes.

It is quite easy to modify the preceding subroutine. There is apparently some wastage of random number generation when less than three crossovers are called for, but this is no more than before since in effect random numbers choosing zero masks were also wasted. If the crossover number table can reasonably be kept as small as 64 words, then with a crossover mask table of 256 words and a maximum of three crossovers, one 31-bit random fraction will cover all the random number requirements for one gamete chromosome (six for the number table, plus a maximum of three times eight, plus one). If the table sizes cannot be kept so small, additional random number generation will be needed.

A revised version of the preceding subroutine would be as follows, the parent being in **E** and the product gamete chromosome in **F**.

p1 = m, the number of loci
p2 = $2^m - 1$, for mask complementation
p3 = n, where 2^n = table size; n now has a maximum value of 8
p4 = first address of crossover number table
p68 = first address of single crossover mask table

The instruction sequence will be

(0); p1→M15; E→D; D down(M15); p0P202 = (j1); J0P202;
(1); H up 1; G = 0; GH up 6; G→M15; p4(M15)→K15;
(*K15* = *number of crossovers required***); J5K15 ≠ 0;**
J4H < 0; D→F; [link and exit]**;**
(4); E→F; [link and exit]**;**
(5); p3→M14; F = 0;
(2); G = 0; GH up(M14);
G→M15; F ≢ p68(M15)→F; and thence as before.

Interference can be applied easily enough to this general method, but requires extra random number generation. The technique will not be described in detail, because the method using sequential crossover formation described in the next section is to be preferred when interference is being considered, partly because it is then faster and also because it provides a better pattern of crossover distribution.

This account refers to the method as first described, with the same maximum number of mask choices being made each time. Remember that any attempt to choose a crossover position may produce a non-crossover.

Suppose one crossover has been produced. Then if a second is produced, the distance between their positions is determined and referred to a probability table. This table gives for the various distances apart the probability that two crossovers would occur so close together, and a comparison of the usual kind between that probability and a random fraction would decide whether or not the second crossover should be allowed to stand. For the longer distances there will be no interference and the probability of survival will be 1.0; it would be a waste of time testing this against a random fraction, and the simplest way of avoiding this would be to have a negative number in the table, the test only being proceeded with if the relevant entry in the probability table is positive. There are two courses of action open if the second crossover is rejected; either it may be treated as no crossover, or a further attempt may be made to produce a second crossover. The former has the effect of reducing the mean crossover number per gamete chromosome, and this will have to be taken into account when calculating the number of zero masks required in the crossover table.

To a lesser extent, replacement may also reduce the mean crossover number, since any replacement attempt may produce a non-crossover mask; however, such non-crossovers could be discarded and the operation continued until a crossover is produced which survives the interference test. The latter would increase even more the extra time which replacement would in any case require.

Where surviving crossovers result from the first two attempts at crossover production, and a third is produced, then interference from either or both of the two previous crossovers will have to be considered. The easiest way of doing this would be to determine the distance from each of the previous ones, obtain the probabilities and where these are both less than 1.0 testing their product against a random fraction. Where the maximum number of crossovers is more than three, this becomes even more involved.

All this obviously involves some awkward programming, because apart from the interference probability test, steps will have to be taken to see that crossover choices are distinguished from non-crossovers (a distinction which without interference did not matter), and crossover positions will have to be retained. Random number economy is less easily managed than before, especially if a rejected crossover is to be replaced, because then additional random numbers will be required for the choice of crossover position. In this case, it would be better to use one subroutine producing integers economically (as we have imagined for **P203** in the next section) for the crossover positions, and a different one producing fractions economically for the interference test. If rejected crossover positions are not replaced the situation is simpler; assuming a maximum of three crossovers, **P202** could then be used as before for the crossover positions, and used separately for the interference test by generating a 31-bit fraction for the first test and shifting this up 15 places with elimination of the sign bit, for use in the second test (there will only be two tests if there is a maximum of three crossovers with no replacement; the 16 l.s. bits in the first test will have no significance at all there).

Sequential Determination of Crossovers

If ample space is available for tables, the same manipulative technique may be used with yet another method of determining crossover number and position. This is to determine crossover positions sequentially from one end of the chromosome according to some mathematical formula or by random reference to an arbitrary table, the first position being determined with respect to the beginning of the chromosome, each subsequent one with respect to that of the preceding crossover.

The sort of mathematical procedure which has been suggested is to relate the distance between the proximal end of the chromosome and the first crossover, and between subsequent crossovers, to some function of a random fraction. The use of such functions is a rather artificial method of generating crossover positions which is not entirely satisfactory. If calculation of the function is to be avoided every time, a large table related to values of the random fraction will still be required, so the method still requires a lot of space. Reference to an arbitrary table is much more satisfactory, and can give a more realistic simulation of crossover distribution. This table, which will be referred to as the position table, will consist of integers representing the positions at which crossovers may occur (in steps of 1 cM for instance, so that several consecutive positions will correspond to crossovers identical in terms of the two loci involved and requiring identical masks); these integers will not have equal frequencies in the table, but frequencies determining the chance of crossover occurrence at the relevant positions. These chances are not equal; for the first crossover in sequence the position is not random (be careful to distinguish 'first' in this sense from 'first' randomly chosen crossover in the previous method—in the latter case the position is random), since when there is more than one crossover the first is more likely to be in the proximal part of the chromosome.

The table will have to be a large one if the realized frequency distribution curve is not to depart too largely from continuity through being stepped. Account will also have to be taken of the possibility of no crossing-over, and this can be achieved by also including in the table with appropriate frequency an integer representing a position beyond the end of the chromosome. Thus if we have a chromosome 142 cM long, the positions for crossing-over will be represented by integers 0 to 141, and 142 will represent a position off the end.

The table will have a size which is an integral power of two, and will be used in the following way. A random choice of a position is made from it, and if this is less than 142 it will be used as a modifier to choose a crossover mask from a table of the kind described earlier. A second integer is then chosen at random from the position table, and added to the first. If the sum is less than 142, it is used to extract a second crossover mask which is added logically to the first as in the earlier subroutine. And so on until a total of 142 for the position integers is reached or exceeded (hence there is no counting to determine when the process is to stop). If the first choice falls beyond the end of the chromosome, then the gamete chromosome is obtained simply by random choice of one of the parent chromosomes. Otherwise the resultant logical sum will be used as before.

This method is better than having zero (non-crossover) masks at the end of the mask table, partly because the latter would then need to be twice as big to cope with position totals from (in the exemplary situation given) 142 to 283, and partly because with the method described the end of crossing-over is recognized slightly earlier, before reference to the mask table.

If two different position tables are used, one for the first and the other for subsequent crossover positions, the technique provides one of the simplest ways of introducing crossover interference. The first crossover position if any having been established, random reference for a second crossover will be to another position table in which entries will represent not actual positions but distances from the preceding crossover. The frequencies at the beginning of this table will be very different from those in the first; the lowest integers will not occur at all, and increasing integer values will then occur with increasing frequency until at about the desired limit of interference the frequencies will be approximately as in the table for the first crossover. Thus there will be a restriction of crossover occurrence increasing with proximity to the previous crossover, becoming complete and preventing altogether coincident or almost adjacnet crossovers.

Obviously, the required pattern and degree of interference can be achieved through the form of the frequency distribution curve at the low end of the table.

A subroutine for the whole operation is quite simple to write. The difficulty and labour involved lie in the construction of the two position tables in such a way that the final outcome produces a linkage map of the required dimensions with the required degree of crossover interference. This will not be discussed, since it is primarily a matter of genetics rather than of computing. Both tables are liable to be rather large, but storage space could be saved by packing the two tables together, at the expense of a little time taken to unpack. Thus for example the position numbers of one table could be stored at the l.s. ends of the words, and those of the other towards the m.s. end. It would not matter if the two tables were of different sizes—the storage space required would be that for the larger table, and some words would contain only the position numbers relevant to that table.

The main problem arising in writing the subroutine is that of random number economy. The method used before is not always practicable, since there may occasionally be more than three crossovers per gamete chromosome, and sometimes it may be desirable to have position tables larger than 2^{10} and so requiring random numbers of more than ten bits. If such economy is required, then the subroutine would either have to keep count of the number of random integers used and generate a new 31-bit number whenever necessary, or more simply use a subroutine which would itself produce random numbers economically from generated 31-bit numbers, using all bits produced and only generating a new number when insufficient bits of the old one are left. The latter technique is discussed in Chapter 13, where a program is given for subroutine **P203** which is such an economical routine, used in exactly the same way as **P200**, with the required number of bits specified in **M15** on entry.

We will suppose the crossing-over subroutine to be general for any number of loci up to 15. If the number of crossover positions is about 140—corresponding to a map of about 140 cM with a precision of 1 cM—the position frequency tables can hardly have less then 2^{10} entries, especially the second one which introduces interference and needs a rather wide range in the frequency of occurrence of the crossover positions. We will suppose that these two tables (whose sizes should for the usual reason be integral powers of two) have 2^{10} and 2^{11} entries respectively and so require 10-bit and 11-bit random integers for reference to them; they will be packed, the position numbers of the second (interference) table occupying the eight l.s. bits of a word (extracted by a mask of decimal value 255), and those of the first crossover table occupying the next eight m.s. bits (extracted by a logical shift down of eight places); the eight bits allow a maximum of 255 for the number of positions.

The size of the crossover mask table need not be an integral power of two since there is now no direct random reference to it, but it should follow the position tables since its length is variable between programs. At entry, the parent will be in **E** and the gamete chromosome will be produced in **F**.

p1 = m, the number of loci
p2 = $2^m - 1$, for complementation of mask
p3 = the number of possible crossover positions, that is the number representing the hypothetical position off the end of the chromosome.
p4 = first address of the two position tables
p2052 = first address of crossover mask table.

The instruction sequence proceeds

(0); p1→M15; E→D; D down(M15); (*chromosomes separated*)**;**
F = 0; M15 = 10; p0P203 = (j1); J0P203; (***H*** = *10-bit random integer*)**;**

```
(1); H→M15; p4(M15)→C; C down 8; (C = first crossover posi-
     tion, and will sum crossover positions);
     J4C<p3; (no jump if no crossover, choose one parent chromosome);
     M15 = 1; p0P203 = (j2); J0P203; (H = 0 or 1 with equal
     probability);
(2); J3H = 0; D→F; [link and exit];
(3); E→F; [link and exit];
(4); C→M15; F≢p2052(M15)→F;
     M15=11; p0P203=(j5); J0P203; (H=11-bit random integer);
(5); H→M15; p4(M15)→H; H&255; (position number unpacked);
     C+H→C; J4C<p3;
     p2→G; F≢G→G; M15 = 1; p0P203 = (j6); J0P203;
(6); J7H = 0; D&G→G; E&F→F; F≢G→F; [link and exit];
(7); E&G→G; D&F→F; F≢G→F; [link and exit];
```

Random Walk

Finally, a brief account may be given of a method of simulating linkage and crossing-over which has been used successfully but which because of the time it requires is of more theoretical than practical interest, although it does have one important advantage in that it makes very little demand on storage space. It deals directly with the chromosomes, and not by way of masks.

If in a genetic map the fractions $k_1\ k_2\ k_3 \ldots$ are deterministically the successive distances between adjacent genes expressed as crossover frequencies, then stochastically each gives the probability that in the formation of a single gamete from a meiosis a crossover will have occurred in the relevant section of the chromosome. This suggests a simulation method known as a random walk by analogy with the idea of somebody walking along one of two parallel lines and at each of a number of specific points a random choice based on a given probability is made of whether he should continue along the same line or should cross over to the other. It is fairly easy to see how this analogy may be applied.

The basic element in the process is the comparison of a crossover frequency with a random fraction, and the test is simple and obvious. We have a crossover frequency k for the region of the chromosome under consideration, and we generate a random fraction r. If r exceeds k there will be no crossover; if it is less than k a crossover is indicated. We can choose which chromosome we begin the walk with by using a starting value k_0 equal to 0.5.

The execution of the crossover, if required, is equally simple. Suppose that at the start the two parent chromosomes are in accumulators **D** and **E,** at the m.s. ends, and that whenever a crossover is indicated the current contents of **D** and **E** are interchanged. Then if we begin with an empty accumulator **F**, each operational stage in the process, after the test for crossing-over and any interchange of accumulators, consists of a double length logical shift up one place of **FD** and a single length logical shift up one place of **E**. The resultant chromosome at exit is at the l.s. end of **F**. The only table required is one of the crossover frequencies, beginning with a value of 0.5 and passed through sequentially in the usual way as the operation proceeds.

Figure 30 shows the flow diagram for a procedure which could carry out this operation, and how this works can be seen by reference to Table 10, which illustrates step by step the process in a heterozygote **ABCDEFGH/abcdefgh**, with crossover frequencies as shown in the table, when the successive random fractions are those shown (given only to two decimal places for simplicity).

This method of simulating crossing-over is obviously expensive on random numbers, and this is the principal reason why it requires an uneconomical amount of time. However, if random fractions can be generated in which all bits are reliably random, considerable economy can be effected, and in view of the low requirements of the method for store space this may be worth doing, although the process will still be comparatively slow.

For a random fraction, one does not need to use all the bits generated. Thus if the precision required for map distances is no better than 1 cM, a random fraction of seven bits giving a precision of 1/128 should be good enough to deal with crossover frequencies in units of 0.01. (But it must be remembered that a scale in units of 1/128 does not match well with a scale

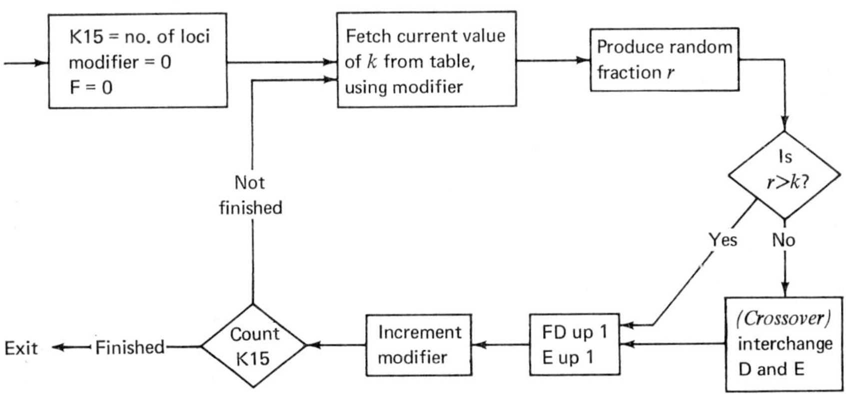

Figure 30. Flow diagram for simulation of crossing-over by random walk. At entry, parent chromosomes are at m.s. ends of **D** and **E**. k is the recombination frequency between acjacent loci. At exit, the resultant chromosome is at the l.s. end of **F**

TABLE 10

Step by step exemplification of the operation of the random walk technique in the production of a single gamete chromosome from a heterozygote **ABCDEFGH/abcdefgh**. See also Figure 30.

Current k	Random fraction	Accumulator contents F	D	E
at start			**ABCDEFGH**	**abcdefgh**
0.50	0.39	**a**	**bcdefgh**	**BCDEFGH**
0.14	0.91	**ab**	**cdefgh**	**CDEFGH**
0.27	0.23	**abC**	**DEFGH**	**defgh**
0.19	0.47	**abCD**	**EFGH**	**efgh**
0.33	0.41	**abCDE**	**FGH**	**fgh**
0.11	0.10	**abCDEf**	**gh**	**GH**
0.22	0.36	**abCDEfg**	**h**	**H**
0.16	0.65	**abCDEfgh**		

in units of 1/100.) This would provide four random fractions from a generated 31-bit fraction and so for an eight locus linkage group the pseudorandom number subroutine would only have to be used twice. If there were no more than eight loci, this could be done quite neatly by generating two 31-bit random fractions before starting the random walk, putting one in **G** and one in **H**. Bits after the seventh would have no important effect and can be ignored, so **H** could be used as the fraction for the test. (If the programmer is worried by the extra bits, it is easy enough to use a copy of **H** from which they have been deleted.) When the test is completed, a double length arithmetic shift up seven places of **HG** with elimination of the sign bit of **H** would produce a new random fraction in **H** ready for the next test. In this way, the random walk loops would only have to shift up and eliminate the sign bit, and no account would have to be kept of the number of fractions used. But if 1/128 were not precise enough, or if more loci were involved, the random walk procedure would need to keep such an account and generate new random bits when the supply ran out—simpler in this particular case than using an economical pseudorandom number subroutine such as **P203**.

Obviously, economy of random fraction generation is essential if the random walk method is to be used. How it is achieved will depend on the circumstances of the experiment, but it is worth exercising programming ingenuity in order to achieve it.

Crossover interference can readily be introduced into the random walk method. If a crossover has occurred in one section, then the chance of one in the next section is reduced, and the random fraction needs to be compared not with the basic value of k for the next section, but some lower value. A second table of crossover frequencies is required, the subroutine controlling reference to one or the other according to whether or not there was a crossover in the preceding section. This could be further complicated to extend the range of interference over more than one section, requiring yet another table.

By this method, crossover interference is unidirectional, in that a crossover in one region affects the chance of one in the following region, but one in the latter does not affect the chance of one in the former. This has to be taken into account in calculating the frequency parameters for the tables, which is not such a simple matter as it might appear to be. The frequencies in the tables must be such that when the subroutine is in operation it will produce those crossover frequencies which were specified for the various regions in the original linkage map. The basic table for instance will no longer be $k_0 k_1 k_2 k_3$ ...—the values for $k_2 k_3$ onwards will have to be increased.

It is clear that the simulation of linkage and crossing-over presents considerable problems in programming, since it requires a great deal of time or space or both. Because the author has never actually introduced linkage into a simulation experiment, the methods of tackling the problem suggested in this chapter should perhaps be taken as no more than suggestions of various procedures which may be used, and should not be regarded as definitive representations of optimum procedures.

A crossing-over subroutine will be used very many times in the course of a simulation program involving linkage, and will take up a considerable proportion of the running time of such a program. It is therefore especially important with such subroutines that they should be programmed with maximum efficiency. In any particular situation, a number of factors will have to be considered and their importance will differ not only according to such things as the number of loci involved, but also according to the computer in use—its storage capacity, instruction speeds, the instructions available in its order code and the way in which it operates. Thus the same genetical situation might best be treated in quite different ways with different computers, because some procedures which might be simple with one might be less so and more time consuming with others, not only because of different facilities in the instruction codes but also because of differences in such things as the way accumulators are used and the relationship between accumulators, stores, counters and modifiers.

The problem calls for programming expertise and each situation must be treated on its merits, with all possible approaches being considered. It is hoped that some of the approaches which have been described in this chapter will be helpful and that perhaps they may suggest other and better possibilities which so far have not occurred to the author.

CHAPTER 9

Examples of simple program

In this chapter, detailed accounts will be given of the conception and development of two programs which the author produced specifically for use in genetics teaching of university classes. They are described in Crosby (1961). Since they were designed to appear as realistic as possible, they have a number of features which would not appear in research programs. For instance, in the latter one naturally uses the computer to classify and score progeny or populations, and print out the results. In these teaching programs, the individuals of the progeny or populations are simulated in the output, and the students are required to classify and score them, and handle the results, just as they would in an experiment with real organisms.

While this chapter will be principally of interest to people wishing to develop programs for use in genetics teaching, it will also describe a number of techniques which may be of wider interest.

The quasi-programs which will be presented will not necessarily correspond precisely with the programs as they were used in experiments described in the paper referred to above. This will sometimes be because the author has since thought of better ways of doing things. Since the programs were first written, they have been adapted for other computers, and the opportunity has been taken not only of improving the programming but of improving the experiments themselves. As a result, those who have copies of the author's program tapes will not necessarily find complete agreement between the procedures used in the programs of those tapes and the corresponding versions presented in this chapter.

Simulation of Meiosis and Three-point Test-crosses

The first experiment which will be described has an obvious relationship with the previous chapter. It simulated linkage with eleven loci which a class could map by means of a series of 3-point test-crosses. It was based on a simulation of chiasma formation during meiosis, and part of the output was designed to demonstrate the connection between chiasma formation and genetical crossing-over. Because of the way the simulation was carried out, it was possible to consider not only chiasma interference, but also non-random distribution of chiasmata resulting from end and centromere interference.

The basis of the simulation of chiasma formation was quite simple. Imagine first how we might illustrate this on a blackboard in front of a class. We might begin by drawing a bivalent in which pachytene has progressed to diplotene by division of the chromosomes but in which chiasma formation has not yet occurred. This is shown in Figure 31a. Our next action we do so

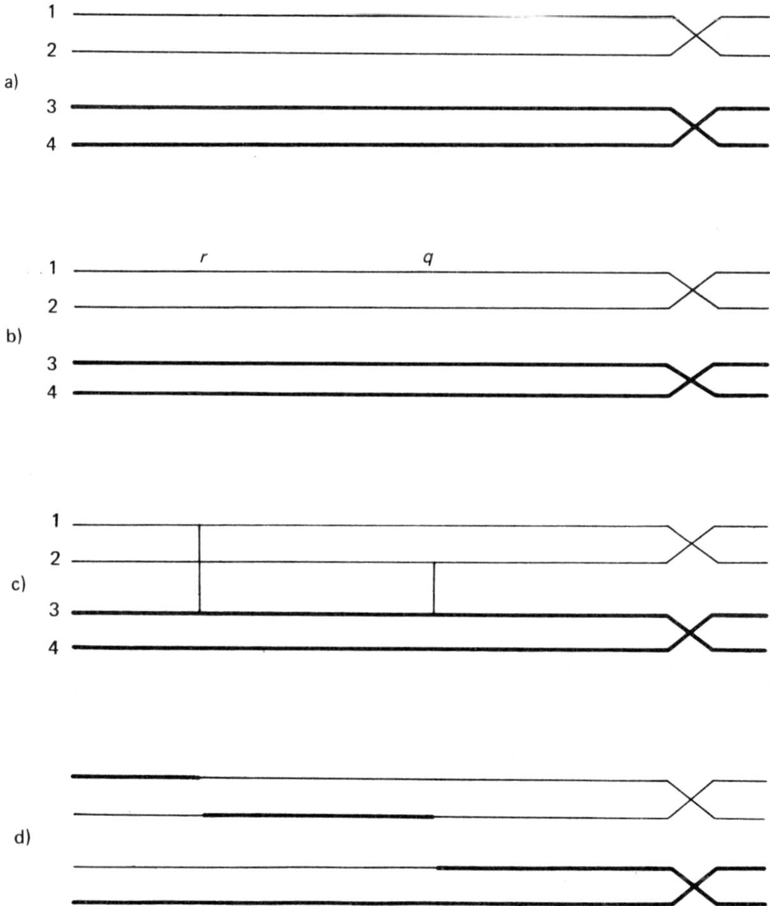

Figure 31. Chiasma formation, as it might be simulated on a blackboard during a lecture

quickly that we seem to do it almost without thinking, but because the analogous decisions have to be taken deliberately and separately by the computer when the process is simulated, we will consider them in the same way now.

Firstly, we have to decide on how many chiasmata there will be. Suppose this to be two. Next we have to decide where these chiasmata shall be and then, for each of them, which pair of non-sister chromatids shall be involved—that is, we have to choose one chromatid from 1 and 2, and one from 3 and 4. Referring again to Figure 31, we decide that the chiasmata shall be in positions *q* and *r* (Figure 31b) and shall involve chromatids 1 and 3, and 2 and 3 respectively, and we indicate this in the usual way by joining the relevant chromatids at the appropriate positions, as in Figure 31c. It is then a simple matter (though the one that needs the most careful treatment on the blackboard) to disentangle Figure 31c and produce the two anaphase I chromosomes in diagrammatic form as in Figure 31d.

With certain rather important reservations, an analogous procedure can be carried out within a computer, if each chromatid of the bivalent is represented by one word. Instead of using lines of different thickness to represent the different homologous chromosomes, we could have produced Figure 31 as efficiently (if more clumsily) by using a string of ones instead of thin lines and a string of zeros instead of thick lines. The obvious logical step is to represent the chromatids of the upper chromosome in Figure 31a by two words each consisting entirely of ones, and the two chromatids of the other by two zero words. The first reservation should now appear—we cannot represent the undivided centromere, since no bit can be shared by two words, which cannot be connected in the way that the chromatids are in Figure 31. The only thing we can do about this is to accept it as inevitable and to make a mental note of this imperfection in the simulation. Figure 31a then becomes (with the 32-bit word we are imagining for XB1) Figure 32a, the centromere bits being indicated by an asterisk.

It is important to note and keep in mind that the bits no longer represent alleles or loci, as they did in the previous chapter, but equidistant points along a chromosome. Later, we will put genes at some of these points, but for the time being we are not considering genes at all.

Keeping to the same number of chiasmata, the same positions (which will now be inter-bit positions) and the same chromatids for each, we can replace Figure 31d by Figure 32b. But going from 32a to 32b is not so simple as going from 31a to 31d. On the blackboard, we virtually deal with the two chiasmata simultaneously; ambidexterity would allow us to convert 31b to 31c by putting in the vertical lines simultaneously, and we do not do any rearrangement of the chromatids until both chiasmata have been drawn in; in the rearrangement to produce 31d we are in effect dealing with the two

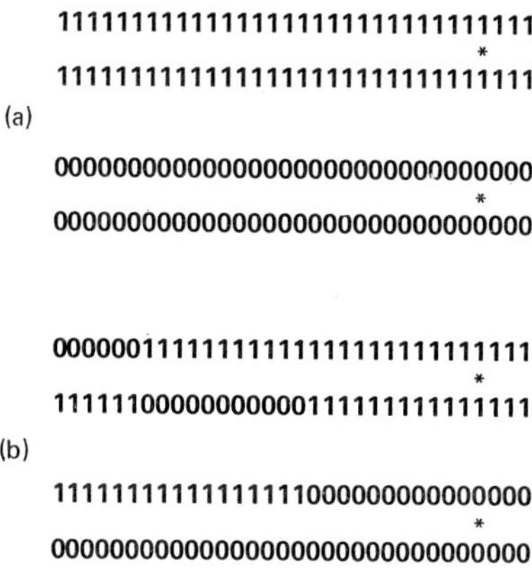

Figure 32. The diagrams of Figure 31a and 31d revised to show how the chromatids may be represented by computer words

chiasmata simultaneously (just as, one presumes, happens in the living meiosis).

But a computer cannot do this. It can only deal with the chiasmata one at a time, and it cannot readily recognize the chromatids as such—it can only recognize words. When more than one chiasma is present in a bivalent, it is important that they are executed in the correct order. This may be illustrated at the same time as the procedure for simulating chiasmata is described, and the point will be made by doing it the wrong way first.

We will suppose that position q (between bits 16 and 17 counting from zero at the m.s. end) is decided upon and executed first. Figure 33a shows the starting position, and the computing operation is to manipulate words 2 and 3 so that their 17 m.s. bits are interchanged. This is quite simple. If the chromatids are stored in **p1**, **p2**, **p3** and **p4** respectively, **p2** and **p3** are transferred to accumulators, say **C** and **D**. Upwards double length logical shifts of 17 places on coupled accumulators **EC** and **FD**, followed by downward double length logical shifts of 17 places on **FC** and **ED** will then effect the exchange. **C** and **D** are transferred back to **p2** and **p3**, and the result of this operation is shown in Figure 33b. A flow diagram is shown later in Figure 40.

The next operation should be the execution of a chiasma at r, between chromatids 1 and 3 which originally were in words **p1** and **p3** and which the computer (unless it has been told to the contrary) will assume are still in those words. But at point r, as a result of the first chiasma, the chromatids in

```
                          q
     p1   11111111111111111111111111111111
                                       *
     p2   11111111111111111111111111111111
(a)
     p3   00000000000000000000000000000000
                                       *
     p4   00000000000000000000000000000000


               r
     p1   11111111111111111111111111111111
                                       *
     p2   00000000000000000111111111111111
(b)
     p3   11111111111111111000000000000000
                                       *
     p4   00000000000000000000000000000000
```

Figure 33. The simulation of chiasma formation. The first (incorrect) stage in an attempt to produce the anaphase I chromosomes of Figure 32b

words 1 and 3 are now sister chromatids, between which chiasma formation (if indeed it could occur at all) is meaningless and the execution of a chiasma by the computer will produce no change from Figure 33b. It would be possible to tell the computer what has happened, but this would involve some intricate programming and waste time. It is much simpler to determine both chiasma positions before any chiasma is executed, and to arrange that the distal one (in this case the one in the m.s. position) is always executed first. In the present example, *r* would be dealt with first, with the result shown in Figure 34; the correct (non-sister) chromatids are still in words 2 and 3 in the neighbourhood of *q*, as required for the second chiasma, and the execution of this would produce the result shown in Figure 32b, as the reader may easily confirm for himself.

```
                r         q
     p1   00000011111111111111111111111111
                                       *
     p2   11111111111111111111111111111111

     p3   11111100000000000000000000000000
                                       *
     p4   00000000000000000000000000000000
```

Figure 34. The simulation of chiasma formation. The correct first stage in the production of the anaphase I chromosomes of Figure 32b

Somewhat similar considerations apply to chiasmata on the l.s. side of the centromere. Execution of a chiasma there in the way described would exchange the centromeres between words, and this might be undesirable especially if segregation in an ordered ascus is being simulated. This difficulty may be overcome by reversing the order of the tandem accumulators and beginning with double length shifts down (the number of places being now 32 minus the position number), interchanging accumulators as before, and then doing the double length shifts upwards. Alternatively, the routine could be performed exactly as before, but on returning the chromatids to their store positions from the accumulators the relationship of these is changed, so that if for example the original transfer was from **p2** to **C** and **p3** to **D**, the return transfer would be from **D** to **p2** and **C** to **p3**, which ensures that the centromere bits return to their original location.

Again, if there are two chiasmata to the right of the centromere (obviously a rare event in this example, but not necessarily always so) the distal one (in this case the l.s. one) must be dealt with first. With one chiasma on each side of the centromere, the order in which they are dealt with is immaterial, except perhaps as a matter of programming convenience.

We have imagined Figure 32b to correspond with figure 31d, and the use of asterisks in Figure 32 serves to make this comparison more clear. But, apart from the figure, those asterisks are purely in the mind; they are certainly not in the computer. If we eliminate them from the figure, then the four chromatids are quite free from one another, and it would be appropriate (and quite proper) to regard the figure as showing not the two chromosomes of anaphase I but the four chromosomes of anaphase II, that is, the chromosomes which will separate and pass one into each of the four products of meiosis. This is how we shall henceforth regard them.

As an element in a teaching program, the simulation of meiosis would have little value unless it could be expressed visually. The author's first use if this program was with a Ferranti Pegasus computer, which had cathode ray tubes which allowed visual examination of the contents of any word. It was easy to arrange that the program should come to a temporary halt at any desired point during and after the completion of meiosis, so that the whole process could be followed directly. Such elegant demonstration of meiosis in the chromosomes of a computer is no longer possible with modern machines, and the best that can be done is to print out the patterns of ones and zeros. This may be done during the process, to illustrate the stages of computer meiosis, but it will usually be adequate simply to print out the four anaphase II chromosomes, with the centromere bit represented by an asterisk instead of a digit.

It is easy to introduce interferences into this model, but before we discuss them readers must be reminded that we are for the moment considering the model in terms of chromosomes and chiasma formation and not in terms of a genetic map and crossing-over. End and centromere interference have no part in the latter, but they may be taken into consideration in the former, and the simplest way of doing this is to determine chiasma position by random choice from a table in which the entries are inter-bit positions (equivalent to real, not recombination, distances from the end of the chromosome) occurring with different frequencies proportional to the chances of chiasma formation in the relevant section of the chromosome; remember that the sections are of equal real length. Thus if the curve in Figure 35 represents the frequency distribution of chiasmata throughout the chromosome, this can

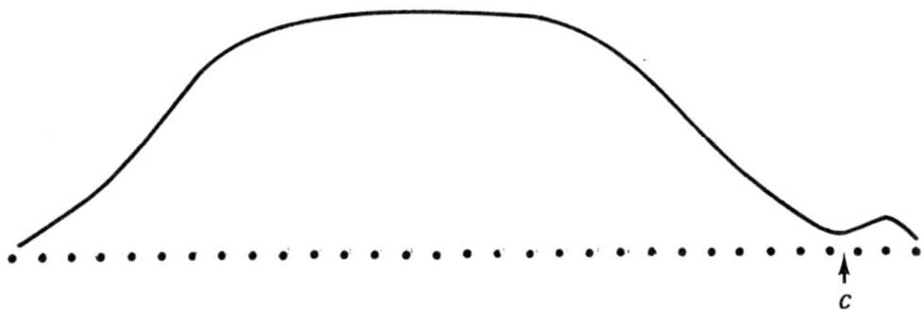

Figure 35. Curve showing a supposed pattern for the relative chances of chiasma formation at various points along a simulated chromosome, with end and centromere interference. The inter-bit positions are indicated on the base line. Table 11 was compiled by proportional translation of the heights of the curve at the inter-bit positions into integers having an overall total of 512. The centromere position is indicated by *c*

be transformed into a table in which inter-bit positions occur with frequencies which may be approximately determined directly from the curve. Approximately, not only because of the usual difficulty of converting fractional frequencies to integers, but also because of the usual need for the table size to be an integral power of two; this requirement may involve some trial and error manipulation of the frequencies of occurrence of the positions in the table.

The realized curve cannot in practice be a smooth one for the usual reason that the number of times any inter-bit position occurs in the table must be integral, although with a very large table it may come fairly close to being smooth. In this particular experiment it will usually be quite practicable to have a large table. Since this is not an evolutionary experiment, no space will be required for storage of population and of zygotes produced by reproduction, and the program instructions themselves do not require a great deal of space. In the KDF9 version of this experiment, with a 48-bit chromosome, a table size of 1024 was used and gave a plausible and fairly smooth distribution curve of chiasma frequency. With a 32-bit word (31 possible chiasma positions), a table of 512 entries would probably be adequate.

As an example, Table 11 shows a possible relationship between chiasma position and frequency based on Figure 35, and assumes that bit 28 (counting from zero) is the centromere, but obviously any distribution can be used at the wish of the programmer. Addition will show that the occurrences total 512, as required.

TABLE 11

The number of occurrences of each chiasma position in a table conforming to the frequency distribution curve of Figure 35. The centromere is between positions 28 and 29

Chiasma position	1	2	3	4	5	6	7	8	9	10	11	12
Occurrences	2	4	6	9	12	16	20	23	25	26	26	27
Chiasma position	13	14	15	16	17	18	19	20	21	22	23	24
Occurrences	27	27	27	27	27	26	26	25	23	20	17	13
Chiasma position	25	26	27	28	29	30	31					
Occurrences	10	7	4	2	2	4	2					

When this experiment was first conceived, it was decided that the maximum number of chiasmata per bivalent should be two and that variation in chiasma number, one or two, should come about solely through chiasma interference, this being effected by suppression or otherwise of one chiasma according to the closeness of the two chosen chiasma positions rather than by deciding on one or two at random and arranging that the second position should be chosen in such a way that it tended to avoid the first; the latter may perhaps be more realistic, but would be more difficult to program, and the former is simpler and perfectly adequate for the purposes for which this experiment was designed. In practice, the method used for implementing chiasma interference produced a mean chiasma frequency per bivalent of about 1.5. The implementation of variation in chiasma frequency by the introduction of zero positions into the table would not work; a choice of two zeros would produce a bivalent with no chiasmata, which is not permissible.

Chiasma interference could have been introduced into the model in several ways, differing in the action after two potential chiasma positions have been chosen.

One method would simply be to decide that the chance of the second chiasma being allowed to stand depended on the distance apart, in terms of bits, of the two chosen chiasma positions, with a minimum distance below which there were never two chiasmata and a maximum distance above which there were always two, the relationship between the intermediate distances and the chance of survival of the second chiasma being ascertainable by table look-up and implemented by reference to a random fraction. In this method, chiasma interference would depend solely on distance apart and be independent of position in the bivalent, and this might be a fair representation of reality.

On the other hand, it might be expected that chiasma interference might be greatest where chiasmata occurred less frequently. This could be implemented quite easily in the following way. The table of inter-bit positions would have these arranged in order, 1, 1, 2, 2, 2, 2, 3, 3, 3, 3, 3, 3... etc., and the distance apart of the chosen words in the table, rather than the distance in terms of bits, would determine whether the second chiasma would be allowed to stand. This method would produce much greater chiasma interference towards the ends of the chromosome than in the centre; how far this would be appropriate would depend on the view taken by the programmer of the cytology of chiasma interference. If it were decided that there was to be absolute interference over a distance of two bits in the centre of the chromosome, then with the chiasma distribution pattern suggested in Table 11 the minimum distance for the second chiasma to survive would be 54 words. This would mean for example that for a first chiasma chosen in position 6 (and for some in position 7), any second choice nearer the m.s. end would always be rejected, and for the next few possible higher numbered positions the number of m.s. second choices surviving would be small. This might well be a good representation of reality, but that is a genetical decision rather than a computing decision. A distance/interference table would be required in which the entries gave the chance of survival relative to the distances apart of the two chosen words in the position table. The first 53 entries would be zero, and subsequent entries would give increasing values for the probability of survival, until the limit of interference is reached. If interference could extend over a maximum of nine positions in the centre of the chromosome, this would be over about 239 words, which would be the required length of the reference table; this table would only be referred to if a check showed that the distance apart did not exceed 239.

Thinking retrospectively, the author now feels that this was the method he should have chosen. However, both methods already discussed each require the production of a further random number to implement the chance of survival of the second chiasma; this occupies time. The actual procedure which was used avoided this, but it was clumsy in conception and had dubious biological justification—although it had a similar basis to the second of the two methods outlined above. But it did produce a plausible chiasma interference effect. For the purposes of a genetics teaching program it was quite satisfactory (provided the students did not enquire too closely about the computer implementation of chiasma interference); for a research project it might be less plausible.

Briefly, the method used and which will be adopted here was as follows. In the chiasma position frequency table, the position numbers for each position were themselves numbered serially beginning with 1, so that each word contained both the position and its serial number. For instance, continuing with the same example (Table 11), with the serial number preceding the stroke, the chiasma frequency table would begin 1/1, 2/1, 1/2, 2/2, 3/2, 4/2, 1/3, 2/3, 3/3, 4/3, 5/3, 6/3... etc.

A second table (interference table) gave for every possible value of the distance (in bits) between the two chosen chiasma positions a positive integer which will be referred to as the interference number. These integers would in the present case range from a maximum value of 28 when the chosen positions are identical, to zero for all distances of more than nine bits. The table is used in the following way. The two chiasma positions having been chosen, their distance apart is obtained and used in a modifier to extract the interference number from this table. The interference number is subtracted from the serial number of the second choice chiasma position, and if the answer is negative the second chiasma is rejected and there will only be one chiasma.

For example, suppose that the numbers in the interference table are, in order from a difference of zero, 28, 27, 25, 23, 20, 17, 13, 9, 6, 3, 0, 0 ... 0. Imagine that the choice of chiasma positions produced the two words 24/12 and 16/7 in that order. The difference between the chiasma positions is five, and the interference number in the table corresponding to this difference is 17. The serial number of the position 7 chosen on this occasion was 16, and since this is less than the interference number 17, position 7 will be rejected and there will be one chiasma, in position 12. The total number of times position 7 appears in the chiasma position table is 20 (see Table 11); 16 of the 20 serial numbers would be less than the interference number of 17 corresponding to a first chiasma five bits distant, so the chance of the second one surviving would have been only 4/20. This may seem a high degree of interference, but in fact the mean degree of interference between chiasmata in positions 7 and 12 is weaker than this. Simulated interference by this technique is not the same in the two directions, especially in the areas of low chiasma frequency. When these two chiasma positions are chosen, this may be in either order with equal probability. Position 12 occurs 27 times in the chiasma frequency table, so if position 7 has been chosen first position 12 has 11/27 chances (serial numbers 17 to 27) of being allowed to stand. The average survival chance is about 0.3. A first choice chiasma in position 8 will prevent any chiasma nearer the m.s. end, but a chiasma chosen second in position 8 could survive a first choice chiasma in positions 1 to 4.

The method is inelegant and biologically speaking its basis is dubious, but with appropriately chosen parameters the result is realistic and the procedure is quick and simple. It will be noted that in this example, although there is no interference over a distance greater than nine bits, we do not attempt to identify such cases and avoid the test—now that no random number is required it is as quick to have zeros in the table for the longer distances and carry out the test (which must always over such distances result in survival of the second chiasma) than to find out if the test is necessary.

If both chiasmata survive, one small operation required will be to reverse their positions if necessary to ensure that they are subsequently treated in the correct order, and also to prepare, should the situation arise, for dealing with chiasmata on the l.s. side of the centromere.

There is one final point to be considered. In maize and *Drosophila* at least, there is no chiasma interference across the centromere. The occurrence of chiasmata on opposite sides of the centromere is easily recognized if chiasma positions on the two sides are distinguished as stored by different sign bits. When the product of two chiasma positions is negative, these positions must be in different arms of the chromosome and no action relating to interference is required.

Before we consider the question of using the simulation of meiosis to produce test-cross families for chromosome mapping, we will confine ourselves to producing a program which will simulate meiosis. Having done that, it may be extended from cytological to genetical simulation.

The program may begin with some 'red tape' operations or specifications required by the particular machine in use, and will then proceed to any similar operations required by the program itself. In this program, a starting number has to be specified for pseudo-random number generation; this must be different for each occasion on which the program is used and will be chosen at random by whoever is using the program, and punched as a parameter to be read with the program. The transfer of this starting number to the appropriate storage location in the pseudorandom number subroutine (**P200** will be used) will be a program red tape operation.

This will be followed by the production of the chiasma position frequency table by use of subroutine **P1**, and subroutine **P2** will print out a visual representation of the pachytene chromosomes, to show how things are at the start. These two subroutines will be used once only. The program will then enter a loop which will simulate meiosis (subroutine **P3**) and print out the four anaphase II chromosomes (subroutine **P4**), repeating this loop according to previous specification in a counter. A general flow diagram is shown in Figure 36. The main program, which consists of little more than the linking together of the four subroutines, could perhaps be written now, but it is better to deal with the subroutines first in case there are any special points about their entry, exit and use which need to be taken into consideration when writing the main program.

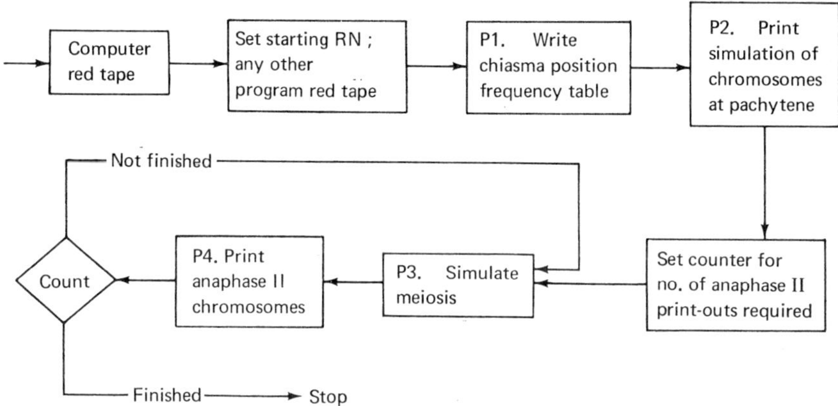

Figure 36. General flow diagram of program for the simulation of meiosis

The program will assume that bit 28 (numbering from zero at the m.s. end) represents the centromere, that chiasma positions will be distributed according to Table 11, and that the interference numbers will be as specified on page 249. These can of course be changed if desired.

The four subroutines will now be dealt with in turn.

P1. *Writing the Chiasma Position Frequency Table*

This table will occupy 512 locations from **s0** to **s511**, and will contain each position the number of times specified in the stores **p1** to **p31** of this subroutine (and we will take them as specified in Table 11). Thus if the contents of **p1**, **p2**, **p3**... are 2, 4, 6... respectively, the first two words of the chiasma position table will indicate position 1, the next four position 2, the next six position 3, and so on. These position numbers will be placed at the l.s. end of each word. In addition, serial numbers will be packed in with the position numbers, beginning with 1 for each position. These serial numbers will be ten bits up from the position numbers; that is, the latter will appear as $m \times 2^{-31}$ and the serial numbers as $n \times 2^{-21}$. Each position number will be held in an accumulator to which 2^{-21} will be added each time the position is written into the table. All chiasma positions to the l.s. side of the centromere will have a **1** added in the sign bit position, and this will be done separately after the table has been set, by addition to the last (**p29**+**p30**+**p31**) words of the table, this total being specified in **p32** (it would be possible for the subroutine to work this total out if **p32** specified instead the centromere position, but it is quicker for the programmer to do the addition himself than to write a section of program to do it for him). **p33** will contain −1.0, which is all zeros except for the sign bit; it could also be specified as **8/20000000000**, which means precisely the same thing.

Although **P1** will be used only once, and therefore could be written in its appropriate position in the main program and entered and left without jumps (and therefore without requiring a link), there is much to be said for treating it quite separately so that all one has to think about in writing the main program is setting the link and jumping. This also allows for any amendment or correction without reference to the main program should the need arise, and since the subroutine is used only once, loss of time in link setting and jumping is negligible.

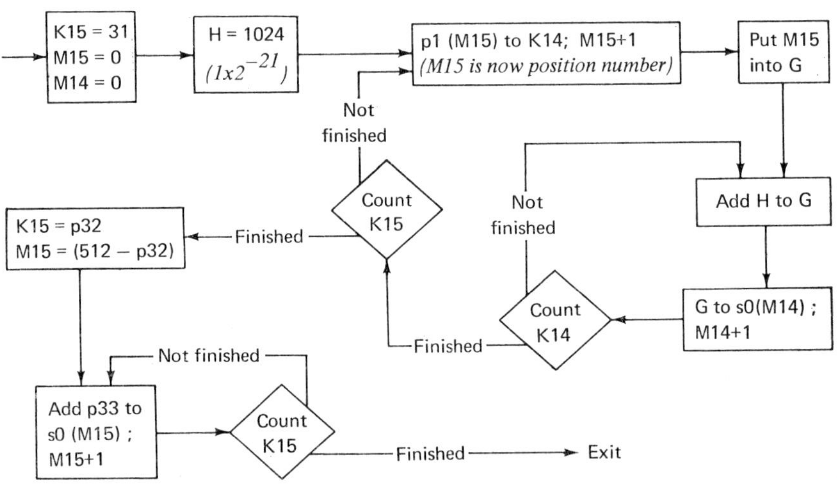

Figure 37. Flow diagram for **P1** which sets the chiasma position frequency table. **p1** to **p31** inclusive give the number of occurrences of each position; **p32** gives the total number of occurrences of the positions on the l.s. side of the centromere; **p33** provides a **1** in the sign position

The flow diagram for **P1** is shown in Figure 37 and the program would be as follows.

```
P1/34;
    0; (for link); 2; 4; 6; 9; 12; 16; 20; 23; 25; 26; 26; 27; 27;
    27; 27; 27; 27; 26; 26; 25; 23; 20; 17; 13; 10; 7; 4; 2; 2;
    4; 2; 8; −1.0;
(0); K15 = 31; M15 = 0; M14 = 0; H = 1024; (for serial number);
(1); p1 (M15)→K14; M15+1; (M15 now = position number);
    M15→G;
(2); G+H→G; (gives serial number); G→s0(M14); M14+1;
    K14−1; J2K14 ≠ 0;
    K15−1; J1K15 ≠ 0;
    p32→K15; H = 512; H−p32→H; H→M15; p33→H;
(3); H+s0(M15)→s0(M15); M15+1; K15−1; J3K15 ≠ 0;
    p0→M15; J(M15);
```

P2. *Printing Simulation of Pachytene*

This subroutine is not essential for this program, and could well be omitted. But it is helpful in demonstration if the class can see a print-out at this stage. How this print-out is executed will depend on the output procedures of the computer in use, and there is little point in giving either flow diagram or program. There is no need for the programmer to be meticulous and refer to a chromatid in order to achieve this print-out. It is quite sufficient to print, without spaces, CRLF (carriage-return, line-feed) followed by 28 ones, an asterisk, three ones, CRLF, 28 zeros, asterisk, three zeros, CRLF and as many further LFs as required to leave blank paper below the print-out.

If desired, pre-chiasma diplotene could also be printed by printing the first line twice followed by the second line twice.

Again, this will be treated as an independent subroutine requiring a link.

P3. *Meiosis*

This subroutine will begin with its **p1** and **p2** all ones (that is, equal to the integral −1), and **p3** and **p4** all zeros. It will execute one or two chiasmata, and **p1** to **p4** will then represent the four resultant anaphase II chromosomes.

There are two major procedures involved, implementation of chiasma interference and chiasma formation. Although these are most conveniently written as though they were separate subroutines, they are best treated as internal subroutines, that is as unnumbered sections within **P3**, since they will both use store locations which may most conveniently be at the beginning of **P3**. In fact, **P3** and its chiasma formation subroutine will refer to the same store locations, and it is simpler not to have to remember and specify a subroutine number when writing these down.

The flow diagram for the whole operation of meiosis, which is shown in Figure 38 without details of the internal subroutines, is fairly involved, and would be little helped by textual description. In following through the diagram, remember that with two surviving chiasmata on the same side of the

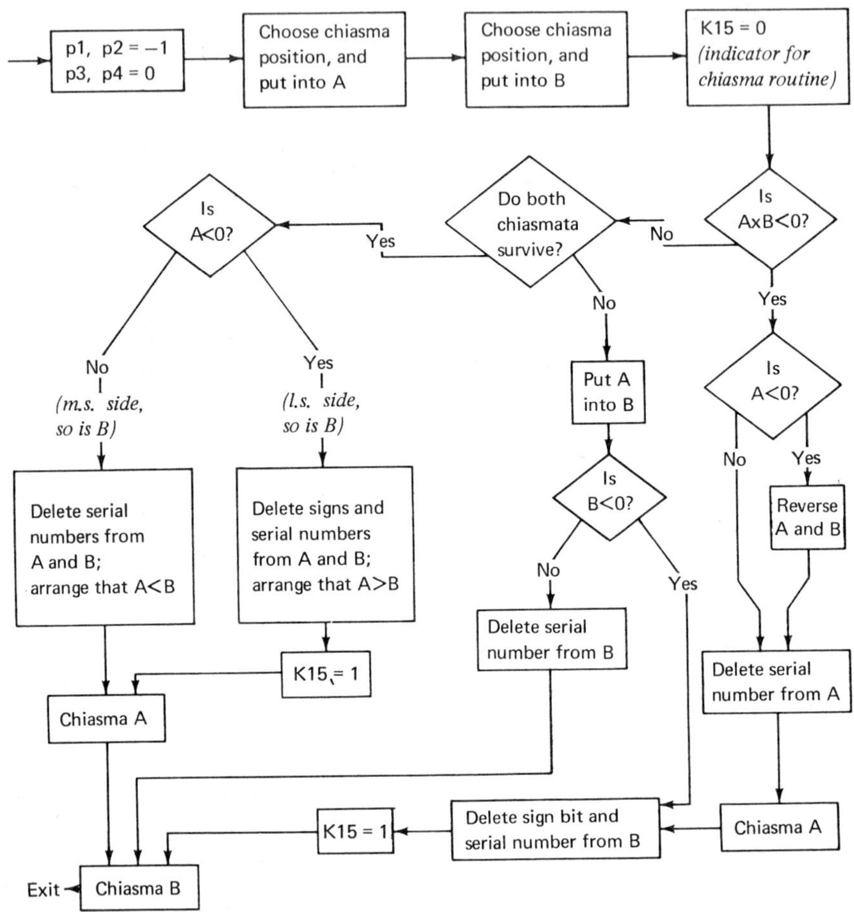

Figure 38. Flow diagram for meiosis subroutine **P3**. If **A** × **B** is negative, the chiasmata will be on opposite sides of the centromere, and there will be no interference; since the contents of **A** and **B** will be required again, the multiplication must be carried out with copies. **K15** is used as an indicator of l.s. (non-zero) or m.s. (zero) side for the chiasma routine will require this information. More detailed flow diagrams for the interference test ('do both chiasmata survive') and chiasma formation are given in Figures 39 and 40

centromere, the one furthest from the centromere must be executed first. With two chiasmata on opposite sides of the centromere, the execution of the m.s. one first is a matter of programming convenience.

The chiasma routine needs to know on which side of the centromere the chiasma position is. It obtains this information from the state of **K15**.

This subroutine assumes that there is no interference across the centromere. With the chromosome assumed in the example and the position frequency table set by the parameters given in **P1**, interference would not allow two surviving chiasmata on the l.s. side of the centromere, and were two such positions chosen an interference test would be redundant. However, the subroutine has been generalized to allow for a different centromere position (achieved by altering the parameters in **P1**) which might allow two surviving chiasmata on either the l.s. or the m.s. side of the centromere. Although this makes flow diagram and program more complicated, it wastes only a negligible amount of time; when the interference test is always redundant, the chance of choosing two chiasma positions on the relevant side is very small anyway. The reader may care to work out how this flow diagram could be amended if it were assumed that the second of two chiasmata on the l.s. side of the centromere could never survive.

Before writing **P3** it is best to write the internal subroutines so that their requirements may be known. Firstly we may consider the interference subroutine, the principle of which has already been described. Since it will be used only once in each meiosis, a link for it will not be essential and it may easily be included in **P3** in such a way that **P3** runs straight on into it with no jump at beginning or end. It is written separately simply because it is easier while writing it to consider it in isolation. It will be supplied by **P3** with the chosen chiasma positions in **A** (the first chosen) and **B**. These will also contain serial numbers and sign bit, and as these will be required later by **P3**, **A** and **B** must remain for the time being unchanged. The chiasma positions may be extracted from copies of **A** and **B** in **C** and **D** by a 5-bit mask (31) in the l.s. position, and the serial number of **B** (which will be required later for the actual test) from a copy by a similar mask 10 places up, which will be stored in **p5** of **P3** as **8/76000**.

The interference numbers, scaled up by a factor of 2^{10} as are the serial numbers in the chiasma position words, are in a table beginning in **p14** of **P3** and having 31 entries.

The flow diagram is shown in Figure 39. Although written first, the program for this internal subroutine will not be shown separately, but in place within **P3** where it occupies the fifth and sixth lines of the instructions, beginning at **A→C**.

The internal subroutine by which chiasma formation is simulated executes the formation of one chiasma in a position supplied to it in **M13**. It begins

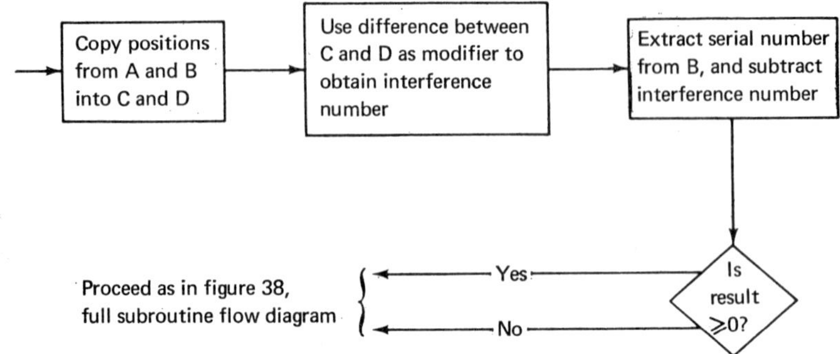

Figure 39. Flow diagram for the interference test—detailed form of 'Do both chiasmata survive' in Figure 38

by choosing at random one of four possible pairs of non-sister chromatids, 1/3, 1/4, 2/3 or 2/4. An eight-word table beginning in **p6** of **P3** carries the integers 1, 1, 2, 2, 3, 4, 3, 4, in that order, and it can be seen that if each of the first four words is coupled with a word four locations later, the four possible choices of chromatids for chiasma formation are specified. The choice is therefore made by generating a random number in the range 0 to 3 and using it as a modifier of **p6** and **p10**. The two integers so chosen will then be used as modifiers of **p0** to transfer the two chosen chromatids to accumulators **C** and **D** and these will be operated on to execute chiasma formation in the way already described in the text.

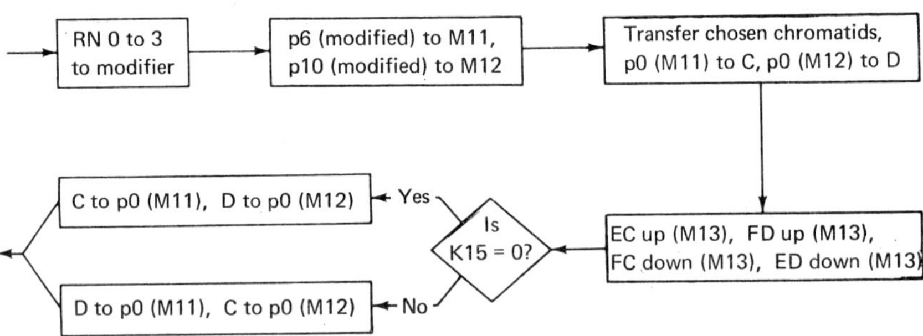

Figure 40. Flow diagram for formation of one chiasma. At entry, **M13** contains the chiasma position, and **K15** is zero if this is on m.s. side of centromere, non-zero if on l.s. side. **p6** onwards contains the chromatid numbers 1, 1, 2, 2; **p10** onwards 3, 4, 3, 4. At the end of the routine **p1** to **p4** will contain the chromatids after chiasma formation. After chiasma **B** (see Figure 38), **p1** to **p4** will in effect be the four anaphase II chromosomes

The resultant contents of **C** and **D** will be returned to the **p** stores, with the same **p**-store/accumulator arrangement as that by which they were removed from the **p** stores if the chiasma position was on the m.s. side of the centromere, and in the alternative arrangement if it was on the l.s. side, the arrangement being determined by the state of **K15** on entry. This ensures that the centromere bit always returns to the **p** store from which it came.

This internal subroutine is used in four different places in **P3**, and therefore requires a link; this may conveniently be set directly in a modifier. The simple flow diagram is shown in Figure 40, and the instruction sequence (which will come at the end of **P3**) will be as follows. At entry, the link is in **M14** (not **M15** which is required by **P200**) and the chiasma position in **M13**.

```
(5); p0P200 = (j4); M15 = 2; J0P200; (H = 2-bit random integer);
(4); H→M15; p6(M15)→M11; p10(M15)→M12; (M11 and
     M12 contain relative addresses of chromatids);
     p0(M11)→C; p0(M12)→D; EC up(M13); FD up(M13);
     FC down(M13); ED down(M13); J3K15 ≠ 0;
     C→p0(M11); D→p0(M12); J(M14);
(3); D→p0(M11); C→p0(M12); J(M14);
```

K15 is set to zero near the beginning of **P3**, and made non-zero prior to the execution of any chiasma on the l.s. side of the centromere.

We are now in a position to write the subroutine **P3** from the flow diagram of Figure 38. There are no particular difficulties now that the two internal subroutines have been written, and it is a question of following through the various routes and making sure that the program does not leave out any route. It would be an excellent exercise for the reader to try this for himself.

p0 = link
p1 to **p4** will carry the chromatids and must be re-set each time the subroutine is used, preferably at the start
p5 = mask for serial number
p6 to **p13** carry the chromatid numbers
p14 onwards will carry the interference table scaled up by a factor of 2^{10}; unspecified locations **p24** to **p44** are compiled as zeros

```
       P3/45;
       0; −1; −1; 0; 0; 8/76000; 1; 1; 2; 2; 3; 4; 3; 4;
       28672; 27648; 25600; 23552; 20480; 17408; 13312;
       9216; 6144; 3072;
  (0); p1 = −1; p2 = −1; p3 = 0; p4 = 0;
       M15 = 9; p0P200 = (j6); J0P200; (H = random integer
       0 to 511);
```

```
 (6); H→M15; s0(M15)→A; M15=9; p0P200=(j7);
      J0P200;
 (7); H→M15; s0(M15)→B; K15=0; A→C; B→D; C×D;
      J8C<0;
      (next two lines, interference test);
      A→C; C&31; B→D; D&31; C−D→C; abs C; C→M15;
      p14(M15)→C; B→D; D&p5→D; D−C→D; J1D⩾0;
      (one chiasma only); A→B; J2B<0; B&31; J15;
 (1); J9A<0; A&31; B&31; J10A<B; A→C; B→A; C→B;
(10); M14=(j15); A→M13; J5; (jump to chiasma routine);
 (9); A&31; B&31; J13A>B; A→C; B→A; C→B; (A now
      needs to be greater than B);
(13); K15=1; M14=(j15); A→M13; J5;
 (8); (chiasmata on opposite sides of centromere);
      J16A>0; A→C; B→A; C→B;
(16); A&31; M14=(j2); A→M13; J5;
 (2); B&31; K15=1;
(15); M14=(j17); B→M13; J5;
(17); p0→M15; J(M15); (exit);
```

This is followed by the internal subroutine for chiasma formation previously written out and beginning with reference **(5)**.

There are several points at which time could be saved by modifying this subroutine, but since the program would probably be used in fairly short runs the overall saving in time would be very slight. Perhaps the only worthwhile change would be to economize in random numbers by using **P203** instead of **P200**.

P4. *Anaphase II Output*

As with **P2** and for the same reasons this subroutine will not be written out, but the flow diagram in Figure 41 indicates the method. With a character-at-time teleprinter, each character (1, 0 or ∗) required will be determined and printed immediately. With a line printer, the appropriate binary code for each character will be stored in sequence, the method of storage depending on the machine in use. The flow diagram is written as if for a teleprinter.

P4 is generalized for any centromere position, which is specified in the main program parameters. These will be transferred to **P4** by the main program. The binary chromosome patterns will be printed directly from **p1** to **p4** of **P3**; since **P4** is program specific, no difficulty arises there. Note how **P4** uses the sign bit to distinguish **0** and **1**. The main program will assume the usual link.

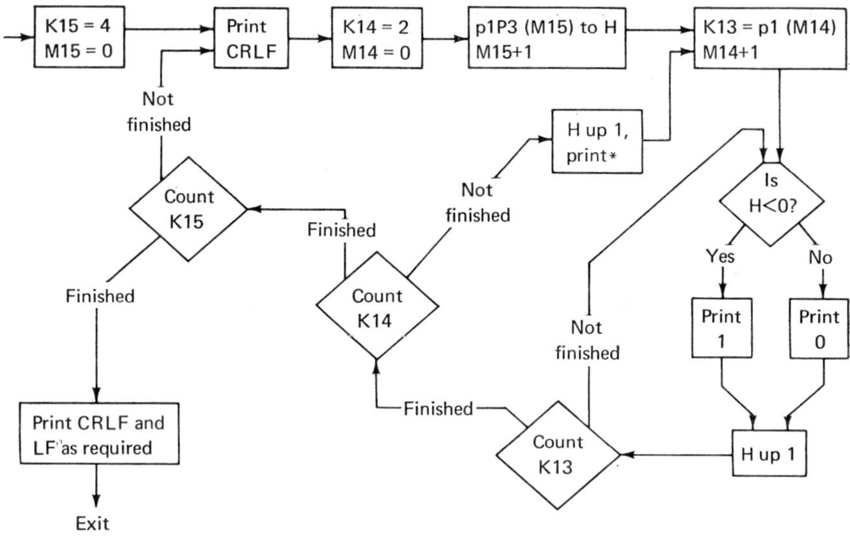

Figure 41. Flow diagram for anaphase II output, **P4.** **p1** gives number of bits on m.s. side of centromere, **p2** number on l.s. side, both being set by main program red tape

Main Program

We may now write out the main program which, after initial specifications and red tape operations consists of little more than the stringing together of the subroutines. It is not possible to write out here any red tape operations which are computer specific; some of these could require some **p** store parameters, so more **p** locations could be needed than those required by the program proper.

p0 = starting random number
p1 = number of anaphase II print-outs required
p2 = number of bits on m.s. side of centromere
p3 = number of bits on l.s. side of centromere

The main program will then read

Meiosis simulation;

s/512;
P0/4; (*more than four* **p** *stores could be required*)**;**
[**p** store specifications]**;**

```
(0); [computer red tape];
     p0→A; A→p1P200; (starting random number set);
     p2→A; A→p1P4; p3→A; A→p2P4; (centromere position to
     P4);
     p0P1 = (j1); J0P1;
(1); p0P2 = (j2); J0P2;
(2); p1→K0;
(3); p0P3 = (j4); J0P3;
(4); p0P4 = (j5); J0P4;
(5); K0−1; J3K0 ≠ 0; STOP;
```

This is then followed by the subroutines **P1**, **P2**, **P3**, **P4**, **P200**, in any order.

Simulation of Test-cross Families

The foregoing program as written is essentially a cytological simulation, producing a series of tetrads of anaphase II chromosomes. With the basic meiosis there, it is not a difficult matter by changing the form of output to arrange for this to be converted to a genetical simulation, producing a test-cross family or a series of such families.

We will consider the matter simply, in the first place, by supposing that our chromosomes have three loci in which we are interested, and that we wish to demonstrate the production of a 3-point test-cross family from which the order of the genes on the chromosome and their genetic map distances may be determined.

Since the essential feature of a test-cross procedure is that the zygotic ratio which is produced is identical with the gametic ratio of the heterozygous parent we do not need to simulate the whole reproductive process. Instead, we simulate the production of the appropriate number of gametes.

Suppose that we have a parent heterozygous at three loci in full coupling, **abc**/+ + +, and that these loci are represented by bits 3, 9 and 21 (counting from zero at the m.s. end). The class of course should not know this, nor even the order of the genes.

It is simplest to use full coupling; for visual demonstration of meiosis it is obviously best to begin with one chromosome all ones and the other all zeros, and if the test-cross simulation is to be tied in demonstration to the meiosis, then retention of the convention that recessives are always represented by **1** necessarily means that the triple heterozygote will be in full coupling. If however for any reason it was desired not to use full coupling, it would not be too difficult to amend the program; the starting chromosomes would have to be mixed ones and zeros, and would have to be reset in a different way by **P3**.

We can produce gametes by simulating a series of meioses and choosing from each at random one of the four anaphase II chromosomes to be the gamete chromosome. This is quite sound biologically, as was pointed out in Chapter 8. We can therefore produce a test-cross simulation program by a straightforward modification of the program which has just been produced. The counter in main program **p1** gives the size of family required. Subroutine **P4** is replaced by one which chooses one of the four products of **P3** at random, and treats it in accordance with our new requirements.

The first of these is the determination of the genotype of the chosen chromosome. This is simple enough. The new subroutine will carry three single-bit masks, with ones in positions 3, 9 and 21 respectively. An LM will be carried out between the chosen chromosome and each mask in turn, and for each the result will be zero if the allele is + and non-zero if it is the recessive.

How we treat this information will depend on the form in which we require the output. If this were a research problem, then the computer would do all the work of scoring and calculation. The genotype as it exists on the chromosome would be converted to a formal representation using the three l.s. bits of a word; if the chromosome were found to carry **a**, four would be added to a zero accumulator, if **b** two would be added, and if **c** one would be added. Otherwise nothing would be added. It is easy to see that the three l.s. bits would then represent conventionally a gamete with three loci, and this could be used as a modifier by which an addition of one could be made to the correct location in a store section of eight words corresponding to the eight possible genotypes, and so the family could be scored. Simple arithmetic would calculate the map distances.

But for the purposes of genetics teaching, this would really be almost pointless. It would be much better to arrange for a print-out which would give a visual representation of the genotypes of the chosen chromosomes in the family (or, expressing it more appropriately, of the phenotypes of the individuals of the family). The class could then score the family as if it were a family of real organisms (which however did not begin to walk about as the effect of ether wore off), determine for themselves the order of the loci by recognizing the double crossovers, and work out the map distances. It is quite easy to produce the output in a suitable form. If the first mask shows the allele to be a **1**, then some kind of symbol may be printed; if the allele is **0**, + may be printed. This will be repeated for the other two loci, different symbols being used for different recessives, but + is the obvious one to use for any normal (in this case dominant) allele. Thus a bracket (for example) could be used for **a** if that were supposed to stand for *arc*, > for **b** if that stood for *bent*, and a comma for **c** if that stood for *curly*. So the gametes **a+c** and **+bc**, for example, would be output as (+, and + >, respectively. A family of 200 individuals printed in this way occupies very little space.

If the class is to be given no clue (other than that provided by the family) to the order of the genes on the chromosome, then the genes should not always be printed out in their cytological order as they were in the above example. The author's program (Crosby, 1961) had eleven genes arranged on the chromosome in an order which was not alphabetical. They were taken in groups of three for the test crosses and in the print-out the order of the genes was alphabetical; sometimes this was the cytological order, sometimes it was not, but the class had no prior knowledge of the situation in any cross.

Thus while dotted, arc, tipsy—symbols : (/—were in that cytological order, the print-out order was (:/. Their low frequencies would show that (+ + and + : / were the double crossovers and establish the order, while + : + for example would be a single crossover between dotted and arc.

The object of that program was to allow the mapping of a chromosome with eleven loci on it, distributed rather unevenly. This was done by using a series of 3-point test-crosses, beginning by taking them at random and then as the picture of the map began to emerge, taking three adjacent loci (or apparently adjacent ones) to obtain maximum accuracy.

This involved some method of informing the output subroutine which three genes were to be dealt with in any particular test-cross, as well as the implementation of that choice. The statement of the choice depended on the computer in use. The first two versions of the program were for fairly slow machines with which it was practicable (and preferable) to use key-board settings to indicate the three loci during temporary halts in the program. A class which was working efficiently could decide which test-crosses were required to bring precision at the closing stages of mapping, without keeping the computer idling for too long (there was plenty of computer time to spare in those days, anyway). But with a fast machine like the KDF9 this was quite impracticable, and it was much quicker to produce a family from each possible test-cross, and extract from the output and deal with those which were required. With eleven loci, there are only 165 different test-cross families, and with line printer output this takes very little time.

P5. *Output one Test-cross Individual*

There are three main problems to be considered. These are how the test-cross is specified in the subroutine, how the specification is conveyed to it, and how it is implemented.

The first and third of these are fairly simple. Three consecutive **p** stores of the subroutine contain 1-bit masks corresponding to the genes involved in the test-cross, and three other consecutive **p** stores contain, in the same order, the binary patterns which determine the output of the appropriate recessive symbol. One of the four anaphase II chromosomes in **p1** to **p4** of **P3**, at the end of a passage through that subroutine, is chosen at random, and an LM performed with each of the masks in turn, + being printed if the LP is zero (dominant allele), the corresponding symbol being printed if the LP is not zero (recessive allele). The values of any bits other than those representing the three genes of the test-cross are of course irrelevant. The flow diagram, Figure 42, is written as if for teleprinter output. For line printer output, the characters would be stored sequentially at this stage for later printing, and this might require the use of a special subroutine to organize the storage.

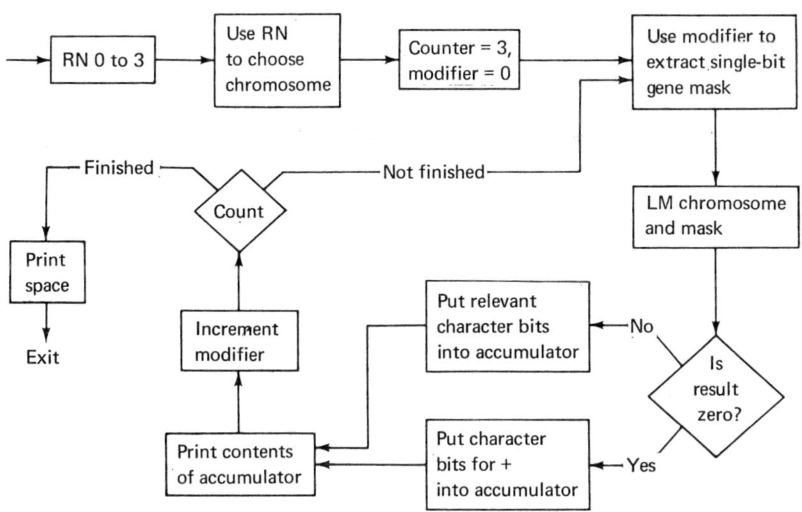

Figure 42. Flow diagram for subroutine **P5** used in test-cross family output. **P5** outputs in character form the phenotype corresponding to one chosen chromosome

The subroutine program would be as follows. Where printing is involved, the action is described in square brackets. **p1** to **p3** are to contain the masks for the genes, and **p4** to **p6** the character bits; these will be set by the main program for each particular test-cross, and will not be written as part of the subroutine. The printing operation will refer to the character bits contained in a specified accumulator; there is no need to store the characters for + and space, since these can have integral equivalents which can be put in an accumulator by the usual instruction, which will be written in the form **F** = [+] or **F** = [space], the appropriate printing (or storage) operation being written as [print **F**].

P5/7;
(0); **p0P200=(j1)**; **M15=2**; **J0P200**; (*H* = *random number* 0 *to* 3);
(1); **H→M15**; **p1P3(M15)→H**; (*H* = *chromosome*); **K15=3**;
  M15=0;
(2); **p1(M15)→G**; **H&G→G**; **J3G=0**; **p4(M15)→F**;
  (*F* = *character*); **J4**;
(3); **F**=[+];
(4); [print **F**]; **M15+1**; **K15−1**; **J2K15≠0**;
  F=[space]; [print **F**]; **p0→M15**; **J(M15)**;

P5 therefore prints out one offspring from each meiosis carried out by **P3**.

P6. *Insert Test-cross Specifications into* P5

The problem of inserting the test-cross specifications into **P5** is more complicated, especially in the present context of a book where several possible ways of getting the information from operator to program have to be considered, but we can begin with the assumption that there is in the store a specification word prescribing the three loci which are to be dealt with, and that this word is to be supplied to a test-cross administration subroutine **P6**.

We will suppose that the linkage group which is to be mapped has a maximum of 15 genes of which any three may be considered at any one time. **p1** to **p15** of this subroutine will contain the masks for the genes. **p16** to **p30** will contain the bits coding for the printed characters, in the same order. From each of these groups of **p** stores, the specified three will have to go into **p1** to **p3** and **p4** to **p6** of **P5** respectively. It is convenient to make the gene order alphabetic; in any case, since the genes have to be specified by their **p** store numbers it is easier and less liable to error if they are arranged in a sensible order, and this should not be the order on the chromosome.

The **p** store numbers of the three required genes will be packed into the specification word. Each will require no more than four bits, and so the 12 l.s. bits can be used for this purpose in three sections of four, and the numbers extracted by LM with 15 after any necessary shift down has been performed. Since the l.s. section of four bits is conveniently dealt with first, the order of the genes as specified in this word (from left to right) is the reverse of their order as printed in the individuals of the family. Thus if we want to specify genes 2, 6 and 9 (identifying numbers, *not* bit positions), the specification word would be **...100101100010**, which we may write shortly as 9/6/2, and if the mask order is alphabetic the print order will be alphabetic.

It is useful to head each test-cross family with the names of the genes (again, most conveniently in alphabetical order), and to show the recessive symbol for each at the same time. This can easily be done if the gene names are short enough for their character bits to be packed into the words in locations **p31** to **p45**.

The flow diagram for subroutine **P6** is shown in Figure 43. The program is quite simple. The main labour is in deciding correctly the contents of **p1** to **p45**. If a linkage group with less than 15 genes is being considered, then superfluous words in the **p** stores will be written as zeros.

At entry, **H** contains the specification word.

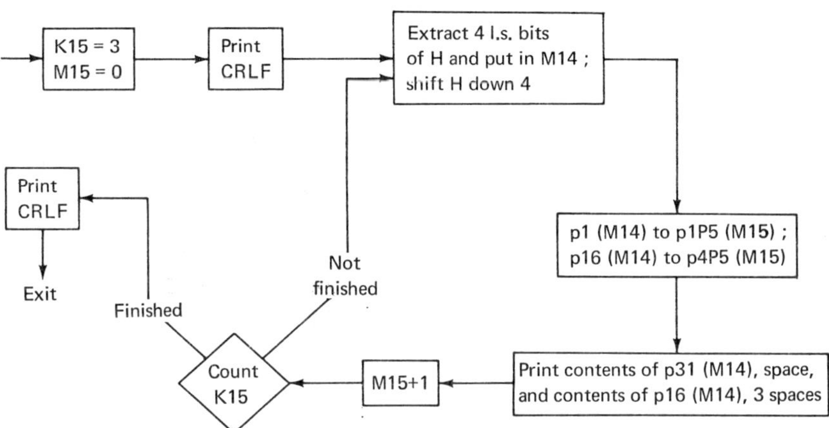

Figure 43. Flow diagram for **P6**, which translates test-cross specification parameters held in specification word into masks and the relevant output character bits, and places these in **P5**. Also prints heading for family. Mask table in **p1** to **p15**, character table in **p16** to **p30**, name table in **p31** to **p45**

```
P6/46;
0; [link]; [p stores as required, gene masks beginning in p1, recessive
characters in p16, gene names in p31];
(0); K15 = 3; M15 = 0; [print CRLF];
(1); H→G; G&15; H down 4; G→M14;
     p1(M14)→G; G→p1P5(M15); p16(M14)→G;
     G→p4P5(M15);
     [print contents of p31(M14), space, p16(M14), three spaces];
     M15+1; K15−1; J1K15≠0; [print CRLF]; p0→M15;
     J(M15);
```

The problems which remain are also administrative, and concern getting the specification word into **H** as required for **P6**, and arranging the printed layout of the family.

How the former operation is performed will depend on several factors, including whether or not keyboard specification is practicable and desirable. This is fairly simple. It is arranged that the program comes to a temporary stop immediately before entry to **P6**; the keyboard switches are then set to correspond to the bit pattern of the required specification word, and the program restarted. Its next actions are to read the keyboard word and then place it directly into **H**. (The starting pseudorandom number may, incidentally, be set by the keyboard in a similar way at the start of the program.) At the end of one test-cross family, the program will return to the same temporary stop for the next family to be specified, and so on.

If keyboard setting is not possible, then setting can be done by input of a card or short section of paper tape, as appropriate. A short subroutine is required which at the temporary stop before entry to **P6** will read three numbers from card or tape, putting the first as it is into **H**, multiplying the second by 16 and adding to **H**, and multiplying the third by 256 and adding it to **H**. **H** is then the required specification word. Thus if we want to specify genes 2, 6 and 9 to be printed in that order, the three numbers in order of input will be 2, 6 and 9 and **H** will come to $2+6\times16+9\times256$, which is the required **...100101100010**. With a fairly slow computer, this is probably the best way of indicating the sequence of test-crosses if the keyboard is not to be used.

If we do not wish to exercise choice while the program is running, but prefer to work from a predetermined order of test-crosses, then we will have a length of tape or a series of cards, and instead of stopping temporarily before entry to **P6** the program will proceed directly to read the next three numbers. A negative number at the end can be used to tell it when to stop.

P7. *Organize Output of all Possible Test-crosses*

If a fast machine with a line printer is available, it would be a prohibitive waste of time to indicate individually the test-crosses required during the running of the program. It would be quickest and simplest to perform and print out all possible test crosses in alphabetical order. It would then be a fairly simple matter to select those required. All that is needed is a routine which will, if the genes are, say, **a b c d e f g h i j k**, arrange that the test crosses are performed in the following order: **abc**, **abd**, **abe** ... **abk**, **acd**, **ace** ... **ack**, **ade** ... **ajk**, **bcd**, **bce** ... **bjk**, **cde**, **cdf** ... **ijk**. This requires a supply of specification words in the sequence 3/2/1, 4/2/1, 5/2/1 etc. This is not a problem of genetic simulation, but one of administration, and it will not be described in detail. The reader may work through the flow diagram of Figure 44 and the program if he wishes to see how it operates.

It has been written to be general for n genes. In the flow diagram and the brief description the last used specification word (which is stored in **p3**) is referred to as $r/q/p$; before the program starts this has the value $n/(n-1)/0$ corresponding to a purely hypothetical specification word, for a reason which the reader should work out for himself, and on the first use of the subroutine the route taken will end at the exit lowest on the right-hand side of the flow diagram.

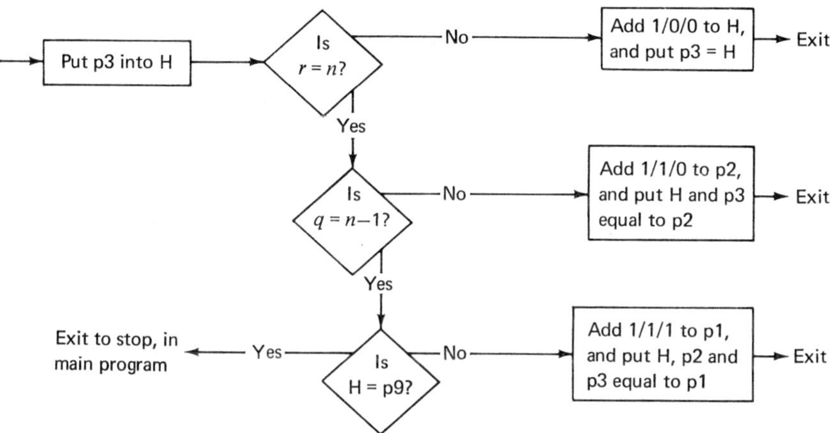

Figure 44. Flow diagram for **P7**, test-cross administration. This arranges that the program performs all possible test-crosses in alphabetical order. Generalized for any number of loci. At entry, **p3** contains the last used specification word, $r/q/p$. The first time **P7** is used, $r = n$, $q = n-1$ and $p = 0$ (where n is the number of loci), while **p1** $=2/1/0$ and **p2** $= 0$. **p9** is always $n/(n-1)/(n-2)$

The **p** stores will be set as follows, using here for clarity the 4-bit section notation.

- **p1** = 2/1/0 (**...001000010000**); before any test-cross is performed this will be changed by the subroutine to 3/2/1, which will be the first used specification word corresponding to **cba**
- **p2** = zero (its specified value is immaterial—it will immediately be made equal to **p1**)
- **p3** = $n/(n-1)/0$
- **p4** = 1/0/0
- **p5** = 1/1/0
- **p6** = 1/1/1
- **p7** = 15/0/0 (mask for r)
- **p8** = 0/15/0 (mask for q)
- **p9** = $n/(n-1)/(n-2)$ (the final specification word)

p10 = $n/0/0$ (to test r)
p11 = $0/(n-1)/0$ (to test q)

The subroutine at exit will contain the specification word in **H** and in **p3**. It will use a link, incremented by one for normal exits, not incremented for final exit to end of program (treated as a failure exit).

The subroutine program will be as follows, **p** store items in square brackets being variable between runs according to the number of genes in the linkage group.

```
P7/12;
0; 8/1020; 0; [n/(n−1)/0]; 8/400; 8/420; 8/421; 8/7400; 8/360;
[n/(n−1)/(n−2)]; [n/0/0]; [0/(n−1)/0];
(0); p3→H; H→G; G&p7→G; (G = r); J1G = p10; H+p4→H;
     H→p3; p0→M15; M15+1; J(M15);
(1); H→G; G&p8→G; (G = q); J2G = p11; p2→H; H+p5→H;
     H→p2; H→p3; p0→M15; M15+1; J(M15);
(2); J3H = p9; p1→H; H+p6→H; H→p1; H→p2; H→p3;
     p0→M15; M15+1; J(M15);
(3); p0→M15; J(M15); (exit to stop);
```

If a second set of test-cross families is required, **p1** and **p3** must first be re-set to their original value. The program can then be re-started at reference **(6)** of the main program (see later). The insertion into the main program of a short re-start subroutine could deal with this. Alternatively, the whole program could be read in again, with a new value for the starting random number.

The question of layout is easily dealt with. A family of st individuals can be printed in s rows of t. All that is necessary is to have two counters, set to s and t. t is decreased by one for each individual until $t = 0$; CRLF is then output, s decreased by one, and the second counter re-set to t. The two counters concerned must not be used elsewhere in the main program loop which produces the test-cross.

The flow diagram for the whole test-cross program is shown in Figure 45, which supposes that each test-cross will be specified by keyboard setting. For execution of all possible test-crosses in sequence, the part within dotted lines is replaced by the part shown separately.

This version of the main program will be as follows.

```
s/512;
P0/3;
[p0 = starting random number; p1 = s; p2 = t];
 (0); [computer red tape];
      p0→A; A→p1P200;
      p0P1 = (j6); J0P1;
```

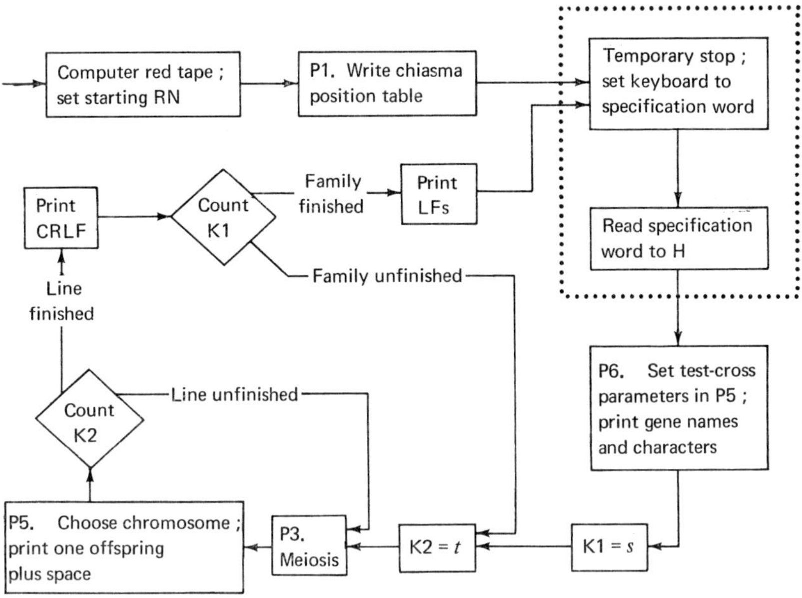

Figure 45. Flow diagram for test-cross program. This assumes that each test-cross family is specified by keyboard setting. s = number of lines of output, t = number of progeny per line.
For execution of all possible test-crosses in sequence, replace the part within dotted lines by single box containing 'P7. Exit to stop if finished, otherwise deliver next specification word to H'.

```
 (6); [temporary stop to read keyboard to H];
      p0P6 = (j7); J0P6;
 (7); p1→K1;
 (8); p2→K2;
 (9); p0P3 = (j10); J0P3;
(10); p0P5 = (j11); J0P5;
(11); K2−1; J9K2 ≠ 0; [print CRLF];
      K1−1; J8K1 ≠ 0; [print extra LF as required];
      J6; (return to temporary stop);
```

Followed by the subroutines **P1, P3, P5, P6, P7** (if fast machine version required), **P200** in any order.

For the fast machine version to print all possible test-cross families, the line beginning with reference **(6)** would be replaced by

```
 (6); p0P7 = (j12); J0P7;
(12); STOP;
```

The reader will note the reference numbers one to five are missing from this version of the main program. The reason for this will shortly be apparent.

Combined Program—Anaphase II Chromosomes and Test-crosses

These two programs could be made more useful for teaching purposes if they were combined into one, so that a number of meioses could be output as anaphase II tetrads, and then by returning to the starting random number the first test-cross family could be produced using the meiosis already performed. When the gene positions have been determined and the class told which bits in the chromosome correspond to the genes, the class can then be shown the relationship between meiosis and offspring since it will be possible to show for each member of the test-cross family which anaphase II chromosome of the corresponding meiosis produced it—or since there is sometimes bound to be ambiguity, which two anaphase II chromosomes included the relevant one.

There is, however, one subtlety—the number of random numbers generated per loop of the two versions of the program are not the same, because of the random choice of chromatids for the test-cross progeny. This means that while the meiosis for the first progeny would use the same random numbers as that for the corresponding anaphase II output, the second progeny meiosis would not, because of the extra random number used the first time. This difficulty can be overcome quite simply by generating an extra random

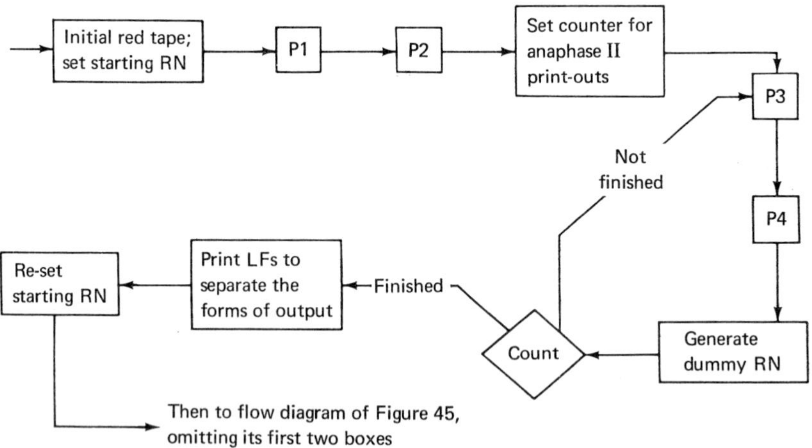

Figure 46. Simplified flow diagram for program combining anaphase II and test-cross outputs

number in each operation of the chromosome print-out loop, and doing nothing with it; if an economical random number subroutine such as **P203** were used, care would have to be taken to call for the correct number of bits (two).

A simplified flow diagram for the combined program is shown in Figure 46. It should be easy enough to write out a new main program. The choice of reference numbers for the original test-cross version removes the necessity for checking against duplication, which of course is not permitted. There will however have to be a change in main program **p** stores, and consequently in the instructions setting **K1** and **K2** in the test-cross section; **p1** to **p3** are used by the anaphase II print-out version, so *s* and *t* will have to go into **p4** and **p5**.

Selection in Inbreeding and Outbreeding Systems

A second program which has been used very successfully in university classes is one which also has a wider applicability and which could readily be adapted to research problems. It may be regarded as essentially a development of the model program described in Chapter 3; the main principles of this kind of program have been discussed previously, and do not need to be dealt with in detail again.

This program was designed to demonstrate the difference between inbreeding and outbreeding populations with regard both to their genetic structure and to their response to selection against recessive alleles. Its first version is described in Crosby (1961), and although it has been modified somewhat in detail in passage from one computer to another, the broad outlines of the program have remained largely the same. It was not, in its latest version for KDF9, as well programmed as it might have been, because certain programming procedures in the early versions were dictated by the nature of the machines used, and rather lazily adapted in writing the KDF9 version instead of being completely revised, which would have meant more effort in programming but a more efficient program.

In the quasi-program in Mendol which is about to be developed, revision rather than adaptation has been used, and it is hoped that the procedures described (although untested) are reasonably efficient. It should however be borne in mind that what is an efficient way of proceeding when using one computer is not necessarily the best way of doing the same thing with another, and the efficiency of this quasi-program is to be considered solely in terms of its quasi-language, Mendol, and its imaginary computer, XB1.

The organisms are imagined to be hermaphrodite and capable of self-fertilization, and they may readily be considered either as plants or as animals.

They have an annual (or single generation) life cycle within which all of them are broadly speaking synchronous, all being simultaneously capable of reproduction during a portion of that life cycle and reproduction being limited to that period. No adult survives beyond its own generation, and all offspring appear and reproduce only in the generation following the one in which they are produced. There is thus no overlapping of generations.

Three genes are considered, each with two alleles .They are unlinked, show complete dominance, and in the author's programs had weak, moderate and strong selection respectively against the recessive homozygote. Although dominance is assumed, it would be quite easy (as explained later) to modify the program to simulate a system without dominance or with partial dominance. Also, although the author assumed no interaction between the three genes in his programs, interaction can be included in the program without alteration simply by choice of suitable fitness parameters.

Fitness is expressed in terms of reproductive capacity, all zygotes surviving but having reproductive capacities related to their phenotypes. Assuming dominance, there are eight different phenotypes, of which the one showing all three dominant characters has the maximum fitness, 1.0. In the absence of interaction, the fitnesses of the three double recessive homozygotes would each be the product of the fitnesses of the corresponding single recessive homozygotes, while that of the triple recessive would be the product of those of all three single recessive homozygotes. But the fitnesses can if desired be assigned arbitrarily or according to any predetermined relationship. For example, if one supposed a favourable interaction between two recessives, the fitness of the double recessive homozygote could be greater than that of either of the singles.

The program is designed to allow the use of various degrees of inbreeding and outbreeding according to a pre-set parameter, which remains unchanged through any single experiment but may be variable between experiments. The required degree of inbreeding is implemented in precisely the same way as with the model program of Chapter 3; inbreeding is self-fertilization, complete outbreeding is random mating. The chance that an individual chosen as female parent is self-fertilized is equal to the degree of inbreeding pre-set for the current experiment; if not selfed, it mates at random.

In preceding chapters it was pointed out that there were often several ways of dealing with any particular operation in writing a program, and the choice would depend on a number of circumstances, including the computer available and the language. We can now consider the question of choice of programming techniques in a definite context and using Mendol with our notional computer XB1.

Firstly, the main choices before us will be outlined, and it will quickly be realized that the choice in one element of the program may affect that in others, so that sections of the program cannot be considered in isolation. It is hoped that the conflict which arises from the fact that a written account in a book has to be presented in a linear sequence will not cause too much difficulty.

Gene Arrangement

Basic to the genetic simulation in this program is a decision as to where the genes are to be located in the word. The gametes will be combined side by side in fertilization, and not interdigitated, but this leaves three main possibilities for their location. These are illustrated as follows. As in Chapter 6, *rrr* and rrr are used in the zygote to represent the genes of the two gametic sets.

(*a*) 0000000000000*rrr*000000000000rrr

(*b*) 0000000000000000000000000*rrr*rrr

(*c*) 0*rrr*rrr0000000000000000000000000

We will decide that the reproduction subroutine used will be one which deals with both parents simultaneously, and the following discussion assumes this.

a has the advantage that the generalized reproduction subroutine for 15 loci developed in Chapter 6 could be used directly and a new reproduction subroutine would not have to be written. It has the disadvantage that the genotype cannot be extracted and used directly for fitness look-up (if we decide to use a genotype/fitness table), but would first have to be derived by shifting the *r* alleles down 12 places and adding them to a word containing only the r alleles. If however the phenotype will be sufficient for table look-up and the genotype not required, then this disadvantage disappears because the phenotype can be derived almost as quickly (the longer shift takes longer) from arrangement *a* as from *b* and more quickly than from *c*. It is less easy to set the initial population with *a* than with the other two arrangements.

b will require a modified reproduction subroutine to be written, but the genotype can be used directly for table look-up if required, without change of position.

c will also require a new subroutine, and the genotype or phenotype can only be used after a shift down of 25 places.

Before we decide on which of these three arrangements is to be preferred, fitness determination should be considered. A table look-up method will be used, and a decision has to be made as to whether this will be based on genotype or phenotype, and whether the fitness will be ascertained each time the individual is chosen as a parent, or whether it will be ascertained once only for each individual and stored with the genotype in the organism word.

Although in situations where we have complete dominance a phenotype/fitness table covers all possibilities of fitness (and requires only eight entries), it has the disadvantage that genotype requires conversion to phenotype before reference can be made to it. With three genes, a genotype/fitness table requires only 64 entries, and this does not normally pose any problems of storage; it can be referred to directly from the genotype, and has the additional advantage that no programming alterations would be involved if it were wished to run an experiment in which there was no dominance (when phenotype/fitness and genotype/fitness tables would of course be identical). The maximum advantage in looking up a genotype/fitness table comes with gene arrangement *b*, since the organism itself can be used directly as the modifier for table look-up. Arrangement *c* can really be ruled out on this account, since an extra instruction would be required for the determination of the fitness and in this particular context it has no special advantage by way of compensation.

If arrangement *b* were used with a genotype/fitness table there would be little point in storing the fitness in the organism word rather than looking it up every time the organism was chosen, since look-up is so rapid, requiring only two instructions. The average number of times an individual is chosen as a potential parent will depend on the degree of inbreeding and on the mean fitness of the population. Even if the population starts with a low mean fitness, the value of this will increase quickly, and in practice the average number of times an individual is chosen is not likely to be very much greater than two in an outbreeding population, and will usually be less in an inbreeding one. If this average number of times is two, then if the viability is determined each time the individual is chosen, a total of four instructions would be required. To determine the viability once and store it with the genotype would require three instructions, two for the determination and one for adding it into the organism word. No extra instruction for extracting the fitness would be required for testing; since the fitness would be stored as a fraction at the m.s. end, the whole organism word would be used; the slight addition to the fitness value made by the genotype bits at the l.s. end would be negligible. An extra instruction would however be required after reproduction; in gametogenesis, **P202** which produces 31 random bits will be used rather than **P200**, since it is quicker and the extra bits in excess of the six actually required are irrelevant; so that although the fitness bits would not interfere with the reproductive process, their debris would remain and appear in the zygote, from which they would have to be removed.

If gene arrangements *a* and *c* were used, then fitness look-up would be a longer process and there might be an advantage in looking up the fitness once per individual and storing it, but again this would rule out *c*, since with that arrangement the fitness would have to be stored as an integer at the l.s. end and would therefore have to be extracted before testing against an integral random number which itself would take longer to produce than a fractional one.

The choice really lies between *a* and *b*; the advantage of an available tested subroutine for *a* is not so great, since the basic principles of the procedure for any number of loci have already been established, and writing one specially for three loci is easy enough. On balance, it has been decided to use arrangement *b* and to determine the fitness from a genotype/fitness table each time the individual is chosen as a potential parent, but it should be pointed out that with other computers and other languages a different decision might have been reached (as it would with KDF9 for example, where the special structure of the Q-stores allowed possibilities which have not been considered here, and where the accumulator structure makes table look-up a slightly lengthier business).

General Account of the Program

A genotype/fitness table with 64 entries takes longer to write down than a phenotype/fitness table, and is more liable to error, both with regards to initial allocation of the fitnesses and in writing the fitnesses down and punching them. Where there is no dominance these difficulties cannot be avoided, but with dominance a genotype/fitness table may be produced by the program as one of its initial procedures using a subroutine which works from a phenotype/fitness table, as explained later.

The degree of inbreeding and the population size (which as will be shown later must be a multiple of 64) may vary from experiment to experiment and will be pre-set as parameters, as will the number of generations for which the experiment is to run. The degree of inbreeding will be set as a fraction. The population size will originally be set as n where the actual size is 2^n, since n is required to specify the number of random bits used in choosing a potential parent from the population, and it is easier to produce 2^n from n (by shifting 1 up n places) than to produce n from 2^n. It could of course be set twice, in both forms, but where program parameters are to be changed from one run to another, there is much to be said for minimizing the number of changes which have to be made. The number of generations required will be set as one-tenth of the actual value, since generation counting will be associated with a form of output produced at ten-generation intervals.

The starting random number raises a question, since both fractional and integral random numbers will be required. One subroutine producing random fractions could be used, since these are strings of 31 random bits and random integers can easily be produced from them by masking. In practice, it is more satisfactory to have this done by the pseudorandom number subroutine, so that one does not have to bother about it when writing the program. Two subroutines will therefore be used, one producing integers and the other fractions, and each will require the initial specification in the main program parameters of a starting random number, different of course for each; **p0** and **p1** will be used for these.

As will be described in detail later, there will be two series of output. One will give a minimum of information each generation; the other will appear at ten-generation intervals and may take either or both of two forms—full population analysis and production of a population sample. Whether a particular form for the ten-generation output will be used or not will be determined by a preset parameter for which a value of zero will indicate that the corresponding form of output will not be used.

The program is designed to allow between but not during experiments different degrees of inbreeding and different population sizes. The object of using this program with a class of students is to compare the effect of differences in the breeding system on population structure and on rate of selection, so a number of experiments will normally be required. This raises a matter of administrative convenience if these experiments are to be performed in one session, as would often be the case. It would then be an advantage if the program did not need to be fed into the computer for each experiment. It would obviously be more convenient if, when a further experiment was to be performed, the main program substituted new parameters for those of the previous experiment and then proceeded directly to the next experiment without operator intervention. As will be seen later, there will be five parameters which will require substitution, and for the first experiment these will be in **p11** to **p15**. The five parameters for the second experiment will follow in **p16** to **p20**, those for the third in **p21** to **p25**, and so on as required. After the first experiment is finished, then if a second one is to be performed the contents of all the parameter stores from **p16** onwards are moved five locations forwards towards the start, so that **p11** to **p15** will now come to contain the parameters for the second experiment, **p16** to **p20** those for the third, and so on.

Since the total number of experiment parameters is variable between runs, according to the number of experiments, they should come at the end of the main program parameter list; definite locations could not be assigned to other parameters coming after them unless a store space of constant but possibly inconveniently large size were allotted to the experiment parameters. As will be seen later, **p0** to **p10** will be required for other parameters, which is why the experiment parameters do not begin until **p11**.

The number of separate experiments to be performed will also be set as a parameter (**p2** will be used) and transferred at the start of the program to a counter. There are plenty of counters available for the program, but care must be taken to see that there is no attempt to use the same one for any other purpose. Since this counter will be reduced by one for counting before the parameters for the next experiment are brought forward five places, the number of parameters which have to be moved will be five times the number in the counter. This operation is simple enough; if **M0** be the modifier, the contents of **p16 (M0)** are transferred to **p11 (M0)**, followed by incrementa-

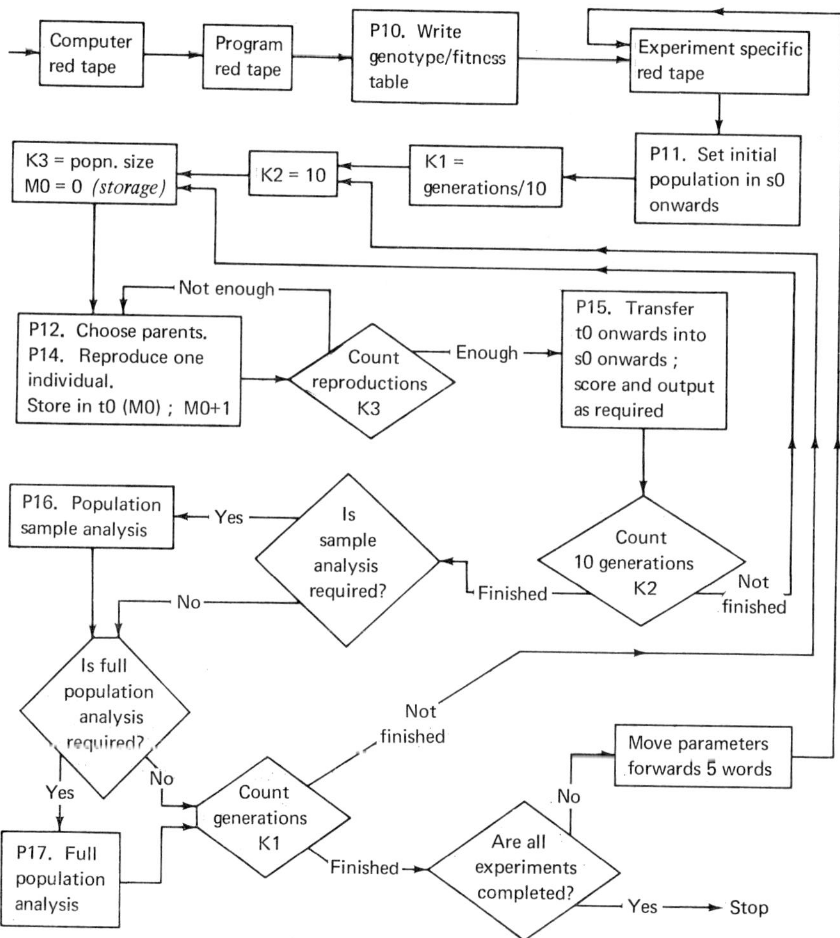

Figure 47. General flow diagram for experiment on selection in relation to the breeding system

tion of **M0** and counting. When all parameters have been moved, the program returns to the appropriate point near the beginning, and starts the new experiment.

The course of the experiment can most easily be described by means of a flow diagram, which is shown in Figure 47. To some extent, a flow diagram such as this cannot be produced in its final form right away, since some of its elements may not be known until all the subroutines are written; for this reason, parts of the figure are retrospective. In one way, it might have been a good idea to have produced a provisional flow diagram at this stage and a revised one later, but it was felt that there might be confusion between the two diagrams if this were done. Program specific subroutines are numbered from **P10** onwards, avoiding possible confusion with subroutines of the program described earlier in this chapter.

Of the major elements of the flow diagram, that simulating reproduction is the most complex, and will itself involve three subroutines (choosing parents, fitness testing, production of a zygote) in addition to those generating random numbers.

The various sections of the program may now be considered in turn. There may be some red tape operations required by the computer; as far as we are concerned, these are imaginary, and there is no point in specifying any. The program red tape will deal first of all with those parameters that will be variable from one run to another, but will be constant between experiments within any one run. These will be the starting random numbers which will need transferring to the pseudorandom number subroutines, the number of experiments which will require placing in a counter, and the phenotype fitness parameters if the genotype/fitness table is to be written by a subroutine, as we will suppose. Since the program is written on the assumption that the fitnesses will be the same for all experiments, the writing of the genotype/fitness table is essentially part of the program red tape, and the subroutine which writes it will use a phenotype/fitness table in **p3** to **p10** of the main program. Fitnesses may readily be changed between runs by altering the parameters specified for this table.

It would not be difficult to arrange for the fitnesses to be changed between experiments; the main program would then have to carry several phenotype/fitness tables, as well as indicators as to whether or not the genotype/fitness table required altering before the next experiment. Figure 47 would then be amended so that if the table required alteration, return to begin a new experiment would be to a point before the table writing subroutine **P10**, the necessary tests for this and any necessary movement of the new phenotype/fitness parameters in **P0** being carried out at the end of each experiment. The simpler view of constant fitness during a run has been taken to avoid excessive complication of the program.

The main program will next have to deal with experiment-specific parameters, some of which will need to be transferred (transformed if necessary) to one or more subroutines, since it is good practice to make the subroutines self-contained as far as possible. This allows independent amendment of main program and subroutines, should amendment be desired. At this stage the requirements for transfer will not be known precisely, and the red tape will not be written until after the subroutines have been written and the necessary information has become available, but it would be a good idea to allot now main program parameter addresses, so that they are known and the parameters more readily referred to as the subroutines are discussed and written. They will be as follows: degree of inbreeding—**p11**; number/10 of generations—**p12**; n, where 2^n = population size,—**p13**; sample size for population sample analysis (zero if none required)—**p14**; indicator for full population analysis (zero if not required)—**p15**.

Information as to requirements for main program action on these parameters will be accumulated and noted as we proceed with the description and programming of the subroutines; it would be a good idea if the reader listed these requirements as he reads on, just as he would have to if he were writing the program.

The main program will also have to take steps, either in its red tape or elsewhere, to ensure that in systems which are fully outbreeding or fully inbreeding time is not wasted in testing whether a chosen parent is to be selfed or crossed, since there will be no choice in the matter. This will be discussed later in the appropriate context.

The main program as a whole cannot sensibly be written until all the subroutines are completed, since its primary function is the organization of subroutine use by the full program.

P10. *Write Genotype/Fitness Table in* **P13**

The first subroutine to be considered is **P10**, which will set the genotype/fitness table in the fitness-testing subroutine **P13** from a phenotype/fitness table held in **p3** to **p10** of the main program, and those **p** stores will correspond respectively to the phenotypes **000**, **001**, **010**, **011**, **100**, **101**, **110** and **111**. Any phenotype used as a modifier of **p3** will direct the extraction of the relevant fitness.

The fitnesses may be assigned arbitrarily, but in the author's current version of his program they were calculated from fitnesses of 0.06, 0.75 and 0.94 for **001**, **010** and **100** respectively, that of **110** for example being 0.75×0.94.

The fitness of **000** appears to present a difficulty, since 1.0 is not permissible. But there is a different point which needs to be considered. Even at the beginning of the experiment (with the population constitution used here), over 40 percent of the individuals are phenotypically **000**, with maximum fitness, and this percentage will quickly increase under selection. To carry out a fitness test involves generation of a random fraction, and when there can only be one answer to the test this is a waste of time; it would be much better if **000** individuals could be recognized as such immediately and the test by-passed. This can be done, but not quite directly since during the experiment the phenotypes of the individuals are not determined. But we can do the next best thing by making the genotype/fitness table give a negative value for all individuals of phenotype **000** and for **P13** to test the sign of the extracted fitness before proceeding to the test. Much less time is wasted on carrying out the sign test on low fitness individuals than by carrying out the fitness test on fully fit individuals. The first address, **p3P0**, of the phenotype/fitness table used by **P10** will therefore be set as a negative number and not as 1.0.

Table writing subroutines have been discussed in Chapters 6 and 7, and **P10** need not be described in detail. Genotypes from 0 to 63 will be produced by adding 1 cyclically to a modifier originally set at zero, and so used to insert into **p1** to **p64** of **P13** parameters which have been read from **p3** to **p11** of **P0** by using the corresponding phenotypes as modifiers.

```
P10/1;
(0); K15=64; M15=0; (l.s. bits of M15 = genotype);
(1); M15→G; G→H; G down 3; G&H→G; (G = phenotype);
     G→M14; p3P0(M14)→G; G→p1P13(M15); M15+1;
     K15−1; J1K15≠0; p0→M15; J(M15);
```

For a situation without dominance, a routine for writing the genotype/fitness table would still be possible if the fitnesses of the whole genotypes could be derived as products of those of the individual genes taken independently (as was assumed in making the basic phenotype/fitness table for this programme). This routine would work from a table giving the fitness values for **AaBBCC, aaBBCC, AABbCC, AAbbCC, AABBCc** and **AABBcc**. It would use an LM for each locus followed by **bits** (as in the scoring subroutine **P15**) to set a modifier for extraction of the relevant fitness elements, and derive the fitnesses of the full genotypes by multiplication.

With interactions, or less simple relationships between genotypes and fitnesses, a table writing subroutine would be impracticable, and the genotype/fitness table would need to be written out in full as part of **P13**.

The genotype/fitness table having been set, the main program deals with the experiment-specific red tape and then comes to **P11**.

P11. *Set Starting Population*

This subroutine sets the starting population, which needs of course to be reset at the start of each subsequent experiment; in this program it will be identical for each experiment.

In the author's programs, the starting population had a very artificial genetic constitution, for the simple reason that evolutionary change cannot be effectively demonstrated unless a population is used which is going to show appreciable change; the same constitution will be assumed here.

At the beginning, for each gene the two alleles will be equally frequent (frequency 0.5) and the 27 possible genotypes will occur in the proportions to be expected on the basis of the independent inheritance of the three genes and completely random mating. It has been decided that the genotype is to be stored in the six l.s. bits of a word, and it can easily be shown that the numbers 0 to 63 when converted to binary will represent all possible genotypes in their correct proportions. (The reader who fails to see this should reflect that the numbers 0 to 7 in binary will represent all possible gamete genotypes, which are equally frequent since the gene frequencies are all 0.5, and that all possible zygote genotypes will, given random mating, be represented by combining each of the three-bit numbers 0 to 7 with each of them in turn, thus producing the octal numbers 0 to 77 once each, which is the same as producing the decimal numbers 0 to 63 once each.)

The population may then be built up from blocks of 64 6-bit numbers equivalent to the decimal numbers 0 to 63, the number of such blocks depending on the population size required, which must of course be 64 or a multiple of 64. To do this is quite simple. We begin with a zero word and store it in **s0**, add one to it and store the answer in **s1**, and continue adding one and storing it at the next address until the required population size has been achieved. But when we have reached 63, the addition of 1 makes 64, which is too large; an LM with a 6-bit mask will convert 64 to zero, and that will be stored in **s64** and the second block of individuals will be produced in the same way as the first, and so on. Strictly speaking, the LM only needs to be performed when the genotype becomes **64**. This would involve a count, and it is hardly worth the bother of setting up a count for this when the subroutine will be used once only in each experiment, and the LM operation requires only one instruction. It is simpler to perform it on every individual produced.

This subroutine is so straightforward that there is no need for a flow diagram. The population size 2^n, transformed from the parameter n in **p13P0**, will have been placed in **p1** of this subroutine by main program red tape.

```
P11/2;
(0); H=0; p1→K15; M15=0;
(1); H→s0(M15); M15+1; H+1; H&63; K15−1; J1K15≠0;
     p0→M15; J(M15);
```

(If it had been decided that the fitness should be looked up once and stored with the genotype, the subroutine would also have had to insert the fitnesses, otherwise the whole population would have zero fitness; this is easily overlooked.)

For any other starting constitution, the population may still be written by a subroutine which will either generate a block in some more complex way than simple unit addition, or may copy as many times as required a block of individuals set in its **p** stores and written down by the programmer as part of the subroutine.

After **P11**, the main program will set three counters, respectively at one-tenth of the number of generations for which the experiment is to run, at ten for the number of generations between major outputs, and at the population size for reproduction; it will then set at zero a modifier for temporary storage of progeny.

It then proceeds to the reproduction cycle, at each execution of which it will produce one individual for the next generation and store it in **t0** onwards.

The reproductive process is fairly involved, and is conveniently broken up into two principal subroutines, one of which (**P12**) will produce one (self) or two (cross) parents, dealing with fitness in so doing by using **P13**, and will be followed by the second (**P14**) which will effect gametogenesis and fertilization.

Where, as in this case, one subroutine (**P12**) contains another within itself (**P13**), it cannot be fully written until all the specifications for the inner subroutine are known. It is therefore good practice, as a general rule, to write the inner subroutine first; this is logically the same practice as writing the main program last. Before proceeding further with **P12**, therefore, we will produce the fitness testing subroutine **P13**.

P13. *Test Fitness of Parent*

Fitness testing has been dealt with in Chapter 7, so **P13** needs little description. The genotype to be tested will be delivered to **P13** in **F**, in which we will arrange that it is produced by **P12**. It will be copied by **P13** into **M14** and used as a modifier for the extraction of its fitness from the table in **p1** to **p64**. We have already decided that full fitness will be represented as a negative number, so after **P13** has extracted the appropriate fitness value, it will inspect the sign of this and exit directly to proceed with **P12** if it is negative. Otherwise, the extracted fitness value will be compared with a random fraction, and **P13** will either exit directly to proceed with **P12** if the random fraction does not exceed the fitness, or (failure exit) discard the chosen parent and return to make another choice if it does exceed the fitness.

A flow diagram is shown in Figure 48 and the program will be as follows, the genotype under test being in **F** at entry. **p1** to **p64** are not specified, since they are written by **P10**. **P13** uses **P202** which requires **G, H** and **M15**.

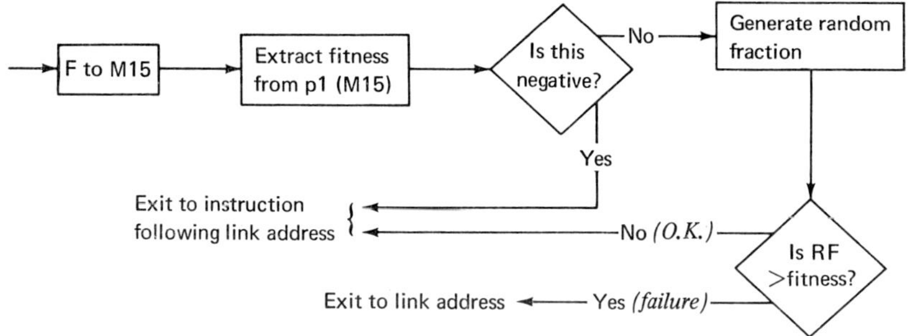

Figure 48. Flow diagram for fitness testing subroutine **P13**. The potential parent to be tested is supplied to it in **F** and is still in **F** at exit. The genotype/fitness table begins in **p1**

P13/65;
(0); F→M14; p1 (M14)→G; J1G<0; p0P202 = (j2); J0P202;
(*H* = *random fraction*);
(2); J3H>p1 (M14);
(1); p0→M15; M15+1; J (M15); (*O.K. exit*);
(3); p0→M15; J (M15); (*failure exit*);

P12. *Choose Parents*

We may now consider the production of parents by **P12**, and this will proceed as follows, a flow diagram being shown in Figure 49.

A prospective parent will be chosen at random from the population of size 2^n by using an n-bit random integer as a modifier. This parent, which will be in accumulator **F**, will be tested for fitness by **P13** and if the test fails will be rejected and a second choice made, and so on until the test is passed. **P12** has to deal with two possible re-entries from **P13**, failure and success, on each occasion that it uses the latter. Two successive instructions in **P12** will be required. The first of these (the address of which is set as the link) corresponds to fitness failure and will cause a jump back to choose another possible parent; the second will be the point of return when **P13** has increased the link by one (fitness O.K.) and will cause **P12** to proceed to the next step.

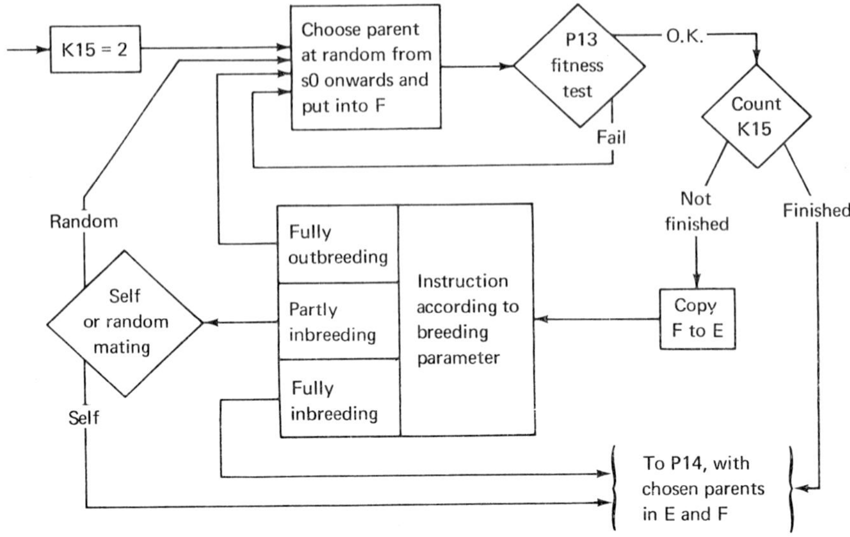

Figure 49. Flow diagram of **P12**, which chooses parents. Version I, which assumes the use of the device of instruction changing to by-pass unnecessary mating test in fully outbreeding or fully inbreeding populations

This section of the subroutine will be used a second time if a second parent is to be chosen at random. Since the same accumulator, **F**, must be used the second time, the parent first produced must at some time be copied into another accumulator, and **E** will be used for this; as a consequence, the first parent will temporarily at least be represented twice, in **E** and **F**. After the first parent has been successfully chosen, **P12** will then determine if the first parent is to be selfed. If so, then since **E** and **F** both already contain the same parent as required for selfing, the subroutine will exit at once and the program will proceed to **P14** for gametogenesis and fertilization. If not, then the subroutine will return to the parent-choosing sequence for a second parent, which will not be copied into **E**, and will exit with two different parents to **P14** as before. Occasionally, of course, especially in a small population, the same parent will be chosen the second time; but that does not matter and is certainly not worth taking steps to prevent.

With random mating, a count is necessary to ensure that the program leaves **P12** after the second parent is chosen.

The implementation by **P12** of the inbreeding parameter is quite simple. If the degree of inbreeding is a fraction f, then a random fraction is generated and the first chosen parent will be selfed if this random fraction does not exceed f; otherwise it will mate at random.

It is however worth introducing a complication which will save considerable time in certain circumstances. In systems which are entirely inbreeding or entirely outbreeding, and therefore in which there is never any choice, it would be a waste of time to carry out the breeding choice procedure. It would obviously be an advantage if those special circumstances could be readily recognized and the choice procedure avoided. There are several ways of doing this.

The most efficient is to make the main program red tape insert according to the value of the inbreeding parameter an instruction in the appropriate location of **P12** which will, after one parent has been produced, either allow the subroutine to proceed directly to the pseudorandom number subroutine, or will cause it either to exit directly with the first parent already duplicated in **E** and **F** (complete inbreeding) or to produce a second one without reference to a random test (complete outbreeding). This is the procedure which has been assumed in Figure 49. It is an operation which demands care, especially in computers where there may be more than one instruction per word or where instructions may be partly in one word and partly in the next. How it may be carried out will be considered after the subroutine has been produced. Meanwhile, **P12** is written with the critical instruction—which follows reference **(4)**—in the form for partial inbreeding.

The parameters **p1** and **p2** must be set by main program red tape, and are therefore not specified in the program which follows.

p1 = n, where 2^n = the population size
p2 = the inbreeding parameter

The subroutine will exit with the chosen parent(s) in **E** and **F**, where **P14** will expect to find them.

```
P12/3;
(0); K15=2;
(1); p1→M15; p0P200=(j2); J0P200; (H = random integer);
(2); H→M15; s0(M15)→F; p0P13=(j3); J0P13;
(3); J1; (fail, return to try again); K15−1; J6K15=0; F→E;
(4); p0P202=(j5); J0P202; (H = random fraction);
(5); J1H>p2; (breeding test, return for random mating);
(6); p0→M15; J(M15); (exit, with parents in E and F);
```

We may now consider the matter of short-circuiting the breeding system test. What has been referred to as the critical instruction is the one indicated by reference **(4)**, namely **p0P202 = (j5)**. If this were substituted by **J1**, this would lead to the choice of a second parent and correspond to full outbreeding. If it were substituted by **J6**, this would lead to exit with the first parent duplicated and correspond to full inbreeding. This substitution has to be carried out by the main program (according to the contents of its own **p11** which contains the breeding parameter), and it must therefore be able to find correct copies of all three instructions (since partial inbreeding may not be the requirement for the first experiment, and the instruction **p0P202 = (j5)** may need to be reinstated). This may be achieved by writing the three instructions, referenced, at the end of the subroutine (in which position they will never be obeyed). So **P12** will end

(7); p0P202 = (j5); (*p11P0* *positive, partial inbreeding***);**
(8); J1; (*p11P0* *zero, full outbreeding***);**
(9); J6; (*p11P0* *negative, full inbreeding***);**

The main program can extract these instructions quite simply, since it can obtain their absolute addresses in much the same way as a link is set. For example, the main program instruction **M0 = (j8P12)** puts the absolute address of the second of these three instructions into **M0; M1 = (j4P12)** puts the absolute address for substitution into **M1**; the pair of instructions **a0(M0)→A; A→a0(M1)** will effect the substitution. The only question is how the main program knows which instruction to substitute. If the parameter for full inbreeding is set as a negative number (it cannot be set as 1.0), then the three possibilities are easily recognizable according to whether the parameter is positive (partial inbreeding), zero (full outbreeding) or negative, and the appropriate part of the main store red tape would read as follows; we can assign reference numbers arbitrarily, so long as we keep note of them.

```
      p11→A; J2A=0; J3A<0; M0=(j7P12); A→p2P12; J4;
(2); M0=(j8P12); J4;
(3); M0=(j9P12);
(4); M1=(j4P12); a0(M0)→A; A→a0(M1);
```

Note that with this by-passing technique, transfer of the breeding parameter to **p2P12** is necessary only in the case of partial inbreeding, and it is appropriately included in the above sequence. Depending on the computer in use, this kind of programming device requires a certain amount of programming confidence.

An effective but less neat and more time-consuming method is for **P12** itself to distinguish the three possibilities each time it is used, directing the program through itself accordingly. For use in this way, the breeding parameter must be in an accumulator or a counter. To transfer it from **p2P12** or **p11P0** each time it is required by **P12** would waste time, and it is advantageous if it is transferred to a counter as part of the experiment's red tape and kept intact during the whole experiment; a counter is used because more counters are available than accumulators and one could not afford to keep an accumulator so tied up throughout a program. Reference to Figure 47 shows that **K0** to **K3** are used by the main program, so **K4** may be used here. The flow diagram for version II of **P12**, shown in Figure 50,

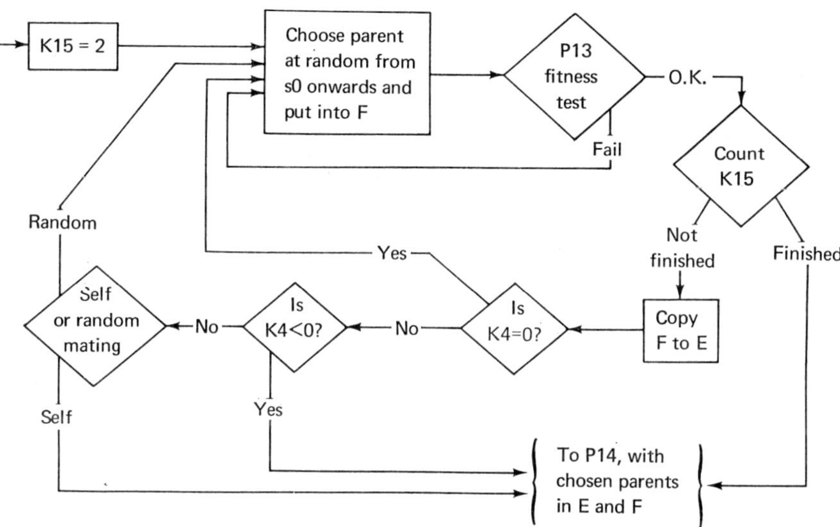

Figure 50. Flow diagram of version II of **P12**, which determines by-passing of mating test or not, according to the content of a counter **K4**, permanently set by the main program to contain the breeding parameter

should require no comments. As before,

p1 = n
p2 = the inbreeding parameter

and with the breeding parameter also in **K4**, the program for version II proceeds

```
P12/3;
(0); K15=2;
(1); p1→M15; p0P200=(j2); J0P200;
(2); H→M15; s0(M15)→F; p0P13=(j3); J0P13;
(3); J1; K15−1; J6K15=0; F→E;
     J1K4=0; J6K4<0; p0P202=(j5); J0P202;
(5); J1H>p2;
(6); p0→M15; J(M15);
```

P14. *Produce one offspring*

From **P12**, whichever version is used, the program (still within the reproduction loop) proceeds to **P14**, which produces one offspring from the parental genotypes (identical or not, as the case may be) delivered to it in **E** and **F**. **P14** should not need a detailed description. It is no more than a modified form of the generalized reproduction subroutine described in Chapter 6, reduced from 15 independent loci to three. A flow diagram is superfluous, that of the upper half of Figure 26 combined with Figure 27 being sufficient illustration, with the 15 and 2 of Figure 26 replaced by 3 and 26 respectively. As mentioned earlier, the random fraction subroutine **P202** will be used—the superfluous bits are irrelevant and **P202** is faster than **P200**. It is essential of course that the l.s. bits of the random fraction are reliably random; **P202** conforms to this requirement.

Beginning with the parents in **E** and **F**, **P14** delivers a zygote in **F**. It uses a link but has no parameters, and proceeds quite simply as follows. (Since the parents have no fitness values stored within them but contain genotype bits only, there are no subsequent complications.)

```
P14/1;
(0); D=0; ED down 3; FD down 3; D down 26; F up 3;
     E≢F→E; (genotypes rearranged in D and E);
     E→F; D&F→F; D≢E→D; p0P202=(j1); J0P202;
(1); D&H→D; D≢F→F; (F = zygote); p0→M15; J(M15);
```

On return to the main program, the new individual is stored in the next vacant position from **t0** onwards, and incrementation of the modifier completes the reproduction loop.

Although we will not write the main program in full until all the subroutines are written, it may help to give now a provisional version of the reproduction loop, keeping a record of the arbitrarily allotted reference numbers. At this stage, **p13** of the main program will contain the actual population size, its original content n having been transformed to 2^n. We will begin with the setting of the counter (**K3**, see Figure 47) for population size and end with the instruction counting the number of individuals produced.

```
      p13→K3; M0=0;
 (8); p0P12=(j9); J0P12;
 (9); p0P14=(j10); J0P14;
(10); F→t0(M0); M0+1; K3−1; J8K3≠0;
```

An Alternative to Temporary Storage

If a very large population is used and there is a shortage of storage space, an alternative to the use of a temporary store, requiring only 64 locations, may be considered. Simply, the zygote genotypes are counted and instead of a later transfer of individuals from temporary store to population store, the new population is constructed according to the genotype counts. If the count is made in **t0** onwards, **t0** to **t63** are cleared at the beginning of each generation, and then counting is by using each zygote genotype as a modifier to add one to **t0** (modified). The new population is produced at the end of reproduction for the whole generation by using the totals in **t0** to **t63** as counters for determining the numbers of each genotype from **000000** to **111111** respectively which are to be placed sequentially in **s0** onwards. This takes rather longer than the use of a temporary store, but not much longer, especially since the genotypes are going to be scored anyway and this may be done just as conveniently at this stage as later.

This method of course is generally applicable in similar situations, but is really only useful when few loci are involved. Five loci would require 1024 locations for counting and a population construction sequence would then involve 1024 separate counting operations, many of them with zero counters. It is not worth while anyway with small populations or when ample store space is available.

Output

The problems remaining are concerned primarily with output, and the first thing to be considered is the information which will be required about the population during the course of the experiment, and the intervals at which it will be required.

It was decided that after every generation, output should treat each gene separately and should give for each the numbers of each of its three possible genotypes, and the frequency of its recessive allele. This enables a quick demonstration of the degree of heterozygosity of each gene in each generation, and allows changes in gene frequency to be seen very readily. After every tenth generation there was additional output, giving or allowing an analysis of the population in terms of genotypes.

P15. *Individual Genes at each Generation, and Progeny Transfer*

We will first consider the generation by generation analysis of individual genes carried out by subroutine **P15**. The first operation is to score the numbers of all 64 possible binary representations of genotypes (64, not 27, because the computer distinguishes between **01** and **10**), and this can most conveniently be carried out as the new progeny are transferred from their temporary store in **t0** onwards into the population store in **s0** onwards. The scoring is carried out in locations **u0** to **u63**, which must first be cleared.

As each individual is transferred, a copy of the genotype is placed in a modifier, and one added to **u0** modified by this genotype. When the whole new population has been transferred and the scoring completed, **P15** inspects the scores in the following way.

A modifier is set at zero, and increased by one after each score in **u0** onwards has been inspected. The number in the modifier at the time of inspection is also, in binary, the genotype relevant to that score, and the

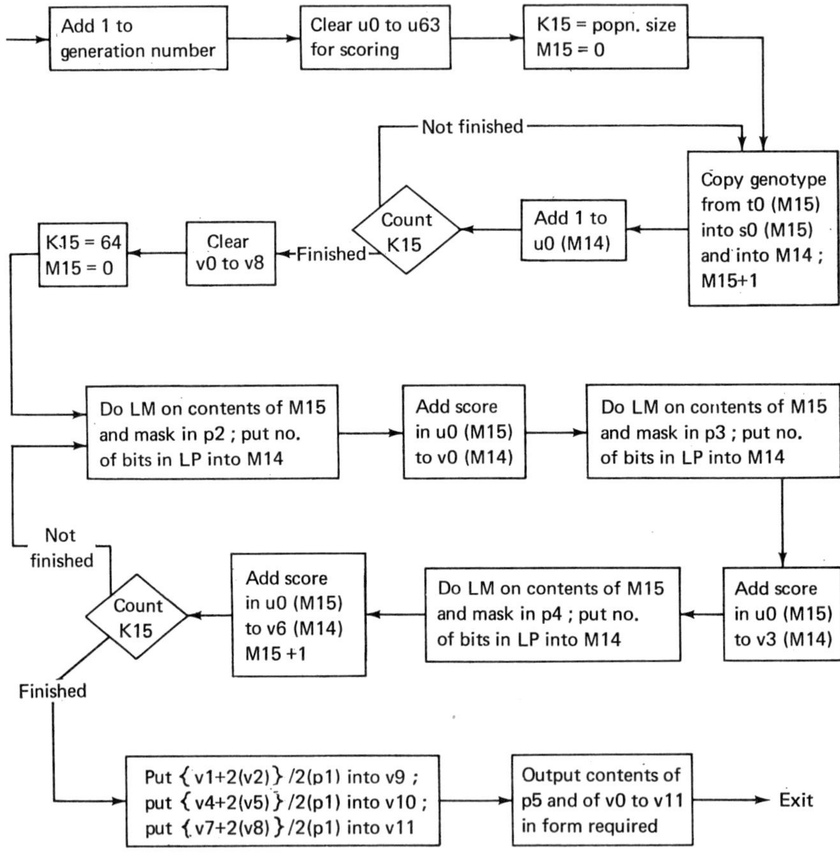

Figure 51. Flow diagram for **P15**, which transfers and analyses the new population each generation, and outputs generation number followed by the genotype and gene frequencies for each gene considered independently. The new population begins in **t0** and is transferred to **s0** onwards. **p1** = population on size; **p2, p3** and **p4** contain the gene masks **...100100**, **...010010** and **...001001** respectively; **p5** contains the generation number

performance of an LM with the properly located binary representation of the recessive homozygote of any gene will extract that portion of the genotype relevant to that gene only. This is followed by the operation **bits**, which will give a result which is zero for the homozygous dominant (**00**), one for the heterozygote (**01** or **10**), and two for the homozygous recessive (**11**). This result is then used as a modifier to add the score which has just been extracted from **u0** onwards to the relevant location which is accumulating the total score for that single-gene genotype. This operation is repeated for each of the other two genes. Thus if the three genes are **A/a**, **B/b**, **C/c**, the totals of **AA**, **Aa**, **aa** may be accumulated in **v0**, **v1**, **v2** respectively (**v0** plus 0, 1 or 2), those of **BB**, **Bb**, **bb** in **v3**, **v4**, **v5** (**v3** plus 0, 1 or 2), and similarly for **CC** etc. **v1** plus twice **v2**, divided by twice the population size, gives the gene frequency of **a**, and similarly for **b** and **c**, and these frequencies may be placed in **v9**, **v10** and **v11**.

P15 then has to arrange for the conversion of the contents of **v0** to **v11** (which will of course be in binary) to decimal, and their output in a convenient layout determined by the programmer. No attempt will be made to describe this operation; binary to decimal conversion subroutines are normally available as library subroutines, and generally incorporated in library output subroutines. The actual method of output will depend very much on the computer in use and its output equipment.

Theoretically, in determining the frequencies of the recessive alleles, the possibility of obtaining a value of 1.0 (which would cause overflow) should be considered, but unless a fitness approaching 1.0 is assumed for one of the homozygous recessives, the chance of any of the dominant alleles being eliminated is so small that it is not worth considering. If however the inclusion of a neutral gene as one of the three was a possible development, then steps would have to be taken to guard against this eventuality arising by random drift. This can be done either by conversion to floating point and doing floating point divisions; or by inspecting for overflow after division and if overflow has occurred expressing the gene frequency provisionally as a negative number. The latter can be recognized during the operations which carry out the conversions from binary to a form suitable for print-out, and will then be simply replaced by the decimal character sequence 1.0. We will ignore this eventuality.

It is helpful if the generation number can also be printed out, at the beginning of the line of frequencies. If **p5** is cleared at the beginning of every experiment, and increased by one each time **P15** is entered, then this will provide the generation number for output.

P15 is illustrated as a flow diagram in Figure 51. The program may be written as follows, the actual output section merely being indicated.

p1 = population size, inserted by main program red tape at the beginning of each experiment

p2 = the mask **...100100**
p3 = the mask **...010010**
p4 = the mask **...001001**
p5 = current generation number, does not require specification

```
P15/6;
0; 0; 8/44; 8/22; 8/11;
(0); p5+1; K15=64; M15=0;
(1); u0(M15)=0; M15+1; K15−1; J1K15≠0; (u0 to u63
     cleared);
     p1→K15; M15=0;
(2); t0(M15)→H; H→s0(M15); M15+1; H→M14;
     u0(M14)+1; K15−1; J2K15≠0;
     K15=9; M15=0;
(3); v0(M15)=0; M15+1; K15−1; J3K15≠0; (v0 to v8
     cleared);
     K15=64; M15=0; (M15 current genotype);
(4); u0(M15)→H; (H = score of current genotype);
     M15→G; G&p2→G; bits G; G→M14; H+v0(M14)→v0(M14);
     M15→G; G&p3→G; bits G; G→M14; H+v3(M14)→v3(M14);
     M15→G; G&p4→G; bits G; G→M14; H+v6(M14)→v6(M14);
     M15+1; K15−1; J4K15≠0;
     v2→H; H×2/1; H+v1→H; p1→G; G×2/1; H/G; H→v9;
     v5→H; H×2/1; H+v4→H; H/G; H→v10;
     v8→H; H×2/1; H+v7→H; H/G; H→v11;
     [output contents of p5, and v0 to v11];
     p0→M15; J(M15);
```

The reader will observe that there is some element of repetition in two sections of this subroutine, and may wonder why this has not been dealt with by a loop. The subroutine as written could be shortened by using a loop executed three times, but the writing would be a little involved and liable to error. It isn't really worth the bother, but it could be done most simply by running through the 64 scores three times, dealing with one gene at a time. The following amendment to the subroutine will serve this purpose it; replaces that portion of the subroutine program *after* the line beginning with reference **(3)**.

```
     K13=3; M13=0; M12=0; p1→G; G×2/1;
(4); K15=64; M15=0;
(5); M15→H; H&p2(M13)→H; bits H; H+M12→H; H→M14;
     u0(M15)→H; H+v0(M14)→v0(M14); M15+1; K15−1; J5K15≠0;
     v2(M12)→H; H×2/1; H+v1(M12)→H; H/G; H→v9(M13);
     M12+3; M13+1; K13−1; J4K13≠0;
     [output contents of p5, and v0 to v11];
     p0→M15; J(M15);
```

The triple pass through the scores would probably be preferred where no **bits** instruction was available. In that case, the following procedure is better than using a short **bits** routine or table look-up.

The result of the LM between full genotype and single recessive homozygote would be used directly as the modifier for the accumulation of the totals. Those for **Aa, aA, aa, Bb, bB, bb, Cc, cC, cc** would be accumulated in **v4, v32, v36, v2, v16, v18, v1, v8** and **v9** respectively, but **AA, BB** and **CC** would all indicate **v0** as the appropriate address for the accumulation of their totals. It would be simplest to complete the totals for one gene before dealing with the next, to avoid this difficulty, and this would mean passing through the scores three times. Rearrangement of the totals would also be necessary to get them into the appropriate locations for output.

It would be possible to accumulate the single-gene genotype totals directly as the organisms are transferred from the **t** stores to the **s** stores, doing the LMs with the three recessive homozygotes separately on each individual zygote genotype, and using the number of bits in each case as a modifier to indicate which location should have its contents increased by one. But except in a small population this would take appreciably longer.

P16. *Ten-generation Population Sample*

Two different forms of ten-generation output have been developed for this program. One of them, which will be described first, is of value only in the context of genetics teaching. The other is appropriate either to teaching or to research. Which is used in any experiment is determined by pre-set parameters.

The output form which was first developed was designed to simulate the experimental methods which would have to be employed by a geneticist investigating the genetical structure of a natural population. There, assuming complete dominance of the genes concerned, determination of the genotypes of phenotypically dominant individuals is not possible directly by inspection, but can only be achieved indirectly by test-crossing the individuals, or a suitable sample, and inspecting the test-cross families for segregation at the individual loci.

In the simulation of this procedure, a random sample is taken from the computer population, and the output gives for each individual its phenotype (which is all that would be recognizable for a real organism), and the phenotypes of the individuals of a family produced from it by test-crossing it with a triple recessive homozygote. If the test-cross family is kept to a reasonable size, all the information relevant to a single individual of the sample may appear on a single line of output, its own phenotype being kept distinct from those of its progeny by suitable spacing. It is then an easy matter for the class to score the test-cross families and deduce the parental genotypes (subject to the proviso that, for example, **Aa** × **aa** may occasionally give a misleading all **A** family).

For each individual in the sample, there are basically two operations: its random choice from the population, and the production of a test-cross family. The first is quite simple, and follows the usual procedure of generating a random integer in the range 0 to $2^n - 1$ for use as a modifier to make the random choice from the population. This choice will be made from the original members of the new generation in the **t** stores, which have been left unaltered during the process of copying them into the **s** stores. This allows the program to avoid sampling the same individual twice, and it does this by putting a negative number into the **t** store position of each individual as it is chosen; the sign of each sampled word from the **t** stores is inspected before any further action is taken, and any negative rejected. To treat the new population in the **s** stores in this way would produce complications, though not very serious ones.

The way in which the test-cross is simulated depends on the extent to which the details of the simulation are to be demonstrated to the class. If the simulation is to be fairly precise, then the sampled individual and a triple recessive homozygote may be sent as parents to **P14**, which will produce one offspring from them, and the phenotype of this will be determined; this is repeated as often as necessary for the desired size of test-cross family. The phenotype of the sampled individual, and those of its test-cross family, are determined and arranged for output.

However, as far as results are concerned, the triple recessive homozygous parent is redundant, since the phenotypes of the individuals of the test-cross family are the same as the genotypes of the gametes produced by the parent under test. Precise simulation may well be abandoned, without in any way affecting the validity of the results, so long as it is not desired to demonstrate the simulation of test-crossing. This has the advantage of allowing a neat trick. If, instead of sending the parent under test and a triple recessive homozygote to **P14**, we duplicate the former and send two copies of it to **P14**, exactly as though we were simulating a self-fertilization, we can obtain two gametes, equivalent to two test-cross progeny, for each entry to **P14**. This is because the individual produced by **P14** is a combination of two gametes which, though formed simultaneously, are in fact formed quite independently (that is, the genotype of one gamete has no relevance to that of the other, except that both must be possible derivatives from the tested parent). All that has to be done therefore to produce a test-cross family of ten individuals is to send the parent under test in duplicate to **P14** five times, extracting both resultant gametes on each occasion. Ten is a reasonable size for a test-cross family, and will be adopted here. There will be a very occasional family which will give from a heterozygote a misleading 10:0 segregation which should be 5:5; enough to be able to make the point to the class when the ten are recessives but not enough for the occasional ten dominants to affect the results seriously. If however the point about misleading segregations is to be impressed on the class, it is easy to amend the program to produce a smaller test-cross family of, say, eight or even six.

The form of output now requires consideration. The method used by the author was essentially that of the chromosome mapping program already described, different printer symbols being used to represent the recessive characters and + being used to represent the dominant character for each gene.

The conversion of a binary representation of the genotype of a gamete into a visual representation of a phenotype is quite easily effected in the usual way by using the genotype as a modifier to refer to an eight-word table of which each word contains in proper sequence the binary codes for the three characters required to represent the phenotype of the relevant gamete, plus a space for separation. Normally, six bits are enough to code a character, so the 32-bit word of XB1 has ample facility for coding three allele characters plus a space. The phenotype of the tested parent is treated in the same way.

```
(++        (++  (+:  (+:  (++  (+:  (++  (+:  (+:  (+:  (+:

+++        +++  +-+  (++  +++  (-+  (++  (-+  +-+  +++  (++

+++        +++  +-+  +-+  +-+  +-+  +++  +++  +-+  +++  +-+

+-+        (-+  +-+  +-+  +-+  +-+  +-+  +-+  (-+  +-+  +-+

(++        (++  (++  (++  (++  (++  (++  (++  (++  (++  (++

+++        +++  +++  +++  +++  +++  +++  +++  +++  +++  +++
```

Figure 52. Example of output of population sample analysis from **P16**. Each line gives the phenotype of the sampled individual on the left, and ten test-cross progeny. The recessive alleles **a**, **b** and **c** are supposed when homozygous to have phenotypic expression as (− and : respectively. It may readily be deduced that the genotypes of the sampled individuals are respectively **aaBBCc**, **AaBbCC**, **AABbCC**, **AabbCC**, **aaBBCC** and **AABBCC**

How these words containing the character bits are transformed by the computer into printed output will depend on the computer in use, and we will proceed no further than the arrangement, into 13 consecutive words, of the parental phenotype, extra separating spaces, ten offspring phenotypes and concluding CRLF, to be dealt with in a manner appropriate to the output devices of the computer. Figure 52 illustrates the form of the output. There is one small subtlety; in practice, the genotype of a triple recessive homozygote would be obvious and we would not bother to test-cross it; it will be arranged that the program will also skip the test-cross for any triple recessive in the sample.

Whether the 13 words for each test-cross are output immediately, or whether all test-cross families from one ten-generation analysis are accumu-

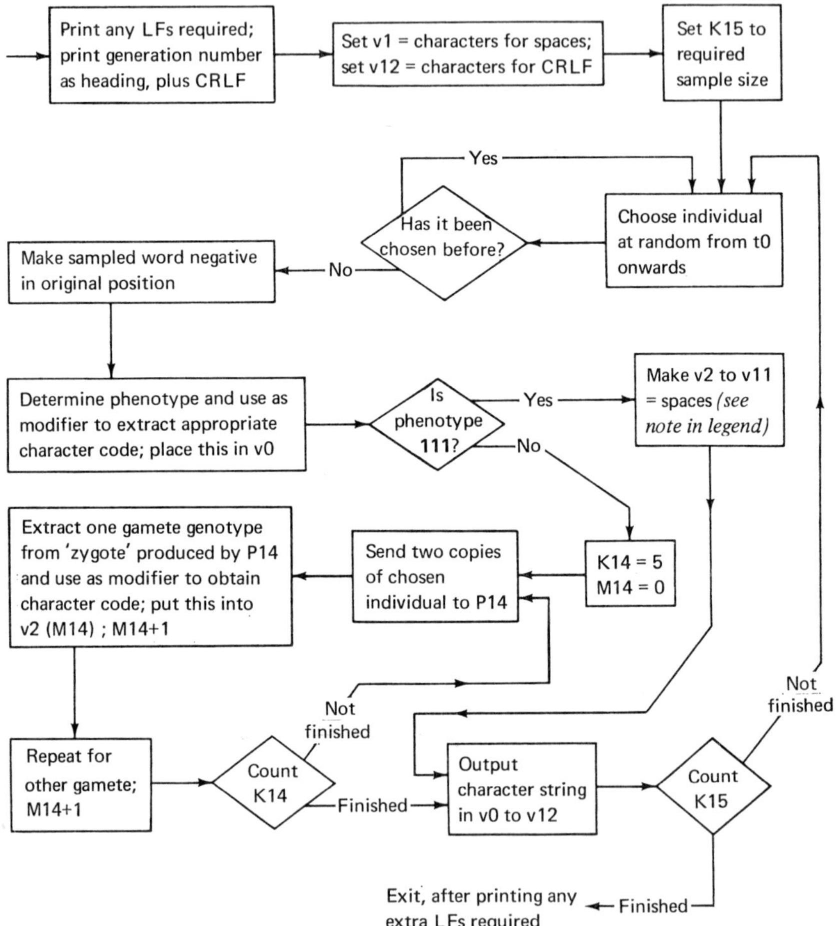

Figure 53. Flow diagram for **P16**, which outputs population sample analysis; see also Figure 52.
Note: if triple recessive, and output is via teleprinter, only **v0** and **v12** should be output; the box in the 'yes' line becomes 'output characters in v0 and v12', and the program will proceed directly to count **K15**

lated and then output, will depend on the output device used; with a line printer, the latter is probably better provided the programmer can write his own output procedures or has access to a really efficient one.

The following program and the flow diagram in Figure 53 assume that the test-cross family is output as it is completed.

p1 and **p2** will be set by main program red tape, and are not specified, being written as zeros.

p1 = n, 2^n being the population size
p2 = size of sample required
p3 to **p10** contain the character codes corresponding to the genotypes indicated in square brackets below, plus a space
p11 contains the character code for four spaces
p12 contains the character code for CRLF

```
P16/13;
0; 0; 0; [p3 to p12—000; 001; 010; 011; 100; 101; 110; 111;
spaces; CRLF];
(0); [print any extra LFs required, print GENERATION, plus generation
     number in p5P15, plus CRLF];
     p11→H; H→v1; p12→H; H→v12; p2→K15;
(1); p1→M15; p0P200=(j2); J0P200; (H = random number
     for sampling);
(2); H→M15; t0(M15)→C; (C = sampled individual); J1C<0;
     t0(M15) = −1; C→G; G down 3; G&C→G; (G = pheno-
     type);
     G→M15; p3(M15)→G; (G = characters); G→v0;
     J3G≠p10; (jump if characters are not those of triple recessive;
     if they are, the following instructions set rest of line as spaces);
     K14=10; M15=0; p11→G;
(4); G→v2(M15); M15+1; K14−1; J4K14≠0; J5;
(3); K14=5; M14=0;
(6); C→F; C→E; p0P14=(j7); J0P14; (F = two gametes);
(7); F→E; E&7; E→M15; p3(M15)→G; G→v2(M14); M14+1;
     F down 3; F&7; F→M15; p3(M15)→G; G→v2(M14);
     M14+1; K14−1; J6K14≠0;
(5); [output character string in v0 to v12];
     K15−1; J1K15≠0;
     [print any extra LFs required]; p0→M15; J(M15);
```

P17. *Ten-generation Full Population Analysis*

While the form of output produced by **P16** is useful in providing a closer approach to the reality of a genetical investigation of a population, it would be inappropriate for research rather than teaching; it might also be less suited to a particular teacher's requirements than a form of output which gave the actual frequencies (or numbers) of all possible genotypes in the whole population.

The relevant information for the latter is produced after each generation by **P15**, and when the program comes to the ten-generation output the relevant scores of all 64 possible binarily distinct genotypes will still be stored unaltered in **u0** to **u63**, since these locations have not meanwhile been touched again by the program. The main problems are in deciding on the layout of the output (the problem here is that of getting a three-dimensional array onto a two-dimensional page) and reducing the 64 binarily distinct genotypes to the 27 genetically distinct ones (for example, there are eight binary forms genetically equivalent to **111000**).

There are several ways of carrying out this reduction, and which one is used may be a matter of personal preference.

If *a*, *b*, *c* represent the numbers of **a**, **b**, **c** alleles in the genotype (determined as before by three masking operations each followed by **bits**), then the use

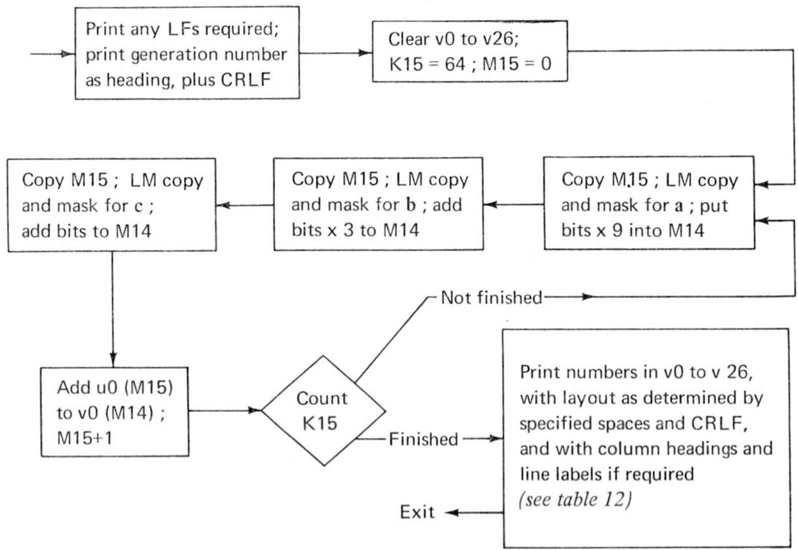

Figure 54. Flow diagram for **P17**, which outputs total population analysis

of $9a+3b+c$ as a modifier will accumulate the totals in a linear sequence corresponding to the genotype series ($9a+3b+c$ in brackets) **AABBCC** (0), **AABBCc** (1), **AABBcc** (2), **AABbCC** (3) ... **AAbbCC** (6) ... **AaBBCC** (9), **AaBBCc** (10) ... **aabbcc** (26). Although this is a somewhat cumbersome operation, it is one which will be performed only infrequently in any one run, and time is of little consequence. It has the advantage over simpler methods using table look-up that it is less liable to errors in table writing and punching.

The procedure is illustrated in the flow diagram of Figure 54, and leaves the totals for the various genotypes in such an order that, taking them in the same order and specifying spaces and CRLF as required, they could be output with the arrangement as in Table 12, the totals having been accumulated in **v0** onwards.

TABLE 12

The arrangement of the genotype totals from full population analysis, as produced in the **v** stores by **P17** in a sequence ready for output

	BBCC	**BBCc**	**BBcc**	**BbCC**	**BbCc**	**Bbcc**	**bbCC**	**bbCc**	**bbcc**
AA	v0	v1	v2	v3	v4	v5	v6	v7	v8
Aa	v9	v10	v11	v12	v13	v14	v15	v16	v17
aa	v18	v19	v20	v21	v22	v23	v24	v25	v26

If some other order is required for the layout, then it is not very difficult to rearrange the numbers or arrange that the output procedure deals with them in some other rational sequence.

If the output is required as frequencies rather than numbers, this is easily managed by shifting each total in the **v** stores up $31\text{-}n$ places—population size $= 2^n$, and up because the word will now represent a fraction and not an integer. This would require n to be set by the main program in this subroutine's parameters and the output section of the subroutine would begin with the integer to fraction conversion loop. Both number and frequency outputs can be produced in turn, simply by outputting the integers, converting them to fractions, and repeating the output process.

There is an advantage in printing out the genotypes as column headings and line labels as in Table 12, but there is a minor difficulty in that only capital letters are normally available for output. One could use + for the dominant and the appropriate (capital) letter for the recessive, so long as there is no danger of confusion; otherwise the recessive allele may be represented by its phenotypic character, as in **P16**.

The binary character codes for the headings, and those for extra spaces and CRLF, will be carried in the **p** stores of this subroutine, 16 locations being required. This will be discussed in more detail after the subroutine has been written out.

With the genotype totals in **u0** to **u63**, and **p1** to **p3** carrying the gene masks **100100, 010010** and **001001**, the subroutine is as follows.

```
P17/20;
0; 8/44; 8/22; 8/11; [p4 to p19 as described later];
(0); [print any extra LFs required, print GENERATION plus generation
     number in p5P15, and CRLF];
     K15 = 27; M15 = 0;
(1); v0(M15) = 0; M15+1; K15−1; J1K15 ≠ 0; (v stores
     cleared);
     K15 = 64; M15 = 0; (M15 also = current genotype);
(2); M15→H; H&p1→H; bits H; G = 9; G×H; H→M14;
     M15→H; H&p2→H; bits H; G = 3; G×H; H+M14→M14;
     M15→H; H&p3→H; bits H; H+M14→M14;
     u0(M15)→H; M15+1; H+v0(M14)→v0(M14); K15−1;
     J2K15 ≠ 0;
     [output contents of v0 to v26, with spaces and CRLF as required
     for layout];
     p0→M15; J(M15);
```

The layout of Table 12, with headings and line labels, can be organized by a fairly simple routine. We will assume that in the headings and line labels the dominant alleles are to be represented by + and the recessives by letters, which will have to be capitals. The characters for the headings are stored consecutively in **p4** to **p16** as follows, *s* representing a space, and CRLF carriage-return line-feed: *sssss*; *s*++++; *s*+++C; *s*++CC; *sss*; *s*+B++; *s*+B+C; *s*+BCC; *sss*; *s*BB++; *s*BB+C; *s*BBCC; CRLF. **p17** to **p19** will be: ++; +A; AA. These will all be output directly.

The integers in **v0** onwards will be sent to an imaginary subroutine via accumulator **H** for conversion to characters, and each will be output in five characters including one or more spaces at the m.s. end, thus occupying the same width as each heading.

The following sequence of instructions and square-bracketed pseudo-instructions replaces the square-bracketed portion at the end of **P17** as printed above.

```
     [output CRLF and characters in p4 to p16];
     K14 = 3; M14 = 0; M13 = 0;
(3); [output characters in p17(M13)]; M13+1; K13 = 3;
```

(4); [output 3 spaces]; **K12 = 3**;
(5); **v0(M14)→H**; **M14+1**; [print **H**]; **K12−1**; **J5K12 ≠ 0**;
K13−1; **J4K13 ≠ 0**;
[output CRLF]; **K14−1**; **J3K14 ≠ 0**;
[output extra LFs if required];

The choice of the form of ten-generation output may be determined by using programs which differ in whether they have **P16** or **P17**. It is neater to have one program incorporating both, and to determine which is used by a preset parameter in the main program. It would also be possible to have two preset parameters relating respectively to **P16** and **P17** and determining use or non-use; **P16** does not touch the **u** stores, so no difficulty arises on that account, and this is the version we shall use.

This completes the program, apart from counting to see whether the run has proceeded far enough, and we may now proceed to write the main program.

The Main Program

This is really little more than initial red tape followed by stringing the subroutines together. It will be assumed that version I of **P12** is used; this will require main program insertion of the appropriate instruction at reference **(4)** in **P12**.

The program red tape has already been described. The experiment-specific red tape has to carry out the following.

The inbreeding fraction (**p11**) has to be placed in **p2P12** unless it is 1.0 or zero, and action has to be taken on the instruction for reference **(4)** of **P12** according to the value of **p11**.

n (**p13**) has to be placed in **p1 P12** and **p1 P16**; it has then to be converted to 2^n and that value placed in **p13** (replacing n), **p1 P11** and **p1 P15**.

The sample size (**p14**) requires to be put into **p2P16**. This (and n to **p1 P16**) would appear to be redundant if **P16** is not to be used, but it is as quick to put it there as to test whether it is needed.

The generation number has to be set at zero in **p5P15**.

With the red tape requirements in mind, and referring to the flow diagram in Figure 47, we come to the program itself. In the **p** store specifications, r_1 and r_2 are the starting random numbers; e is the number of experiments to be performed; b_1 b_2 etc. are the degrees of inbreeding in experiments 1, 2 etc.; g_1 g_2 etc. are similarly the number/10 of generations required; n_1 n_2 etc. are the population parameters where the actual population size is 2^n; s_1 s_2 etc. are the sample sizes (zero if **P16** is not required); f_1 f_2 etc. are 1 or 0 according to whether **P17** is required or not.

```
P0/5e+11;
s/2^n; t/2^n; u/64; v/27;
    r1; r2; e; -1; .06; .75; .045; .94; .0564; .705; .0423;
    (p3 to p10 = fitness parameters); b1; g1; n1; (eventually 2^n); s1;
    f1; (p11 to p15 = experiment parameters); b2; g2; n2; s2; f2; b3;
    etc.
 (0);  [computer red tape];
       p0→A; A→p1P200; p1→A; A→p1P202; p2→K0;
       p0P10=(j1); J0P10; (program red tape completed);
 (1);  p11→A; J2A=0; J3A<0; M0=(j7P12); A→p2P12; J4;
 (2);  M0=(j8P12); J4;
 (3);  M0=(j9P12);
 (4);  M1=(j4P12); a0(M0)→A; A→a0(M1); (instruction in P12
       set);
       p13→A; A→p1P12; A→p1P16;
       A→M0; A=1; A up(M0); A→p13; (p13 now 2^n);
       A→p1P15; A→p1P11;
       p14→A; A→p2P16; p5P15=0;
       [print inbreeding fraction]; (end of experiment red tape);
       p0P11=(j5); J0P11; (set population);
 (5);  p12→K1;
 (6);  K2=10;
 (7);  p13→K3; M0=0;
 (8);  p0P12=(j9); J0P12;
 (9);  p0P14=(j10); J0P14; (F = zygote);
(10);  F→t0(M0); M0+1; K3-1; J8K3≠0;
       p0P15=(j11); J0P15;
(11);  K2-1; J7K2≠0;
       p14→A; J12A=0; p0P16=(j12); J0P16;
(12);  p15→A; J13A=0; p0P17=(j13); J0P17;
(13);  K1-1; J6K1≠0;
       K0-1; J14K0≠0; STOP;
(14);  K0→A; B=5; B×A; A→K1; (K1 = 5e); M0=0;
(15);  p16(M0)→A; A→p11(M0); M0+1; K1-1; J15K1≠0;
       (move experiment parameters up 5 places);
       J1; (return to start new experiment);
```

If version II of **P12** is used, then the four lines beginning at reference (1) are replaced by

```
(1);  p11→A; A→p2P12; A→K4;
```

In the program as given, the inbreeding fraction is printed out at the start of each experiment. There is something to be said for printing it at the head of each sequence of ten genotype and gene frequency outputs, and at the head of each 10-generation output. This reduces the possibility of confusion if the output of one experiment is dismembered for distribution among a class of students. Alternatively, an experiment may be given a key number, and that printed as suggested.

CHAPTER 10

Algebraic Simulation

Although this book concentrates deliberately on the simulation of populations through the digital simulation of the genotypes of the individual organisms composing them, some account must be given of algebraic simulation, since there are certainly situations where such a technique may be very appropriate and if methods can be found of overcoming its principal drawbacks it could become used more widely and with greater fidelity to biological systems.

It is not proposed to say very much about the derivation of algebraic expressions by which genetical or evolutionary systems may be represented. In this field, the author's experience is as limited as his ability, and there are many people more qualified mathematically, and perhaps biologically, than he.

The dangers inherent in algebraic simulation have been referred to in Chapter 2. The most serious of these is the temptation to indulge in sophisticated mathematical techniques which, while they may (mathematically speaking) have considerable aesthetic merit and expertise, may at the same time fail for various reasons to represent with sufficient fidelity the biological situation. The speed of a computer not only allows, but encourages, that kind of mathematical complexity which may not only become master of the biological element in the system but which is also so far beyond the comprehension of most biologists that they are unable to check for themselves the validity of the algebra as a representation of the biology.

Yet, in a sense, the speed of the computer reduces the necessity for the use of sophisticated mathematical techniques in 'simplifying' the algebraic treatment. If a genetical system can be represented by a number of simple algebraic expressions or equations, all interconnected in a complex and perhaps at first glance confusing way, then a computer can deal with these piecemeal, though of course this may require intricate and patient organization through the programming. Simplification of such a system to one or a few complex expressions may make programming easier (though the amount of preceding mathematical work may be greatly increased) and save computer time, but unless it is done with absolutely no change in the interpretation of the biology of the system and in a way which readily allows an inspection of its validity, it is better not done at all. Striving for elegance and simplicity is natural enough for a mathematician, but it seems possible that sometimes at least its application to algebraic simulation of a biological system could involve more work than the direct programming of an unsimplified system. Computer programmers are equally liable to the temptation to strive for elegance; the author once spent several happy programming hours in minimizing the time wasted during a program in reading from the drum of a Ferranti Pegasus computer to the computing store, an exercise which saved 20 minutes of computing time in the days when ample computing time was available; his satisfaction with his technical expertise was matched only by its practical futility.

Where mathematical refinement does not reduce the validity of a simulation, it does no harm. But where there is any loss of validity, or any doubts about this, then it is positively objectionable. If it is to be of any value, the development of algebraic simulation must proceed along the lines of using the computer as a means by which mathematical refinement may be avoided and the situation simulated in a piecemeal manner.

Stochastic Transformation

An algebraic simulation of a genetical system, whether refined or not, is primarily deterministic and the basic problem which has to be faced is to transform this simulation into a stochastic one. It is surprisingly difficult to find an efficient solution to this problem, since except in fairly simple situations the transformation consumes so much time that the apparent advantage of the algebraic method, its speed, may be very largely lost.

The problem has already been stated in Chapter 2, but will be restated in a simple form for more detailed consideration. Imagine a system in which two genotypes **R** and **S** are involved, having in one specified generation frequencies r and s $(r+s = 1)$. We produce an algebraic simulation of the genetics of the situation which allows the calculation of values r_1 and s_1 for the genotype frequencies in the next generation. This is a deterministic solution, and r_1 and s_1 are the frequencies which would be obtained in an infinitely large population. Real populations are not infinitely large, and may often be very small. The solution which we require is a stochastic one which would have some other values r_1' and s_1' which might have occurred by chance in a finite population of a stated size when the deterministic expected frequencies were r_1 and s_1. What is required is a procedure which would, over a large number of occasions when the expected frequencies were r_1 and s_1 produce various values of r_1' and s_1' in frequencies distributed according to the rules of statistics.

We may illustrate the problem by considering this over-simple situation further, and show how it might be dealt with *in that particular situation.* Suppose we have a population of eight individuals and that deterministic calculation leads to the expectation of equality in numbers, four **R** and four **S** ($r = s = 1/2$). In fact, we know that we might get any assortment from eight **R** and no **S** to no **R** and eight **S**, and that the likelihood of any particular assortment is given by the expansion of $(\mathbf{R}/2+\mathbf{S}/2)^8$, in which for each item in the expansion the exponents of **R** and **S** would indicate their numbers in the population, and the coefficient would indicate the likelihood of obtaining that constitution.

We can therefore quite easily carry out in this particular case a stochastic transformation by random reference to a 256-word table, each word of which contains (suitably packed) two integers totalling eight and corresponding to an **R**:**S** ratio, the nine possible ratios occurring in the table with frequencies equalling their expectations as indicated above; that is, 0:8 would appear once, 1:7 eight times, 2:6 twenty-eight times, and so on.

A very little thought will show that this technique has limitations. An obvious one is population size. Eight would be ridiculously small for almost any simulation experiment, except where the study of small populations was the deliberate object of the investigation. But for each increase in population size by one individual, a doubling in size of the table of ratios is required. However, this is not so serious as it might seem, because a population can easily be built up by multiple random references to a small ratio table. Thus the sum of 128 ratios randomly chosen from the 256-word table would produce a population of 1024. If the population size were a multiple of ten, then 100 references to a larger table based on the expansion of $(\mathbf{R}/2+\mathbf{S}/2)^{10}$ would serve, but that table of course would occupy 1024 words. However, packing could reduce the table size at the cost of increase of time required for reference to the table.

A much more serious difficulty, which to the author with his rather limited knowledge of statistics appears to be severe, arises when the two genotypes are expected in some ratio other than equality, that is when $r \neq s \neq 1/2$. The ratio table now required for a population (or population fraction) of eight individuals corresponds to the expansion of $(r\mathbf{R}+s\mathbf{S})^8$ and will require many more than 2^8 words unless there are substantial rounding approximations in the ratio frequencies. During the course of an evolution experiment the values of r and s will change, and the program would require a separate table for each possible expected ratio. It is completely impracticable for all possible tables to be stored with the program. It would certainly be possible for the appropriate ratio frequency table to be produced at each generation by calculation of the appropriate expansion once the value of r had been calculated. This table might be quite large unless there were rather drastic rounding approximations; such approximations would not necessarily be objectionable since inexactitudes would probably tend to even out over many generations.

A logical development of this technique would be to consider a population fraction of one individual, and to produce that fraction as often as the number of individuals in the population. This requires no calculation of a table—it does not even require a table; it merely requires comparison of r with a random fraction. This is in fact a simple form of the procedure described later in the chapter for dealing with multi-class populations, but it is of course slow in that it requires as many random fractions as individuals in the population.

TABLE 13

The expected frequencies of the various **R**:**S** ratios to be expected in a population of 16 individuals when the deterministic ratio is calculated to be 0.71**R**:0.29**S**

R	S	
16	0	0.00416998
15	1	0.02725167
14	2	0.08348224
13	3	0.15912578
12	4	0.21123388
11	5	0.20706870
10	6	0.15505849
9	7	0.09047678
8	8	0.04157472
7	9	0.01509442
6	10	0.00431573
5	11	0.00096151
4	12	0.00016364
3	13	0.00002056
2	14	0.00000180
1	15	0.00000010
0	16	0.00000000

There is however a quite different approach to the problem and this also can probably best be illustrated with reference to an example. Imagine a population of size 16, and an expected value for r of 0.71. Then the probabilities for the different possible ratios are derived from the expansion of $(0.71\mathbf{R}+0.29\mathbf{S})^{16}$, and are shown in Table 13. The expected ratio of **R**:**S** is 11.36:4.64; the actual numbers have to be integral. As will be shown, we need to work from the most likely ratio, and this is 12**R**:4**S** which is expected to occur with a frequency of 0.21123388. If we now generate a random fraction, then the probability of this being less than 0.21123388 is of course 0.21123388. So we generate a random fraction and subtract 0.21123388 from it. If the answer is negative, our population will become 12**R**+4**S**. If not, then we subtract successively the expected frequencies of 11**R**:5**S**, 13**R**:3**S**, 10**R**:6**S**, 14**R**:2**S** and so on (remembering that we get to 16**R**:0**S** before we have finished in the other direction) until we get a negative answer; we take as the new population ratio the one whose frequency subtraction produced that negative. The alternation in direction of deviation from expectation means that we are subtracting the expected frequencies approximately in order of magnitude, and thereby tending to minimize the number of subtractions which have to be made; it is important to realize that this does not affect the validity of this procedure as a random process, provided the pseudo-random fraction is reliable.

Taking a numerical example in the situation described, suppose we generate a random fraction 0.92174031. Subtracting 0.21123388 from this we get a positive answer, 0.71050643, so we do not take 12**R**:4**S** as our new population. Successive subtractions of 0.20706870, 0.15912578, 0.15505849, 0.08348224 and 0.09047678 still leave a positive answer, 0.01529444, but now the further subtraction of 0.02725167 gives a negative answer and so the new ratio for our population is 15**R**:1**S**.

There is no reason why this method should not be used for much larger populations. It does not take so long to operate as might be supposed. For a population size of a thousand and a value for r of 0.5, then as often as not the number of subtractions required will be less than 22; as many as 62 would be required less than once in twenty times, and 105 subtractions would be needed with a frequency of about once in a thousand. For other values of r the average number of subtractions would be less.

A problem which will have occurred to the reader is that different values of r will require different versions of Table 13, and that for a population of a thousand the table will require 1001 entries, and these will have to be calculated. In fact, this problem can be avoided, since such tables require neither complete calculation, nor even temporary storage.

Consider the situation in which the deterministic expectation for a population of size n is $r\mathbf{R}:(1-r)\mathbf{S}$, as before. Then the frequencies of the possible assortments of **R** and **S** are given by the expansion of $\{r\mathbf{R}+(1-r)\mathbf{S}\}^n$. For the expected ratio, the expected numbers of **R** and **S** are rn and $(1-r)n$ respectively, and we will suppose that the nearest integral approximations are $(n-j)$ and j respectively. Then the term in the expansion which will correspond to the first subtraction we would wish to make is that containing $\mathbf{R}^{(n-j)}\mathbf{S}^j$, and this is the $(j+1)$th term which is

$$[n!/j!(n-j)!]\,[(r\mathbf{R})^{(n-j)}\{(1-r)\mathbf{S}\}^j].$$

The probability of the population actually being $(n-j)\mathbf{R}:j\mathbf{S}$ is therefore $[n!/j!(n-j)!]\,[r^{(n-j)}(1-r)^j]$, and this is the first value to be subtracted from the random fraction.

This would appear to involve a very considerable calculation, but the $n!/j!(n-j)!$ part of the expression can be dealt with by the production, at the beginning of the program, of a table giving all values of this for all values of j up to and including n; each value may readily be calculated from the preceding one, since $n!/(j+1)!(n-j-1)! = n!/j!(n-j)! \times (n-j)/(j+1)$. It is important during this process (and during all subsequent calculations) to carry the calculation to ample significant figures to minimize the possible effect of cumulative rounding errors.

The $r^{(n-j)}(1-r)^j$ part of the expression may also be calculated fairly quickly if a suitable subroutine is written, generalized for any value of j; obviously, one does not actually need to perform $n-j-1$ multiplications in order to obtain $r^{(n-j)}$.

A difficulty which arises is that of scale. If n is large, then some values of $n!/j!(n-j)!$ will be very large indeed, and some values of $r^{(n-j)}(1-r)^j$ will be very small indeed. For example, if $n = 1000$ and $r = 0.5$, then $r^{(n-j)}(1-r)^j = 0.5^{(1000)}$. In fixed point working, this will involve the use of scaling factors. In floating point, overflow and underflow may occur, since there are limits to the range of numbers which can be expressed in floating point as a hardware operation, depending on the computer in use. Special action may therefore have to be taken by the programmer to deal with this; a special floating point subroutine would be one possible answer.

If $[n!/j!(n-j)!]\,[r^{(n-j)}(1-r)^j]$ is calculated, and leaves a positive answer on subtraction from the random number, then the stochastic transformation subroutine must continue subtracting frequencies calculated from alternately higher and lower values until a negative answer is obtained. This would be done by having two internal subroutines, one for increasing and one for decreasing values of j, these being used alternately.

The new value for the factorial part of the frequency expression is easily obtained from the appropriate location in the table of $n!/j!(n-j)!$. The new value for $r^{(n-j)}(1-r)^j$ is obtained for increasing values of j by multiplying by $(1-r)/r$, and for decreasing values of j by multiplying by $r/(1-r)$.

Clearly, this method of stochastic transformation in a system in which r is variable is complicated, requires careful programming, and is not quick. But for large populations it would be significantly faster to reproduce a new population in this way than it would be to reproduce one of the same size in a program using digital genotype simulation of individual organisms. But its practical application is severely limited because it is directly relevant only to situations with two possible genotypes, and these are obviously uncommon. Examples would be where all but two genotypes were lethal, where the gene concerned was relevant to the breeding system, or where haploid organisms are being dealt with.

It could be applied to a 2-class gamete pool. If for the gametes of any one sex the expected ratio of the two classes over the population is calculated, an observed ratio for the n gametes which will participate in the formation of the next generation may be produced by this method of stochastic transformation. The same may be repeated for the gametes of the other sex (often, but not necessarily, with the same expected ratio). This gives two stochastic gamete pools, and they may be combined rapidly but deterministically by simply multiplying together their observed ratios, or the full stochastic treatment may be given by combining non-algebraically the two pools at random. The latter is a time-consuming procedure, especially if the two allelic classes are of nearly the same size, but one way of doing it is as follows.

The n eggs (say) are arranged in the store in a random sequence, and are combined with the sperm which are notionally arranged (they need not be actually arranged) in a non-random sequence (one random sequence is enough). The random arrangement of the eggs may be produced as follows. n consecutive store locations are made zero; using a random number in the range 0 to $n-1$ as a modifier, as many non-zero numbers as there are eggs in the smaller class are placed at random in zero locations; if on any occasion the random number indicates a non-zero location further tries will be made until a zero location is found. The outcome of this will be a random sequence of n locations in which the numbers of zeros and non-zeros are equal to the numbers in the two classes among the eggs. If the numbers in the two classes of sperm are r and $n-r$, then from the numbers of zeros and non-zeros in the first r locations of the randomized egg store, and their numbers in the last $n-r$ locations, a stochastic ratio for the three zygote genotypes among the n individuals of the new generation may easily be derived.

The method described for a 2-class population could be applied to a 3-class population in the following way, but this would seem to be more of theoretical interest than practical usefulness. Suppose we have a population in which three genotypes **R S T** are expected with frequencies $r\ s\ t$ respectively $(r+s+t=1)$. Then we could begin by treating this as a 2-class population, **R** and (**S**+**T**) with expected frequencies r and $(s+t)$, the latter of course being $(1-r)$. By using the method described previously we can arrive at a number for **R**. Suppose this to be m and the population size to be n. We then repeat the process for a population of size $n-m$ consisting of **S** and **T** individuals expected with frequencies of $s/(s+t)$ and $t/(s+t)$ respectively, by putting $s/(s+t)$ for r and $(n-m)$ for n. This will give us a value for the number of **S** individuals, whence **T** is derived by subtraction.

This process could in fact be carried out for any number of classes, dealing with one at a time and with a residual population which gets smaller at each operation. The drawback to this approach is that after the first class (**R** in the example above) has been dealt with, subsequent, operations become much slower because there is no longer available a table comparable to that for $n!/j!(n-j)!$, since it is only for the first operation that the working population size is constant and known (n). $(n-m)$ is neither known in advance nor constant, and it would obviously be impracticable to construct (and store) at the beginning of the run of a program a table of $(n-m)!/j!(n-m-j)!$ for every possible value of $(n-m)$. We would be faced with the complete initial calculation of $[(n-m)!/j!(n-m-j)!][(r')^{(n-m-j)}(1-r')^{j}]$ at each generation (r' being the expected frequency of each successive class in the residual population). Possible, but time-consuming.

The author's excuse for dealing at length with a method of such limited use and applicability is that the problem of a reliable and fast method of stochastic transformation is an important one, and if satisfactorily solved it could lead to an extensive development and application of algebraic techniques of simulation which, it must be remembered, have except in this one respect the considerable advantage over digital techniques of speed, especially with large populations. It seems to the author that the method described suggests a way in which this problem might usefully be tackled, perhaps successfully by some-one better equipped algebraically than himself.

What we would like to have, of course, is a method of generating random fractions distributed not with uniform density but having some other specified distribution over the range from 0 to 1.0. Since random fractions as generated have uniformly dense distribution, the problem becomes one of transforming such fractions into random fractions with some other pattern of distribution. This is discussed by Buslenko and Sragovich (1964), and will only be touched on briefly here.

If the required distribution pattern is capable of mathematical expression as a density function, then in principle the problem is capable of solution, sometimes fairly easily, sometimes very laboriously.

A normal distribution may be obtained easily enough by generating a number of random fractions and taking their mean value. As the number of random fractions used increases, the distribution of their mean about 0.5 rapidly approaches normality, and it can be shown that the standard deviation of this distribution is $\sqrt{(1/12N)}$, where N is the number of random fractions used. Since the standard deviation of the frequency of one class in a two-class family of size n expected to segregate in a 1:1 ratio is $\sqrt{(1/4n)}$, then the frequency distribution of the ratios obtained from such a segregation can be simulated with the correct standard deviation by the distribution of the mean value of $n/3$ random fractions. A little thought will show that a stochastic transformation of a deterministic ratio of $n/2:n/2$ in a family or population of size n can be obtained by generating $n/3$ random fractions and multiplying their sum by three, which will give the number of individuals in one class arbitrarily decided beforehand, that of the other being obtained by subtraction.

Unfortunately, this method is only practicable for two classes expected in a 1:1 ratio, since the problems of calculation become very much greater when the required mean value for the stochastic fraction is no longer 0.5. Consequently the technique of transforming the distribution pattern of random fractions is of very limited use in the stochastic transformation of calculated genotype ratios.

On the other hand, it may be useful in producing generation to generation variability in factors involved in the genetical or evolutionary system under investigation. For example, in the simulation of models involving mixed selfing and random mating, Jain and Marshall (1968) used various transformations of uniformly distributed random fractions in order to treat outcrossing rate and selective values of homozygotes stochastically. It is worth noting that once the values of these factors had been decided stochastically for any one generation, treatment of the subsequent production of the genotype frequencies for the next generation remained strictly deterministic.

Random numbers may be transformed, even when the required distribution is not expressible mathematically as a density function, by the simple technique of random reference to a table in which the number of occurrences of each item corresponds to its required frequency. The table may be an arbitrary one, or based on some mathematical density function. Examples of this technique have appeared previously in this book; the ratio table based on $(\mathbf{R}/2+\mathbf{S}/2)^8$ referred to earlier in this chapter was one instance; the progeny tables for simulating reproduction by use of table look up (Chapter 6) provide another; and the table used in choice of chiasma position in Chapter 9 was an example with an arbitrary basis. Unfortunately, the size of table becomes prohibitively large if there are more than a few classes and precision in achieving the required frequencies is desired, a point which has been discussed in Chapter 8. A transformation to a normal distribution could be achieved quite easily and quickly in this way if no great precision was required.

Transformation of random numbers for various purposes may be as important in digital genotype simulation as in algebraic simulation. In the program described in the next chapter table look-up transformation of random numbers is used to determine distances of seed dispersal and pollen transport.

Two-class segregations in large populations in ratios other than 1:1 can in theory be treated by an approximate method described by Buslenko and Sragovich (1964), though in practice it may be complicated and its use limited. It is described here not so much by way of instruction, as with the thought that it may perhaps suggest ideas.

Figure 55 represents the distribution curve of the frequency a of one class (S) in a two-class population of a given size n expected to have the ratio r**R**:$(1-r)$**S**. The vertical divisions below the curve enclose equal areas, and therefore a random choice has equal likelihood of falling in each of the areas over the sections a_0-a_1, a_1-a_2, a_2-a_3 etc. The random choice is easily made in the usual way by random reference to a table in which successive words carry the values of a_0, a_1, a_2 etc. So far, no approximation is involved, but once a section has been chosen we have to make a further choice of a point within that section and we do this by an approximation which supposes that the values of a are distributed over that section with uniform density.

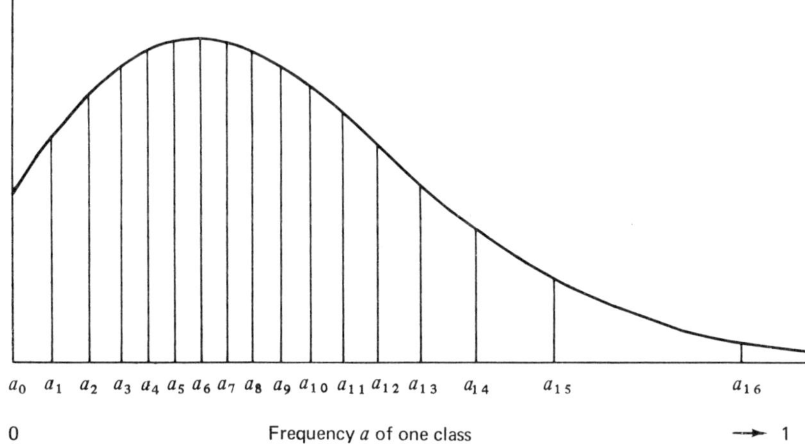

Figure 55. Hypothetical frequency curve of the distribution of two-class ratios relevant to one given expected ratio, to illustrate a method of transforming random numbers into a desired probability distribution. The sections under the curve are of equal area; one is chosen by the generation (in this example) of a random integer m in the range 0 to 15. A random fraction will then directly indicate a position on the base line between a_m and a_{m+1}

All we need then is to generate a random fraction which will indicate directly how far along the section is the required value of a. If the first random choice leads to the section beginning at a_m, and the random fraction generated is f, then the indicated value of a is $a_m+f(a_{(m+1)}-a_m)$. If the approximations are to be reasonably accurate, the number of sections must be fairly large; inaccuracy is worst at the ends of the distribution.

Once the table has been produced, this is quick and easy. The difficulty is the construction of the table, and this requires that the density function of a

shall be capable of convenient mathematical expression. If there are k sections of equal area, the total area under the curve being 1.0, then the integral of the density function between a_m and $a_{(m+1)}$ will be the same, $1/k$, for any value of m. a_0 being known (zero), it is therefore possible to determine the value of a_1, and thence a_2 and so on. This is laborious, but practicable if only one table is required which is going to be referred to many times. Unfortunately, in the study of evolutionary systems the density function of a is not capable of convenient mathematical expression and the table is more difficult to construct; it would in any case be used once only since the density function of a will be different from one generation to another (since the value of r will vary).

We come to the basic problem. What we really need is the ability, given a random fraction f, to find a value $a = t$ such that the integral of the density function from $a = 0$ to $a = t$ is f. The density function, unfortunately, is $n!r^{(n-an)}(1-r)^{an}/[(n-an)!\,(an)!]$, meaningful only when an is an integer.

Stochastic Transformation by Frequency Subtraction

There is quite a different approach to the whole problem of stochastic transformation, which is of general use and simple to apply. Although it is much more time-consuming than the previous method with a two-class population, it would normally take much less time than the production of a digitally simulated population of the same size. Each new individual requires one random number, but this is obviously better than five or more (two random parents, each fitness tested, plus reproduction) as required in many digital simulation experiments.

The big advantages of this method are that it is not limited to two classes and is quite untroubled by varying ratios. Imagine a population consisting of five classes, **A**, **B**, **C**, **D** and **E**, expected with frequencies a, b, c, d and e (totalling 1.0). Then we can perform a stochastic transformation by simulating the random choice of the required number of individuals from an infinite population in which the five classes occur with their expected frequencies. We cannot of course set up such a population within the computer, but we do not need to; the procedure used may readily be illustrated by an analogy. Consider a line of length 1.0, made up of five sections of lengths a, b, c, d and e corresponding to classes **A**, **B**, **C**, **D** and **E** respectively.

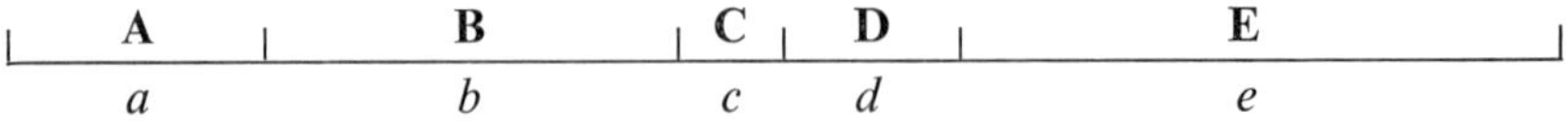

A	**B**	**C**	**D**	**E**
a	b	c	d	e

All we need to do is to choose at random the appropriate number of points on this line, corresponding to the number of individuals required for the experimental population. The number of points falling in each section will indicate the number of individuals belonging to the corresponding class. We can do this quite easily for each random point by generating a random fraction (which of course measures the distance of the random point from the zero end of the line) and cumulatively subtracting from it in turn a, b, c, d and e until the answer becomes negative, when the subtraction which produces the negative answer indicates the chosen class. The whole operation is repeated until the required number of individuals have been produced. These are not actually stored as individuals, but are merely counted, the final result giving the numbers of individuals of each class in the new population, easily transformed to frequencies a', b', c', d' and e' as required.

A subroutine for carrying out this operation is quite simple. We will suppose that the calculated frequencies a, b, c, d and e are stored in **t0** to **t4** respectively, and that the numbers of the genotypes for the new generation will be accumulated in **t5** to **t9**, which must be cleared at the start of each generation. Random fractions will be produced by **P202**.

Only four subtractions are necessary, since if the fourth leaves a positive answer we know that the fifth will not and we do not need to perform it. If any genotype comes to be fixed with a frequency of 1.0, division will produce overflow which may be detected and the run stopped since further generations would be pointless; the overflow register must be cleared in advance.

p1 contains the population size. The instruction sequence would be

```
(0); t5 = 0; t6 = 0; t7 = 0; t8 = 0; t9 = 0; p1→K15;
(1); p0P202 = (j2); J0P202; (H = random fraction);
(2); H−t0→H; J3H<0; H−t1→H; J4H<0; H−t2→H; J5H<0;
     H−t3→H; J6H<0; t9+1; K15−1; J1K15≠0; J7;
(3); t5+1; K15−1; J1K15≠0; J7;
(4); t6+1; K15−1; J1K15≠0; J7;
(5); t7+1; K15−1; J1K15≠0; J7;
(6); t8+1; K15−1; J1K15≠0;
(7); K15 = 5; M15 = 0; p1→H; J8V; (clear overflow);
(8); t5(M15)/H; J9V; M15+1; K15−1; J8K15≠0;
     [link and exit];
(9); [exit to print information and stop experiment];
```

It would have been possible to have written the subtractions as a loop; the program would have looked neater, but would take more time to execute since extra instructions are involved. The seven lines beginning with reference **(1)** would be replaced by

```
(1); M14 = 0; p0P202 = (j2); J0P202;
```

(2); H−t0(M14)→H; M14+1; J2H ⩾ 0; t4(M14)+1; K15−1; J1K15 ≠ 0;

(**t4** for the addition, not **t5**, since **M14** has been incremented.)

For this version of the subroutine, it is essential that the calculated original frequencies should total not less than 1.0. The subroutine could be made general for any number of genotypes by accumulating the scores in **u0** onwards instead of **t5** onwards, and having that number set as a parameter for use in setting **K15** in the line beginning **(7)**.

Time could be saved by making double use of each random fraction. Unless the population size is very large and the calculated frequencies need to be expressed to more than 15 binary places, then 31 bits can provide two adequate random fractions. The random fraction is used the first time as generated (the 16 l.s. bits are insignificant and need not be removed) and a second time after a shift up of 15 places with elimination of the sign bit. The original version of the subroutine would be modified as follows. **p2** will contain the mask **8/17777777777** and the line beginning with reference **(1)** would be replaced by

(1); p0P202 = (j10); J0P202;
(10); H→G; G up 15; G&p2→G; K14 = 2;

and each **t***n***+1** would be followed by **G→H; K14−1; J2K14 ≠ 0; K15−2; J1K15 ≠ 0; J7**. Obviously, the population size must be an even number.

In an early application of this method of stochastic transformation, which will be discussed later in this chapter, the author (Crosby, 1960), being not entirely confident about pseudorandom numbers, added a further random element by choosing at random for each individual the sequence in which the calculated frequencies for the different classes were subtracted. This of course lengthened the running time and it is very unlikely that anything was gained by doing it.

A contrary procedure, which will save time and should be perfectly satisfactory if the pseudorandom number subroutine in use is reliable, is to arrange the expected frequencies in decreasing order of size at the beginning of the stochastic transformation for each generation, and to subtract them in that order, which remains unchanged thoughout the whole generation. This will minimize the number of subtractions to be performed, and although the time saved may not be very great in relation to the time required for the generation of a random fraction, it is still worth saving, especially if the number of genotypes is large or if one or two of them have much higher frequencies than the rest. In the example which has been illustrated earlier, the frequencies would be subtracted in the order *e*, *b*, *a*, *d*, *c*, when on average just over two subtractions would be required for each individual instead of three with the order as in the illustration.

Unfortunately, rearranging the frequencies in order of magnitude is a lengthy and complicated operation, even when these are few. The following routine, which is given without description, will rearrange five frequencies which have been placed in a standard sequence in **t0** to **t4**. The standard sequence is the one in which the algebra, and the output subroutine, expects to find them. It is therefore important for the program to know how they have been rearranged, and track can be kept of this if the three l.s. bits of each frequency are cleared, and replaced by the integers 0 to 4 respectively; these will act as suitable tags which can be used for identification when required. Care must be taken to see that this tagging operation still leaves a total overall of not less than 1.0.

There are no parameters, and the instruction sequence proceeds

```
(0); t0→D; t1→E; t2→F; t3→G; t4→H;
     J1D>E; D→C; E→D; C→E;
(1); J2E>F; E→C; F→E; C→F; J2D>E; D→C; E→D; C→E;
(2); J3F>G; F→C; G→F; C→G; J3E>F; E→C; F→E; C→F;
     J3D>E; D→C; E→D; C→E;
(3); J4G>H; G→C; H→G; C→H; J4F>G; F→C; G→F;
     C→G;
     J4E>F; E→C; F→E; C→F; J4D>E; E→C; F→E; C→F;
(4); D→t0; E→t1; F→t2; G→t3; H→t4; [link and exit];
```

This subroutine would be much faster if an instruction were available (as on some computers) which would examine two registers and reverse their contents if the first-named were not the larger.

The benefit of re-ordering the frequencies increases as the number of genotypes increases, but so unfortunately does the difficulty and time required for the re-ordering, very much more so. Techniques have been developed for the re-ordering of long sequences, but for our purpose an approximate rearrangement into size classes will be good enough.

The easiest way of doing this is to sort the frequencies into classes by size: above 0.5, 0.5 to 0.25, 0.25 to 0.125, and so on; or, in binary, those frequencies beginning **0.1**, **0.01**, **0.001**, and so on as required. This is done by scanning the frequencies the required number of times. During the first scan, each frequency is copied and the copy shifted up one place; any negative number is recognised and the corresponding frequency (beginning **0.1**) stored; obviously, there will not be more than one of these, but it would complicate the program to try and cut the scan short if and when it is found.

During each scan, the frequencies are closed up as those in the current class are recognized and transferred; this means that in the following scan only those frequencies which remain to be re-examined will be looked at—the number of them will be known. If the latter is zero, the job is finished early and the program will leave the subroutine forthwith.

For the second scan, each frequency copy is shifted up two places, and negatives now correspond to frequencies beginning **0.01** (any beginning **0.11** having been eliminated). For the third scan, the shift is three places and negatives now correspond to the **0.001** class, any beginning **0.111** or **0.011** having been eliminated. And so on as required.

When the chosen number of scans have been made, there may still be some even smaller frequencies left, which will also need to be stored in the new sequence unless they are zero (actually to store the zeros would be pointless). In fact, with the possible exception of the original first frequency, no frequency will appear as zero because of the position tag; if there are a lot of zero frequencies, it is worth while making sure that they are (notionally) at the end of the new sequence, and they can be recognized simply by eliminating the tag with a mask. If there are to be more than eight genotypes, then more than three bits will have to be left for the position tags. Seven bits, as supposed below, will allow for 128 tags.

The following routine will produce the required approximate ordering by classes, for any number of frequencies. The calculated frequencies are in **t0** onwards and the new sequence in **v0** onwards.

p1 = number of scanning passes required
p2 = number of genotypes
p3 = the mask **8/17777777600**
The instruction sequence is
(0); p1→K15; M15 = 0; M14 = 0; p2→M12;
(1); M15+1; M12→K14; M12 = 0; M13 = 0;
(2); t0(M13)→H; M13+1; H→G; G up(M15); J3G<0;
 H→t0(M12); M12+1; J4;
(3); H→v0(M14); M14+1;
(4); K14−1; J2K14 ≠ 0;
 M12→H; J5H ≠ 0; [link and exit]**;** **(***early finish***);**
(5); K15−1; J1K15 ≠ 0;
 M12→K14; M13 = 0;
(6); t0(M13)→H; M13+1; H→G; G&p3→G; J7G = 0;
 H→v0(M14); M14+1;
(7); K14−1; J6K14 ≠ 0; [link and exit]**;**

During the subsequent stochastic transformation, the numbers of the genotypes will be accumulated in the **u** stores in the same order as the frequencies in the **v** stores. As these new genotype numbers are converted to frequencies, the new frequencies will be placed in the standard order in the **t** stores by using the tags of the corresponding old frequencies as modifiers of **t0**.

The method of stochastic transformation described in this section, which first seems to have been used by Crosby (1960) in the study of primrose populations described in the next section, is a very reliable one. Its principal disadvantage is that it is time-consuming, and this becomes increasingly severe as the number of genes increases since the number of possible genotypes then increases exponentially and consequently so does the maximum number of subtractions which would be required for each individual produced. This may not matter if most of the genotypes are rare since a negative answer will usually be reached quickly if the genotypes are properly ordered; but if none are rare, the time required for the subtractions may substantially exceed the time required to generate the random fraction, and the time taken to produce one individual may be as great as that by the genotype simulation technique. There can be no doubt that the latter has the advantage in dealing with situations of genetical complexity.

One point which may be noted is that in the techniques described in this chapter, the stochastic effects due to all causes are here lumped together and dealt with in a single operation, whereas in the digital genotype simulation technique the stochastic effects operating through fitness, choice of mate, segregation, for example, are dealt with separately. It would of course be possible to separate these various effects in algebraic simulation, but this would require greater complexity of programming, would occupy much more time, and wouldn't make any difference anyway.

Simulation of Evolution in *Primula* Populations

Brief reference has already been made to this work, which will now be taken as an example and discussed in more detail. It illustrates the use of stochastic techniques in algebraic simulation in the study of evolution in groups of populations between which there is gene flow. For a full description of the work, reference should be made to Crosby (1960); the account here will deal primarily with matters of computing interest.

The problem concerned an area of populations of the primrose, *Primula vulgaris*, in the west of England. This is normally an outbreeding species, exhibiting dimorphic heterostyly, being indeed the classic example of this. The short-styled high-anthered *thrums* (**Ss**) are almost completely self sterile and sterile with other thrums; they are almost always fertilized by pollen from the long-styled low-anthered *pins* (**ss**) which themselves are about 90 percent fertilized by pollen from thrums and about 10 percent self fertilized. In the west of England, over an area of about 600 square miles, there occur large numbers of fully self compatible long-styled high-anthered *homostyles* which may be **s′s′** or **s′s**. (Strictly speaking a complex of closely linked genes is involved, but we may treat the situation as determined by one gene with three alleles.) Homostyles are almost exclusively self-fertilized as female, but outcross as male onto pins. Only the four cited genotypes need be considered, and it could be shown theoretically that homostyles (heterozygotes and homozygotes) should increase in frequency in any population in which they appear, and that homostyly should spread outwards by centrifugal gene flow into neighbouring populations, so increasing its range. That is, there should be evolution from outbreeding to inbreeding over a steadily increasing area. Broadly speaking, the distribution of homostyly in the area agreed with the theoretical expectation, suggesting a final equilibrium which was largely (but not entirely) inbreeding and contained about 80 percent of homostyles, 20 percent pins and no thrums.

But there were some anomalies which demanded explanation. The most obvious of these was that as one moved through a series of primrose populations the gradients of homostyle frequency were often far from smooth, not always in the expected direction, and there were many examples of pairs or small groups of populations quite close to one another showing striking differences in homostyle frequency which would apparently not fit in with the idea of a steady gene flow.

A possible explanation came from a consideration of the theoretical calculations of the rate of change of homostyle frequency within a population, the calculations being well supported by evidence from the natural populations. At first, when homostyle frequency is low, the rate of increase is very slow; but as homostyle frequency increases so also does the rate of increase, very rapidly, slowing down again as thrums near extinction with the approach of equilibrium.

The theoretical curves had been calculated some years previously (Crosby, 1949) as a purely deterministic procedure, but reconsideration of homostyle evolution as a stochastic process quickly led to the conclusion that random fluctuations in homostyle frequency in the early stages could make considerable differences to the time by which the period of very rapid homostyle increase would be reached and so to the rapidity with which homostyles become established at high frequencies. Thus in one population with a low homostyle frequency a fortuitous increase over expectation of a few homostyles might lead to an early and considerable acceleration in the evolutionary process and the rapid attainment of a high frequency of homostyles; while in another perhaps only two or three hundred yards away an equally fortuitous shortage of homostyles might considerably delay the arrival of the population at the stage of rapid acceleration. Unless there were substantial gene flow between them, two neighbouring populations might easily and rapidly come in this way to have strikingly different homostyle frequencies.

It seemed likely that it would sometimes happen that homostyles would be fortuitously eliminated altogether from a population, which would remain strictly heterostyle until the **s**′ allele arrived once again from some other population.

It was reasonable to suppose that an explanation along these lines might account for the most obvious anomalies in homostyle distribution, but the problem was that of actual theoretical justification of the idea. An electronic computer (the newly installed Ferranti Pegasus in the Newcastle Division—as it then was—of Durham University) provided the opportunity. From our point of view, the interest of this project is that it was designed primarily as a stochastic operation, the deterministic work having long since been done. It was not a case of stochastic transformation being applied simply to make a deterministic computer simulation more realistic. The computer was used because its great speed (great, that is, in the late 1950s by comparison with electric desk calculating machines) and its ability to produce pseudorandom numbers made possible the investigation of homostyle evolution as a stochastic process, with particular reference to the effect of random fluctuations in gene frequency on the rate of evolution.

If at any one time the frequencies in the population of the genotypes **ss**, **Ss**, **s′s** and **s′s′** are represented by p, q, r and s, then on the basis partly of knowledge of the breeding system and reproductive capacities, and partly from a knowledge of the genetical constitutions of natural populations at various stages of the evolutionary process, fairly simple expressions could be produced which would allow the deterministic calculations of the frequencies p_1, q_1, r_1 and s_1 to be expected in the offspring of that population.

The primrose introduces a complication of a kind we have not so far considered in that it is a perennial plant with overlapping generations. The early deterministic calculations took no account of this, and treated the generations as non-overlapping; to have done otherwise would have involved a great increase of work with only desk calculating machines then available.

For the computer simulation experiments, it seemed desirable to treat the primrose properly as a perennial. It was known from the author's own work (unpublished) that about 15 years was a reasonable estimate of the average life of a primrose plant. Of course, there would be a great deal of variability between individual plants; it would have been possible to introduce such variability, but this would have involved some complicated programming at a time when the author was still a programming novice. It was decided that all plants should be supposed to live for the same length of time; a non-flowering year of development from the seedling stage preceded 16 years (a convenient binary round number) during which the plant flowered with equal vigour every year. This gives an average generation time of $9\frac{1}{2}$ years—not $8\frac{1}{2}$ as stated in the paper.

In fact, it now seems likely that after the first few years flower production and seed set on average do not remain constant from year to year in the primrose, but fall off markedly with age. This would have the effect of shortening the average generation time and making evolution to homostyly more rapid in terms of years. It would have been easy enough to have taken account of this. Scaling factors related to age and applied to the number of plants in each age group would have been used to weight the contribution of each age group to the reproductive output of the whole population.

Age distribution within the population was uniform, so that 1/17 would be first year and non-flowering, 1/17 second year and flowering, and so on. The total population size was $2^n + 2^{(n-4)}$, so that the actual reproducing population size on which the deterministic calculations were based was an integral power of two, 2^n.

The numbers of the four genotypes in each age group were carried in a block of four words; seventeen consecutive blocks in sequence of age and with identical totals of plants constituted the population. For the smallest population size investigated, 17, there was only one plant in each age group. In all experiments, whatever the population size, the starting point was the natural heterostyle equilibrium which has slightly more pins than thrums, and all age groups were as nearly identical in genetical constitution as the necessary use of integers permitted; a single heterozygous homostyle replaced one thrum in the youngest (non-flowering) age group.

If we number the age blocks from 1 to 17, then at the beginning of an experiment block 1 carried the numbers of the oldest plants (those due to die at the end of the first year) and block 17 the youngest (not due to flower until the following year). A further block, 18, carried the total numbers of the four genotypes currently in flower, that is *at the start* the totals of blocks 1 to 16.

Reproduction was carried out yearly, the number of new plants each year being $2^{(n-4)}$ replacing the $2^{(n-4)}$ which died. From the frequencies p, q, r and s obtained from the total numbers of the flowering genotypes in block 18, a deterministic calculation gave values p_1, q_1, r_1 and s_1; but these were not the frequencies for the new generation, they were those for the plants required to replace the oldest ones which were due to die. So the stochastic transformation on p_1, q_1, r_1 and s_1 produced not a number of individuals equal to the population size, but a number equal to 1/16 of the size of the flowering population. Thus in a total population size of 272, with 256 flowering plants, the stochastic transformation would produce 16 plants; for the smallest population size investigated, only one plant was produced each year.

During the first year, the plants due to die were in block 1. At the end of the year their numbers were subtracted from the totals in block 18 and they were replaced in block 1 by the new plants. The numbers of the plants in block 17, which were due to flower for the first time the following year, were added to block 18 which thus maintained the total of flowering plants. So in the second year, block 1 carried the new plants not yet in flower, block 2 those due to die at the end of that year, and block 17 those flowering for the first time. In the third year, the corresponding blocks would be 2, 3 and 1. And so on, each block becoming in effect a year older until the age of 17 when its contents were replaced by seedlings and it started life afresh. In effect, blocks 1 to 17 were treated as though arranged in a circle, the point of death and replacement moving clockwise one block in each year, the organization of this being controlled by a simple routine.

The arithmetic of the deterministic calculation was a straightforward computing operation and needs no comment. Stochastic transformation was carried out by the method of frequency subtraction described in the last section, but with some differences of detail. The frequencies were not in fact treated as fractions, but were scaled up by a factor of 2^{12} and rounded to 12-bit binary integers. To produce an individual, they were then subtracted successively from a random integer in the range 0 to $2^{12}-1$. In effect, this is the same as retaining the frequencies as fractions but rounding them to 12 binary places and subtracting them from a random fraction of 12 places. The reason for so treating them was that the pseudorandom number subroutine used (from the Pegasus library) delivered its products (which did not occupy all 39 bits of the Pegasus word) in a form which led naturally to their interpretation as integers, and it never occurred to the author to treat them otherwise. These pseudorandom numbers consisted of 31 bits, and each was used economically in four sections of 3, 12, 3 and 12 bits respectively (one bit being wasted), to produce two individuals.

In an attempt to improve the randomness, the order of subtraction of the calculated frequencies was varied at random from one individual to the next by using the 3-bit random number to select one of eight orders of subtraction (arbitrarily chosen from the 24 possible orders). As pointed out earlier, this was almost certainly a waste of time as there is no reason to doubt the reliability of the pseudorandom number subroutine used, and it would have been more efficient to have arranged for the frequencies always to have been subtracted in descending order of magnitude.

Only an indication will be given of how the method actually used was carried out, rather than a detailed account. Each sequence was decided by random choice of one word from a table of eight, each containing four packed integers 0 to 3 in different orders. The extraction and use as modifiers of these integers in the same order as in the word determined the order in which the four frequencies were taken for subtraction, and also where the one was to be added in counting the genotype. Only eight possible orders of subtraction were used because the small immediate-access (computing) store of the Pegasus computer left no room for a bigger table.

Ordinarily, a quicker method would be to have eight versions of the subtraction procedure (it was very short, so not much programming labour would be involved), and to use the 3-bit random integer to direct a jump to one of the eight at random; but the small size of the Pegasus computing store would not then have given an advantage, since a great deal of slow main store to computing store transference would have been involved, and moreover the way modification operated in Pegasus was particularly advantageous for the method actually used.

The complete stochastic transformation for one year having been carried out, the new plants substituted for the dead, and the necessary amendment made to the totals in block 18, the frequencies derived from the new totals in block 18 were used to calculate the frequencies p_2, q_2, r_2 and s_2 for the next year and these were stochastically transformed, and so on over succeeding years until either homostyles (fortuitously from a low frequency) or thrums (in the course of evolution) were eliminated.

A long series of stochastic runs was performed on flowering populations of various sizes ranging in powers of two from 16 to 1024 (except 512), each beginning with a single heterozygous homostyle. The computing time required for each successful experimental run (from the introduction of a homostyle at the beginning to the elimination of thrums at the end) varied from about eight minutes for the largest population to a few seconds for the smallest.

The results strikingly confirmed the theoretical expectation and showed that a purely deterministic interpretation of the homostyle populations was quite inadequate.

By way of illustration, some of the results may be briefly considered. Of 80 runs with the largest population (1024), 40 were 'unsuccessful' in reverting to pure heterostyly by loss of homostyles altogether within the first few generations, usually within the first two. After 119 years, the remaining 40 populations varied strikingly in constitution with homostyles ranging from 1.3 percent (with thrums 48.4 percent) to 63 percent (thrums 7.6 percent). The former took 44 generations before thrums were eliminated and this was the slowest run; the latter took 22 generations, which was two generations longer than the fastest run.

As would be expected, the effect was more striking with the smaller populations. In 31 out of 71 runs at size 64, homostyles failed to establish themselves and were lost, usually within the first two generations, but one run went on for ten generations before all homostyles were lost, having had at one stage as many as four homostyles in its population. After 68 years (which corresponds to the 119 years of the largest population—both populations began with one homostyle and the smaller one therefore had a higher starting frequency and so on average made more rapid initial progress) the populations in the 40 successful runs had homostyle percentages ranging from 5 (41 percent thrums) to 81 (3 percent thrums). The former took 26 generations to lose its thrums (the longest run at this population size) while the latter was one of the five populations to finish in the shortest time of ten generations.

With the smallest population of only 16 flowering plants, 19 out of 53 runs failed to make permanent progress and lost their homostyles, but one of these kept going for ten generations and at one time five of its plants had been homostyles. Of the 34 runs which went to final extinction of thrums, only seven were longer than that failed run (18 generations being the longest), while three had eliminated thrums by the fourth generation.

Although the results from these stochastically transformed algebraic models of isolated homostyle populations would seem to be sufficiently conclusive, they did not exhaust the possibilities. While they clearly demonstrated that isolated populations starting simultaneously with identical homostyle content could quickly come to differ very considerably, they failed to take into account that, barring repeated spontaneous origin of homostyly which can be ignored as a very remote possibility, completely isolated populations would never come to contain homostyles anyway.

Two points arise. Gene flow between populations would tend to smooth out the stochastic fluctuations in gene frequency, and this might go some way towards reducing the force of the conclusions drawn from the use of models of isolated populations. A more interesting point emerging from the consideration of gene flow is that this must also be a stochastic process. In the primrose, dispersal of seed probably plays little part in gene flow, which takes place very largely through pollen transport from one population to another, the principal vector s(in the region in question) being bee-like diptera.

It is obvious that there will be considerable variation in vector activity from day to day, from year to year, and from place to place, depending particularly on weather conditions, size of the vector population, primrose density, and the detailed topography of the area in which the populations occur.

Anomalies found in the pattern of homostyle distribution might have arisen through random fluctuations not only in the rate of evolution within populations, but also in transport of pollen between populations and so in gene flow, with obvious consequences on the rate of spread of homostyly both from place to place and from time to time.

It was therefore desirable that the model should be elaborated so as to allow the treatment simultaneously of several populations between which pollen transport was allowed on a stochastic basis.

This problem was first explored in a simple way, mainly to establish the possibility of the construction of such a model, and to see whether the stochastic treatment of gene flow would produce results which would justify the construction of a more complex model simulating a large number of populations occurring in a diverse countryside.

The first approach was to consider a single lane along which were seven primrose populations at varying distances apart and varying in size from 64 to 256. For this and the more complicated later models, the refinement of simulating the first year of non-flowering development was dropped; there was no reason for supposing that it had any significant effect on the results, it complicated the programming, and the extra age blocks would have used valuable storage space which was in rather short supply in Pegasus and would have meant that fewer populations could have been dealt with in the later experiments.

This imaginary lane was isolated from other primrose populations. It was supposed that pollen could pass between adjacent populations, but not between non-adjacent ones, and pollen transport was simulated by supposing that for any one population the pollen parents involved in its seed production would include in addition to its own plants a fraction of the plants in its immediately neighbouring populations, the equations constituting the model being revised accordingly. Clearly, the amount of pollen transport and consequently the rate of gene flow would be determined by the size of these adjacent population fractions, and random fluctuations in the sizes of the fractions would introduce the desired stochastic element.

The problem was to decide, on the basis of knowledge of pollination in the primrose, how the deterministic sizes of the population fractions should be arrived at, and how these should be dealt with stochastically. Unfortunately, very little was known about the behaviour of the pollen vectors, which was of course the critical factor in the situation. Treatment of the problem had therefore to be based to a considerable extent on reasoned guesswork. Retrospectively, in the light of greater familiarity with the primrose populations, it seems to the author that some of his guesses were not very good, and he could certainly produce now a more realistic model of the system. But for our immediate purposes, we are less concerned with biological accuracy than with the way the problem was tackled and the technique of translating the biological interpretation of the system into a stochastic model.

The description which follows provides a good example of the amount of biological detail which has to be taken into account in constructing a model of this kind, and the point must be emphasized that where any of the relevant biological facts are unknown or cannot be confidently assumed, *something* has to go into the program—they cannot just be ignored as they might be in a theoretical discussion between people or on paper.

The questions which had to be answered can be discussed by referring to two hypothetical populations A and B, and considering the fraction of B

which was to be regarded for purposes of pollen supply as part of the population of *A*.

Firstly, how long do the pollinating insects stay in the same population before leaving it? If they stay for a fairly long time they would pollinate many flowers and it would be expected that most of the seed would result from intra-population pollination; correspondingly, there would be a relatively low number of flights between populations, which is another way of looking at the same thing. If they stay a short time, then few flowers will be pollinated at any one visit to the population and there will be more flights between populations; this would mean a larger amount of interpopulation pollination. The former possibility would correspond to a slow rate of gene flow, the latter to fast gene flow. In the absence of any basis for an informed decision on this point, two versions of the model were made, one with slow gene flow and one with fast. This was simple enough to implement—it merely required substitution of the population fraction parameters.

The sizes of *A* and *B* (in terms of the numbers of plants) would also be expected to have an effect on the amount of gene flow between them. For any particular size of *B*, the fraction of *B* which ought to be reckoned to contribute pollen to *A* might not be the same for all sizes of *A*. For example, smaller populations would possibly be visited less frequently than larger ones. The logic of the situation is not so simple as it might appear to be, and it seems to the author in retrospect that his logic was open to question and his solution of doubtful validity. The difficulty was two-fold: the behaviour of the pollinating insects was inadequately known, but even if it had been known, any interpretation in terms of gene flow would have been a very uncertain process.

This particular problem would be tackled quite differently today, not by any attempt at logical reasoning but by constructing a stochastic model of the individual genotype simulation kind with various population sizes of *A* and *B*, simulating the behaviour of pollinating insects within and between them; conclusions from experiments with such a model would then be incorporated into the algebraic model. This would be easy enough to do now, but would have been difficult when this work was carried out, even if the idea had occurred to the author. In the event, he decided that the fraction of *B* to be considered as contributing pollen to *A* should be independent of the size of *B* but, other things being equal, should be proportional to the square root of the size of *A*.

To what extent would the size of the population fraction of *B* depend on the distance apart of *A* and *B*? Would a pollinating insect on leaving population *B* tend to return if it did not quickly find more primroses, or would it tend to keep on flying away from *B*? In the former event, the fraction would fall off rapidly with distance apart. In the latter, it would depend on whether the insect's direction of flight was random or whether it would tend to fly more frequently over ground suitable for primroses. If random it might fly across fields and meet no more primroses for a considerable distance. The pollen of *B* might then under natural conditions reach many more distant populations, but only a small part would reach *A* unless *A* and *B* were very close together; the fraction of *B* donating pollen to *A* would fall off rapidly with distance. At the same time, *A* would receive small quantities of pollen from many different populations. The concept of an isolated lane would then be unrealistic, and we would be dealing with a situation in which the direction of gene flow was random and the spread of homostyly would be fairly regularly centrifugal. This would have been contrary to the hypothesis about homostyle distribution which was to be tested.

If vector flight was non-random, then it might for example continue along the same hedgerow until the next population was reached, so that if *B*'s pollen was going anywhere it would be very largely to *A* or to a population in the opposite direction, and *A* would receive pollen from similarly restricted sources. In that case, the fraction of *B* to be considered as providing pollen for *A* would not fall off so quickly with increasing distance apart. There were grounds for believing that the pollen vector's flight was non-random, but no knowledge at all as to how far it might prospect before returning to the original population. There was little better to be done than make a guess, and this guess involved the supposition that under conditions of slow gene flow the effect of distance would be greater and pollen transport would fall off much more rapidly with distance.

The way in which the required fraction sizes were arrived at was first to visualize and draw (without any calculation) for each of the two rates of gene flow a curve relating distance apart of two populations and the rate of gene flow from one to the other (expressed as population fraction) on the basis of a recipient population size of 256. The general shape of the curves was based rather inadequately on what was then known of the range of insect pollination (Bateman, 1947a and b), inadequately because the pollen vectors of the primrose are not the same as those discussed by Bateman.

Since distance apart and recipient population size were the only factors entering into the determination of the donating population fraction for a particular rate of gene flow, for a pair of populations *A* and *B*, the fraction of *B* considered as donating pollen to *A* was obtained simply by reading off from the graph the fraction corresponding to the distance apart, and scaling this for the size *N* of the recipient population *A* by multiplying by $(N/256)^{\frac{1}{2}}$.

In addition to the age group and total population blocks, there was stored for each population the reference number of its adjacent populations and the deterministic size of the pollen-donating fraction of each of those. The fraction sizes were not calculated and inserted by the program, but calculated on paper as part of the programming operations and written into the program as parameters. This was because the nature of the computing and backing stores of Pegasus meant that it was easier to calculate the parameters than to write a program to do it. When it was desired to modify the rate of gene flow, new parameters were calculated, and it was an easy matter to amend the program after it had been read by the computer. With modern machines, it would be simpler to have a table corresponding to the appropriate gene flow curve stored with the program in the machine, and to have the population fraction parameters calculated by the program and inserted where required. Change of gene flow rate, or any other relevant amendments, would then be much simpler, since it would only be necessary to amend the table. The table would give the size of the population fraction for each combination of distance apart and recipient population size.

This use of an arbitrarily drawn curve to determine quantities dependent on the different values of a variable is particularly useful in simulation techniques. Calculation of such quantities, particularly if they are not simple ones, might involve a great deal of time if performed whenever the factor is required, and reference to a table is clearly preferable. But this has the corollary that it is not necessary for the items in such a table to be calculated; they could equally well be arbitrarily assigned so long as they conform with the biological requirements of the situation. This means that we can deal with parameters which have no simple mathematical relationship with the variables on which they depend, or even no mathematical relationship at all. In the case we are considering, range of pollen transport, it is much better to work from a curve which looks as though it might reasonably fit the situation than to try to force the biology into a mathematical mould and produce some mathematical formula of which the implications (unlike the curves) are difficult to visualise and the fidelity to the natural situation is difficult to judge and probably inadequate. This is as true for algebraic simulation as for individual genotype simulation techniques.

For each population along the lane, there was determined the number of plants from each of the populations on either side of it which were to be added to its own plants for cross-pollination purposes (one side only for the end populations). Whence, from the current population constitution of the relevant population, the frequencies of the different genotypes among all its pollen parents could easily be calculated each year for use in the generating equations.

It should be pointed out that the incoming pollen is relevant only to the fertilization of pin primroses, which may be successfully pollinated by thrum or homostyle pollen (it was assumed that the only pin pollen effective on pin stigmas was own pollen). Homostyles were supposed always to be self-pollinated, and thrums can only be successfully pollinated by pin pollen and unless the incoming pollen leads to an increase in seed set by thrums (and this was assumed not to be the case) it is irrelevant where the pin pollen comes from.

Stochastic Variation in Gene Flow

It is now necessary to consider how gene flow may be treated stochastically in this model. There would already be a stochastic element in the gene flow in that the stochastic transformation of the calculated genotype frequencies of the offspring implies random choice among all pollen, native and immigrant. But the variability to be expected in gene flow would be much greater than that to be expected simply on a random sampling basis. It would result primarily from variation in pollen vector activity, arising from such quasi-random causes as changes in weather, from causes partly random and partly non-random as far as the vector is concerned but effectively random as far as the primroses are concerned (for example, variation in vector numbers), and from causes not necessarily random as far as the primroses are concerned (for example, changes in number and vigour of primrose plants in a particular area).

In this investigation, it was decided only to consider those factors which were effectively random as far as the primroses were concerned, and it was clear that variability in gene flow could be best expressed primarily as a random variability from year to year and from population to population in the sizes of the donating population fractions and so, for any one population, in the relative proportions of native and immigrant pollen contributing to its seed production.

The problem was how this was to be implemented. A simple random variation in size of the donating population fraction (not necessarily normal but corresponding to any pattern which seemed reasonable) could easily be imposed, but it was felt that there would also be greater variability between the different genotypes involved than that simply due to random sampling from the revised population fraction. The argument for this was that an insect leaving a population would not carry a random sample of pollen from the donating population, but an excess of pollen from the genotype last visited. The conclusion drawn from this argument was largely faulty except perhaps for two populations far apart under conditions of slow gene flow, when there would be only a few vector flights between them. With many flights between them, the total pollen carried over would of course be an approximately random sample of the pollen of the donating population. It now seems to the author that he may have introduced too much intergenotype variability into gene flow, and that he should have confined his stochastic treatment of gene flow to treatment of the size of the donating population fraction.

The method which he did in fact use was clumsy and based on biological premises some of which now seem to be lacking in sense. Although some of the programming techniques are of interest, the procedure is not going to be described here because it is felt that the element of irrationality in the biological reasoning is likely to confuse the reader, as it has confused the author in looking back over his notes and programs. Instead, an account will be given of the way in which the author thinks he might more reasonably have tackled this problem; this will include some of the same techniques as were actually used.

In the original method, the stochastic transformation of gene flow was carried out for a recipient population after the calculated donations from its neighbours had been added together. This implied identical variation in the contributions from the two neighbours of a population but also at the same time that its own contributions to those two neighbours varied independently (since the stochastic transformations on the pollen donations to those neighbours were separate operations). This is illogical, but an examination of the situation shows that the illogicality is not easy to resolve. Consider three populations in a row, *A*, *B* and *C*. Then we have four items of pollen movement to consider, *A* to *B*, *B* to *A*, *B* to *C* and *C* to *B*. To what extent would we expect these four to vary independently? It might be thought that since the pollen movements *A* to *B* and *B* to *A* are over the same territory, they would tend to vary together; but a period with persistent wind from the same direction might influence insect movement and increase pollen flow in the direction of the wind and decrease that against the wind. If for example there was a prevailing wind in one season from *A* to *C*, we might expect (other things being equal) that both *A* to *B* and *B* to *C* pollen flows would be higher than usual and the *C* to *B* and *B* to *A* pollen flows to be less than usual. Under different conditions the relations between the variabilities in pollen transport might be quite different. Differences in vegetation and topography along the lane (such as those affecting exposure to wind) might be expected to result in considerable differences in magnitude of the variabilities. These and other possibilities could be taken into account, but this would have required some intricate programming (especially in the more complex versions to be discussed later), and this is the sort of situation to which should be applied the golden rule 'keep it simple to begin with, so long as it is sensible; when it works, then is the time to think about elaboration'.

The simplest assumption is that variability in any one pollen transport situation is independent of any other. We can then consider a hypothetical example, say pollen flow from *B* to *A*, and decide how variability may be superimposed on the fraction of *B* calculated as contributing pollen to *A*. The principles having been determined, they would be applied in the same way to all the other instances of pollen transport between adjacent populations.

One question is whether the variability should be related to the calculated number of plants in the fraction or to the size of the donating population.

For example, consider two population fractions of 40 plants from populations of sizes 64 and 1024. Would one expect the variabilities to be of the same magnitude? The vector flight distances will be quite different (which is why the fraction sizes are the same), and this may affect the variability as much as the question of mere numbers from which the fractions are derived. In thinking about this from various points of view, the author came to two opposite and apparently equally reasonable conclusions, thus emphasizing another gap in his knowledge of the biology of the situation. The obvious solution seemed to be the one which required the less involved programming, which was to make the variability independent of the population size and related only to the fraction size expressed as number of plants.

The next thing to be decided is the extent of the variability and its form. It could be decided that variation should be gaussian, in which case its magnitude would be fixed by specification of the standard deviation. It is simpler to consider a specific fraction size (again in terms of number of plants) and draw a curve giving a reasonable representation of the variability which might be expected. A plausible curve relating to a calculated fraction size of 64 is shown in Figure 56, and this would be implemented in the program by conversion into a frequency table of the usual kind.

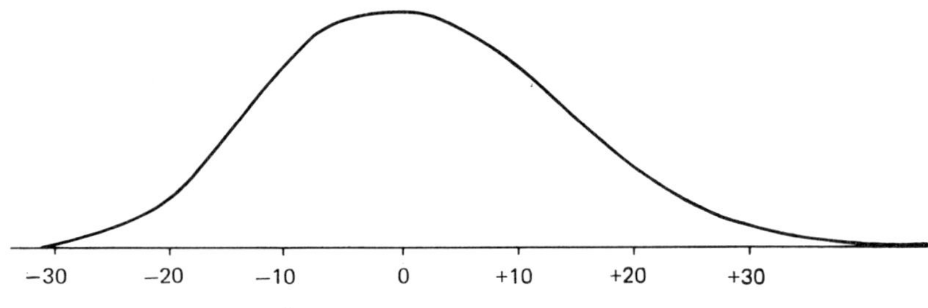

Figure 56. Arbitrarily drawn curve representing the frequency distribution of pollinating fraction sizes when the calculated expected size is 64. This is translated into a table in the program, and random reference to this will produce a stochastic fraction size, readily convertible for any other expected fraction size as explained in the text. The curve is slightly skew, as it might reasonably be expected that variation upwards would be over a greater range than variation downwards, especially where the expected fraction size was much smaller than the size of the donating population

In the figure, the abscissae represent numbers to be added or subtracted to 64, so changing the fraction size, and the ordinates give the number of times each abscissa value should appear in the table. The total number of entries in the table will be a power of two, so that it may readily be referred to at random. Such random reference will produce the amending values with probabilities corresponding to the ordinates of the figure.

The amending value extracted at random will (in the example given) be relevant to a population fraction of 64 plants, and will need scaling for other fraction sizes. The scaling factor required is not linearly related to the fraction size; an obvious relationship would be to its square root, the randomly extracted value being multiplied by $(N/64)^{\frac{1}{2}}$ for a fraction of N plants. There is a point which has to be watched: for very low values of N, stochastic amendment could produce a negative answer. This must be recognized when it occurs, and substituted by zero. Any other relationship could be used according to how the programmer felt that variability would depend on the calculated fraction size.

Since the basic (deterministic) population fraction is constant for each donor/recipient pair, and calculated and inserted during the writing of the program, the scaling factor can also be calculated or arbitrarily decided and stored permanently with the population fraction.

As an example of scaling, and supposing that we assume the square root relationship, if a value of -7 is extracted from the table, then for fraction sizes of 13 and 87 this value would become on rounding -3 and -8 respectively and the stochastic fraction sizes would be 10 and 79.

The population fraction now needs to be converted into numbers of the four genotypes by reference to the current constitution of the donating population. If computing time is of little consequence, the best way of doing this is by the same method as used for stochastic transformation of the yearly calculated genotype frequencies, the appropriate number of plants being chosen by that number of genotype frequency subtractions from random fractions. Unfortunately, this is very time consuming and would more than double the running time for the program; remember that for annual reproduction the plants to be produced number only 1/16th of the population size. For fast gene flow the donating population fraction was usually bigger than this and could be more than one half, so that by this method more frequency subtraction operations would be required per annum for the pollen fractions than for the transformation of the calculated frequencies at the end of the year's reproduction.

A very much quicker alternative would simply be to multiply the final fraction number by the genotype frequencies of the donating population, leaving stochastic variability among pollinating genotypes to be absorbed and dealt with in the single operation following reproduction. Not only does this probably produce (in effect) too low a genotypic variation in the pollen donating fractions, but it introduces a more serious disadvantage when homostyles are rare (it doesn't matter if they are common). If after the multiplication of the fraction number by the genotype frequencies the resultant genotype numbers are rounded to integers (which would be the natural thing to do since they are to be added to integers) a rare genotype would usually round to zero, especially if it only occurred once in the donating population. In that case it would have no opportunity of donating pollen while it was still scarce, and this is important in the case of homostyles since it seems highly likely that one of the factors determining irregularity in homostyle distribution may be fortuitous differences in the time taken for the homostyle allele to reach a new population, and one must allow the possibility of it spreading even when homostyles are scarce. Even a single plant must be allowed the possibility of fathering a seed in the next population. The genotype numbers resulting from multiplication must therefore not be rounded to integers, but only to at least one and preferably two decimal places. If the resultant value for homostyles is very low, then obviously the deterministic frequency for homostyles in the year's reproduction output for a population in which homostyles have hitherto been absent will be very small, and the chance of the stochastic transformation producing the first homostyle in the population will also be very small. But it will at least be possible. It may well be that 12-bit random fractions would now not be long enough for the stochastic transformation.

Once the logical basis for the stochastic treatment of the population fractions has been arrived at to the programmer's satisfaction, the programming presents little difficulty though it may be laborious. It is now not particularly difficult to introduce random annual variations in pollen transport. This will arise from such causes as the number of vectors available and their activity, and the latter in particular will depend on the weather; it is simplest and not altogether unreasonable to assume that variation will be broadly the same in magnitude and direction for all populations in any one year. The easiest way of dealing with this would be to have a table of scaling factors, distributed normally or in some other way about a mean value of 1.0; one of these factors would be selected at random and used to amend by multiplication each calculated population fraction before the stochastic operation on it. This would produce an overall change in the basic gene flow which would differ from one year to the next. It would also mean that since the population fraction size which is to be subjected to stochastic amendment will vary from year to year, the scaling factor for that operation will also no longer be constant, and strictly speaking should really be calculated afresh every year. Unless annual variations in the rate of gene flow are likely to be substantial, this is probably a subtlety not worth bothering about.

The method of introducing annual variation actually used was not a very good one. It simply assumed that all variability was in the same direction in any one year, but with the direction varying at random from year to year, either the positive side or the negative one of the curve as in Figure 56 being used.

There is one point of technique which should be mentioned here, as it saved considerable computing time in the early stages of each run, especially in the larger models to be mentioned later. Considering a particular recipient population, if there are no homostyles either in itself or in the donating populations, there is little point in carrying out on that occasion any calculations and stochastic operations, whether of gene flow or reproduction, since random fluctuations in pin: thrum ratio will have little effect of any significance on subsequent homostyle evolution, and certainly not enough to warrant spending computing time in dealing with them. It was a simple matter to introduce a routine check on this point into the program, short-circuiting the pollen transport and reproduction operations where appropriate.

This outlines the basic points involved in the stochastic treatment of gene flow in primrose populations. The application to gene flow along identical lanes of the rather cruder version actually used produced widely different rates of spread of homostyly and demonstrated clearly the importance of random fluctuations in gene flow as well as in rate of evolution.

One question we have not considered is output of results. This presents no problems in any of the experiments, including those yet to be described. Unlike the situation with genotype simulation, the need to score the population does not arise. All the information required for output is there with the population either in the appropriate form or easily ascertainable by simple arithmetic, and it is only a question of outputting the genotype frequencies when required in a sensible sequence and tagged with the population number.

Populations in a Simulated Countryside

It was now a fairly simple matter to adapt the program to deal not merely with an isolated lane but with an imaginary section of countryside involving lanes, hedgerows forming field boundaries, a wood and a stream. Thirty-seven populations of various constant sizes were distributed unevenly in appropriate locations in this imaginary countryside, and the system was dealt with in essentially the same way as the simpler single lane version. There was no actual representation of the countryside within the computer. All that was needed was the information as to which populations could donate pollen to each other, and the deterministic sizes of the relevant population fractions.

At the beginning there was one homostyle only, in a population in the centre of the area. There had to be a safety routine in the program to deal with the possibility that homostyly might be fortuitously eliminated at the beginning of a run; in that case, a homostyle would be re-inserted into the central population and the run automatically restarted.

It was assumed that pollen vector movement would take place only along lanes, hedgerows, streams and through woods, and not across fields and open spaces. Adjacent populations, between which there could be pollen flow, would thus be directly connected by lane, hedgerow, stream or wood. Populations on opposite sides of a field would not be considered adjacent unless the route from one to the other round the sides of the field was devoid of other populations.

There were now situations where one population could donate pollen to (and receive it from) three other populations, and in one case four. But apart from the greater complexity involved in dealing with the population fractions and the organization of the operations involving them in the program, there was no essential difference between the lane and the countryside programs, and the results from the latter confirmed and amplified the conclusions drawn from the former.

It was thus clearly demonstrated that algebraic computer simulation techniques, with suitable stochastic variation, were valuable not only in dealing with evolution within isolated populations, but could also be used for the study of evolution in groups of populations which were not genetically isolated and which were considered not in abstract but in geographically specified positions in a topographically diverse region where ease of gene flow could vary in ways related to that diversity. A further development of this model provided an even more striking demonstration.

The 37-population model was a comparatively simple one, and it was decided to construct a much larger model bearing a closer resemblance to a naturally occurring area of primrose populations, and where pollen transport might occur over a wider range than between adjacent populations. This time the model countryside, which included two woods, had 150 populations of constant size ranging from 32 to 1024. At the beginning, one population had a single homostyle. The general rules for pollen transport were as before, except that pollen could now pass not merely from one population to the next, but to the next but one, that is across an intervening population. As before, for each pair of populations between which pollen transport was possible, the fraction of one to be considered as donating pollen to the other was primarily determined by the distance apart and the size of the recipient population, but where there was an intervening population the fraction was reduced by a factor which depended on the size of this. It was considered that the chance of pollen passing across an intervening population would vary contrary to the latter's size which would be expected to influence the possibility of whether a pollen vector would fly over rather than visit it. For the smallest size of this intervening population pollen transport was reduced by five percent, and by 80 percent for the largest.

This increase in complexity of the model was achieved without modification of the basic operations of the program, and provided a good example of the way in which a model sensibly constructed with a view to later elaboration can, once it is working satisfactorily, readily be adapted for the simulation of more complex situations. However, the fact that the basic simulation procedures required no modification did not mean that little work was involved in adapting the model. Increase in the range of pollen transport now meant that some populations might receive pollen from ten or more others, and with 150 populations in the model there were just over 500 distinct pairs of populations which had to be dealt with. Considerable labour was involved in preliminary calculations, and in the intricate organization within the program which was necessary for the efficient manipulation of the pollen transport operations.

Pollen transport was now administered differently from the way it had been dealt with in the earlier experiments. All pairs of populations between which pollen movement was possible were listed in the computer, with all relevant information about each pair, and the pairs dealt with in turn by running through the list. This probably took more computing time, but by way of compensation was much easier to program than would have been the case had the procedure been to list with each recipient population the possible donating populations and parameters, dealing fully with each recipient population in turn, extracting the relevant information as required and acting on it. Stochastic amendment of the immigrant pollen fractions was carried out for each recipient population as a single operation on their total, not independently on the fraction for each donating population.

With 150 populations and only just over 4,000 words of store in the Pegasus computer which was used, tight packing of the genotype numbers in the age groups was necessary. Each population required four items (genotype numbers) in each of 16 age groups, and eight further items for the overall genotype frequencies and accumulation of the total numbers of immigrant pollen genotypes. Clearly, each item could not occupy a word, since that alone would have required over 10,000 words.

The program was run once, for 198 years—at which point there was a computer failure, but evolution had gone far enough. Since the result of this run with the large model has not been published elsewhere, it is illustrated here in Figure 58, with for comparison a map of real homostyle distribution in natural populations, Figure 57. It illustrates very well the power of algebraic simulation techniques in the investigation of this kind of complex evolutionary problem.

The question may now be asked as to whether the problem could not have been tackled by digital genotype simulation techniques, and if so whether or not this would have provided a better approach. The simple answer to both these questions is, in principle, yes. But at the time when this work was begun the author was not aware of the possibilities of digital simulation, and even if he had been a digital simulation model would have required much more computing time and for the largest model an amount of storage space very much greater than was available on the Pegasus computer. The 150 populations included just over 40,000 plants.

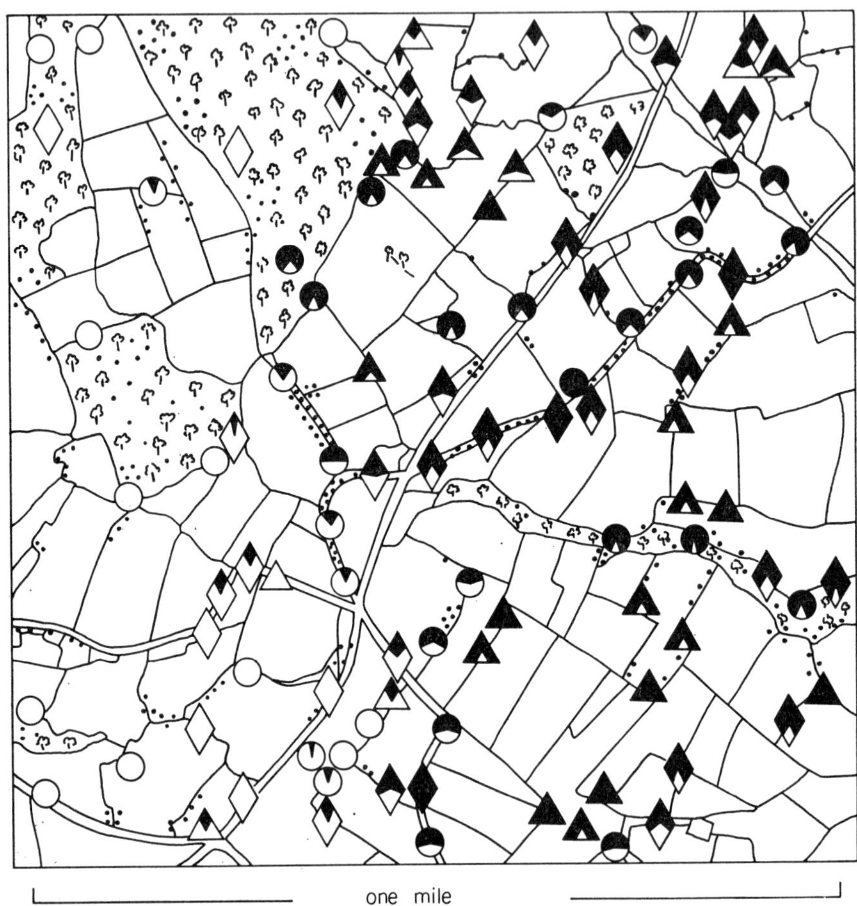

Figure 57. A small part of the distribution map of homostyly in Somerset. Single lines are usually hedges, double lines are roads or lanes, trees indicate woods. Symbol shapes indicate number of plants in the sample scored, roughly the population size for the first two; △ 11 to 40; ◊ 41 to 90; ○ over 90. The degree of blackness of these symbols indicates the extent of evolution—from all white (no homostyles) to all black (no thrums). Dots show where primroses were present but not scored. (Reproduced from *Phil. Trans.*, 1960, B.242, p. 555, permission of the Royal Society.)

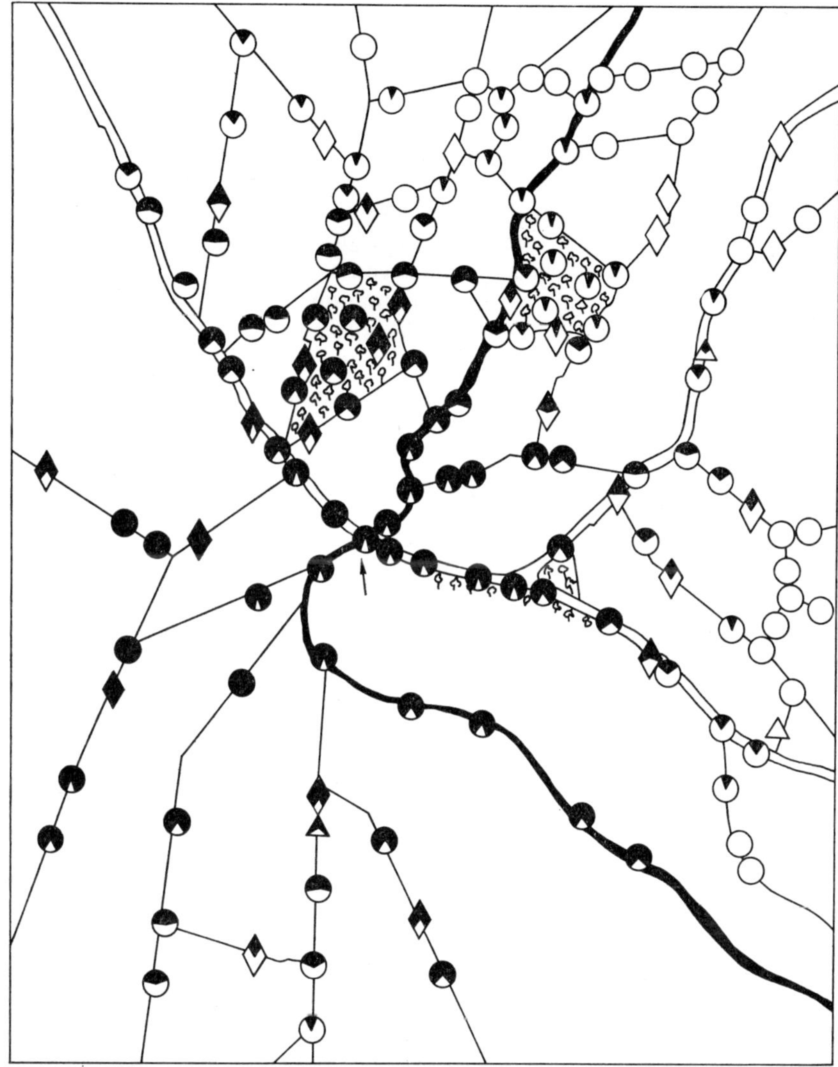

Figure 58. Imaginary map of the distribution of homostyly after 198 years of simulated evolution from a beginning in which there was only a single homostyle; this was in the population indicated by an arrow. Single lines are hedges, double lines lanes, the thick black line is a stream, trees indicate woods. Symbols show population sizes; △ 32; ◊ 64; ○ 128 to 1024. Degree of blackness of the symbols indicates the extent of evolution, as in Figure 57

To simulate this model on a digital genotype basis would certainly have been possible, and in some respects might have been easier. The basic simulation of reproduction within a population would have presented no difficulty. It has in fact since been carried out successfully as a student exercise in programming, using a KDF9 computer, with results confirming those of the original algebraic simulation, but no attempt has been made to elaborate on this; to do so might be a tempting intellectual exercise, but otherwise pointless in view of the satisfactory operation of the algebraic models. In any case, the much greater time which the digital model would require would still be an important consideration, because as the speed of computers increases so does the demand for computing time.

It seems clear that algebraic simulation has an important part to play in the theoretical study of systems of this kind. But there are many evolutionary systems to which the application of algebraic simulation would appear to be impossible and for which only digital genotype simulation is practicable. Such a system will be described in the next chapter. It is another example involving the introduction of geographical space and the possibility of topographical diversity, but applied at the level of individual plants, not of populations.

CHAPTER 11

A Complex Model — Position, Distance and Genetic Discontinuity

The previous chapter showed how algebraic simulation techniques could be used for the investigation of a system in which the spatial relationships of interbreeding populations were of primary importance, but in which no consideration was taken of the distribution of individual plants within a population. Although there was an evolutionary change in the breeding system from outbreeding to inbreeding, the one species involved remained genetically continuous, with gene flow occurring both within and between populations, freely in the former case, less freely in the latter because of the need for transport of pollen by insect vectors from one population to another.

In this chapter an account will be given of the development of a program in which the evolution of genetic discontinuity within a species is studied, and in which the position within a population of the individual plants composing it is a matter of primary importance.

A full account of the biological ideas and implications of this work, together with detailed results obtained from the models which were developed, is given in Crosby (1970). This chapter will deal primarily with the construction of the model and the computing methods which were used, giving only sufficient of the biological background for that purpose. The cited paper and this chapter should be regarded as complementary to one another.

The Problem

The problem under consideration concerns the population genetics and the possible evolutionary consequences when subspecies of a single species, having become genetically somewhat different from one another during a period of geographical isolation, come into contact with one another and hybridize freely with the formation of hybrids of low fertility. The production of such hybrids involves wastage of gametes, and it might be expected that natural selection would favour any genotypes which reduce the possibility of hybridization between the subspecies, with consequential reduction in gamete wastage.

This would be a second-order selection, and therefore weak, and the question to be answered was whether the theoretical expectation of the selection of barriers to hybridization (and thus to gene flow) between the subspecies, with consequent evolution of genetic discontinuity, was in fact capable of practical realization.

The hypothetical situation to be investigated was one in which the two subspecies (which will be referred to as *A* and *B*) had come into contact with some interpenetration and free hybridization in the zone of contact. We may, for the sake of argument, regard this as being a single population; but since the zone of contact formed, initially at least, a boundary (not necessarily sharp) between *A* and *B*, the distribution of *A*, *B* and hybrids was non-random within this population and neither pollination nor seed dispersal could any longer be regarded as random. Whether wind or insect pollinated, a plant would be more likely to receive pollen from nearer plants than from more distant ones, and seed dispersal equally would be related to the position within the population of the plant which produced it.

Clearly, the evolutionary system was one in which simulation had to take into consideration the actual position of each plant within the population, and therefore had to be on an individual basis. Digital genotype simulation and not algebraic simulation was the technique required here, and it also allowed the introduction of genetic complexity well beyond the scope of algebraic treatment.

The problem was tackled in two stages, for two reasons. One was the immediate practical reason that when the problem was conceived only the slow and small Pegasus computer was available, and it would have been quite impracticable on grounds both of speed and of storage capacity to think of using it for a model of the scale and complexity which was envisaged. The other reason was that a number of simulation techniques which would be basic to the problem had to be worked out, and there is a great advantage in working out such techniques in a relatively simple context providing this is biologically sensible.

It was therefore decided to begin with a pilot model on a small scale and to consider only the question of whether genetic barriers to interbreeding could be selected. In this pilot model the positions of the individual plants were not considered and the two subspecies were supposed to be mixed at random within a small population through which seed movement and (initially) pollen transport were random. It was also felt by the author (but almost certainly wrongly) that if genetic barriers to cross-pollination between *A* and *B* were not selected in such a simplified system, then they would probably not be selected in the more complex and realistic situation ultimately to be dealt with, and it would be a mistake to embark directly on the much more complex model before demonstrating that such selection would be effective in the simple one.

This having been demonstrated by the pilot model, the latter was used as the basis for the construction on a large scale of a more complex model in which the positions of the individual plants were taken into account, and pollen transport and seed dispersal were no longer random. This model was designed for and used on a KDF9 computer.

Although many of its basic ideas and procedures were first conceived in relation to the pilot model on Pegasus, and some (but not all) of the procedures were adapted with little change for the KDF9, the following account will be written as though the program had been designed for KDF9 in its complex form from the start, with no pilot model, in order to reduce the risk of confusing the reader by reference to two very different computers. Techniques specific to Pegasus are of very little interest nowadays.

In a few cases, the procedures used with the KDF9 model were inefficient, usually because they had been adapted from Pegasus procedures without sufficient thought and did not take full advantage of KDF9 possibilities. In such cases, the more efficient procedure will be described even though it was not the one used; the differences will be purely of programming technique and without biological significance.

There is, though, one important point which must be mentioned now and which is relevant to the whole of this chapter. The word length of the KDF9 was 48 bits, and some of the methods used in the program for representing and dealing with the individual plants would not be possible on a 32-bit machine, such as our notional XB1. It would be possible to redesign the procedures so that they could be written in Mendol for XB1, but there would be considerable risk of error in so doing, especially since the new procedures would be more complicated than the old ones and would also be untestable.

The procedures will therefore be described and the flow diagrams produced as for a 48-bit word machine. For this reason, no quasi-programs in Mendol will be given for the subroutines and procedures of this program. Mendol terminology will however be used in the flow diagrams where it does not conflict with the procedures used and satisfactorily explains what is going on, since this should help the reader who has by now become sufficiently familiar with this quasi-language.

The Genetics of the Model System

As usual, the first step in the development of the model was to imagine a sensible biological system on which such an investigation could in principle be carried out if unlimited time were available. The next operation was to consider how this system could be represented by a model.

The model was clearly going to be a fairly complex one, and it seemed therefore desirable to use maximum biological simplicity for those parts of the system which would be expected to have little bearing on the problem under investigation. The most convenient organisms to deal with were annual hermaphrodite flowering plants which, apart from considerations of position, bred at random (panmictically) and with no generation overlap, the seed of one year all germinating in the next. It was assumed that the two subspecies were equally well adapted to their environment which was uniform over the whole area of the population and that there was no selective advantage of one over the other in this respect. These were assumptions which could easily be modified later if desired.

Flowering time, known to provide an effective genetic isolating barrier in nature, was chosen as the potential isolating barrier in the model.

Two independent elements of the genotype had to be considered. Firstly, there were the genes which determined the subspecies characteristics and which would, directly or indirectly, be concerned with the low fertility of the hybrids. Broadly speaking, and taking extreme possibilities, low hybrid fertility could be considered to arise either from irregularities during meiosis resulting from a relatively low degree of homology between the chromosomes of *A* and *B*, or from genetic imbalance produced by a mixture of alleles from *A* and *B*; the latter could be expressed as low fertility of pollen and ovules resulting from meiotic disturbance, or as a general lowering of reproductive activity (with or without a lowering of vegetative activity) expressed perhaps as a smaller production of flowers.

However the cause of low hybrid fertility is imagined, the genetical treatment could be the same. Since the F_1 hybrids between *A* and *B* were not to be completely sterile, the population would come to contain F_2 plants and back-crosses between hybrids and the pure subspecies; in subsequent generations there would be progeny derived from all of these. All possible intermediates between *A* and *B* come into consideration. If low fertility is taken to be due to meiotic failure resulting from chromosomal differences, then for any particular plant this would be expected to depend on where in the range of genotypes between pure *A* and pure *B* the plant lies; in this case, the subspecies-characteristic genes could be considered simply as indicators of the degree of impurity of the plant and so of its fertility. If low fertility is taken to result from genetic unbalance, then the subspecies-characteristic genes can be considered as directly determining the fertility. In either case, the appropriate fertility for any plant in the model population can be determined immediately by reference to its subspecies-characteristic genotype. The relationship could be a simple arithmetic one, or one decided arbitrarily, visualized as a curve, and stated in the program in the usual way in the form of a table. A simplifying assumption which was made was that lowering of fertility affected pollen and ovules equally.

The way in which the subspecies-characteristic genes were to be dealt with was a matter of considerable importance, since it would affect the ease of program writing, storage requirements, and speed of the program. The simplest possible treatment was used. Though to some extent unrealistic, it was biologically sensible, and there was no reason for supposing that a more realistic simulation which would have required more complex treatment would have enhanced the validity of any conclusions to be drawn from the model. It provides a good illustration of the roles of simplicity and sense in computer models.

It was decided that there should be eight unlinked loci, called the **G** loci, which should be concerned with characterization of the subspecies and with the expression of fertility. Reference to Chapter 8 will make it clear why all the genes in this model were unlinked. In its bit representation within a word, the whole genotype was arranged so that the two parental gamete contributions were side by side and not interleaved, and this arrangement will be used below when expressing the genotype (in whole or in part) symbolically.

The genotype of one subspecies was

$$\mathbf{G}_1\mathbf{G}_2\mathbf{G}_3\mathbf{G}_4\mathbf{G}_5\mathbf{G}_6\mathbf{G}_7\mathbf{G}_8\mathbf{G}_1\mathbf{G}_2\mathbf{G}_3\mathbf{G}_4\mathbf{G}_5\mathbf{G}_6\mathbf{G}_7\mathbf{G}_8$$

and that of the other

$$\mathbf{g}_1\mathbf{g}_2\mathbf{g}_3\mathbf{g}_4\mathbf{g}_5\mathbf{g}_6\mathbf{g}_7\mathbf{g}_8\mathbf{g}_1\mathbf{g}_2\mathbf{g}_3\mathbf{g}_4\mathbf{g}_5\mathbf{g}_6\mathbf{g}_7\mathbf{g}_8.$$

It was decided that the eight genes should have equal effect, both in determining the relationship of a plant to the pure subspecies, and in indicating its fertility. There was also to be no dominance. The contributions of the **G** alleles to the phenotype were therefore identical and their expression additive, and so were the contributions of the **g** alleles. Thus the three plants of genotypes

$$\mathbf{G}_1\mathbf{G}_2\mathbf{g}_3\mathbf{G}_4\mathbf{G}_5\mathbf{G}_6\mathbf{G}_7\mathbf{g}_8\mathbf{G}_1\mathbf{g}_2\mathbf{g}_3\mathbf{g}_4\mathbf{G}_5\mathbf{G}_6\mathbf{G}_7\mathbf{G}_8$$
$$\mathbf{G}_1\mathbf{g}_2\mathbf{g}_3\mathbf{G}_4\mathbf{G}_5\mathbf{g}_6\mathbf{G}_7\mathbf{G}_8\mathbf{G}_1\mathbf{G}_2\mathbf{G}_3\mathbf{G}_4\mathbf{G}_5\mathbf{g}_6\mathbf{g}_7\mathbf{G}_8$$
$$\text{and } \mathbf{g}_1\mathbf{G}_2\mathbf{G}_3\mathbf{G}_4\mathbf{G}_5\mathbf{G}_6\mathbf{G}_7\mathbf{G}_8\mathbf{G}_1\mathbf{g}_2\mathbf{G}_3\mathbf{G}_4\mathbf{g}_5\mathbf{g}_6\mathbf{G}_7\mathbf{g}_8$$

would be considered as occupying the same positions in relation to pure *A* and pure *B*, and they would all have the same fertility. Their genotypes could all be expressed quite simply as 11**G**5**g**. With **G** alleles represented digitally by **0** and **g** alleles by **1**, these three genotypes (and any others having the same relationship to *A* and *B*) may be given a numerical value equal to the number of **g** alleles, namely five, readily ascertainable by a **bits** instruction and easily handled when required, for example for table look-up or for population scoring for output. Plants with genotypes of identical numerical value would have identical fertility, but the numerical value is not in any way a measure of the fertility; it is an expression of taxonomic status which may be used to ascertain the fertility.

Although this treatment of the genetics of the model system is clearly by comparison with natural systems a considerable simplification, a little thought will show that departure from such simplification would have resulted in a disproportionate increase in complexity of the program.

We may first consider dominance, and continue with the convention of attributing all **G** alleles to one subspecies and all **g** to the other. If all the **G** are dominant, then the phenotype of the F_1 hybrid is the same as that of one subspecies, and we cannot use its phenotype either for classification or fertility determination. It would of course be quite easy to recognize the F_1 hybrid, whose bit representation would be **0000000011111111**, by separating the two parental sets of alleles and performing an LA followed by **bits**, which would give the answer 8 indicating heterozygosity at all eight loci. But this would introduce a distinction between the F_1 hybrid and an equally intermediate plant such as the completely homozygous $\mathbf{G_1G_2g_3G_4g_5g_6G_7g_8G_1G_2g_3G_4g_5g_6G_7g_8}$. It might of course be reasonable to suppose that fertility might be related not only to the **G**/**g** proportions, but also to the degree of heterozygosity, but it should be noted that the last cited genotype, being completely homozygous, would in terms of heterozygosity be indistinguishable from either pure **A** or pure **B**. Handling the genotype for purposes of fertility determination would thus involve consideration both of phenotype and of degree of heterozygosity.

An alternative would be to suppose that only half the **G** (say $\mathbf{G_1}$ to $\mathbf{G_4}$) are dominant, and the other half recessive. The phenotype of the F_1 hybrid would then be 4**G**4**g** and (all **G**s still being **0** and all **g**s **1**) its **bits** value 4; but this phenotype could not be determined in the usual way by an LM, since the LM would again produce a completely zero result. An alternative system, making **A** homozygous for $\mathbf{G_1}$ to $\mathbf{G_4}$ and $\mathbf{g_5}$ to $\mathbf{g_8}$ with **B** having the complementary arrangement, would be even more awkward to handle.

All these difficulties (and others not mentioned) could be overcome by a combined use of clever programming and table look-up methods. It is difficult to see that anything useful would have been gained from the considerable extra work required in programming. But in any case, if we choose to regard the **G**/**g** alleles merely as indicators of degree of hybridity, the question of dominance is irrelevant.

Another elaboration of the program might have been to suppose that the eight **G**/**g** loci did not make equal contributions to the phenotype and so to fertility. We have a little earlier introduced the concept of numerical value (then easily determined of a genotype, both as an indicator of its taxonomic status and allowing ready determination of its fertility. The numerical value is in fact a way of representing the genotype and, as far as the subspecies-characteristic genes are concerned, its phenotype. Now, with different phenotypic effects of the loci the numerical values of the phenotypes of (for example) the three plants 11**G**5**g** shown a little earlier would be different, and could not be determined by a **bits** operation; they would have to be determined by some other method such as table look-up.

The availability of a **bits** instruction made the derivation of fitness from genotype so rapid that although the assumption of different phenotypic effects of the **G**/**g** loci would not have involved any very complicated operations, the saving in time resulting from the simpler view of genotype/phenotype relationship was by no means negligible. Although the simple view was taken in designing this model system, the way in which the more elaborate situation might have been tackled may be of some general interest, and will be described here.

Suppose we have assumed a numerical value of zero for the phenotype of **A**, and of 1.0 for that of **B**, by assigning a value of zero to each **G** allele and various positive values to the eight different **g** alleles such that these values add up to 0.5 (the diploid complement of **B** totalling 1.0). There is no point in assigning values other than zero to **G** as well as to **g**—that would only increase the work without affecting the result.

The numerical phenotypic value for any plant can then be obtained by adding together the values corresponding to those **g** alleles in its genotype. But we do not need actually to determine which alleles are present and perform the addition—this would bc too slow.

We can perform the operation quickly and neatly by direct table look-up, using a table relating genotype to phenotypic value. The whole genotype does not need to be dealt with in a single reference to this table; indeed, in the example under consideration it would be impracticable to use such a table which would require 2^{16} entries for a genotype of 16 bits and would require far too much storage space. Since the phenotypic value is derived additively, and since the two parental sets of alleles have the loci in precisely the same order, it is possible to obtain the full phenotypic value by separately determining the values for each of its parental sets of alleles and adding them together. This then requires a table of only 2^8 entries, which will not usually involve any great problem of storage space.

The problem that is posed is the construction of the table, which is best done by program procedure in the following way, rather than by preliminary calculation and incorporation of the table as part of the written program. The binary representation of each set of parental alleles is of course also the relative address in binary of the corresponding address in the table, and a little thought will show that its m.s. bit must be **0**($\mathbf{G}_1$) for the first half of the table (0 to 127) and **1**($\mathbf{g}_1$) for the second half (128 to 255). The next m.s. bit is **0**($\mathbf{G}_2$) for the first and third quarters of the table (0 to 63 and 128 to 191) and **1**($\mathbf{g}_2$) for the second and fourth quarters (64 to 127 and 192 to 255). And so on down to the l.s. bit which alternates at successive addresses between **0**($\mathbf{G}_8$) and **1**($\mathbf{g}_8$), being **0** for the first address.

The table is then constructed by first clearing completely the relevant area of store, and then adding the value for $\mathbf{g}_1$ to positions 128 to 255, that for $\mathbf{g}_2$ to positions 64 to 127 and 192 to 255, and so on, finishing with the addition of the value for $\mathbf{g}_8$ into each odd-numbered position.

The numerical value for a particular genotype having been obtained by two references to this table, it must be converted into the corresponding value for the fitness. It may be asked why we cannot go directly from the genotype to the fitness instead of first having to determine a numerical value for its phenotype. The reason is simply that the relationship between the numerical value and the fitness is non-linear; the fitness has two maxima, corresponding to the extreme numerical values for the phenotype, and this means that the fitness could not be derived by table reference for each parental set of alleles separately. Writing the genotypes with the two sets separately, 8**g**8**g** and 8**G**8**G** would have equal maximum fitness, and if those fitness values were obtainable by adding fitness values for 8**g** in one case and 8**G** in the other, then 8**g**8**G** would obviously have the same maximum fitness. Direct determination of fitness from genotype would therefore involve taking the whole genotype at one time for reference, which would require a table of 2^{16} entries, which as already pointed out is impracticable.

If the numerical values assigned to the **g** alleles are carefully chosen, the numerical value/fitness table need not be very large, For example, if they could be expressed as fractions of 64 so that the maximum value for a parental set (that is, for 8**g**) was 32, then a table with 65 entries would be adequate. If a wider range of numerical values for **g** alleles is required, the table would be larger.

In deciding whether or not the **G**/**g** loci should have equal phenotypic effect, the choice would lie between a simple **bits** operation followed by a single reference to a bits/fertility table, and an operation involving two half-genotype extractions with shifts to the correct position for use in modification, and three table look-ups.

It is difficult to see that departure from the assumption of equal effect of the eight **G**/**g** loci would have had any significant bearing on the problem under investigation and would almost certainly not have been worth the extra running time that would have been involved.

Having decided that the fertility-determining values of the different **G**/**g** loci should be equal, it then remained to consider the relationship between the genotype (its numerical value expressed as the number of **g** alleles) and the fertility. The relationship could be a mathematical one, or decided entirely arbitrarily. One fairly obvious step was to arrange that the determination of fertility from genotype should be carried out in such a way that the fertility parameters could subsequently be changed with minimum alteration to the program.

The easiest way of doing this would be to have a numerical value/fertility table, which could be amended easily enough whether or not the relationship was an arbitrary one. This table would be referred to by using the number of **g** alleles as a modifier, and since that number ranged from 0 to 16, the table would be a small one with only 17 entries. In the basic version of the program, minimum fertility occurred in the F_1 hybrid and in equally intermediate plants, that is those of genotype 8**G**8**g** and numerical value 8. The values in the fertility table would therefore begin with a maximum value at location 0 (genotype 16**G**, fully fertile subspecies), fall to a minimum at location 8 (8**G**8**g**) and rise again to a maximum at location 16 (16**g**, the other fully fertile subspecies).

The relationship between fertility and the numbers of **g** alleles was decided by drawing a curve which looked reasonable and was symmetrical about 8**G**8**g**, where the fertility was at a minimum of 0.25, that of the pure subspecies being 1.0. The values required for the fertility table were then simply read off from this curve and rounded slightly so that they could be expressed in relatively few binary bits (they were subsequently to be stored with the genotype, and some economy of space within the word was essential).

In practice, the fertility table could not be constructed in quite such a simple way because, as will be seen later, the figure required for fitness testing was not the full reproductive capacity, but the reproductive capacity available in one week, and that depended for any given fitness value on the number of weeks for which the plant flowered. But the principle of reference from the number of **g** alleles to the fertility remains the same.

We may now turn to the second element in the genotype, that dealing with the potential isolating barrier, flowering time. If *A* and *B* have identical flowering periods, there are two processes which can be involved in the development and establishment of a difference. One subspecies may come to flower earlier, the other later; and when this process has started, both can shorten their flowering periods and so decrease the time during which their flowering periods overlap. Obviously, the less simultaneous the flowering, the less the amount of hybridization.

It was decided that three genes, called the **D** genes, should control the date of flowering. For the same reasons as were discussed with the subspecies-characteristic genes, these were unlinked, of equal effect with the effects strictly additive, and there was neither dominance nor interaction. $\mathbf{D_1D_2D_3D_1D_2D_3}$ plants (6**D**) were the earliest flowerers, and $\mathbf{d_1d_2d_3d_1d_2d_3}$ (6**d**) were the latest.

For both subspecies, flowering could occur during and only during a period which was divided into eight equal consecutive sections considered to be weeks (it makes no difference to the model what they are called). No plant could flower throughout the whole period, the maximum being six weeks and the minimum two, according to the genotype; the model was treated as though each plant came into flower at the beginning of its first week of flowering and finished at the end of its last, flowering evenly throughout the whole period. Control of length of flowering was by two genes, and as before these were unlinked, of equal effect with the effects strictly additive, and there was neither dominance nor interaction. These genes were called the **W** genes; the number of weeks for which a plant flowered was equal to the number of **w** alleles plus two, $\mathbf{W_1W_2W_1W_2}$ (4**W**) flowering for two weeks and $\mathbf{w_1w_2w_1w_2}$ (4**w**) for six. If there was selection for genetic isolation through flowering time, both subspecies would be expected to evolve towards 4**W** and elimination of **w** alleles, provided that length of flowering period had no effect on reproductive capacity.

This is an important proviso which must be considered in detail. It would naturally be expected that the longer a plant flowered the more flowers it would produce and so the greater would be its reproductive capacity. But in that event, there would be an element of selection in favour of longer flowering. Since this would be first order selection it would swamp the second order selection resulting from the disadvantage of hybridization, and it was in any event irrelevant to the problem under investigation. Clearly, the model had to be constructed in such a way that the reproductive capacity was determined solely by the subspecies-characteristic genes **G**/**g** and was quite independent of the length of the flowering period (but preferably constructed so that if desired it would be easy, with a minimum of program revision, to investigate the effect of allowing some increase in reproductive capacity with length of flowering period).

Thus, if we suppose that for all plants of a given fertility the total production of good ovules by each was n, then for any such plant the mean weekly production of good ovules would be n/m where m was the length of its flowering period in weeks. The same would apply to pollen production. The point then to be decided was whether the reproductive capacity should be spread evenly over the m weeks of flowering, or whether it should start lower than average, rise to a maximum at the middle of the flowering period, and decline towards the finish, as it would be expected to do in nature. Thus for a plant flowering for three weeks we might have, say, successive weekly values of $n/4$, $n/2$ and $n/4$; for one flowering for six weeks we might have something like $n/16$, $3n/16$, $n/4$, $n/4$, $3n/16$ and $n/16$; but the pattern need not be symmetrical.

At the time the program was developed, it was felt that it would have raised programming difficulties to have allowed the weekly reproductive capacity to change during the flowering period, and it was decided that for each plant its weekly reproductive capacity should be the same for each week in which it was flowering, that is n/m. In fact, it would not have been particularly difficult, though it would have added a little to the running time of the program. Since when the flowering times have come to differ somewhat, simultaneous flowering would now have involved lower intensity periods of each subspecies (beginning of one, end of the other), one effect might have been to reduce the selection pressure in favour of a shorter flowering period, and so perhaps have produced results somewhat different quantitatively from those which were obtained. In retrospect, this seems to have been a situation where it would have been preferable to have sacrificed a little simplicity for an increase in realism.

One final assumption which needs to be stated explicitely relates to pollination. It was assumed that the pollen vectors were entirely without taxonomic discrimination, and that their movements from flower to flower were unrelated to the genotypes of the plants concerned.

The Outline Flow Diagram

With the basic features of the model in mind, we can now consider the construction of an outline flow diagram, and this is shown in Figure 59. This is the final form of this flow diagram, corresponding to the program actually used. (Tentative versions drawn up during its development will not be discussed.)

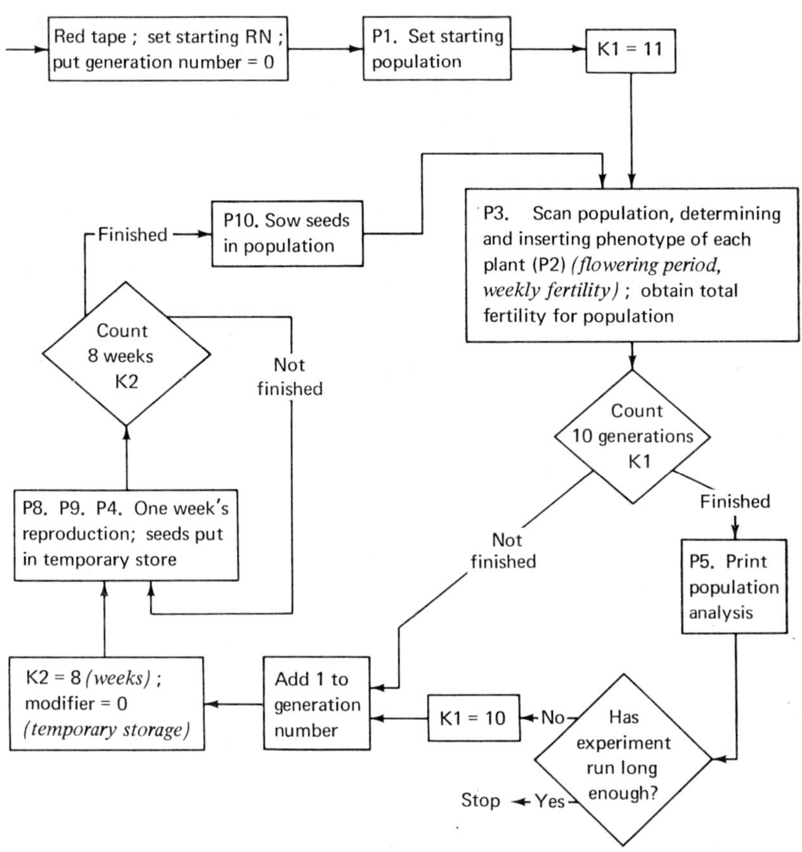

Figure 59. Outline flow diagram for the model described in this chapter

Broadly speaking, the account which follows will deal with the program as though it were being written now, having already been fully conceived. It would not be practicable to describe the way in which it was actually written, since there was a great deal of interconnection between subroutine requirements, and when first writing one subroutine it was not always apparent in detail how it would be affected by the requirements of others to be written later, and consequently earlier written subroutines often required amendment. This means that the writing of some subroutines will be described with hindsight and references will occasionally be made to requirements of others still to be described or to later requirements by the main program; the precise significance of some operations may not always be clear until the later subroutines are described. The sections of the program will be dealt with in the order in which they occur in the program, and not in the order in which they were written, which was to some extent haphazard. The subroutine numbers given correspond to those of the actual program and to the order in which they were written rather than to the order in which they will be dealt with here.

After initial red tape, the first operation is to set the starting population which is of course an array of individuals represented by digital simulation of their genotypes.

During the process of reproduction of the population, it will be necessary to know the phenotype of each individual (its fitness, and the weeks during which it is in flower). Since the determination of this from the genotype is a somewhat lengthy operation and (as will be seen later) the phenotype of each plant needs to be referred to several times, it is more efficient to determine it once and for all and store it in some numerical form with the genotype.

This operation could have been done quite easily for each original plant as it was put into the population, but since it was known that there would be a subroutine which would scan the population whenever required, performing the necessary determination and insertion of the phenotype for each plant in turn, it was preferable to keep population setting simple and insert the phenotypes as a separate operation using that subroutine. There was the added advantage that if at some future date it was desired to alter the fertility relationships or flowering characteristics of the different genotypes this would require amendment of only one subroutine and not two. The important thing is not to forget to insert the phenotypes for the starting population. The consequences of forgetting are dramatic, as the author well knows—all plants have zero fitness and the program goes into a permanent loop as it tries in vain to perform the first act of reproduction.

The phenotype having been determined and inserted, the population can now reproduce, and this operation is performed on a weekly basis by repeating eight times (corresponding to the eight successive weeks during which flowering is possible) a cycle in the course of which only the plants flowering in the relevant week are considered for reproduction. During reproduction, the seeds, represented by their genotypes, are sent to a temporary store.

When reproduction for all eight weeks is completed, the existing population is replaced by the new generation by means of a subroutine which sows the seed, not entirely at random but for each seed with regard to a predetermined pattern of dispersal about its point of origin within the population.

With the old generation dead, and the seed of the new one dispersed in the population store, the program comes back to the determination and insertion of the phenotypes, which in effect represents seed germination and growth.

It would have been easy to have dealt with phenotype determination and insertion for each plant as its seed was sown, and this would normally be the natural way for the author to deal with it since it would mean that each plant would have to be handled only on one occasion instead of two. But as the seed sowing subroutine was rather an intricate one the author preferred to deal with the two operations separately. The extra time required by having to handle each plant a second time was only a few seconds in a run of an hour. Provided there is no significant loss of time there is much to be said for separating complex procedures; for one thing, if it subsequently becomes necessary or otherwise desirable to amend or re-write one procedure, this can be done without having to consider any possible effect on the program of the other which may require a consequential amendment (always a fruitful source of error). Neatness of program is in this context a secondary consideration.

We come next to the question of output. For the moment we are not concerned with its nature, except that it is going to be complex and bulky; this will be discussed later. All we need to consider now is how frequently output will be required. The pilot experiment had taken about 80 generations to complete its evolutionary sequence, and it was felt that the large-scale model would take several times as long since in contrast to the situation in the former, most of the plants of each subspecies were now, initially at any rate, not in contact with those of the other and so the proportion of hybridization (which was producing the selection pressure) was less. It was known that output was likely on each occasion to occupy four pages, and take about twenty seconds with a line printer. Apart from using too much time, output every generation would produce a quite indigestible mass of figures. As a first guess, it was decided that output every tenth generation would be adequate, and this proved to be the case.

So by using a counter set to ten which is tested immediately after the phenotype determination and insertion procedure, there will be output of a detailed population analysis after every tenth cycle of reproduction. When no output is required the program goes straight on to produce the next generation; if output is required, this is carried out and then the program either re-sets the counter and goes on to the next generation, beginning another 10-generation sequence, or if it has gone on long enough it stops.

Stopping can be determined in two ways. The natural way would be dependent on a length of run pre-determined by number of generations (or rather, in practice, by the number of outputs, a counter being set to one-tenth of the desired number of generations). Actually, it was determined rather differently. The author really had no very precise idea for how long each experiment ought to run, particularly in the early testing runs with the model before he had experience to guide him, and in any case an experiment subject to random fluctuations is as unpredictable in terms of evolution rates as in other respects. KDF9 had a hardware clock, which could readily be referred to by the program and this was used to determine when a run should be stopped. Usually, each run was timed to finish immediately following the first output after 30 minutes, when the whole program (current population as well as instructions etc). was transferred to magnetic tape. The results so far could then be considered at leisure, and if the experiment had not gone far enough the program was read from the magnetic tape back to the computer, restarted where it had left off, and run for a further 30 minutes. And so on until it was considered to have gone far enough. 30 minutes corresponded to about 150 generations, and most experiments were run for a total of an hour and a half. The techniques for dealing with transfer to and recall from magnetic tape vary a great deal from computer to computer, and there is little point in discussing them.

The flow diagram of Figure 59 requires a little comment. It would seem from the diagram that population analysis and output was carried out (when required) at the beginning of a reproductive cycle (generation) and not at the end which would be the natural place for it. In fact of course, before and after have no significance when going round in a circle, and the apparent position of the population analysis and output is determined by the point at which the reproductive cycle is first entered after the initial population has been set. This point of entry must be immediately prior to the determination and insertion of the phenotypes, and this is naturally followed by execution or avoidance of population analysis. This also explains the curious initial setting (before the reproductive cycle is entered) of the generation counter at 11; no analysis of the population is required at the start; at the first count the counter is reduced to 10 and not to zero, and is therefore then at the correct value of 10 to give the first output at generation 10. During the rest of the run the counter is re-set at 10 only, within the reproduction cycle after analysis and output. The difference between the generation counter and the generation number should be noted. The former is used only to count ten generations to determine output, and is re-set at 10-generation intervals. Generation number begins at zero and is increased by one at each generation, so that the current generation number may be printed as a label with each population analysis output. (It is preferable to count by adding one at each generation rather than by adding ten at each output, because if it is decided to change the interval of output only the setting of the generation counter needs to be altered, not the value added to the generation number.)

We may now consider each of the major elements of the program in turn, For most of these there are still important decisions to be made on the biology and the relevant simulation procedures.

The Initial Population. P1.

The first of these major elements is the routine which sets the initial population, and here there are two distinct aspects to be considered. These are how the spatial distribution of the individual plants is to be represented in the computer, and what the genetical structure of the population is to be.

In order to keep the programming as simple as was compatible with the introduction of the concept of position and distance, it was decided that as far as pollen transport and seed dispersal were concerned the population should be treated as though it were linear. It was also decided that some provision should be made to allow variation in plant density, both through the population and from time to time, while keeping the overall population size approximately constant. Since reproduction was going to take place on a weekly basis and involve only plants actually in flower at the time, the number of plants taking part in reproduction would vary and this would mean that random choice would rarely be from an array of plants which was a power of two. There was therefore no point in having an overall population size which was a power of two. The chosen size was 2560, half to be of one subspecies, half of the other.

This population was considered as being arranged in a long narrow rectangle of 256 rows, each row containing initially ten plants but having places for 15; although the population would start with a uniform density, during the course of an experiment the number of plants in any row could vary from zero to 15.

There was to be no lateral restriction (that is within the row) of pollen and seed movement (at least, it was originally intended that there should be no lateral restriction of pollen flow, but as it turned out the way in which pollen transport was simulated did introduce some kind of lateral restriction); only movement along the population (that is between rows) was subject to that restriction of distance on dispersal which was one of the essential features of the system.

Since throughout the population some words will represent plants and others unoccupied places, with differences from one generation to the next, it is necessary that the program should know which are which. This could be done by tagging each unoccupied word so that it could be recognized when inspected, but there would be some waste of time if every word has to be examined whenever the population is scanned, since one third of the population store consists of unoccupied words. It would also be necessary to ensure that after the seed has been dispersed and sown each word left unoccupied is in fact tagged; it would not be sufficient that unoccupied words would be zero (all plants of the previous generation are made zero when they have finished flowering—see later), because such a word would be indistinguishable from a zero genotype (16**G**4**W**6**D**) before the phenotype has been added in.

It is therefore preferable to keep a tally of the number of plants in each row as the seeds are sown. The places in each row are filled sequentially from one end, the current value of the tally indicating the next vacant word. Since the plants in a row then occupy words from the beginning with no gaps between them, the population can be scanned row by row with the appropriate tally being used as a counter for each row and only the words occupied being scanned. The other words in the row are thus never inspected in that generation and their contents are irrelevant.

The row tallies could be produced and maintained as required by using a 256-word section of store, each word holding the number of the plants currently in the relevant row; in some ways this might be easier than the method which was used. The population is in fact stored in a consecutive sequence of 4096 words, in 256 sections of 16 words. For each 16-word section, the first word is the tally and carries the number of plants in the following 15 words which represent the row; the words which contain plants always follow immediately after the tally word, with no gap, the distal words being the unoccupied ones, if any.

It was decided that the two subspecies should not overlap, but merely be in contact (overlapping would have been easy enough to arrange, and was in fact done for one experiment, but it made no difference to the results—without overlapping the subspecies quickly came to interpenetrate slightly by virtue of seed dispersal). Setting the population thus involves setting 128 sections (rows) of 16 words of which the first carries the tally number 10, the next ten each contain a plant of subspecies A, and the remaining five are to be regarded as zero, although their actual contents are irrelevant as previously explained and they do not need to be set at zero (they could have been left non-zero by a previous program). Then follow 128 sections which are arranged identically with the first except that A is replaced by B.

Before deciding on the way to do this, we need to consider how the genotype is to be represented, and what the genetical structure of the population is to be. The subspecies-characteristic genes present no difficulty, since one subspecies is to be 16**G** and the other 16**g**.

The time of flowering genes however have to be considered rather carefully. In the pilot experiment it had been decided to begin with the subspecies genetically identical in respect of the date of flowering genes **D**/**d** (with the same genetical variability), mainly to see if a difference in flowering time could come about between the two subspecies purely by random change in gene frequency. In a deterministic model, such a start would produce no evolutionary change, since there can be no selection for difference in flowering time as a barrier to hybridization until such a difference exists. But if such a difference can arise in a stochastic model, then selection can come into operation and increase it. The pilot model showed that this in fact could happen.

One of the difficulties which might arise from waiting for a flowering time difference to appear as a consequence of random change in gene frequency would come directly from the nature of the process—it might take a very long time. In any case, it is unlikely that two previously separated subspecies would have precisely the same flowering periods. *A* and *B* are therefore given at the start slightly different average **D/d** genotypes, and the question under investigation now is whether under the circumstances of the more complex model system selection can increase this difference in response to the disadvantage of hybridization. The same argument does not apply to the length of flowering genes **W/w** and the two subspecies start with mean flowering periods identical in length, namely four weeks, and with the same variability.

The desired genetical variability in the population can be satisfactorily represented in an array of ten plants, and the simplest way of setting the population is to specify in the written program a row containing ten plants of *A* and a row containing ten plants of *B*, and copy each of these rows into the appropriate 128 rows of the population. Since the ten *A* plants are not identical among themselves with respect to **D/d** and **W/w**, and nor are the ten *B* plants, each subspecies will be genetically variable across the population (that is along the row) but, subject to this, genetically uniform throughout its length.

Representing for the moment the genotypes of the plants in contracted form, the 11 words required to specify a row of subspecies *A* are as follows, the first word being the tally:

10; 16**G**1**W**3**w**5**D**1**d**; 16**G**2**W**2**w**4**D**2**d**; 16**G**2**W**2**w**3**D**3**d**; 16**G**3**W**1**w**3**D**3**d**; 16**G**3**W**1**w**3**D**3**d**; 16**G**2**W**2**w**4**D**2**d**; 16**G**2**W**2**w**2**D**4**d**; 16**G**1**W**3**w**2**D**4**d**; 16**G**2**W**2**w**3**D**3**d**; 16**G**2**W**2**w**4**D**2**d**.

For subspecies *B*, the 11 words are:

10; 16**g**1**W**3**w**4**D**2**d**; 16**g**2**W**2**w**4**D**2**d**; 16**g**2**W**2**w**2**D**4**d**; 16**g**3**W**1**w**3**D**3**d**; 16**g**3**W**1**w**3**D**3**d**; 16**g**2**W**2**w**3**D**3**d**; 16**g**2**W**2**w**2**D**4**d**; 16**g**1**W**3**w**1**D**5**d**; 16**g**2**W**2**w**2**D**4**d**; 16**g**2**W**2**w**3**D**3**d**.

These 22 words are written sequentially in the subroutine program as parameters. The genotypes cannot however be written in the form in which they have just been presented, for two reasons. One is that this would be unintelligible to the compiler which needs them in a form which it can convert directly into a binary pattern, that is as a decimal number, an octal number, or a pattern of letters. The other reason is that the contracted forms of the genotypes which have been given do not sufficiently specify the genotype because not only do they fail to distinguish the alleles of the two parental gamete sets, but also for the **D/d** and **W/w** loci they do not specify which bits are **1** and which **0**.

Thus there are 15 different binary representations which could give **4D2d**. It is therefore necessary, having decided in general terms what the genotypes are to be, to make these more specific as regards the actual loci involved. The $\mathbf{w}_1$ and $\mathbf{w}_2$ frequencies will be identical for the whole population, and so will the $\mathbf{d}_1$, $\mathbf{d}_2$ and $\mathbf{d}_3$ frequencies within each subspecies. As nearly as is possible with ten plants, it will be arranged that for each of the five **W**/**w** and **D**/**d** loci among those ten plants the proportion of heterozygotes to homozygotes will be that to be expected in a panmictic population; the correct (stochastic) proportions will be reached automatically after the first generation.

With the two parental sets of alleles lying side by side, the sequence in each set will be the eight **G**/**g** alleles, the two **W**/**w** alleles and the three **D**/**d** alleles. When the program was written, it was decided that the phenotypes could be handled more easily at the l.s. end of a word, and the genotype was therefore put at the m.s. end (but excluding the sign bit).

Thus if the bits of a word are numbered from zero at the m.s. end, the **G**/**g** loci will occupy bits 1 to 8 (for one parental set) and 14 to 21 (for the other), the **W**/**w** loci bits 9, 10, 22 and 23, and the **D**/**d** loci bits 11 to 13 and 24 to 26. To make this clear, we may write out the bit patterns which were actually used for the fourth and fifth *B* plants, remembering that we are now dealing with the 48-bit word of KDF9. Spaces are used here to separate the different components of the genotype. The genotypes of these two plants were expressed above identically as **16g3W1w3D3d**, but they were in fact not identical, being in bit form

0 11111111 10 101 11111111 00 100 000000000000000000000

and

0 11111111 01 001 11111111 00 011 000000000000000000000.

Ignoring the **g** alleles which were the same for both, the two plants were thus $\mathbf{w}_1\mathbf{W}_2\mathbf{d}_1\mathbf{D}_2\mathbf{d}_3\mathbf{W}_1\mathbf{W}_2\mathbf{d}_1\mathbf{D}_2\mathbf{D}_3$ and $\mathbf{W}_1\mathbf{w}_2\mathbf{D}_1\mathbf{D}_2\mathbf{d}_3\mathbf{W}_1\mathbf{W}_2\mathbf{D}_1\mathbf{d}_2\mathbf{d}_3$ respectively.

These binary patterns had to be written in a form acceptable to the compiler, and the easiest way of doing this is to write them as the octal numbers 3775377440000000 and 3772377430000000 respectively (the spaces in the binary patterns above are irrelevant and are ignored).

The string of 21 unused bits at the l.s. end of each word will subsequently contain the phenotype—fertility and flowering period.

The flow diagram for the population-setting subroutine **P1** is quite simple and is shown in Figure 60. A modifier is first set to zero, to pass sequentially through the population, and then a counter is set to count half the rows in the population. For each row, a counter is set at 11 and a modifier at zero, to copy the appropriate 11 parameter words into the row, and when that copy is complete the first modifier is incremented by five to skip the unoccupied words at the end of the row. When the first 128 rows have been dealt with, the first counter (but not the first modifier) is re-set and the second half of the population receives its *B* plants in the same way as the first half received *A*.

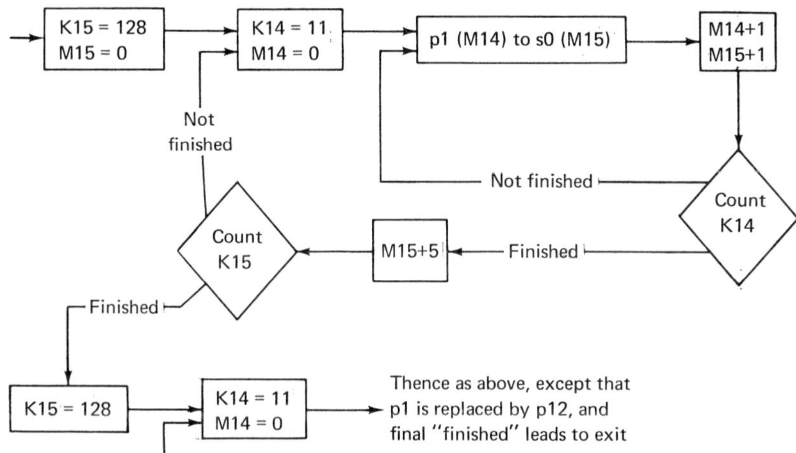

Figure 60. Flow diagram for subroutine **P1**, which sets the starting population in **s0** onwards, from row tally plus row of *A* plants stored in **p1** to **p11**, and row tally plus row of *B* plants stored in **p12** to **p22**

If at some subsequent stage it is desired to change the genetical constitution of the starting population, then provided it is still possible to keep the *A* rows identical and the *B* rows identical, all that would be necessary would be to amend the appropriate genotypes in the parameter list of the subroutine. If it is desired (as it was in a later experiment) to mingle *A* and *B* at the beginning instead of having them non-overlapping, this can be done quite easily by using the same subroutine but adding a procedure which comes into operation when the population has been set as above. With *A* originally in rows 0 to 127 and *B* in 128 to 255, this additional procedure interchanges rows 127 and 128, 125 and 130, 123 and 132, and so on according to how much interpenetration of *A* and *B* is required.

Phenotype Determination and Insertion. P2, P3.

The starting population having been set, the next major operation is to determine the phenotype of each plant and store it for future reference. In a computer with a smaller word size than the KDF9, for example our notional 32-bit XB1, there would be no room for the phenotype in the same word as the genotype, and phenotypes would have to be stored elsewhere in parallel with the population. With the sign bit and genotype occupying 27 bits of the 48-bit KDF9 word, 21 bits are left available for the phenotype and when it has been determined it is simply added in to the genotype word at its l.s. end. When required later in the program it is extracted by use of the appropriate masks.

We need to consider what information about the phenotype will be needed by the program. What we may call the taxonomic element of the phenotype is directly determinable by a **bits** operation on the **G**/**g** section of the genotype, and this need not be considered further.

The other information which the program will need is the fertility and the actual weeks during which the plant will be in flower. Six bits are allocated for the expression of the flowering period element of the phenotype, three being used to specify the week in which flowering is to start and the other three the number of weeks over which flowering will extend. This way of expressing the flowering phenotype is very convenient for the program to handle and was decided upon with subsequent procedures in mind. There was, however, a better way of doing it which was explained towards the end of Chapter 7.

Neither element of the phenotype is quite so easy to deal with as it might seem. We may consider fertility first. Reproduction is dealt with on a weekly basis, and when a plant is chosen as a possible parent it is not its total fertility which is required for the fertility test, but the amount of fertility available in that particular week, or putting it less clumsily, its reproductive capacity for that week. This value will be called the weekly fertility.

This weekly fertility is to be tested against a random number to determine whether on any particular occasion on which it has been chosen a potential parent is to be used or rejected. To avoid unnecessary rejection, plants with maximum weekly fertility (that is, either of the pure subspecies flowering for only two weeks) need to be used every time they are chosen, and are therefore assigned a weekly fertility value of 1.0. Since this is a purely operational quantity, there is no inconsistency in allocating a value for the weekly fertility equal to that for the total fertility. For any plant therefore, if f is its total fertility, its weekly fertility is $2f/m$, where m is the number of weeks for which the plant is in flower. (We have earlier discussed the decision that the weekly fertility of a plant should be constant over all weeks in which it is in flower.)

The weekly fertility is thus obtained from the **G**/**g** genotype (which allows f to be determined) and the **W**/**w** genotype (which gives m), but it would be a waste of time to look up f and then divide it by $m/2$ (m is the number of **w** alleles plus two). It is much simpler to have a table giving the weekly fertilities directly, being referred to by use of a modifier which combines the **G**/**g** and **W**/**w** elements of the genotype. What is required therefore is a table of five sections, each section giving the **G/g** : weekly fertility relationship for one of the five possible lengths of flowering period (two weeks to six weeks). If g is the number of **g** alleles, each section of the table has 17 entries covering all values of g from zero to 16. If w is the number of **w** alleles, then the simplest way of combining the relevant two elements of the genotype for table look-up is to use the value $g+17w$ as a modifier. For two weeks of flowering ($w=0$), the relevant weekly fertilities will be in words 0 to 16 of the table, for three weeks in words 17 to 33, and so on.

Although 21 bits were available for the phenotype in the 48-bit KDF9 word, they were not all allocated for this purpose, partly because it was felt desirable to hold some bits in reserve in case they should be required for possible future modifications of the model and also because it might be necessary for other information to be carried temporarily by the plant. With the flowering time phenotype occupying six bits (3+3), seven of the remaining 15 were allocated for the weekly fertility, being the seven l.s. bits of the word. Seven was fixed on for no better reason than that this had been used in the pilot model on Pegasus whose word size did not allow of the use of more than seven bits for this purpose. To keep this number for the KDF9 model was a silly decision made without sufficient thought; it raised problems, because while it was easy enough to arrange that all the values for the total fertility could be expressed precisely in seven bits, this was not possible for all values of $2f/m$, since m could have any of the values 2, 3, 4, 5 and 6. This meant that in some cases the weekly fertility was a rounded approximation, and thus the basic assumption that the total reproductive capacity was independent of the length of the flowering period could not be strictly adhered to. Since one of the objects of the investigation was to see whether there was selection for shorter flowering period purely on the basis of avoiding hybridization, it was obviously important that the rounding errors involved in specification of the weekly fertilities did not confer any advantage on shorter flowering. All rounding of $2f/m$ was therefore carried out in such a direction that any effect on selection would tend slightly to favour longer rather than shorter flowering period and not invalidate any conclusions to be drawn from shortening of the flowering period if that should occur. More bits should have been allocated to the weekly fertility, to diminish the effect of the rounding errors, but by the time it was realized that more bits would be available for this, several parts of the program were already committed to the 3+3+7 bit structure for the phenotype, and to have changed this and made all the consequential amendments would have been arduous and liable to the introduction of error. In the event, it seems likely that the rounding errors did weaken slightly the selection of shorter flowering period; but it was clear enough from the results that such selection had nevertheless taken place, so no real damage was done.

The use of seven bits at the l.s. end to represent the weekly fertility means that the latter is expressed as an integer but treated as a fraction of 128, and it appears in the fertility table as an integer i in the range 0 to 127. For the fertility test, this integer will be compared with a 7-bit random integer in the range 0 to 127, and the plant rejected when this random number exceeds i. The actual weekly fertility is thus $(i+1)/128$. In the written program, the fertility table appears as a string of integers in the parameter list of the subroutine **P2** determining and inserting the phenotype. Amendment of this table, to change either the total fertilities with respect to **G**/**g** genotype or the weekly fertilities with respect to length of the flowering period, would be a simple matter not requiring amendment to any other part of the program. It is worth pointing out that such a table could not accommodate fertilities both of 1.0 and zero (the minimum value zero for i gives a true weekly fertility of 1/128; a negative value could not be used for i because although a negative integer could be packed into the word carrying the genotype, it would be awkward to handle when required). This did not raise any difficulty, as zero fitness was never required.

The construction of the table for determination of the flowering period was also not completely straightforward. We will follow the usual programming practice of numbering the weeks of flowering from 0 to 7. This makes identification of plants about to come into flower a simple matter, as will be explained later (in Crosby's 1970 paper, numbering was from 1 to 8 to avoid confusing readers with no experience of computing.)

For plants flowering for only two weeks, there is no difficulty; 6**D** plants would flower in weeks 0 and 1, 5**D**1**d** in weeks 1 and 2, and so on, with 6**d** plants flowering in weeks 6 and 7. But for plants flowering for three weeks, if the same principle were followed with 6**D** plants flowering in weeks 0 to 2, 6**d** plants would flower in weeks 6 to 8 which is not possible since it exceeds the limit of the flowering period. It should be clear that in this case two different **D**/**d** genotypes would need to have identical flowering periods. The extreme situation arises with plants flowering for six weeks, when only three different flowering periods (0 to 5, 1 to 6, 2 to 7) are available for seven different **D**/**d** genotypes. The determination and manner of use of flowering time phenotype in this model has been used as an example and discussed in Chapter 7. That discussion may be amplified by considering how the table of flowering time phenotypes was produced.

To begin with, a diagram was made showing genotypes and actual flowering periods, allotting the latter to the former in a way which seemed to give a sensible visual impression. This is illustrated in Table 14, and it will be noticed that (except for the 6-week flowering periods) no pair of **D**/**d** genotypes had identical flowering periods for more than one **W**/**w** genotype; thus 5**D**1**d** and 4**D**2**d** had identical flowering periods when they were flowering for

TABLE 14

The flowering periods, and their octal representations, for all combinations of **W/w** and **D/d**. In the octal representation, the m.s. digit gives the first week of flowering, the l.s. one the number of weeks

W w	**D d**	0	1	2	3	4	5	6	7	Octal
					Weeks					
	6 0	—	—							02
	5 1		—	—						12
	4 2			—	—					22
4 0	3 3				—	—				32
	2 4					—	—			42
	1 5						—	—		52
	0 6							—	—	62
	6 0	—	—	—						03
	5 1		—	—	—					13
	4 2			—	—	—				23
3 1	3 3			—	—	—				23
	2 4				—	—	—			33
	1 5					—	—	—		43
	0 6						—	—	—	53
	6 0	—	—	—	—					04
	5 1		—	—	—	—				14
	4 2		—	—	—	—				14
2 2	3 3			—	—	—	—			24
	2 4				—	—	—	—		34
	1 5				—	—	—	—		34
	0 6					—	—	—	—	44
	6 0	—	—	—	—	—				05
	5 1	—	—	—	—	—				05
	4 2		—	—	—	—	—			15
1 3	3 3			—	—	—	—	—		25
	2 4			—	—	—	—	—		25
	1 5				—	—	—	—	—	35
	0 6				—	—	—	—	—	35
	6 0	—	—	—	—	—	—			06
	5 1	—	—	—	—	—	—			06
	4 2	—	—	—	—	—	—			06
0 4	3 3		—	—	—	—	—	—		16
	2 4			—	—	—	—	—	—	26
	1 5			—	—	—	—	—	—	26
	0 6			—	—	—	—	—	—	26

four weeks and when they were flowering for six weeks, but otherwise the former began flowering one week earlier than the latter.

It was easy enough to translate the lines in the table into a 2-digit octal number, the m.s. digit giving the first week of flowering and the l.s. one the number of weeks. It then remained to list in the written program these octal numbers in a form in which they could be compiled into a table.

This presented no difficulty with KDF9, whose compiler would accept a specification giving the octal number and the position which its l.s. bit was to occupy in the word. Consider the genotype 3**W**1**w**4**D**2**d**. This begins in week 2 and flowers for three weeks, the octal representation being 23. The weekly fertility is to occupy the seven l.s. bits of the word carrying the plant and the flowering time parameter the six next m.s. bits. The latter should be in its proper position for adding to the plant without any shifts being required, and in binary would therefore be **...010 011 0000000**. In the 48-bit word (bits numbered 0 to 47), the l.s. bit of the octal number is in position 40, and the KDF9 compiler would accept and correctly interpret the specification **B23/40**, **B** indicating the octal nature of the **23**.

With Mendol it would have been less easy since octal representation has to take the binary bits in threes from the l.s. end; the example given would be **8/4600**, and clearly great care would have to be taken in translation. The safest way would be to specify all flowering parameters as if the were at the l.s. end—**8/23** in the present example— and have a short procedure at the start of the program which would shift all the table entries up seven places.

As explained in Chapter 7, the table is referred to by using $8w+d$ as a modifier, w and d being the numbers of **w** and **d** alleles in the genotype ascertainable by **bits** operations after extraction with the appropriate masks. But for this purpose the table in the program could not be exactly as shown in Table 14. If we consider genotype 1**W**3**w**2**D**4**d**, $8w+d$ comes to 28, but the relevant entry in Table 14 is (beginning with zero) in line 25. This is because Table 14 does not include the non-existent genotypes with 7**d**, and therefore needs expanding by insertion of a dummy word (any value, it will never be referred to) after every item corresponding to 6**d**, except the last which does not matter. The full length of the table is then 39 words. This is better than using $7w+d$, which requires a multiplication instead of a simple shift of w.

Having decided on how the genotype is to be represented and how it is to be determined by table look-up from the various elements of the genotype, the next step is to consider how the addition of the phenotypes to the words representing the plants may be effected, and the broad structure of the operative procedure.

Basically, two distinct operations are involved, and since they are distinct there is a good deal to be said for using separate subroutines, since each operation can then in writing the program be dealt with more or less independently of the other.

One subroutine, **P3**, will scan the population, extracting each plant in turn. As each plant is extracted, **P3** will call in **P2** (which is thus internal to **P3**) to determine and add the phenotype. The scanning subroutine will then return the plant to its original position in the population store. The only considerations which **P3** has to take of **P2** are the presentation of the plant in the accumulator required by the latter, and providing the jump instruction (link setting is automatic in KDF9). The contents of the phenotype subroutine are irrelevant to the scanning subroutine so long as they correctly perform the required operation.

There is however one other operation which has to be performed by this whole procedure, which is not immediately apparent. It illustrates the point that although one can use subroutines to segment and simplify the writing of a complex program, they cannot always be considered in isolation, since requirements of one part of a program may have repercussion elsewhere. At a later stage of the program, reproduction will be taking place on a weekly basis, and it will be necessary to know how many seeds will have to be produced for each particular week. Now it is known how many seeds will have to be produced for each generation; that will be the population size, 2560. This total will be made up of eight different weekly instalments of seed production, and the proportions of these will not be the same from one generation to another if our basic hypothesis is correct that there will be a change in flowering times, since that will mean that for any particular week the number of plants in flower (and consequently the seed that is set) will vary from generation to generation. Further, the mean reproductive capacity of the plants in flower in any particular week may also vary from generation to generation. Clearly, the seed to be produced in any specified week will depend on the total reproductive capacity (fertility) available in that week, and can be determined by multiplying 2560 by the ratio of the total of the weekly fertilities of plants flowering in that week to the grand total of weekly fertilities for all plants over all eight weeks.

In any week, the sum of the weekly fertilities of plants flowering in that week can be obtained as they are identified for reproduction. The grand total of the weekly fertilities is most conveniently accumulated during the operation of phenotype insertion. This could be done by summing over all plants the product for each one of its weekly fertility and the number of weeks of flowering.

The method actually used is quicker, but the slight rounding errors that were involved in calculating the weekly fertilities have to be ignored. It is to determine for each plant, in addition to its actual weekly fertility, the weekly fertility it would have had with the same **G/g** genotype if it had been flowering for two weeks only, and this is done by making a second reference to the fertility table using g as the modifier instead of $g+17w$ (this is the same as taking $w=0$). The value so obtained is actually the total reproductive capacity of the plant—remember that the weekly fertilities have been scaled up by a factor of two so that the maximum weekly fertility is 1.0.

The sum of these values over all plants will give a value equal to half the required grand total of the weekly fertilities; the necessary doubling of the sum can be executed when it is required, which is less work than doubling each value as it is obtained.

So after **P2** has determined the phenotype and added it to the plant sent to it by the scanning subroutine, it returns the plant to the latter and also provides in another accumulator the relevant fertility value required for the grand total.

Of the two subroutines, the internal one, **P2**, which determines and inserts the phenotype will be considered first, following the usual practice.

P2 accepts (in a specified accumulator) a plant from the scanning subroutine, inserts its phenotype (weekly fertility, first week of flowering, and number of weeks of flowering), and returns it to the scanning subroutine in one accumulator together with its total reproductive capacity in another. We have already discussed how the elements of the phenotype are related to, and how they may be determined from, the relevant elements of the genotype. We only need to consider how the subroutine operates.

Three masks are required, corresponding to genotypes 16**g**4**W**6**D**, 16**G**4**w**6**D**, and 16**G**4**W**6**d**, to extract the **G**/**g**, **W**/**w** and **D**/**d** sections of the genotype preparatory to the **bits** operations which determine the numbers of **g**, **w** and **d** alleles respectively, previously designated as g, w and d. From these, the appropriate modifiers for table reference are derived. The phenotype values in the tables are in their proper bit positions, and on extraction are simply added to the word containing the genotype. Since g and w are required twice, a copy of each is stored to avoid the need for redetermination. A copy of the plant has also to be retained, since not only is it needed three times for genotype extraction, but it has to be returned with added phenotype to the scanning subroutine.

The two phenotype tables are stored as part of the subroutine parameter list. The weekly fertility table occupies 85 words, the flowering period table 39. The flow diagram of **P2** is shown in Figure 61.

In considering the scanning subroutine **P3**, it must be remembered that **P2** uses **M15**, and this therefore cannot be used by **P3** unless such use is quite separate in time from use of **P2**. The latter uses accumulators **E**, **F**, **G** and **H**; **G** and **H** are used for communication with the scanning subroutine and so their use by the latter at the relevant time is prescribed.

For the first time the scanning subroutine is used, which is to add the phenotypes to the plants of the starting population, the population consists of 256 rows with ten plants each. But subsequently this will not be the case, since the population will have reproduced and the number of plants per row will not remain constant.

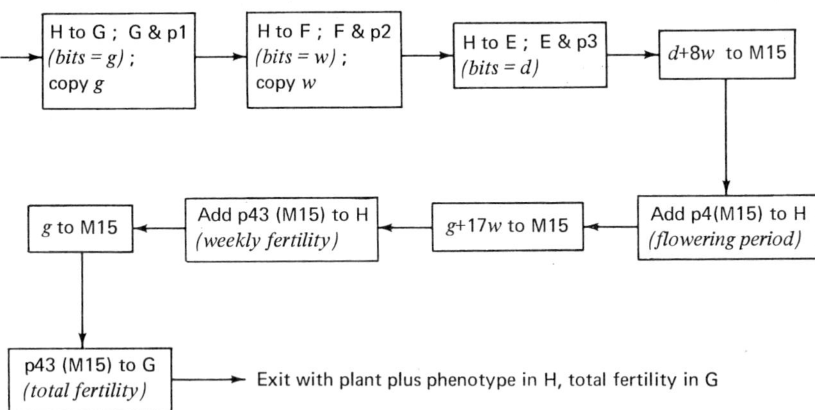

Figure 61. Flow diagram for subroutine **P2**, which adds weekly fertility and flowering time phenotype into a plant supplied to it in accumulator **H**. **p1**, **p2** and **p3** contain the masks for **g**, **w** and **d**. Flowering period table begins in **p4**, weekly fertility table in **p43**

Every sixteenth word of the population block will give the number of plants in the corresponding row, that is in the next 15 words. So the subroutine needs to execute 256 times a loop in which the number k (the tally) in address **s**n (where n is zero or a multiple of 16) is used as a counter to deal with the plants in the next k words following **s**n. The value of **s**n needs to be advanced by 16 at each execution of the loop, but it is also advanced by one each time a plant or k is dealt with. The obvious way of doing all this would seem to be add one to the modifier as each plant or k is extracted, and when all the plants in the row are finished to increment the modifier by $15-k$, the number of unoccupied places in the row. This is rather clumsy since it involves a subtraction and an extra addition to a modifier. Where, as in KDF9 user code, an address may be referred to by two modifiers, there is no problem; one modifier is incremented by 16 at each execution of the loop, while the other begins each loop at zero and is incremented by one as each plant or the tally is extracted.

Where this is not possible, the simplest method is to use an accumulator to store a number which is initially zero, is incremented by 16 after each execution of the loop, and is put into a modifier at the beginning of the loop, this modifier being used relative to the address **s0** (the first word of the population store) and incremented by one each time *k* or a plant is extracted; the number in the accumulator is not incremented during these latter operations.

The subroutine is quite straightforward, and there should be no difficulty in following it from the flow diagram, Figure 62.

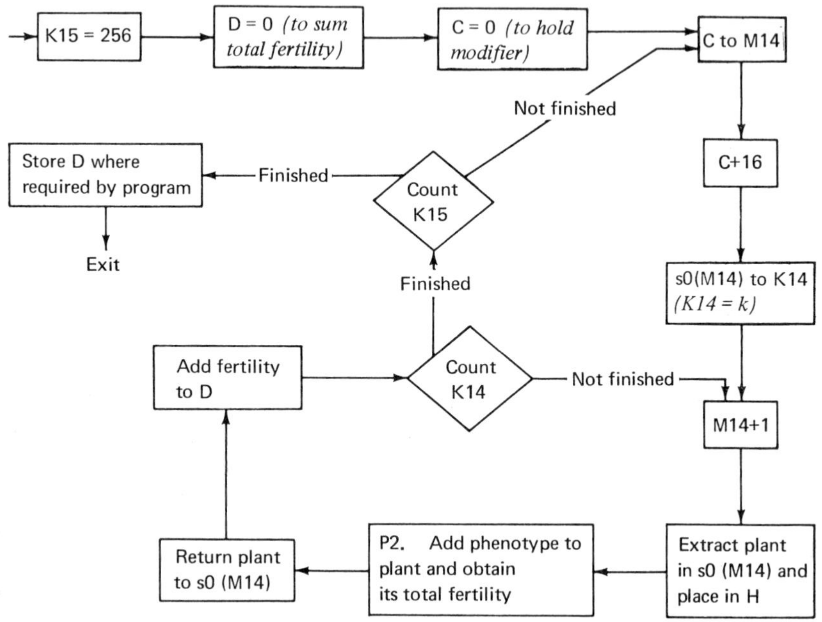

Figure 62. Flow diagram for subroutine **P3**, which scans the population row by row avoiding empty places, and uses **P2** to add phenotype to each plant which it replaces in its original position in the population. The population begins in **s0**. *k* is the row tally

The Reproduction Cycle. P8, P9, P4.

The population is now set, and the phenotypes of all plants determined and inserted. Reference to the flow diagram of Figure 59 shows that the next stage is the decision as to whether or not population analysis and relevant output is required, and if so the performance of this. But essential though this process is, it is not really part of the model of the evolutionary system, and we will leave consideration of it until we have completely dealt with the model proper. That is, we will read the flow diagram along the line which by-passes population analysis.

This brings us at once to reproduction which will replace the current generation by the next one. This is a fairly complicated operation, and consists of an eight-fold repetition of a basic procedure—the identification of the plants flowering in a specified week and the production of the appropriate number of seeds from them. Clearly, a counter will need to be set so that the cycle may be performed eight times.

We may now consider in detail the basic procedure—one week's reproduction. To carry this out, the first operation must be to scan the population to determine which plants are in flower during that week, and so are available for reproduction; copies of these plants will be stored separately as a sub-population, and the sum of their weekly fertilities must be obtained so that the number of seeds required from them during that week may be determined.

The sub-population will not be arranged in the same way as the actual population, mainly because a random choice from a populations with gaps in it would be awkward (the gaps being due both to non-flowering plants and to unoccupied places in the actual population). The plants will therefore be stored serially in the sub-population (in the same sequence as in the actual population), with no gaps. This also saves space. The number so stored will need to be recorded, since this is the number from which a random choice of seed parent has to be made.

From the weekly sub-population, potential seed parents will be chosen (subject to fertility test) at random, which is a fairly simple matter. For each of these a pollen parent (similarly subject to fertility test) will be chosen, which is not a simple matter since this choice will not be entirely at random but will depend on the position of the relevant seed parent in the population and the pre-determined pattern of pollen transport. For this purpose, the row position in the actual population of each seed parent must be known at the time of reproduction, and therefore as the weekly flowering plants are recognized and copied into the sub-population, the copies must be tagged with the number of the row in which the plant was growing. (This information will also be required later when the seed is sown, and will need to be transferred to the word carrying the seed.)

The two parents having been chosen, they will then produce a seed, using a method which has already been described in Chapter 6 for the simulation of gametogenesis and fertilization in two parents simultaneously, but adapted for 13 loci at the m.s. end (excluding sign bit) of a 48-bit word.

The seed will then be stored serially in a temporary store; this serial storage must be maintained through all eight weeks, and therefore the storage modifier must be set before the eight-week cycle is commenced, and not be re-set during it.

Figure 63 shows a flow diagram for the weekly reproduction, and we may now proceed to deal with each of its elements in turn. The first of these is the determination of which plants are flowering in any particular week.

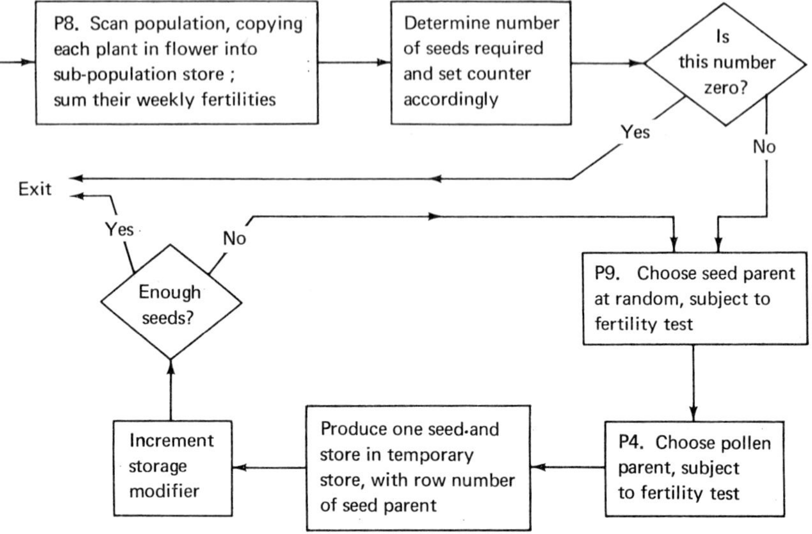

Figure 63. Flow diagram for that section of the main program which deals with one week's reproduction

Determination of Plants in Flower. **P8.**

Although we have used a population scanning procedure previously during this program, the nature of the operations which will now be performed during the scanning are rather different, and it is better to write a new scanning procedure rather than use the old one. This will be easy enough since the same principles apply and the old procedure can form a basis for the new; this does not need discussion in detail. The new element in the operation is the determination of whether a plant is currently in flower or not, and this involves inspection of its phenotype.

The principles of this operation have been described briefly by way of example at the end of Chapter 7, Figure 28 showing a flow diagram of the operation for a single plant. The flowering phenotype which has been inserted by **P2** as an octal number seven places up from the l.s. end of the word may be represented as *ab*; *a* gives the first week of flowering and may be extracted by use of 7×2^{10} as a mask; *b* gives the number of weeks and may be extracted by use of 7×2^{7} as a mask. We never need to know the actual values of a and b; all that is necessary is to know when they are zero. During the course of the eight-fold reproduction cycle, a is reduced after inspection each week by one (by subtracting 1×2^{10} in situ) until it is zero, which will indicate on inspection the following week that flowering is due to start; when flowering has started, b is the number of weeks of flowering left and is reduced each week by one (by subtracting 1×2^7 in situ) until it is zero, which will indicate that flowering has finished. It can now be seen why the weeks are numbered 0 to 7 and not 1 to 8; a plant due to flower in the first week is immediately recognized by the value of zero for a; another reason is that 8, being **1000**, would require four bits.

As soon as the plant is in flower, it is made negative by making the sign bit **1**, which allows speedy recognition of its status (quicker than extracting a and testing that), and does not affect the genotype or subsequent reproduction operations in any way, the m.s. bit having been left vacant for just this sort of use.

As soon as flowering is finished, the plant is made zero, again allowing speedy recognition which saves a good deal of time, especially with plants which finish flowering early; a plant which has finished flowering will never be required again, and there is no possibility of confusion with a plant of zero genotype which has not finished flowering since that will always carry the maximum fertility value and can never be zero.

The reductions of a and b, addition of negative sign bit, and change to zero are carried out on the copy of the plant being tested for flowering, and the amended copy replaces the original version in the population store, so that the effect is the same as if these amendments had actually been carried out on plants in the population store.

During each week that a plant is recognized as flowering, a copy is sent to the weekly sub-population. This copy does not need the flowering time section of its phenotype, but it does need to be tagged with its row number in the full population. The former is therefore eliminated from the copy of the plant by extraction of genotype plus weekly fertility (required later for fertility test); then the row number scaled by a factor of 2^7 is added, that is the row number will take over the bits originally occupied by a and b plus the next two m.s. bits. The row number, occupying a maximum of eight bits, would just fit in between the genotype and the flowering phenotype, which would then not need to be deleted. But at the time this procedure was written the author had in mind subsequent experiments which would deal with more loci. Had the row number been placed between genotype and phenotype, **P8** would then have needed to be rewritten. With the row number replacing the flowering phenotype, **P8** would serve unaltered for larger genotypes. The value for the row number is obtained from the accumulator holding the scanning modifier (C in Figure 62); the number in that accumulator, before incrementation, is the address of the first word in the row (holding the tally value) and is 16 times the row number. It therefore needs shifting up three places to produce row number $\times 2^7$. C+16 would need to be later than in Figure 62, immediately before the count on **K15**.

During each week that a plant is flowering, its weekly fertility needs to be added in to the running total for that week, since the total will be required for calculation of the number of seeds required from that week.

Another set of information which will be required later for **P4** (which chooses the pollen parent) is the number of plants currently in flower in specified sections of the actual population. This can be provided by the production of a table of 257 entries (**u0** to **u256**); the words of this table correspond sequentially to the rows of the actual population, and each word gives the total number of currently flowering plants which have been discovered in the rows up to but not including the row corresponding to that word. Thus **u0** is always zero; **u256** is always the total of the weekly flowering sub-population (it corresponds to a non-existent row beyond the population); **u21** would give the number of flowering plants in the first 21 rows (row 21 being the 22nd row, counting beginning at zero); and the number of flowering plants in rows 34 to 43 inclusive would be given by **u44-u34**. The table is quite easily produced by using the modifier which controls sequential storage of the weekly sub-population; before the scanning of each row is started, the number in this modifier (which begins at zero and is incremented by one as each flowering plant is stored) is the number of flowering plants so far, and this number is simply put into the appropriate word of the table.

One final piece of information which will be needed later is the size of random number required for choice of seed parent from the weekly sub-population. The size of the latter is of course variable and will only occasionally be a precise power of two, whereas random numbers as generated will be in the range 0 to 2^n-1 where n is an integer; what has to be determined for each weekly subpopulation is the least value of n such that 2^n-1 is equal to or greater than the size of the sub-population for that week. This has been discussed in detail in Chapter 6, and a method given for determining the required value for n. If there are no flowering plants in that week, this operation is unnecessary and is omitted.

Determination of n may be carried out independently in the program, or included as part of the subroutine we have just been discussing. There is much to be said in terms of convenience for adopting the latter course, which while it adds to the length of the subroutine does not complicate it, since it is merely added on at the end.

P8, having discovered and stored the plants currently in flower, will then supply the information for the next stage, namely the total weekly fertility for that week, the size of the flowering sub-population, and the number of bits required for the random numbers.

The weekly flowering sub-population having been established, the program proceeds to the act of reproduction, of which there are essentially three stages—choice of seed parent, choice of pollen parent, production of one seed—the whole being repeated to produce the required number of seeds. Before proceeding, this number has to be determined, unless there are no plants flowering during that week. In the latter case, the total weekly fertility for the week, as delivered by the preceding subroutine, is zero; no seeds are then required and the remainder of the reproduction process can be by-passed for that week. If it is not zero, then the number of seeds required is determined by dividing the current weekly total by the grand total of the weekly fertilities (as determined by **P3**), and multiplying the answer by 2560, the population size.

Choice of Seed Parent. **P9.**

Choice of seed parent is simply the random choice of one plant from the weekly sub-population, followed by a fertility test (based on its weekly fertility), with rejection and repetition of random choice if that test fails.

Programming is simpler if the fertility test is carried out by a short separately written subroutine (**P7**) to which the plant is sent, success or failure determining the point of return to **P9** and subsequent action by the latter. **P7** extracts the seven l.s. bits of the plant and compares them with a 7-bit

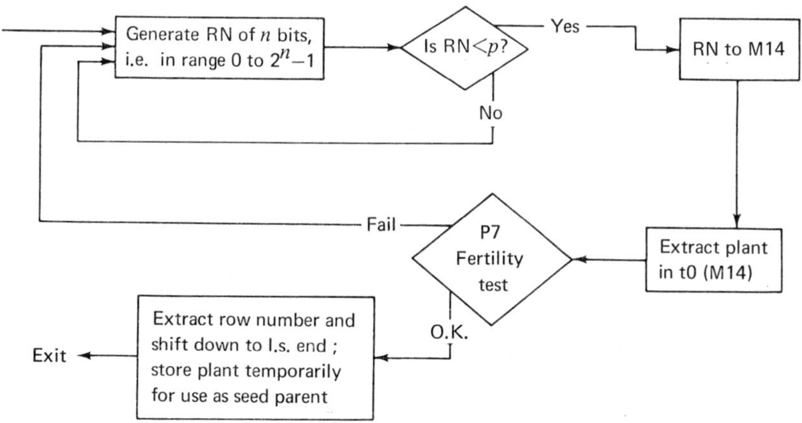

Figure 64. Flow diagram for subroutine **P9** which chooses one seed parent. n = number of bits required for random integer; p = size of weekly flowering sub-population which is stored in **t0** onwards

random integer, the plant failing the test if the random integer is larger. This could be done equally well as part of **P9** and would take less computing time, but if **P7** is written it may also be used for testing potential pollen parents, which avoids rewriting the testing procedure as part of **P4**.

If the fertility test succeeds, the seed parent is stored temporarily in the subroutine **P9**. Its row number in the actual population and its position in the weekly sub-population must be extracted and delivered to the program ready for use by the next subroutine which will require them.

The seed parent subroutine is thus quite short and uncomplicated. Figure 64 shows the flow diagram, which does not require detailed comment.

Choice of Pollen Parent. **P4**.

The choice of pollen parent to go with the seed parent which has just been produced is much more complex, and biologically speaking is one of the two most critical operations in the whole program, the other being seed dispersal. These two procedures introduce into the biological operations the concept of position within the population.

So far in this book it has been possible to keep fairly distinct the two basic elements in genetic simulation—the concept of a model which represents a system in a biologically sensible way, and the translation of that model into a computer program. In the development of the pollen parent subroutine these two elements could not easily be separated, and had to be considered together. Whatever the spatial relationships of seed and pollen parents, and the biology of pollination, these had to be considered with close regard to the arrangement of the plants in the model population in the computer and the way in which these plants could be handled by the program. Further, this subroutine was clearly going to be fairly complex, and it would be used more than 2560 times in each generation since some of the chosen pollen parents would fail the fertility test and would be rejected. It was therefore important that the simulation of pollination should be treated as simply as was compatible with the maintenance of biological sense, that the subroutine should be programmed efficiently, and that no time should be wasted in its execution.

In the event, it seems possible that the compromise between biological plausibility and programming expediency may have been too much on the side of the latter, but when the whole program was written and working, and could be considered critically, it seemed that the simulation of pollination actually achieved was reasonably sensible and realistic in its effect.

The account which follows is based closely on the subroutine which was actually used. In retrospect, the author thinks that neither biology nor programming were perfect. Some of the imperfections will be pointed out. Readers may care to consider how they would have produced a more satisfactory subroutine.

The problem is fairly simple to state. We have already decided that, subject to differences in reproductive capacity and the need for simultaneous flowering, pollination is random as between genotypes. It is not random with regard to position; a plant is more likely to be pollinated by onc close to it than by one farther away, and we therefore have to make a choice of pollen parent which while basically random is weighted in such a way that it is more likely to fall on a near neighbour than a distant one. We apparently have to consider proximity within the row (lateral distance) as well as distance in terms of the number of rows apart (longitudinal distance).

When the author first approached this problem, he assumed without thinking about it too closely that to tackle pollen transport on a two-dimensional basis in a single operation would be too difficult, as indeed it would have been with the population arrangement in which the rows were filled serially rather than in a haphazard sequence. (The full implications of serial filling and possible relevance to other operations were not realized when that part of the program was written.) In fact, with rows filled in a suitable way it is not too difficult to deal with pollen transport on a two-dimensional basis, and a method for doing this is described at the end of this section.

Since the experiment involves a long narrow population, and the interest is primarily in longitudinal gene flow, one obvious simplification was to treat distance as relevant only in a longitudinal direction, with lateral pollen movement fully random. The method which them immediately suggests itself is a random choice of row for the pollen parent weighted so that it is most likely to fall on rows closest to the seed parent, followed by a fully random choice of a plant within the selected row. But this will not do, because the chance of a plant being chosen as a pollen parent will then depend on the number of plants in its row as well as on its longitudinal distance from the seed parent; other things being equal, the fewer the plants in its own row the better would be its chance of being chosen, which is not biologically sensible.

This difficulty was eliminated in the following way, though it should be clear to the reader that the method used does not entirely conform with the actual population structure.

For the purpose of choosing the pollen parent it was supposed that the weekly flowering sub-population, instead of being arranged in rows, was actually arranged as a single line with no gaps between the plants, the first flowering plant in any one row following immediately after the last flowering plant in the preceding row. This is of course precisely the way in which the sub-population has been stored in the computer. For the moment, we will not consider the biological implications of this, and will first deal with the procedure as it was used.

It would then seem that choice could be effected quite simply by random reference to a table of numbers, each of which represents the position of a plant in the linearly arranged sub-population relative to its distance from a reference point (the seed parent for the time being), and occurs in the table with a frequency corresponding to the chance of a plant in that position becoming the pollen parent on any one occasion. This sort of procedure is already familiar. The addition of the number randomly chosen from the table to the actual position of the seed parent in the sub-population would give the position of the pollen parent.

This however is altogether too simple, and carries implications which must be carefully considered. Since such a table would be a permanent one, it would always refer to a range of pollen transport which would be constant in terms of plant numbers. But since density of plants in flower may vary from one part of the population to another and will certainly vary from one week to another, this range of pollen transport when translated into rows of the actual population would not be constant but would also vary, sometimes considerably. For example, at the beginning of the experiment there will be relatively little flowering of either subspecies during the first and last weeks, and density of flowering plants throughout the population will then be relatively low; a fixed range based on numbers of plants would, in terms of actual distance, correspond during those weeks to a considerable range of pollen transport which might even be possible over the whole length of the population. Also, when the flowering times of the two populations are becoming differentiated, a seed parent close to the territory of the other subspecies will often have very different densities of plants in flower on either side of it, with corresponding differences in the distance from which pollen might come if a fixed table giving pollen range in terms of the number of plants were used; it might then be pollinated by a plant deep within the other subspecies which had a flowering time not typical for its kind. All of this might well be a true reflection of what could happen in a natural system, but it did not commend itself to the author who at that stage wished to exclude the possibility of long range pollination.

It seemed reasonable to suppose that the activity of pollinating insects would be greatest where there was greatest density of flowering plants, and that where the densities on either side of a seed parent differed, pollen was more likely to come from the side with the greater density. It was decided therefore that the range of pollen transport should be kept constant in terms of rows of the actual population, and that the chance of pollen coming from one side rather than the other should be based on a direct comparison of the densities on the two sides. The maximum range of pollen transport was to be seven rows on each side of the row containing the seed parent, and the density on either side was to be expressed as the number of plants in flower during that week in the relevant seven rows, easily determinable from the table set up (in **u0** onwards) during the establishment of the weekly flowering sub-population. Suppose we are looking at the population from the side, with the low-numbered rows to our left. If the number of flowering plants in the seven rows left of the seed parent (that is, lower numbered) was a and the number on the other side was b, then the chance of the pollen coming from the left rather than the right was $a/(a+b)$, and was implemented by reference to a random fraction in the usual way. If the seed parent was less than seven rows from the end of the population, then a (or b as the case might be) was the number of plants in flower up to that end of the population.

The application of a table based on a fixed number of plants to a situation with a variable number of plants in a fixed number of rows, when the choice has actually to be made in terms of plants, was quite simple. The table used had 256 entries; the numbers 1 to 8 each occurred five times, 9 to 20 four times, 21 to 40 three times, 41 to 76 twice and 77 to 98 and the even numbers from 100 to 126 occurred once. Each number was treated operationally as if it were the numerator in a fraction of which 128 was the denominator. The procedure was then to use an 8-bit random integer to pick a number from the table; this was multiplied (fixed point) by $-a$ or b (according to which side the pollen was to come from) and the integral answer divided by 128 by shifting down seven places arithmetically (the sign must be maintained).

This would give an answer in the range $-a$ to 0 or 0 to b respectively, and the addition of this to the number of the position of the seed parent in the weekly sub-population store would give an answer (to be used in a modifier) which would be the number of the pollen parent in that store. A little thought will show that the chosen pollen parent could not be more than seven rows from the seed parent, and that the choice could not be directed outside either end of the population.

In estimating a and b, plants in the same population row as the seed parent were ignored; they could however readily be chosen as pollen parents, as could the seed parent itself if the rounded scaled-down value of the product were zero, as it was liable to be if a or b were small and a low number was chosen from the table.

It may have occurred to the reader that the determination of the direction of pollen transport by reference to the number of plants in flower on either side is apparently incorrect, because the direction should rather depend on the amount of pollen available (proportional to the number of flowers open) than on the number of plants in flower, that is it should depend on the total weekly fertilities in the two 7-row sections. To draw this conclusion however would be to overlook the fact that the chosen potential pollen parent still has to be submitted to a fertility test; if it fails this test it will be rejected and a second choice made, beginning with a redetermination of the direction of pollen transport. The direction from which the pollen will come will thus on average depend on the total weekly fertilities in the 7-row sections and not simply on the numbers of flowering plants.

One point which required consideration was whether the realized reproductive capacity of a plant would depend on the density and fertilities of the potential pollen parents in its range. There was reason to believe that, as a general rule, unless plants are really isolated they usually manage to set plenty of seed, especially if capable of self-fertilization, and that therefore density would have little effect on the amount of seed set per plant. If there were no possible pollen parents within range of the chosen seed parent, then it would be self-fertilized.

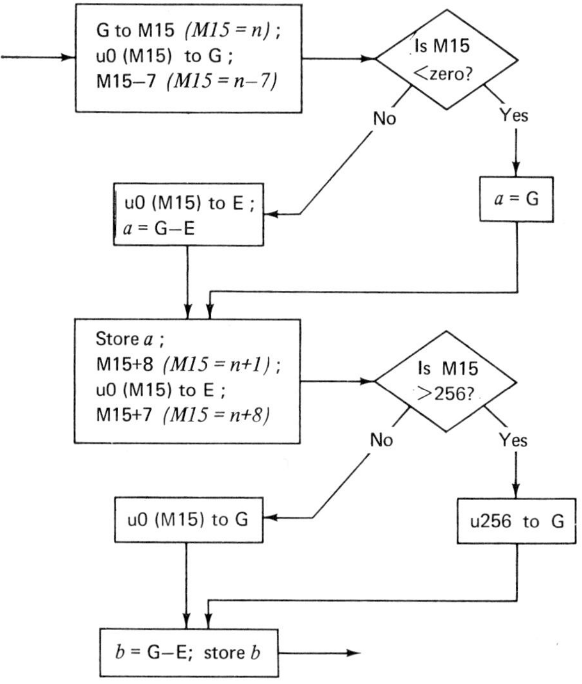

Figure 65. Part of flow diagram for subroutine **P4**. This section determines *a* and *b* which are the numbers of plants in flower in the seven rows on either side of the seed parent, being supplied with the row number *n* of the seed parent, in **G**. For explanation see text. A more efficient version would use an extended position table in the **u** stores. **u0** would become **u7** and the program would proceed straight through the column of boxes, omitting the questions about **M15**

On the other hand, if low fertility came about at least in part through bad pollen, this might provide a mechanical obstacle to good pollen on the stigma, and (other things being equal) seed set per plant might tend to be disproportionately lower in areas of lower fertility. This was partly taken account of in the following way. As has been pointed out, if a pollen parent fails the fertility test, it is rejected and a new choice made; however, a limit of three was set on the number of attempts to provide a pollen parent for each chosen seed parent; after three failures the seed parent was rejected and a new one chosen.

It will be easier to discuss further biological implications of this subroutine when it has been described in detail, and this will be done with the aid of the flow diagrams in Figures 65 and 66. There are three main sections: the determination of a and b (see above); the determination, for each attempt to choose a pollen parent, of the direction from which the pollen is to come; and the actual choice of pollen parent.

The determination of a and b in the author's program was rather more complicated than it need have been, and wasted some time. It will be remembered that the subroutine **P8** identifying the weekly flowering sub-population produced a table beginning in **u0** in which each word in turn gave the running total of flowering plants discovered up to but not including the corresponding row of the actual population. If the chosen seed parent is in row n, then a = **u**n**−u(**n**−7)** and b = **u(**n**+8)−u(**n**+1)**. **P4** is provided on entry with the value of n from **P9**, and it is a simple matter to put this into a modifier and with the appropriate additions and subtractions to use this modifier to extract the required values from the table beginning in **u0**.

Difficulty arises when $n<7$ or >248, that is when there are less than seven rows between the seed parent and an end of the experiment and therefore **u(**n**−7)** or **u(**n**+8)** would be outside the table of running totals. In the former case, a would be given by **u**n and in the latter b would be **u256−u(**n**+1)** (since **u256** carries the total for the week). This situation was dealt with rather clumsily in the original program by simply recognizing when $n-7$ was negative or $n+8$ was greater than 256, and taking the appropriate action. This involved two conditional jump instructions, and could easily have been avoided with a little more thought during the writing of **P8**—the purpose of the table beginning in **u0** was of course known at the time of writing that subroutine. It would be better for this table to begin in **u0** with **u0** to **u6** all zeros, the table proper running from **u7** to **u263**; **u7** (also zero) would correspond to row 0, **u(**n**+7)** to row n, **u262** to the final row 255, and **u263** would carry the total for the week as would **u264** to **u270**.

The modifier would, as before, be supplied with $n-7$, n, $n+1$ and $n+8$ as appropriate, but the address modified would now be **u7** and not **u0**. Negative values for $n-7$ and values of $n+8$ greater than 256 would not need to be distinguished, since they would always produce the required values zero and weekly total respectively. This section of the subroutine would then require no jumps.

This improvement is obvious enough, but like some other instances it quite failed to occur to the author until he came to write this book.

a and b having been determined, the next step is to decide on which side of the seed parent the choice of pollen parent is to be made. The choice is to fall left of (that is at a lower address than) the position of the seed parent with a frequency (subject to chance) of $a/(a+b)$, this frequency to be imple-

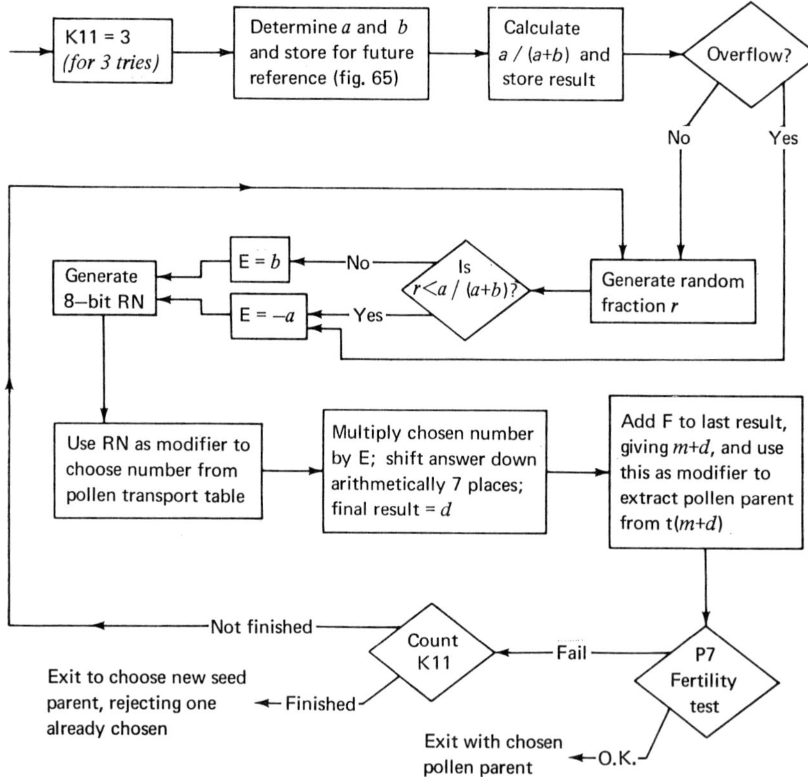

Figure 66. Flow diagram for **P4**, which chooses pollen parent. At entry, **F** contains the position m of the chosen seed parent in the weekly population store. a and b are the numbers of plants in flower in the seven rows on either side of the seed parent. Note that the calculated value of d will be negative if the pollen is to come from the left of the seed parent

mented by comparing the fraction with a random fraction; if the random fraction is smaller than $a/(a+b)$, then the choice will fall to the left; otherwise to the right.

When the side has been determined, random choice from the table of integers in the range 1 to 126 gives a number which is scaled down by multiplication by $-a/128$ or $b/128$ as the case may be (an arithmetic shift must be used for the division by 128, because the sign must be maintained).

If the chosen seed parent is in location **t**m of the weekly sub-population store, then **P4** will have been provided with the value of m from **P9**, and this is added to the scaled product just produced. The result is then used as a modifier of the address **t0** to extract a pollen parent. If the integer randomly chosen from the table is p, then according to which side the pollen is to come from, the address of the pollen parent will be $\mathbf{t}(m-ap\mathbf{2}^{-7})$ or $\mathbf{t}(m+bp\mathbf{2}^{-7})$, $ap\mathbf{2}^{-7}$ and $bp\mathbf{2}^{-7}$ being properly rounded to integral form. Because of the way in which a and b have been determined, the choice cannot fall outside the flowering sub-population for the current week.

There are three special circumstances which must be considered: when $a=0$, when $b=0$, and when both are zero. One of the two former situations will always occur when the seed parent is in an end row of the population, and may also occur when it is close to an end or when it is near the end of the distribution of its subspecies and the two subspecies are tending to flower at different times. The situation when both a and b are zero will occur very infrequently, and only when very few plants are flowering or when the seed parent is isolated from other plants flowering at the same time. But however remote such a contingency, steps must be taken to deal with it or to ensure that it does not upset the running of the program.

In none of these three cases is a choice of side (involving random number generation) necessary, since pollen must come from after, before, or the same plant respectively. Usually when such contingencies are uncommon it is in practice quicker to make a choice which is occasionally superfluous than to carry out a test for superfluity on all occasions. But in this case there are difficulties arising from the values of $a/(a+b)$.

There is no problem when a is zero, for then the fraction has a zero value and if a choice is made it will always fall correctly on the b side. But when b is zero, the value of $a/(a+b)=1$, and if fixed point division is used this will produce overflow and the correct value will not be produced and so cannot be tested against the random fraction. Floating point division would give the correct answer, but not only would the use of floating point require extra time, it could not deal with the situation when $a+b=0$, $0/0$ producing overflow both with floating and with fixed point.

The simplest way of dealing with this situation is probably to carry out the division $a/(a+b)$, and then to test to see if overflow has occurred. If it has not, then b is not zero (a may be) and the program can proceed directly to compare $a/(a+b)$ with a random fraction, sending $-a$ or b to the next stage according to the outcome of the comparison.

If overflow has occurred, then b at least is zero and the pollen parent must always either come from the a side or be the seed parent itself; this is ensured by directly multiplying the randomly chosen integer by $-a/128$, no comparison with a random fraction being required (or indeed possible).

When there are no flowering plants within range of the seed parent, a as well as b will be zero, and with the same action after overflow as before the result of the subsequent multiplication by $-a/128$ will be zero and the chosen pollen parent must then of course be the seed parent, so producing the obligatory self-fertilization.

Whatever the route by which the pollen parent has been chosen, its weekly fertility is then submitted to test in the usual way, using **P7**. If the test fails, and this is the third failure for the one seed parent, then the latter is discarded and the program returns to choose a new seed parent. If there have not yet been three failures, the subroutine tries again by returning to the generation of a random fraction, the values of a, b and $a/(a+b)$ having been retained in store by the subroutine. If the fertility test succeeds, then pollen and seed parents are passed to the gametogenesis and fertilization subroutine.

Before proceeding to this next stage, we must consider some other biological implications of this subroutine, and an account will also be given of quite a different way by which the choice of pollen parent could have been tackled.

The way in which a and b were calculated and used had two implications. One was that pollen never came from more than seven rows away. In a real situation, pollen might be expected occasionally to move over a longer distance, but there does not seem any reason for supposing that to allow occasional long distance travel would have any significant effect on the problem under investigation. Had it been decided to allow it, the way would have been occasionally to choose the pollen parent simply at random from the whole of the weekly sub-population.

The second implication was in a sense complementary to the first. It would seem to be likely that in real life the range of pollen transport would be shorter the greater the density of flowering plants, since it would be expected that the average length of flight between visits to flowers would then be less, although it must be remembered that an insect will carry pollen from flowers other than the one last visited. With this subroutine, pollen always had the opportunity to travel seven rows (so long as there were plants in the seventh row and not too many in the seed parent row) whatever the density of flowering plants. Consider a situation in this model population in which the mean flowering plant densities on the two sides of a seed parent are different, but in which the plants are evenly distributed in each of the two seven row sections. The expected mean distances of pollen transport for the two sides will be the same, and thus quite independent of the density difference between the two sides. But if we consider a seven row section on one side of a seed parent when the plants are unevenly distributed over the section, then because of the way in which the final random choice is applied, distance of pollen transport will now depend on the density, being less when the highest density of plants is close to the seed parent and greater when the lowest density is near the seed parent. These two conclusions are clearly inconsistent, but nevertheless the latter situation probably provides the closest approach to reality achieved by any part of the subroutine.

Another point about this method is that pollination within the row is not random, since the rows are considered as arranged end to end and the chance of pollination is then determined by the resultant notional distance in terms of plants. For example, consider the three adjacent rows of Figure 67, which indicates the plants currently flowering by means of letters, the sequence as they are treated in choosing the pollen parent being alphabetical. If *I* is the seed parent, the sequence is *ABCDEFGH I JKLMNOP*. Consider the plants *D E H K* and *P*, which in terms of real distance from *I* would be in the order *KEHDPI*, but which in terms of distance as used for determination of the chance of being pollen parent would be in the order *PDEKHI*.

	A			B	C					D				
E		F					G	H			I	J		
K	L			M				N	O		P			

Figure 67. Diagram to illustrate the point that choice of pollen parent within the row is not random—for explanation see text. The diagram shows three adjacent rows in the population, here supposed to run from top to bottom. Letters indicate plants currently in flower, blank squares have non-flowering plants, or are empty

P is very close to *I* but is less likely to be chosen to pollinate it than the distant *K*, while *E* and *K* at very similar real distances have quite different chances of pollinating *I*. This is clearly quite unrealistic, but as will be shown later there is little or no correlation between genotype and position in row, and considered over many pollinations and many generations the irrationalities tend to cancel out and the effect of this subroutine is to produce a reasonable simulation of gene flow. It may be reflected that nature is not always rational but nevertheless seems to work fairly well.

−7:−7	−6:−7	−5:−7	−4:−7	−3:−7	−2:−7	−1:−7	0:−7	1:−7	2:−7	3:−7	4:−7	5:−7	6:−7	7:−7
0	**0**	**0**	**0**	**0**	**1**	**1**	**1**	**1**	**1**	**0**	**0**	**0**	**0**	**0**
−7:−6	−6:−6	−5:−6	−4:−6	−3:−6	−2:−6	−1:−6	0:−6	1:−6	2:−6	3:−6	4:−6	5:−6	6:−6	7:−6
0	**0**	**0**	**1**	**1**	**1**	**1**	**1**	**1**	**1**	**1**	**1**	**0**	**0**	**0**
−7:−5	−6:−5	−5:−5	−4:−5	−3:−5	−2:−5	−1:−5	0:−5	1:−5	2:−5	3:−5	4:−5	5:−5	6:−5	7:−5
0	**0**	**1**	**1**	**2**	**2**	**3**	**3**	**3**	**2**	**2**	**1**	**1**	**0**	**0**
−7:−4	−6:−4	−5:−4	−4:−4	−3:−4	−2:−4	−1:−4	0:−4	1:−4	2:−4	3:−4	4:−4	5:−4	6:−4	7:−4
0	**1**	**1**	**2**	**3**	**4**	**5**	**6**	**5**	**4**	**3**	**2**	**1**	**1**	**0**
−7:−3	−6:−3	−5:−3	−4:−3	−3:−3	−2:−3	−1:−3	0:−3	1:−3	2:−3	3:−3	4:−3	5:−3	6:−3	7:−3
0	**1**	**2**	**3**	**5**	**8**	**11**	**12**	**11**	**8**	**5**	**3**	**2**	**1**	**0**
−7:−2	−6:−2	−5:−2	−4:−2	−3:−2	−2:−2	−1:−2	0:−2	1:−2	2:−2	3:−2	4:−2	5:−2	6:−2	7:−2
1	**1**	**2**	**4**	**8**	**13**	**18**	**21**	**18**	**13**	**8**	**4**	**2**	**1**	**1**
−7:−1	−6:−1	−5:−1	−4:−1	−3:−1	−2:−1	−1:−1	0:−1	1:−1	2:−1	3:−1	4:−1	5:−1	6:−1	7:−1
1	**1**	**3**	**5**	**11**	**18**	**28**	**37**	**28**	**18**	**11**	**5**	**3**	**1**	**1**
−7:0	−6:0	−5:0	−4:0	−3:0	−2:0	−1:0	0:0	1:0	2:0	3:0	4:0	5:0	6:0	7:0
1	**1**	**3**	**6**	**12**	**21**	**37**	**0**	**37**	**21**	**12**	**6**	**3**	**1**	**1**

<table>
<tr><td>−7:1
1</td><td>−6:1
1</td><td>−5:1
3</td><td>−4:1
5</td><td>−3:1
11</td><td>−2:1
18</td><td>−1:1
28</td><td>0:1
37</td><td>1:1
28</td><td>2:1
18</td><td>3:1
11</td><td>4:1
5</td><td>5:1
3</td><td>6:1
1</td><td>7:1
1</td></tr>
<tr><td>−7:2
1</td><td>−6:2
1</td><td>−5:2
2</td><td>−4:2
4</td><td>−3:2
8</td><td>−2:2
13</td><td>−1:2
18</td><td>0:2
21</td><td>1:2
18</td><td>2:2
13</td><td>3:2
8</td><td>4:2
4</td><td>5:2
2</td><td>6:2
1</td><td>7:2
1</td></tr>
<tr><td>−7:3
0</td><td>−6:3
1</td><td>−5:3
2</td><td>−4:3
3</td><td>−3:3
5</td><td>−2:3
8</td><td>−1:3
11</td><td>0:3
12</td><td>1:3
11</td><td>2:3
8</td><td>3:3
5</td><td>4:3
3</td><td>5:3
2</td><td>6:3
1</td><td>7:3
0</td></tr>
<tr><td>−7:4
0</td><td>−6:4
1</td><td>−5:4
1</td><td>−4:4
2</td><td>−3:4
3</td><td>−2:4
4</td><td>−1:4
5</td><td>0:4
6</td><td>1:4
5</td><td>2:4
4</td><td>3:4
3</td><td>4:4
2</td><td>5:4
1</td><td>6:4
1</td><td>7:4
0</td></tr>
<tr><td>−7:5
0</td><td>−6:5
0</td><td>−5:5
1</td><td>−4:5
1</td><td>−3:5
2</td><td>−2:5
2</td><td>−1:5
3</td><td>0:5
3</td><td>1:5
3</td><td>2:5
2</td><td>3:5
2</td><td>4:5
1</td><td>5:5
1</td><td>6:5
0</td><td>7:5
0</td></tr>
<tr><td>−7:6
0</td><td>−6:6
0</td><td>−5:6
0</td><td>−4:6
1</td><td>−3:6
1</td><td>−2:6
1</td><td>−1:6
1</td><td>0:6
1</td><td>1:6
1</td><td>2:6
1</td><td>3:6
1</td><td>4:6
1</td><td>5:6
0</td><td>6:6
0</td><td>7:6
0</td></tr>
<tr><td>−7:7
0</td><td>−6:7
0</td><td>−5:7
0</td><td>−4:7
0</td><td>−3:7
0</td><td>−2:7
1</td><td>−1:7
1</td><td>0:7
1</td><td>1:7
1</td><td>2:7
1</td><td>3:7
0</td><td>4:7
0</td><td>5:7
0</td><td>6:7
0</td><td>7:7
0</td></tr>
</table>

Figure 68. Notional grid used as a basis in the simulation of insect flight from one plant (in position 0:0) to another. The grid is translated into a table with its positions occurring in different frequencies (shown below the position figures) depending on distance from 0:0, and this is operated in the usual way by random reference to it

Pollen Transport Considered Two-dimensionally

There is quite a different method by which the problem of pollen transport could have been tackled, which would have been more realistic and certainly easier to program. It would probably however have required more running time, though as will be seen later this is rather difficult to judge. Since the technique may have wide application, it will be described in some detail.

The method was developed for investigation of a problem related to the present one, with essentially the same population structure. Instead of flowering time difference, discrimination by pollen vectors between different flower colours and pattern was considered as the potential isolating barrier. The model had to simulate the flight of an insect, since it involved the assumption that pollen from several recently visited flowers might be carried at any one time. It seemed essential that lateral as well as longitudinal range of pollen transport should be considered, and this appeared to present fewer problems in the context of a situation in which all plants were flowering simultaneously for the same length of time; this is the context in which this technique will be considered.

The basic operation was the decision, given an insect visiting a particular plant, which plant it should fly to next.

Although the implications are somewhat different, and in a sense the direction is reversed, the practical problem is exactly the same as that involved in the decision, given an ovule, as to where the fertilizing pollen grain was to come from.

In the new model, range was again limited to seven rows longitudinally and seven plant positions (that is including empty positions) laterally in either direction; it was assumed that the distance between plants in a row was the same as the distance between rows.

Insect flight (equivalent to choice of pollen parent in the flowering-time model) was operated in the following way. A squared grid was drawn up, corresponding to a section of population 15 rows $\times$15 plants (seven rows and seven plants on either side of the reference plant, that is the one we imagine the insect to be currently visiting). The positions in this grid were numbered relative to the central square of the grid, by row and plant, the central position being 0.0 and representing the position of the reference plant. This is illustrated in Figure 68. The position numbers were stored in the program as a table with frequencies corresponding to the chance of a plant being visited by an insect directly from the reference plant (equivalent for the purposes of the flowering-time model to providing pollen to the central plant). Obviously, those positions close to the centre would appear most frequently in the table, the distal positions least frequently, and positions in the corners not at all.

Each entry in the table will have the row and plant numbers packed. Packing of negative numbers presents no problems. In the present example the range of numbers to be packed runs from -7 to 7. If the four l.s. bits of any number are packed, then the m.s. of these four bits will show the correct sign. Thus 7 will be packed as **0111** and -7 as **1001**.

Unpacking is less simple because for negative numbers the appropriate sign bits must be dealt with. The easiest way of doing this is to pack the two numbers at the m.s. end, but leaving a zero between them. The latter is essential since otherwise, while subsequent arithmetic shift down would retain the correct sign of the m.s. number, it would also cause spurious rounding if the l.s. number were negative. The m.s. number is unpacked by an arithmetic shift down to the l.s. end of the word; the l.s. number is unpacked by a logical shift up to the m.s. end followed by an arithmetic shift down to the l.s. end. Thus $-5:-4$ would be packed as **101101100**... The proper arithmetic shift down of the m.s. number will give **11...1011**; logical shift up five places will give **1100**... and this arithmetically shifted down will give **11...1100**, as required. The shift up could also be arithmetic, but would cause overflow.

The frequencies used are shown as the lower figures in the squares of Figure 68. It might appear that plants near the central position, with their high frequencies, had their chances greatly overweighted, but it should be pointed out that not only does the chance diminish with distance but that at greater distances there are more plants among which the chance is to be divided. Thus within closest range there are four plants, and at the most distal range 32.

The distances, which determine frequencies, are direct distances from the central position. The frequencies were arrived at by first sketching one side of an approximately normal curve giving for any distance d the chance of a flight over that distance. For a single position at distance d from the centre of the grid, the chance was read from the curve and then divided by d which is proportional to the number of plants at that distance, since that number will be proportional to the circumference of a circle of radius d. The number of times a particular position should appear in the table was then derived from this answer by direct proportionality to the total number of entries in the table. There had to be some manipulation of the answers, partly because the final figure for any position had always to be integral and partly because the total number of entries in the table had to be a power of two, for the usual reason.

Obviously, the basic frequencies could be assigned in any way one cared to choose, either on the basis of a formula or purely arbitrary. It will be noticed that the table derived from Figure 68 apparently would not allow self pollination. This would be true for the flowering-time model, but it did allow selfing in the experiment for which it was designed since it was supposed that an insect might return to a plant after visiting one or two other plants and still carry some pollen from it. For the flowering time experiments where we might have a situation in which no other plants were flowering within range of the seed parent, the table would either have to be amended to allow self-pollination or special steps would have to be taken to deal with this contingency which would not arise with simultaneous flowering unless there was something drastically wrong with the program causing almost complete depopulation in one part of the model (this has happened!).

With the introduction of this new technique, the population arrangement was modified by using all 16 positions as potential sites for plants, the row tallies being kept in a separate section of the store—a method which would have been preferable for the original program.

The use of the table in choosing a pollen parent was simple in that no consideration had to be taken of the numbers of plants available within range, so no question arose of estimation of these nor of calculations involving them; but empty positions had to be recognizable and this was managed simply by clearing the population store before seed dispersal. The table was used by choosing from it at random a word containing a row/position parameter, and adding this to the actual position of the seed parent in the population, the result giving the actual position of the pollen parent chosen. Thus if the seed parent is in position 67/11 and random reference to the table produces $5/-4$, the position indicated for the pollen parent is 72/7 and this plant is extracted by using $72 \times 16 + 7$ as a modifier.

But difficulties could arise. The final address could be one in which there was no plant; this was easily dealt with by trying again. The position indicated could have been outside the population, either laterally (position in row <0 or >15), or longitudinally (row number <0 or >255), or both; this was dealt with by supposing that when an insect reached the edge of the population it would fly back into the population as though it were internally reflected from the side or end of the population according to the laws of light, the total flight distance being unchanged. Reflection was supposed to take place at the boundary, not at the centre of a square. Thus, remembering that the extreme positions of a row are 0 and 15 and extreme rows are 0 and 255, the non existent positions (row given first) $2/-3$, $-4/14$ and 257/17 would become 2/2, 3/14 and 254/14 respectively. This required that every determined position should be tested to see whether it was within bounds, and that appropriate action should be taken if not.

The situation could have been avoided altogether and the whole procedure made much simpler if the population, instead of occurring in a long narrow rectangle, occupied the whole of the surface of a torus (using the geometrical sense of the term). The population would then have no edges and no ends, but there would be two different places where the two different subspecies come into contact.

Provided the number of rows and the number of positions in each row were integral powers of two, no problems would arise from the addition of the chosen value from the table to the actual position in the population. The row and position numbers in the table would be centred not on 0/0 as in Figure 68, but on 256/16 if there were 256 rows and 16 positions in each row. 256/16 would in fact be the same position as 0/0, and its use would avoid the difficulties involved in getting negative answers and allow the required address to be determined simply by taking the eight l.s. bits of the determined row number and the four l.s. bits of the position number. For example, suppose the actual position of the reference plant is 254/4 and the value obtained from the table is 259/11 ($\equiv 3/-5$ based on 0/0), we get by addition the position 513/15 (which would have been 257/-1 if we had used a table based on a central reference 0/0; this would refer to a position outside the population if we were not dealing with a torus). Using only the eight l.s. and four l.s. bits respectively (that is, taking the numbers modulo 256 and modulo 16) 513/15 becomes 1/15 which now refers to a position within the population. 1/15 would appear to be a long way from 254/4, but is actually quite close because the population is on the surface of a torus.

It may seem to be a rather unnatural mathematician's trick to have the population on a torus, but there is no reason for believing that biology on the surface of a torus would be very different from biology anywhere else, other things being equal.

In the flowering-time experiment, where pollen movement is not dealt with by actual simulation of insect flight, there would probably be little point in so involved an approach as the use of internal reflection to deal with out of bounds addresses. It would be simplest and probably quite satisfactory to reject any such address and try again, exactly as for an unoccupied position. Every address would still, however, need to be tested to ensure that row and position numbers were always within bounds.

With the use of the grid technique of choosing pollen parents, the original method of arranging plants in the row would be inappropriate. The population-setting routine of the flowering-time experiment and the method of seed dispersal (to be described later) involved the filling of each row serially from one end, so that plants were not dispersed uniformly across the population. There is no difficulty in arranging for the rows to be filled non-serially, as will be shown later in this chapter.

The main objection to applying the grid technique to the flowering time model is that a great deal of time would sometimes be wasted in choosing addresses at which there were no plants in flower at the same time as the chosen seed parent. This waste cannot be eliminated and may be considerable, especially if selection leads to most plants having the minimum flowering period of two weeks. When flowering-time differences have developed between the subspecies, there will be occasions when a chosen seed parent in an area occupied largely by the other subspecies will have within range very few plants flowering at the same time as itself, and sometimes many attempts may have to be made before choice lights on an address occupied by a plant in flower. On the other hand, the method involves only one random number generation instead of two, and the programming is altogether simpler, so there is some gain in speed to offset the waste of time. To what extent these balance one another, and where the advantage in speed would really lie, it would be difficult to estimate; the easiest way of finding out would be experimentally by trying both.

If the grid method were used, since it is applied directly to the actual population, the determination and establishment of the weekly sub-population could be eliminated, but this is not so straightforward as it might seem. At first glance, it would appear that all that would be necessary would be to choose two plants and make sure that their flowering periods had at least one week in common. This is easy enough to establish if the flowering-time phenotype is expressed as a bit pattern (p.209); if two plants are not in flower together at any time, then the LP between their flowering-time bit patterns will be zero. But this is not sufficient. Consider two plants flowering for three weeks; the chance of them reproducing together will be less if only one of the three weeks is common to both of them than if their flowering periods exactly coincide.

The best way of dealing with this would seem to be as follows, the potential seed parent having already been chosen at random from the population and fertility tested against its total reproductive capacity. A potential pollen parent is chosen in the way described using the grid. If its total reproductive capacity is a and it flowers for b weeks of which c coincide with flowering of the seed parent, then the fertility test on the potential pollen parent is performed with reference to ac/b. (N.B. a/b is half the value of what was previously designated as the weekly fertility; it is in fact the true weekly fertility.) a/b does not require determination on every occasion—it may be determined once and stored with the genotype like the rest of the phenotype.

Since in this method of choosing the pollen parent the seed parent has been chosen from the whole population without regard for the weeks in which it is flowering, variability is allowed in the distribution of seed production through the flowering period, in contrast with the week by week procedure used in the flowering-time experiment which required adherence to a calculated and specified seed production for each week.

The grid method of determining pollen movement is clearly capable of giving biologically more realistic simulation than the one-dimensional technique actually used. It is well adapted for use in a situation simulating environmental differences through a population, and is efficient in application when all plants flower simultaneously. It would clearly involve loss of time in the flowering-time model by leading to a high proportion of ineffective choices, but this loss has to be weighed against the extra random number and other calculations required by the one-dimensional procedure.

Fertilization

After the involved procedure of choosing a pollen parent, the remainder of the reproduction process is relatively simple. An account has already been given in Chapter 6 of the simulation of the production of one zygote from two parents with many loci, carried out in a single operation. All that is required is a slight modification of the subroutine there described so that it can deal with 13 loci and a genotype situated at the m.s. end of a 48-bit word. This presents no problems.

The seed having been produced, it is then stored serially in a temporary store, each week's seeds following on directly from those of the preceding week, that is, the storage modifier is set at zero before any reproduction for the current generation has taken place and is not re-set at the end of each week.

Before this temporary storage, the seed must have added to it the row number of the seed parent, since this will be the reference point for its dispersal. This row number was added to the seed parent by the subroutine which chose it, and is readily extracted and added to the seed.

When enough seeds have been produced for the current week, a count will show whether or not any more weeks remain to be dealt with. When reproduction for the eight weeks is complete, the number in the storage modifier (provided it has been incremented after the last seed stored) will be equal to the number of seeds stored, and will be required for the next subroutine. It will not necessarily be exactly 2560, because it will depend on how the estimations of the weekly requirements have been rounded in each particular week.

Seed Dispersal. P10.

The next step is for the seeds to be dispersed and sown, and although like the pollen parent subroutine this involves position and distance, it is a very much easier matter. In considering distance of seed dispersal, only longitudinal dispersal (that is in terms of rows from the row of origin) was taken into account. This was achieved quite simply by the familiar device of using a table based on a distribution curve. The curve was roughly normal in shape and expressed the probability of a seed being dispersed to various rows distant from its row of origin. The table of 64 words contained the numbers -12 to $+12$ in various frequencies, -12 and $+12$ occurring once each and zero (dispersal within the row of origin) having the maximum occurrence of six times.

The table was applied in the usual way by use of a 6-bit random number in a modifier to select a number from the table; this added to the row of origin of the seed (that is the row of the seed parent) gave the number of the row to which the seed was to be dispersed.

It is at this point that difficulties begin. The most obvious of these is that the indicated row might be outside the population, that is <0 or >255. Various courses of action are open here.

All seeds falling outside the population could be considered lost. But this might produce gene flow and change in gene frequency which would be quite irrelevant to the evolutionary properties of the system and therefore undesirable. This would come about in the following way. With the rows near the ends of the population having the population average of 10 plants per row, the expected number of seeds lost would be about 21 from each end, and this would lead to a population of less than the specified size of 2560. But 2560 seeds would still have to be produced in the next generation. The mean number of seeds produced per plant would thus be just over 1.0, and this mean would be consistent through the population (subject to differences in fertility); but the mean number per plant of seeds contributing to the next generation would not be so consistent, being lower near the ends of the population because of loss of seeds falling outside the population. This would give a greater rate of effective reproduction to plants away from the ends of a population and a selective advantage to any alleles more frequent in the centre of the population than at the ends. Again, this might represent biological reality, but was not relevant to the problem under investigation and could have been positively misleading. The two consequences would be an increase in frequency of those alleles which are most frequent in the centre of the population (unless stronger selective forces were acting otherwise), and a slow but steady gene flow outwards since the end rows would tend to have fewer plants in them (because of lost seeds) and other things being equal plant density would tend to even out over the population.

An obvious alternative method would be to try again for the same seed repeatedly until it fell within the population. Biologically, this would be rather as though seed from identical plants outside the population were falling inside it in numbers compensating precisely for those lost. This would seem to be acceptable, but only if there is no objection to the effect which this procedure has in reducing plant density at the ends and increasing it a short distance in from the ends. This method was in fact the one used, with one modification; a limit of five was set on the number of attempts at dispersal for any one seed and if all of these failed then the seed was discarded. There is no logical point in this modification, but it was felt that if failure might occasionally arise from an unusual and unforeseen combination of circumstances (about which the author was thoroughly vague and is now quite unable to visualize), the program might get itself into a state of perpetual failure and make no progress—an improbable but undesirable contingency. This restriction to five attempts still allowed a slight seed loss, but this was so small (averaging one third of a seed at each end per generation) as to be negligible.

A third method, which either did not occur to the author or which he rejected for some reason which now escapes him, is quicker and more satisfactory in that it does not affect the evenness of plant density at the ends of the population. As before, it corresponds to seed lost being exactly compensated for by immigration from identical plants just outside the population, but is more accurate in terms of dispersal and does not require more than one random number per seed (thus saving time). Any seed which would be lost off the end is treated as though it were internally reflected, travelling the same total distance that it would have done had it landed in the place originally indicated. For example, seeds which the dispersal operation indicates should land in rows -1, -4 or 257 would be treated as landing in rows 0, 3 and 254 respectively (the reflection taking place at the external boundary of the terminal rows, not at their centre line).

This is achieved quite simply. Suppose the originally produced dispersal row is n, and a test shows this to be negative, then the row to which the seed is actually dispersed is $-(n+1)$. If n is greater than 255, then the actual row for seed dispersal is $(511-n)$; this is done by testing to see if $255-n$ is negative and adding 256 to the answer if it is. This is the method which will be used in constructing the flow diagram of this subroutine.

The row having been determined, the seed is then sown in the first vacant position in that row, rows being filled serially from positions 1 to 15. Clearly, a running tally has to be kept for each row of the number of positions filled, partly because the subroutine will need to know where the next seed for that row is to be placed, and partly because the final total for each row is required by other parts of the program, as described earlier. This tally is held in position 0 for each row, and so if the population begins at address **s0**, the running tallies are at addresses **s0**, **s16**, **s32** etc., that for row n being at $16n$. Since all running tallies must be at zero before any seed is dispersed, these addresses must be cleared before any dispersal is begun.

n having been determined as described, the next step is to obtain $16n$ by shifting it up four places; this value is used to modify **s0** to extract the tally for the row. If the latter is p, then positions 1 to p in the row are already filled, and the seed has to go into position $p+1$. The tally is increased by one, and the seed is put into the word at address **s0** modified by $(16n+p+1)$.

This is quite straightforward until p reaches the value of 15, when a full row presents a second difficulty. Two ways of dealing with this immediately present themselves. We can try again until we find a row with a vacant place; there will be some random fluctuations in density through the population, and the contingency we are discussing is most likely to arise in regions of high density; the try again action helps to perpetuate fortuitous high densities, and we might even find a situation in which all rows within range of the seed parent were full; this would require special action to prevent the program going permanently into an unsuccessful loop.

Alternatively, we could reject any seed which falls on a full row. This would have the advantage of providing some check against density build-up, but if applied in the most direct way would have disastrous consequences for the experiment by introducing an entirely spurious element of selection. The seeds as they are produced are stored serially in the temporary store, beginning with those produced in the first week and finishing with those produced in the last. If the seed dispersal subroutine deals with this store in the same sequence, and rejects any seed falling on a full row, then the seeds which are dealt with last and therefore have the greatest liability to rejection will be those produced late in the season and so come from the latest flowering plants. There will then be some selection both against late flowering and a long flowering period. It is clearly imperative that any such spurious selection should be eliminated.

This could be done satisfactorily if it were possible to store all seeds falling on a row and, if the final number exceeded 15, eliminate some at random to bring the total down to 15. This is not practicable, as there is no sensible way of temporarily storing the surplus, but the following approximation may be used.

When a seed falls on a full row, it is made to replace one of the existing seeds at random by generation of a random number r in the range 0 to 15 and use of $16n+r$ as the modifier of **s0** unless r is zero, in which case it is the new seed which is eliminated. Thus if in the course of one generation 16 seeds fall in one row, elimination of one seed is entirely random. However, this technique does not deal perfectly with all possibilities, since if more than 16 seeds fall in a row elimination is no longer entirely random, seeds produced late in any year now having a slight advantage. Suppose 19 seeds are allocated by the subroutine to one row. This requires four random replacements; the first 16 seeds allocated will be at risk four times, the 17th three times, the 18th twice and the last only once. This effect may be minimized by dealing with the temporary seed store not serially, but in the sequence (supposing it to begin in **v0**) **v0, v64, v128** ... **v2560**; **v1, v65, v129** ... **v2561**; **v2, v66, v130** ... **v2562**; ... **v63, v127, v191** ... **v2623**. This is still not perfect, but very slight selection of late flowering does not matter much since we are looking for selection in opposite directions, and slight selection of a longer flowering period also matters little since it is contrary to the expected direction and while it may slightly retard selection it will not lead to a spurious indication of selection for a shorter flowering period. The apparently unnecessary extra words in the temporary store are to deal with the possibility that excessive upwards rounding of the weekly requirements may sometimes produce more than 2560 seeds; with this procedure, 64 is the minimum number for the extra words. So that unfilled words in the temporary store may be recognized as such by the dispersal subroutine, they are made nega-

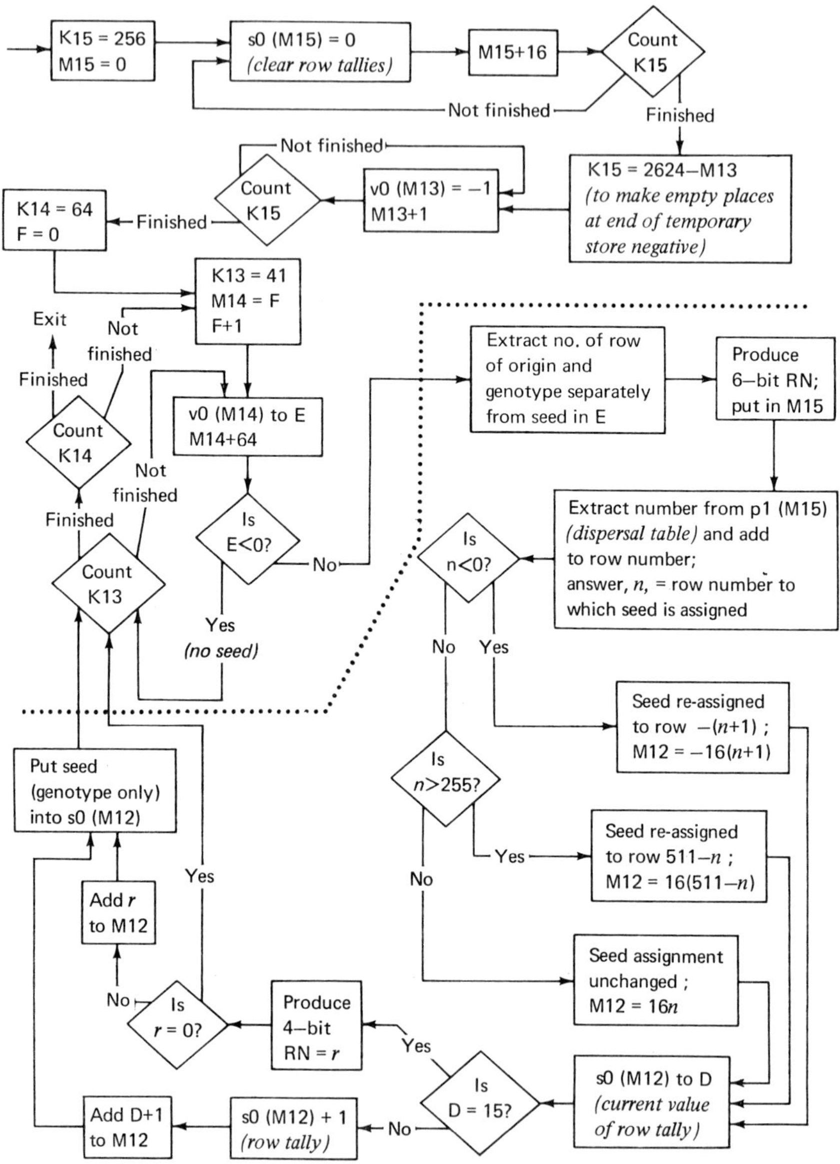

Figure 69. Flow diagram for **P10**, which passes through the temporary population in **v0** onwards in the manner described in the text, and sows seed in **s0** onwards. **M13** was used for temporary storage, and contains the number of seeds produced. Area below the dotted line deals with a single seed

tive; this is easily done immediately after the generation's reproduction either by the main program or as a preliminary activity by the dispersal subroutine. The number of seeds actually produced will be in the modifier used for temporary storage, and this allows both calculation of the number of unfilled places (by subtraction from 2624) and use of the same modifier to tag the unfilled words with a negative number; zero will not do, since there may be zero genotypes, phenotypes not having been added at this stage.

The whole subroutine, including clearance of tally addresses and making negative the surplus words in the temporary store, is illustrated in the flow diagram of Figure 69.

It would have been possible, at the cost of extra time or storage space (or both), to have dealt with the temporary store in a random order. With seed dispersal dealt with in a sequence which is sufficiently close to random, there is no danger of spurious selection arising as a consequence of over-filled rows. It would in fact simplify the dispersal procedure to the extent that all seeds arriving in a filled row could now be discarded directly instead of being made to replace at random an earlier arrival.

Random progress through a table may be carried out in several ways. One apparently obvious way is to pass through the table in a sequence each step of which is indicated by a random number generated at the time. For a temporary store of 2560 seeds (0 to 2559), a pseudorandom number generator producing the integers 0 to 4095 in a 4096-step cycle (that is, each occurring once and once only) would seem to be fairly efficient, though numbers higher than 2559 would have to be rejected. But to consider a pseudorandom cycle of this size as providing a truly random sequence is really very dubious; the pattern of the sequence would be the same from one generation to another, although that could easily be overcome by entering the cycle at a randomly determined point at each generation, so that there would be random differences between dispersal sequences of different generations. Apart from objection to the small cycle size, the technique applied precisely as described wastes time, since it involves a great deal of extra random number production in each generation. Since the pattern of the cycle would always be the same, whatever differences may result from randomization of entry points, it would be more efficient, if storage space is available, to produce the random sequence at the beginning of a run and store it in the form of a table. This table would have to occupy storage space equal to that of the temporary seed store (that is in our case rather more than 2560 words, to allow for surplus seed production arising from excessive rounding up, unused words in any generation being made negative as before), and would contain the relative addresses of the seed store produced in random order by operation of the 12-bit pseudorandom number generator with rejection of superfluous high numbers. It would be used in the following way. The subroutine would pass through this table serially, each word giving in turn a relative address which would be used in a modifier to extract from the temporary store the next seed to be dealt with. Since the relative addresses are in random order, the seeds would be dispersed in a random order, or at least in an order as nearly random as the short cycle permitted.

Random differences between generations could be effected by starting each serial passage through the random table of addresses at a point chosen at random; care would have to be taken to ensure that when the last word in the random table is reached the subroutine goes to the first word in the table, not to the next word in the store which would be beyond the table. This could be done either by comparing on each occasion the modifier used in passage through the table with its maximum permissible value, and making it zero when this is exceeded; or by simply calculating the number of words in the random table beyond the entry point and using this to provide a counter to determine when the end of the table is reached, and the number of the entry point as a counter to complete the passage from the beginning. With ample store space available, a quicker way of achieving the same end would be to duplicate the random table, the second following on immediately after the first with the random addresses in the same order. Passage from the first table to the second would have exactly the same effect as going back to the start of the first, and would require neither recognition nor special action. This device, though space-consuming in this example, is very useful with small tables when serial passage from random starting points is required, since problems of store space are then less serious.

A better approach to randomness could apparently be obtained by using a large-cycle pseudorandom number generator (obviously, in practice, the one used throughout the rest of the program) to produce 12-bit numbers, again discarding those greater than the size of the temporary population. The difficulty here is one of time, since such a procedure does not in producing 4096 consecutive numbers produce each possible 12-bit integer once and once only—some will occur more than once and some not at all. This would really make it quite impracticable to use the technique afresh at each generation, using 12-bit random numbers each indicating in turn the address in the temporary store of the next seed for dispersal; the difficulty quite simply is that by the time most seeds have been dealt with the random number would usually indicate seeds already dispersed, and the last few seeds would require very many random numbers to find them (the last one over four thousand, on average). In fact, on average more than 25,000 12-bit random numbers would have to be generated to produce every number from 0 to 2570 at least once.

The same difficulty would arise in preliminary establishment of a random position table, to be used for all generations with random points of entry as before. Such a table would be constructed by assigning the integers 0, 1, 2 ... 2570 (if that were the size of the temporary store) in sequence to randomly chosen addresses in the table, but on average the same number of random integers as before would be required to complete the table. This of course would be much less serious if it were done only once, at the beginning of a run.

But there is a much simpler and quicker way of running through a table or section of store in a random sequence. That is to shuffle the contents of the table or store at random, and then run through the table serially from the beginning, Shuffling requires only as many random numbers as there are addresses in the table (apart from waste when the number of addresses is not an integral power of two). Each address in the table is considered in turn, and its contents exchanged with those of another address in the table chosen at random; as progress is made, both addresses involved in an exchange are increasingly less likely still to have their original contents, and although every address will have its contents exchanged at least once, it will occasionally happen that an address will in the end have its original contents returned to it.

This shuffling procedure could be carried out on the temporary store at every generation immediately after reproduction was completed. Clearly, this would add running time to the program, but only to the extent, very approximately, of doubling the time required for seed dispersal. If economy of time was more important than economy of storage, then the shuffling would be carried out once at the beginning of a run on a table of integers, the shuffled table being entered at a random point for each generation and used to direct the sequence of seed dispersal from the temporary store in the way previously described.

It may well seem to the reader that too much time has been given to the elaboration of a rather trivial point. But the point is not trivial, and it cannot be emphasized too strongly that in experiments involving selection, especially where (as in the present case) selection pressures are low, it is important to make sure that spurious selection is not introduced in the construction of the model. The liability that this may happen is one of the disadvantages that sometimes arise in genotype simulation models, but it is usually much easier to recognize than it is in algebraic models where it may also happen as a result of mathematical manipulation, the fine consequences of which are by no means always apparent.

It is one of the facts of genotype simulation techniques that programming complexity may bear little relation to the relative biological importance within the system of the process being simulated. It is no more difficult to conceive and write a subroutine producing a zygote from two parents than it is to devise in the present program a procedure which ensures that no spurious element of selection arises in the seed dispersal subroutine.

During discussion of the grid technique for choice of pollen parent, it was pointed out that this could not operate properly if the rows were filled serially. It is easy enough to arrange for the row to be filled not serially, either in a predetermined order or with an element of randomness, at the cost of a small increase in program complexity and time.

The object is to ensure that, however many plants are in the row they are spread either fairly evenly or at random over it. In the insect flight program (in which 0 was a plant position, not the row tally), each row was filled in the predetermined sequence 5 8 14 2 10 0 6 12 4 15 1 9 3 11 7 13, which achieved the object desired as far as each row was concerned, but meant of course that there would be a pattern through the completed population in that there would almost always be a full line of plants in position 5 (unless there were empty rows), and that the line in position 13 would always have fewest plants. This sequence was achieved by having a 16-word table in the subroutine (beginning, say, in **p65** immediately after the row number frequency table) containing in the sequence previously given integers corresponding to positions in the row. Then, referring to the flow diagram of Figure 69, instead of adding to **M12** the new total for the row (1 + the number in **D**) in order to place the seed, the number in **D** is used as a modifier of **p65** to choose a number from the 16-word position table, and that value is added to **M12** and so used to put the seed in **s0(M12)**. The flow diagram would then be modified as follows. 'Add **D+1** to **M12**' would become 'put **D** into **M11** and add the contents of **p65(M11)** to **M12**' (With all 16 locations in a row being used for plants, instead of only 15, the flow diagram would require some other modifications, especially in the action to be taken on finding the row already full, which will be dealt with later.)

A completely random sequence of filling a row could be achieved by making a random choice of position for each seed at it is to be sown. Although this would also achieve randomness in distribution sequence between rows, it is not really practicable for the same reason that we have encountered on a much larger scale. It would involve generating 4-bit random numbers indicating positions in a row and discarding those already occupied; by the time the row is nearly full, several attempts would have to be made for each seed in order to find a vacant position.

A 4-bit pseudorandom number generator will not do (that is one producing all the numbers 0 to 15 in a single 16-stage cycle), however applied. So short a cycle cannot simulate randomness; if the cycle sequence is maintained through different rows we face the same difficulty that we started with when considering an arbitrary order of filling the row; if the rows operate individual but identical cycles, differing among themselves at random only on the point at which the cycle is first entered, then we have essentially the same procedure as the one about to be described but with the disadvantage that a random number has to be used to place each seed in its row.

The following partly random method provides a reasonable compromise, but raises a difficulty discussed later. In addition to the 256-word table with row tallies, a second 256-word table, also with sequential word/row correspondence, will be filled at some stage in each generation prior to seed dispersal with 4-bit random numbers (0 to 15) produced by the large-cycle subroutine used generally in the program, and so not repetitive in 16-word sequences. For any row, the number will be constant throughout the seed dispersal operation for any one generation but may vary from generation to generation if the table is filled as stated, or may be kept entirely constant if the table is filled once and for all at the beginning of a run.

The procedure is basically as in the predetermined sequence method with the incorporation of the appropriate random number from the second of the 256-word tables in one of two possible ways. It may be added to the current seed total for the row and the four l.s. bits of the sum used in the modifier in making the choice of position from the table beginning in **p65**; or alternatively it may be added to the number chosen from that table and the four l.s. bits of that answer taken to indicate the position for the seed. Either method will ensure that the 16 positions in any row are taken in some sequence without repetition, that at any time the seeds already present in the row will be dispersed fairly evenly through it (this of course is not at random), and that adjacent rows will usually not be filled in identical sequences. On the other hand, there will only be 16 different filling sequences in the population, instead of the 16! which are theoretically possible. A random sequence of numbers in the table beginning in **p65**, rather than one carefully chosen to favour even dispersal in the row, would not help. There would still only be 16 different filling sequences, all based on one random sequence and therefore still non-randomly related to one another.

Effective randomness of seed positions in a row may be achieved after the generation's seed dispersal has been completed. The seeds are dispersed in the way described for the program as actually used, that is serially in each row. When all have been dispersed and sown, the contents of each row in turn are shuffled at random by exchanging each seed (or unfilled position) in turn with another chosen at random from the same row—the same procedure in fact as described for a much larger table. Obviously, this adds time to the seed dispersal procedure (possibly doubling it), and whether the advantage of a random sequence of filling the positions in each row is worth the extra time involved is a matter for the programmer's judgment. This disadvantage could be substantially reduced if the same random pattern of dispersal within rows were used in each generation, but the time saved would be at the considerable expense of store space. At the beginning of a run, a dispersal table equal in size to the actual population store would be set up numbered serially from 0 to 4095; that is, corresponding to 256 rows of 16 positions. For each notional row in turn, the words and thus the serial numbers would then be shuffled at random in the way described, and the table in this revised form would be permanent for that run. In any generation, when a seed had been assigned to a row and was the *m*th seed to fall in that row, it would be referred to the *m*th word in the 16-word sequence in the table corresponding to that row in the actual population. The integer in that *m*th word would then be used as a modifier of **s0** to sow the seed in its proper place in the population.

For example, suppose that after shuffling the 16-word sequence in the dispersal table corresponding to row 5 of the population reads 93 89 87 95 94 83 88 82 81 84 91 85 80 86 90 92. The eighth seed to fall in row 5 would be referred to the eighth word in the notional row, which contains the number 82. With this as a modifier of **s0**, the seed is placed in position **s82** in the actual population (which would be the third position in the actual row).

Excess seeds would be dealt with by random replacement of a seed already in that row in the actual population; but when, as we have supposed, all 16 positions in the row are used for seed, a difficulty unfortunately arises. It illustrates very well the sort of irritating difficulty which crops up and has to be dealt with since in a really irrelevant way it affects the biology of the situation. With 15 available positions in a row, when these are filled and a 16th seed falls there it takes its chance of elimination equally with the other 15 by virtue of a random number zero corresponding to a non-available position. However, with 16 positions available there is no choice which will lead to the elimination of the 17th seed if a 4-bit random number is used, and its genotype will thus be at a selective advantage.

One rather clumsy way round this difficulty would be to generate a 5-bit random number, and subtract 15 from it. If the answer is negative, the random number is rejected and a new one generated; if the answer is zero, the 17th seed is rejected; if the answer exceeds zero it is decreased by one and used as a modifier to indicate which seed in the row is to be replaced by the 17th. In itself rather time-consuming, this method would not lead to much loss of time since it would not need to be used many times in a generation. Of course, if seeds in the temporary store are dispersed in random sequence, this difficulty no longer arises, since any surplus seed may be immediately rejected.

It must not be forgotten that for any method in which the rows are filled non-serially with the object of using a grid technique for choice of pollen parent, the whole population must be cleared so that filled and unfilled positions may later be distinguished.

It would be simplest to clear the whole population store to zero and to determine and add the phenotypes to the genotypes as the seed is sown, thus avoiding ambiguity which could arise from zero genotypes. If the phenotypes are not added at this stage, the population store may be set entirely at a negative number; also, in adding the phenotype the entire population store will have to be scanned, since the row tallies will no longer indicate which row positions hold plants—this will take more time but the scanning procedure will be simpler than it was in the original program.

Population Analysis and Output. P5.

The seed having been dispersed and sown, the generation cycle is completed, and the program now comes round again to phenotype determination and insertion, and thence to a further generation's cycle of reproduction.

There is one important element of the program of which we postponed consideration, partly because it is not a biological operation and therefore does not involve simulation, and partly because it does not come into effect at every generation. This is population analysis and output, and is performed at 10-generation intervals immediately after the phenotype determination and insertion subroutine.

In many ways, the subroutine for population analysis and output was the most intricate one in the whole program to produce, and only the population analysis section is going to be considered in detail here. As has been pointed out elsewhere, programming for output depends to a great extent on the computer in use and its output equipment, and useful generalization is not really practicable.

In deciding on the output for this program, there were two basic considerations: what information was required from the population analysis, and how it should be presented. It was clear that any useful analysis would require a great deal of output. From the very nature of the experiment, the population was not uniform throughout its length, and the output would therefore have to present a clear picture of variation in population structure and genetic constitution from one end of the population to the other.

Because there would be so much output following each analysis, considerable thought was given to the problem of organizing its layout in such a way that a broad impression of evolutionary changes and the current evolutionary situation could be obtained by visual inspection of the output without detailed examination of the actual figures. The reason for this was two-fold. During the development of the program, the first thing required from any set of results was information as to whether the program was making biological sense; if a superficial inspection of the results showed that this was not the case, then work to amend the program could often proceed immediately without the need to go into a detailed and time-consuming inspection of the results. Later, when the program was satisfactory, it was run in 30-minute stages, at the end of each of which it was dumped onto magnetic tape in such a way that it could readily be resumed later; after each stage a quick inspection of the results would show whether the experiment had gone far enough or whether a further stage should be run; in the latter case, the ability to make a quick decision meant that the run could be resumed with a minimum of delay.

An output giving rapid information about the course of an experiment by direct visual impression is particularly valuable where the experimenter is operating the computer and has because of this some control over the experiment while it is in progress—not simply by stopping it but for example by changing parameters or other properties of the model. This however generally applies to the older and slower machines, and not to the faster and more complex machines (such as the one used for the experiment under discussion).

The output subroutine actually developed was in fact perhaps too effective. The layout presented apparently so clear a picture of the situation that it led to two tactical errors by the author which were unfortunate, although they had no effect on the validity or conclusions ultimately drawn from the experiments. Firstly, at the end of each 30-minute stage the picture of the genetical state of the population usually seemed so clear that the author did not at the time inspect with sufficient care the earlier 10-generation outputs; had he done so he would have realized then (instead of much later when he decided that the time had come for detailed consideration of the results) that evolution was not proceeding so steadily as it appeared to be, and that several things of considerable interest were happening which were not at all apparent to the casual eye.

From a practical point of view, the second error was more serious. Because the layout apparently presented so clear a picture, the author assumed that he had arrived at the optimum decision on the information to be provided by the population analysis and the way in which it was to be presented. It was not until he came to write the work up for publication that he realized that general visual impressions, however accurate, cannot readily be presented in the limited space available in a scientific journal, and that graphs can only be drawn and tables and diagrams produced when the appropriate figures are available.

For his own purposes, the expansive output appeared to be satisfactory, and in the sense that it sufficiently enabled him to follow the course of an experiment in progress and to plan future experiments, this was true. But it did not provide in a rapidly available form all of the critical figures which were essential both for the written description and for the illustrations and tables. For example, the progress of one experiment is summarized in Table 2 of the published paper (Crosby 1970), and this has 14 items of information for each of five selected points during that run. Of these 14 items, two could be obtained directly by inspection of the output, and three could be obtained fairly easily by simple addition; the remainder were certainly obtainable from the output, but only by laborious calculations (it would have been even more laborious at that stage to have produced a program for further analysis of the output and to prepare the output for treatment by it). It is true that no information which was needed for the description and interpretation of the course of the experiment was missing; it just required a great deal of work to get it out.

Perhaps because of the clear picture to himself of the course of his experiments presented by the output, the author quite failed to consider the picture he would need to present in a written paper. If at an early stage of development of the programs he had stopped to consider output in the light of this requirement, he would have realized that certain summarizing calculations were highly desirable and it would have been practicable at that stage to have amended the analysis and output procedures to include them. As an example, the output gave for each of a series of sections of the population the various gene frequencies for each of the two subspecies. But the subroutine made no calculation of the mean gene frequencies for the whole of each subspecies over the entire population; these values had to be derived subsequently from the sectional figures, and since the sections had variable numbers of plants this involved a great deal of work.

The moral is obvious. Output, especially in a complicated experiment, requires a great deal of thought. In the early days of computing before line printers had been introduced, output was at the rate of one character at a time and was a lengthy process which could add very considerably to the running time of a program. Where a great deal of output was required, even economy in the use of spaces was essential, and analysis and output routines had to be designed to give the maximum of information with the minimum of output.

With the advent of the line printer, the situation changed considerably. A line (of, say, 120 characters) was now printed in a single operation and took the same sort of time as that formerly required by a single character. Also, once the material to be output had been properly assembled and the instruction to print had been given, the actual printing operation was independent of the central processor of the computer which could continue with the program (provided there was no immediate call for further output). For example, in the author's program under discussion, the output from a single population analysis consisted of 176 lines of 120 characters each, occupying four pages. The results of the analysis having been properly assembled in the store by the subroutine, printing was initiated by a single instruction. Immediately this instruction was put into operation, printing became quite independent and the computer proceeded to leave the subroutine and get on with the next section of the generation cycle, although the line printer spent the next 18 seconds in printing the output. Since output was at roughly 100-second intervals, the mechanical operation of printing caused no delay to the program. It is perhaps worth pointing out that this sort of efficiency was achieved because the author wrote his own output procedure; library subroutines which were available would have been much less efficient.

One consequence of this change of speed of output has been a change in attitude to output, the general philosophy apparently being that since (up to a point) it does not waste much computer time, one might as well have as much output as possible. One always has the suspicion that other people, with their great wads of output, are getting far more figures than they will ever be able to study or comprehend. This is not entirely fair because sometimes (as in the present case) the visual pattern presented by the figures can convey much information that could not so easily be conveyed in any other way. But there is no point in producing a great mass of figures which convey little or nothing on casual inspection unless they are really needed. Although there are of course occasions when only a few are actually needed but all have to be printed because it is impossible to tell in advance which will be the critical ones. It should be an important objective to have as much inspection and analysis of the results as possible carried out by the program, to achieve economy of output, to ease the labour of appraisal, and to make sure that useful information is not lost because the output is so massive that its effective appraisal is impracticable.

One cannot overemphasize the importance of careful preliminary thought and planning in the organization of population analysis and output, nor the need for careful consideration of the results even from early trial runs to confirm or otherwise that analysis and output are providing in a readily comprehensible form all the information which is required. Obviously, especially with a complex evolutionary situation, it is not always possible to foresee what information will be required, especially when there is uncertainty about the course which evolution will take, so that it is still desirable to present results in sufficiently detailed form to permit further analysis should this prove to be desirable; intelligent anticipation may indicate what possibilities should be left open. There is a great deal to be said, if the possibility exists, for dumping onto magnetic tape or disc, on each occasion of population analysis, either the whole population intact or so detailed an analytical summary of it that should the unexpected occur and demand reconsideration of the course of the experiment in terms of other information not adequately dealt with in the original analysis, this would still be possible.

The population analysis and output subroutine in the author's program, although providing a good visual picture, certainly fell short of those standards, though not by a great deal. It is perhaps not surprising that it fell short; it was much the most complicated population that he had to deal with, and one cannot learn by experience until one has had the experience. There were no precedents to follow and the author was then on largely unexplored territory. In the description of this subroutine which follows, detailed flow diagrams will not be presented. An account will be given of the information which was required from the analysis, of the way in which it was decided that it should be output, and of the general principles of the techniques used in the population analysis.

Before describing the output further, it may be as well to recapitulate the genetics of the situation. There are three groups of genes. There are eight **G**/**g** loci, determining the taxonomic position of the individual and its fertility, 16**G** being pure subspecies *A*, 16**g** being pure subspecies *B*, and 8**G**8**g** for example being (among other possibilities) the F_1 hybrid, and having the lowest fertility. There are three **D**/**d** loci determining date of flowering and two **W**/**w** loci determining the length of the flowering period.

If within each of these groups all loci are of equal value, as was specified, and we are only interested in the numbers of **G** and **g**, **D** and **d**, and **W** and **w** alleles in any particular individual, there are 17 **G**/**g** genotypes, seven **D**/**d** genotypes and five **W**/**w** genotypes to be considered (using 'genotype' in a rather improper sense, but 'phenotype' is not quite right either). Taking these together, there are 595 different genotypes, and one thing that is clearly going to be impracticable is the output of a detailed analysis of sections of the population in terms of the frequencies of the different genotypes; and a little thought will show that in any event so detailed an analysis would not be particularly comprehensible.

The potential mass of genetic information was reduced to intelligibility in two ways, and there were two different forms of output which were printed side by side (though not precisely matched) partly to minimize the physical quantity of output in terms of paper and partly to facilitate the consideration more or less simultaneously of both forms of output for a particular section of the program.

One form of output was concerned primarily with gene frequencies, and for this purpose the 17 taxonomic **G**/**g** genotypes were reduced to five groups, three of which were considered for output and two of which were not. The three groups for output comprised the genotype ranges 16**G** to 14**G**2**g**, 10**G**6**g** to 6**G**10**g**, and 2**G**14**g** to 16**g**, and were treated as subspecies *A*, hybrids, and subspecies *B* respectively. The two groups in between these were omitted because it was felt (correctly as it happened) that there would be few plants with those constitutions and that their genotypes would be of no particular interest anyway; their exclusion reduced the page width required for output in this form and left room for the second form of output to be placed by the side of the first. But in any case, the second form of output gave adequate information about them.

This gene frequency output dealt with the population in a linear sequence of 128 consecutive sections of two adjacent rows, giving the mean number per individual of **g**, **w** and **d** alleles. These are the alleles represented by **1** in the simulated genotype, and for each individual their numbers are readily obtained by use of the appropriate masks followed by **bits**.

There were four main columns of output. The first gave for each two-row section the total number of plants in those two rows, and the mean numbers per plant of **g**, **w** and **d** alleles respectively. The other three main columns dealt with the three considered taxonomic groups, *A*, hybrids and *B*, giving for each two-row section the number of individuals in each of those groups and the mean numbers per individual of **w** and **d** alleles.

This form of output (which is illustrated later in Table 15) made it possible to see rapidly for any part of the population the numbers of *A*, *B* and hybrids, and their mean genetic constitution in respect of date and length of flowering period, and to obtain an overall picture of how these varied through the population—in particular to see to what extent the two subspecies were interpenetrating and the extent of hybridization. In practice, the first main column gave much less useful information than the other three (because it lumped all the **G**/**g** genotypes together) and could perhaps have been dispensed with, but it was occasionally useful on later detailed analysis and it did allow a check to be made on the numbers of unconsidered **G**/**g** genotypes. The other three columns gave a rapid and clear picture of the current evolutionary stage reached by the population.

The analysis required to arrive at this output was fairly straightforward. The population was scanned two rows at a time. For each two-row section, the total number of plants was readily obtained from the row tallies, and each plant was dealt with in the following way, most of the information being accumulated in a 51-word store which for purposes of description we will suppose to begin in **z0**.

This store, cleared at the beginning of each two-row analysis, was divided into three 17-word sections beginning in **z0**, **z17** and **z34**, the words in each section corresponding serially to genotypes having 0 to 16 **g** alleles respectively. **z0** to **z16** accumulated the number of individuals in each **G**/**g** genotype, **z17** to **z33** the total number of **w** alleles in each **G**/**g** genotype, and **z34** to **z50** the total number of **d** alleles in each **G**/**g** genotype.

As each plant was examined, the number of **g** alleles was obtained and added to an accumulator (to give the total of **g** for those two rows and allow the mean number of **g** for all plants in those rows to be calculated); it was also put in a modifier, say **M15**. Then one was added to **z0(M15)** to count the number of individuals of that genotype, the number of **w** alleles was added to **z17(M15)**, and the number of **d** alleles to **z34(M15)**; the numbers of **w** and **d** alleles were also added into separate accumulators to give their totals over all plants in the two rows. It will be realized that this operation was performed on all **G**/**g** genotypes including those for which no output was required; there were so few of these that it was simpler to deal with them than to test each plant in order that they might be recognized and ignored when they appeared.

When all plants in the two rows had been dealt with, the required means were easily calculated. The overall means were obtained from the total number of plants and the accumulated totals of **g**, **w** and **d**.

Using z_0, z_1 etc. to represent the contents of **z0**, **z1** etc., $(z_0+z_1+z_2)$, $(z_{17}+z_{18}+z_{19})/(z_0+z_1+z_2)$ and $(z_{34}+z_{35}+z_{36})/(z_0+z_1+z_2)$ gave the number of individuals of subspecies *A* (16**G** to 14**G**2**g**) and the mean number per *A* individual of **w** and **d** alleles respectively.

$(z_6+z_7+z_8+z_9+z_{10})$, $(z_{23}+z_{24}+z_{25}+z_{26}+z_{27})/(z_6+z_7+z_8+z_9+z_{10})$ and $(z_{40}+z_{41}+z_{42}+z_{43}+z_{44})/(z_6+z_7+z_8+z_9+z_{10})$ did the same for the hybrids, and $(z_{14}+z_{15}+z_{16})$, $(z_{31}+z_{32}+z_{33})/(z_{14}+z_{15}+z_{16})$ and $(z_{48}+z_{49}+z_{50})/(z_{14}+z_{15}+z_{16})$ for subspecies *B* (**2G14g** to **16g**).

That completed the analysis for the two rows, but the results were in binary. Before output, the means were rounded to one decimal place and all results converted into a binary coded form of the relevant decimal characters for output. Standard library subroutines are usually available for such conversion, which presents no problems, the binary number to be converted simply being sent with any necessary parameters (such as number of significant figures or decimal places) to the subroutine, which will deliver the characters for output in coded form in the proper sequence.

Each result in character coded form was then sent to its correct place in a large table occupying a section of the store. This table had been designed so that when completed everything within it was in the correct order for the line printer, which would deal with its contents in serial order and transform them into printed output in a predetermined layout. Overall, this was a fairly complex operation. The table had to hold the results for both forms of output since both were printed simultaneously—a line printer cannot print one form of output down one half of a page and then go back and print the other so each continuous section of the table representing one line of output would have to carry the characters for both forms of output.

The structure of the table had to be planned carefully. Since the editing characters (spaces, line-feeds, page-throws) were the same for every generation's output, they could be put into the table once for all and left there. The structure having been planned, the control procedure for each generation had then to be developed. This involved precise manipulation of counters and modifiers running in parallel with the population analysis operations in such a way that as each character coded form of a result was produced it was sent to its proper position in the table.

The rounding of the means to one decimal place for output was to avoid crowding the layout. One decimal place was generally adequate, since great precision in gene frequency was not necessary, but it did mean that where there were more than 20 plants of the relevant genotype in a two row section, a single allele would come out as a mean of zero, and this could be misleading in wrongly indicating absence of that allele. Actually, this only happened in a few cases and only affected the mean value of the **g** alleles for all plants in a section. Except occasionally where there were very few plants in a row, the mean value for **w** and **d** over all plants never reached zero or their maximum. For the mean value of **w** and **d** among *A* and *B* (hybrid numbers were never large enough to matter), **w** never reached zero except when numbers were very small, and when the means for **d** reached zero or 6.0, again the numbers of the relevant plants were small because these values only came about when A and B occurred together; the number of the relevant plants was never more than twenty for these extreme values for **d**. It would have been possible to add a second decimal place for each mean, but the output would then have been very crowded and less amenable to visual interpretation.

False indication of zero by using too few decimal places in output is something that needs to be guarded against where it is important not to be misled. This is most likely to happen when a program is modified to give a larger population size, and the effect of this on output is overlooked.

In the present case it did not much matter because only the **G**/**g** alleles were affected (though the author was not to know this beforehand) and the second form of output allowed the occurrence of a misleading zero or 16.0 to be recognized.

The second method of analysis also dealt with the population in sections, but not all of the same size. For each section, a small table of eight rows and 17 columns was produced, the rows corresponding serially to the weeks of flowering, and the columns to the **G**/**g** genotypes. It showed, for each genotype, the numbers of individuals flowering in each week; or putting it another way, for each week the number of individuals of each genotype flowering during that week.

There is a debatable point involved here. The results showed the numbers of individuals, without regard to reproductive capacity. Thus in any week a count of one could equally indicate a plant of a pure subspecies with a total flowering period of two weeks or an F_1 hybrid with a total flowering period of six weeks, although the weekly reproductive capacity of the latter would only be one twelfth of that of the former. The table therefore presented a picture of the number and kinds of plants in flower at any time, and not of the reproductive capacity at that time and its distribution over the various **G**/**g** genotypes. In some ways the latter would have presented a truer picture but would have involved lengthier analysis by the program and would have required the items in the table to be presented as fractions and not as integers. This would not only have required more space, but because there would have been more and crowded figures the table would have been less readily comprehensible. The method showing number of plants in flower was therefore preferred; there was little danger of the author being misled as where small numbers were involved it was usually fairly obvious how many weeks plants were in general flowering. If a more precise picture were required, it could be obtained by making use of the first form of output. However, the author is not entirely sure now that he made the right decision.

The sections into which the population was divided were determined on the basis that the centre of the population was the area of most interest, since there the two subspecies were in contact or interpenetrating, and any differences in flowering period between the different **G**/**g** genotypes would have maximum significance. The sections in the centre of the population were therefore smaller, allowing a more detailed analysis of the population. The central half of the population (taken symmetrically) was dealt with in sections of eight rows. Next to these, moving outwards, were two sections of 16 rows each on each side and a terminal section of 32 rows at each end. As events turned out, it might have been better to have dealt with the whole population in sections of eight rows—this would not have meant an excessive increase in quantity of output.

Each section was scanned in the usual way, and each plant encountered was dealt with as follows. It should be remembered that by this time it carries not only its genotype but its full phenotype as well, of which first week of flowering and number of weeks are required in this operation.

The numbers of the genotypes flowering in each week are accumulated in the 8-row × 17-column table. We will suppose that this table (which must be clear at the start of each section of the population) begins in **z0** and occupies 136 words (the previous use of **z0** onwards for the gene frequency output is quite finished and so the same area of store may be put to this other use). **z0** to **z16** will sum the numbers of individuals of genotypes with 0 to 16 **g** alleles respectively flowering in the first week (week 0), **z17** to **z33** respectively those in the second week (week 1), and so on.

As each plant is taken, the number of **g** alleles is determined by use of the appropriate mask and a **bits** operation, and this number is then put into a modifier, say **M12**. The first week of flowering is then extracted, multiplied by 17, and the answer added to **M12**. The number of weeks of flowering is then extracted and put into a counter in order to execute the appropriate number of times a loop in which one is added to **z0(M12)**, **M12** being incremented by 17 on each execution of the loop. Thus suppose we have a plant of genotype **12G4g3W1w4D2d**. This plant begins flowering in week 2 and flowers for three weeks (Table 14). There are four **g** alleles, so **M12** first receives the value 4. The first week of flowering is week 2, so 34 is added to **M12** making a total of 38, and one is added to **z0(M12)** on three occasions, **M12** being cumulatively increased by 17 for the second and third of these. One is thus added to **z38**, **z55** and **z72**. If this plant were the only one of that constitution flowering during any of those weeks, it would be shown in the printed output table by a 1 in each of the third, fourth and fifth lines of the fifth column. An example can be recognized in section *Q* of Table 16.

The analysis of a section being completed, it remained to transform the binary integers in the stored table into their decimal character coded form, and to put them into their correct position ready for output.

The whole analysis being completed and ready, it was output. Immediately the instruction for output had been given, the program inspected the clock and if it had run long enough it dumped itself onto magnetic tape, entirely and precisely including of course the population, with a record of the state of accumulators, counters, modifiers etc. where the contents of these had to be maintained. If desired, the program would then be resumed at a later date exactly as if there had been no interruption.

If it had not yet run long enough, then it proceeded to begin another 10-generation cycle.

To illustrate the way in which the layout of results allowed a quick appraisal of the situation, a section of the output for generation 140 of run 16 is shown in Tables 15 and 16. Column headings and reference letters to sections have been added so that the tables may be followed more readily. The sectionalization in the output shown in Table 15 was for convenience and had no other significance.

Each of the five sections of Table 16 concerns eight rows of the population and corresponds to four lines (half a section) of Table 15, the precise correspondence being indicated by letters. It will be noticed from Table 15, by comparing the total plant count for each two-row section (left-hand column) with the sum of the corresponding counts in the other three main columns, that there were five intermediate genotypes (there were no others in the whole population), one in the second line of section *QR*, and three in the fourth line and one in the fifth line of section *ST*. These plants can be identified in sections *Q*, *S* and *T* respectively of Table 16, and flower respectively for 3, 5, 3, 3 and 4 weeks, the first of these being the plant we took as an example. In section *S* (Table 16) fourth column, we know that this is one plant flowering for five weeks and not two flowering consecutively for two and three weeks, because we know from Table 15 that there are only three intermediates in section *S* and there must be two in the fourteenth column. If the results in Table 15 were not available, we could not be sure about the fourth column of *S* in Table 16, but we would still know that the fourteenth column represented two plants flowering for three weeks and not three for two weeks, since the latter could not produce the sequence of figures 2 2 2—it would have to be 3 3 0, 0 3 3, 2 3 1 or 1 3 2.

Table 15 shows very clearly the extent of interpenetration of the two subspecies and the amount of hybridization (the diffuse boundary between *A* and *B* had moved from its original position—the two tables cover the whole extent of interpenetration and hybridization.) The same table shows clearly the differences between *A* and *B* in **d** frequencies and that this is strikingly greater where the two subspecies are actually occurring together (some mean values for *A* being zero and some for *B* being at the maximum of 6.0). The fall in frequency of **w** from the starting value of 2.0 is very obvious in *B*, less so in *A*; indeed, the *A* plants nearest the territory of *B* show on average an increased value for **w**.

To interpret Table 15 in terms of flowering period would not be an easy matter, but Table 16 shows the situation very clearly. Although there is a considerable overlap in flowering period, *A* plants are tending to flower most strongly in the earlier weeks, mostly appearing in the upper five rows of each section (first five weeks), *B* plants tending to flower more strongly later, mostly appearing in the bottom five rows (last five weeks).

TABLE 15

Part of one form of output showing for consecutive section of two rows the numbers of all plants, of the subspecies, and of the hybrids, and the mean gene frequencies per plant. This and Table 16 are part of the actual output figures of a run after 140 generations, and appeared precisely side by side, the letters *P* to *T* indicating correspondence between the two tables. In both cases the centre of the population is at the bottom of the table. *g w d* are the mean frequencies per plant of the alleles **g w d**. *A* = 16G to 14G2g; hybrids = 10G6g to 6G10g; *B* = 2G14g to 16g

	All plants				*A*			Hybrids			*B*		
	no.	*g*	*w*	*d*	no.	*w*	*d*	no.	*w*	*d*	no.	*w*	*d*
	17	0.0	2.4	2.4	17	2.4	2.4	0			0		
	15	0.0	1.8	2.3	15	1.8	2.3	0			0		
	21	0.0	2.0	2.5	21	2.0	2.5	0			0		
	17	0.0	1.5	2.4	17	1.5	2.4	0			0		
	16	0.0	2.4	3.2	16	2.4	3.2	0			0		
	16	0.0	1.8	2.3	16	1.8	2.3	0			0		
	23	0.0	2.2	2.3	23	2.2	2.3	0			0		
	23	0.0	1.9	3.0	23	1.9	3.0	0			0		
	10	0.0	1.2	3.2	10	1.2	3.2	0			0		
	17	0.0	1.7	2.9	17	1.7	2.9	0			0		
	8	0.0	2.1	2.1	8	2.1	2.1	0			0		
	9	0.0	1.7	3.3	9	1.7	3.3	0			0		
	18	0.0	1.3	2.6	18	1.3	2.6	0			0		
	9	0.0	1.1	2.2	9	1.1	2.2	0			0		
	11	0.0	1.0	2.1	11	1.0	2.1	0			0		
	11	0.0	0.9	1.3	11	0.9	1.3	0			0		
	11	0.0	1.0	2.2	11	1.0	2.2	0			0		
	10	0.0	0.9	2.2	10	0.9	2.2	0			0		
	10	0.0	1.4	1.7	10	1.4	1.7	0			0		
	9	0.0	1.7	2.0	9	1.7	2.0	0			0		
	11	0.0	1.2	2.1	11	1.2	2.1	0			0		
P	11	0.0	1.8	2.1	11	1.8	2.1	0			0		
	10	0.0	1.5	2.4	10	1.5	2.4	0			0		
	8	4.1	1.0	2.0	6	1.0	0.7	0			2	1.0	6.0
	3	10.7	1.3	3.3	1	2.0	0.0	0			2	1.0	5.0
	5	3.8	1.0	2.6	3	0.7	1.7	0			1	2.0	5.0
Q	6	6.2	1.7	3.5	4	2.3	2.3	0			2	0.5	6.0
	9	8.2	1.9	3.9	4	2.3	2.0	1	3.0	5.0	4	1.3	5.5
	5	15.6	0.6	5.2	0			0			5	0.6	5.2
	7	12.6	1.0	4.6	1	2.0	0.0	1	1.0	3.0	5	0.8	5.8
R	5	14.8	0.6	5.0	0			1	0.0	4.0	4	0.8	5.3
	13	13.7	1.0	4.2	0			4	1.8	3.0	9	0.7	4.8
	9	15.0	1.3	4.3	0			1	2.0	2.0	8	1.3	4.6
S	17	14.4	0.6	3.7	1	3.0	0.0	1	1.0	1.0	15	0.4	4.1
	16	14.6	0.6	3.9	0			3	1.0	1.7	13	0.5	4.4
	15	13.6	0.7	4.2	1	2.0	0.0	0			11	0.3	5.5
	22	15.7	0.9	4.3	0			0			21	0.9	4.5
T	17	15.4	0.8	4.7	0			1	2.0	1.0	16	0.8	4.9
	26	16.0	0.8	5.2	0			0			26	0.8	5.2
	22	15.9	0.7	5.0	0			0			22	0.7	5.0

TABLE 16

Part of the second form of output showing for consecutive sections of eight rows the numbers of plants of the different **G**/**g** genotypes flowering in each week—the lines in each section of the output corresponding to the eight possible weeks of flowering, the earliest week at the top.

See also caption to Table 15; the letters *P* to *T* indicate correspondence between the two tables.

	Number of **g** alleles																
	0	1	2	3	4	5	6	7	8	9	10	11	12	13	14	15	16
	8	0	0	0	0	0	0	0	0	0	0	0	0	0	0	0	0
	19	0	0	0	0	0	0	0	0	0	0	0	0	0	0	0	0
	30	1	0	0	0	0	0	0	0	0	0	0	0	0	0	0	0
	29	1	0	0	0	0	0	0	0	0	0	0	0	0	0	0	0
P	23	1	0	0	0	0	0	0	0	0	0	0	0	0	0	0	0
	11	0	0	0	0	0	0	0	0	0	0	0	0	0	0	0	2
	5	0	0	0	0	0	0	0	0	0	0	0	0	0	0	0	2
	2	0	0	0	0	0	0	0	0	0	0	0	0	0	0	0	2
	2	0	0	0	0	0	0	0	0	0	0	0	0	0	0	0	0
	6	0	2	0	0	0	0	0	0	0	0	0	0	0	0	0	0
	8	1	3	0	1	0	0	0	0	0	0	0	0	0	0	0	0
	5	1	3	0	1	0	0	0	1	0	0	0	0	0	0	1	3
Q	3	1	3	0	1	0	0	0	1	0	0	0	0	0	0	1	3
	2	1	2	0	0	0	0	0	1	0	0	0	0	0	0	1	6
	1	0	1	0	0	0	0	0	1	0	0	0	0	0	0	1	7
	1	0	0	0	0	0	0	0	1	0	0	0	0	0	0	0	5
	1	0	0	0	0	0	0	0	0	0	0	0	0	0	0	0	0
	1	0	0	0	0	0	0	0	1	1	0	0	0	0	0	0	1
	1	0	0	0	0	0	0	0	1	2	0	0	0	0	0	0	3
	1	0	0	0	0	0	0	0	2	3	0	0	0	0	0	1	3
R	0	0	0	0	0	0	0	0	2	3	1	0	0	0	0	1	6
	0	0	0	0	0	0	0	0	1	1	1	0	0	0	0	3	12
	0	0	0	0	0	0	0	0	1	0	0	0	0	0	0	3	17
	0	0	0	0	0	0	0	0	0	0	0	0	0	0	0	1	11
	2	0	0	1	0	0	0	0	0	0	0	0	0	0	0	0	1
	2	0	0	1	0	0	0	0	3	0	0	0	0	2	1	0	6
	2	0	0	1	0	0	0	0	4	0	1	0	0	2	1	0	10
	2	0	0	1	0	0	0	0	4	0	1	0	0	2	1	0	11
S	1	0	0	1	0	0	0	0	3	0	0	0	0	0	0	0	10
	0	0	0	0	0	0	0	0	0	0	0	0	0	0	0	2	17
	0	0	0	0	0	0	0	0	0	0	0	0	0	0	0	3	30
	0	0	0	0	0	0	0	0	0	0	0	0	0	0	0	3	23
	0	0	0	0	0	0	0	0	0	0	0	1	0	0	0	0	1
	0	0	0	0	0	0	1	0	0	0	0	1	0	0	0	0	3
	0	0	0	0	0	0	1	0	0	0	0	1	0	0	0	0	14
	0	0	0	0	0	0	1	0	0	0	0	1	0	0	0	1	27
T	0	0	0	0	0	0	1	0	0	0	0	0	0	0	0	3	37
	0	0	0	0	0	0	0	0	0	0	0	0	0	0	0	3	42
	0	0	0	0	0	0	0	0	0	0	0	0	0	0	0	4	58
	0	0	0	0	0	0	0	0	0	0	0	0	0	0	0	1	42

One other thing which is obvious in both tables is that where the two subspecies interpenetrate, there is an overall shortage of plants. This arises from the average low reproductive capacity resulting from hybridization in that region.

By closer examination of these results, more detailed information about the then current state of the population could be obtained, but the main point to be made from Tables 15 and 16 is how careful attention to layout can help to produce a rapid appraisal of a situation.

Further Developments of the Program

The discussion of this program has been lengthy, but it is hoped that it has served to show how a simulation model of a fairly complex evolutionary system can be built up.

A program of this kind should be constructed in such a way that it may be modified with little trouble and little risk of programming error when it is desired to investigate variations on the original system. Where possible, the properties of the system should be controlled by parameters stored in such a way that they may be easily amended without any need for alteration of the actual program.

Sometimes it seems simplest to write a parameter directly in a subroutine, for example where it is an integer designed for counting or actually forming part of, say, a shift instruction; from the point of view of running time it is likely to be quickest. But if such parameters involve properties of the model system which are likely to be changed either in order to vary the model to investigate a different form of the system, or in development of the initial program before their most satisfactory values have been decided, it is best to store them in a well defined (and well remembered!) location, from which the program will extract them when required. There are two good reasons for this; one is that it is easier to find the correct location in a parameter list and alter it than to search for and find the point in a written program where the parameter is used; the second and more important one is that where the parameter is used several times there is still only one alteration to be made and there is no danger of error arising from overlooking one of the occasions on which the parameter is used.

It was easy enough in the present case to change the reproductive capacities of the hybrids and other intermediate genotypes, the pattern of pollen transport and the pattern of seed dispersal simply by substituting the appropriate tables. A simple amendment to the fertility table with no alteration of any kind to the program allowed the investigation of the consequences of an assumption that shortening of the flowering period might not be entirely compensated for by increased flower production per week; that is, that there might be a slight selective advantage in longer flowering. The question was whether this would be sufficient to outweigh any advantage shorter flowering might have in the avoidance of hybridization. It was.

The introduction of differences in ecological preference between *A* and *B*, expressed as differences in reproductive capacity in different parts of the population, was easily achieved by the introduction of a small subroutine which where appropriate amended the weekly fertility of an individual according to its genotype and its location in the population. This is discussed in more detail in Chapter 12.

More substantial alterations to the program, but with no essential change to its basic structure or many of its subroutines, allowed the plants to be treated as perennials. Still more radical reconstruction (but still with the original model as a firm foundation) allowed variation in thc breeding system to be introduced as an element of major importance.

It is not of course always easy to foresee the way in which one may want to develop a model of this kind—for one thing, development may be determined by previous results. But experience makes it easier to keep programs flexible and to assesss where flexibility is likely to be of most value.

CHAPTER 12

Some Miscellaneous Genetical Procedures

In this chapter, some general notes will be presented on methods of introducing into simulation models some features of genetic systems which so far have not been referred to or have only been lightly touched upon.

Ecological Heterogeneity within a Population

A development of the program described in Chapter 11 considered a situation in which the environment was not uniform and the two plant subspecies had different ecological preferences. The object of this was not the obvious one of investigating the effect on the model of ecological heterogeneity, but the practical one of discouraging the two subspecies from invading each other's territory on anything but a small scale. In the original version of that model, once the two subspecies had evolved an effective barrier to hybridization they interpenetrated considerably, one of them eventually occurring throughout the whole length of the population. It was desired to investigate the situation when in spite of the barrier to hybridization there was little interpenetration, and the obvious way of doing this was to put each subspecies at a selective disadvantage when in the other's territory.

To arrange this presented no difficulty. It will be remembered that in the earlier model the population occupied the area of a long rectangle, with subspecies *A* originally occupying one half and *B* the other.

This area was now divided into three sections, *A*-preferred, *B*-preferred and a smaller neutral section in the centre. It was supposed that each subspecies in its own territory or in the neutral zone had the reproductive capacity originally assigned to it according to its **G**/**g** genotype, but when in the territory of the other subspecies its reproductive capacity was reduced by 25 percent. Hybrids could grow equally well anywhere.

This was managed easily enough. When seed had been dispersed, the program came to a revised version of the phenotype determination and insertion subroutine. This scanned the population in three sections, no special action being required in the central neutral zone. In the other two, when the weekly fertility of a plant had been determined, the subroutine checked whether or not the plant belonged to the 'wrong' subspecies. If so, then the weekly fertility was reduced by a quarter; otherwise no action was taken.

It would not be difficult to introduce much greater and less regular ecological diversity into a model. Suppose we wished to imagine that a population covered eight distinct kinds of habitat to which the different genotypes were variously adapted. It would make little difference whether we chose to regard the population as simply divided into eight different areas which could be scanned consecutively, or into many smaller areas distributed regularly or at random, or if we took the extreme view that different habitats should be assigned to individual positions (addresses) within the population without any sort of pattern.

Instead of the simple scaling procedure described above, the best method now would be to have eight different genotype (or phenotype)/fitness tables, each relevant to one habitat. The program then has to make sure that each plant is referred to the table appropriate to its position in the population.

We will consider that, as in the previous chapter, the population is arranged in transverse rows occupying a long rectangle. The ecologically different areas may be scanned consecutively when the boundaries between them are parallel to the rows and do not cut across them, that is when the different areas of the population consist of blocks of entire consecutive rows. This is the simplest case and presents no difficulty. The areas need not be the same size and any kind of habitat may occur more than once. There will be a parameter table giving the number of plant positions in each area (or the number of rows if that is more convenient) and some form of reference to the appropriate fitness table; the numbers are used as counters during the scanning, determining when a switch shall be made from one fitness table to the next.

There are several ways of effecting reference to the correct fitness table. The appropriate parameter may give the address of the first entry in the table, and this is added to the reference derived from the genotype of the plant, the sum being used as a modifier in the usual way. Alternatively, there could be different short order sequences each giving references to one table, and the parameters would be used as modifiers to direct jumps to the relevant sequence.

The difference between the situation when each kind of habitat occurs once only, and when each may occur several times (not necessarily the same number of times for each) in an irregular order, is one of degree only—the latter situation merely requires a longer parameter list. When the population is not so neatly subdivided, and the area boundaries may run in any direction, a different approach has to be used. This situation may arise when a long narrow population is unsuitable and one wishes to use a population more nearly as broad as long. Essentially the same problem is presented and the same solution appropriate when habitats are assigned without pattern to individual positions.

One way of dealing with this is to tag each position in the population according to habitat with a parameter directing access to the correct fitness table. This can be done by starting the program with a population store containing no plants but with each position correctly tagged. The words containing the plants must always have the bits in the tag position zero, and they will be added to the store location; so that in effect each plant will carry its correct habitat reference. When the store is cleared of plants, this must be done by a masking operation which leaves the tag intact.

If store space is available, it is better to have a store parallel to the population and containing the parameter tags in the proper sequence, so that the same modifier applied to different base addresses will extract plant and parameter separately. This has two advantages; bits for the tag do not have to be reserved in the word carrying the genotype, and the population store can be cleared in the usual way—the parallel parameter store will be left intact throughout the program (unless the possibility of environmental change during the course of an experiment is introduced).

Whichever way this is done, the setting of the tags involves a great deal of labour. If there is no pattern about the distribution of the ecological areas, then the tags cannot be set by the program. They must be written out and punched for the whole population store. It would probably be worth while considering whether, even if the areas were many and small, it would not be better to have some sort of pattern which would allow the tags to be set by the program. Alternatively, if habitat distribution is to be entirely at random one could have a small table of habitat parameters and the population dealt with serially and tagged by parameters chosen at random from the table for each position; or if the habitats are to be in predetermined proportions but otherwise assigned at random, the population could be tagged in a regular arrangement and then shuffled at random.

Another difficulty with an unpatterned arrangement would arise in population analysis and the design of an output layout readily intelligible in relation to the distribution of the different habitats.

Where a complex ecological structure has been introduced into a model, the grid method for choice of pollen parent is essential, and a corresponding method must be used for seed dispersal, since that also has to be on a two-dimensional basis. Seed dispersal may now be a longer operation, since there can now be no possibility of distributing seed to known vacant places as there is when distribution is one-dimensional in terms of rows. At the beginning of seed dispersal, little time will be wasted; but later, as the population fills, more and more choices will fall on occupied positions. How serious this will be will depend on the ratio of the total number of plants in the population to the total number of available positions. The action to be taken in the event of a seed falling on an occupied position will depend on the view taken by the programmer of the biology of the system.

Insofar as position means anything in animal populations, ecological differentiation may be applied in the same way as for plants.

Distance and Position in Animal Populations

Distance and position are fairly easy to deal with in plant populations, since most plants stay where they are once germination has taken place, so that the position of a plant may be defined permanently until its death.

Most animals move. If we suppose they move a great deal, then we can take the easy way out by ignoring position and supposing that the whole population is mating at random without regard to position and distance.

Where this would be unrealistic, the problem may become formidable. It is a difficult one to generalize about, because there are so many different patterns of animal movement and mating behaviour. One approach would be to consider the population broken up into sub-populations, adjacent or with some degree of separation. Within each sub-population mating would be at random, and position and distance would only come into consideration when dealing with gene flow (through the movement of individuals) between populations, which would be restricted and only partly random. This has something in common with the algebraic model of primrose populations described in Chapter 10.

To try to bring position and distance down to finer limits and deal with them on an individual basis requires care and a firm understanding of the biology of the system being simulated if one is to avoid the risk of inaccurate models which could be seriously misleading. This sort of approach to the simulation of animal populations is really only relevant where the animals are relatively sedentary, or where even if they move about a great deal they have fairly constant positions for mating and producing young. From the point of view of the genetics of the system, movement which is irrelevant to reproduction does not need to be incorporated into a model. In this context, the positions of most significance for an animal are where it originates, where it looks for a mate, where it finds a mate, and where it reproduces. Where it goes in the meantime (migrant birds, for example) may be quite irrelevant, even if this involves travels of thousands of miles.

It is not difficult to set up an animal population with each individual in a definite position, and then to simulate movement wholly at random or partly so in relation to some predetermined pattern. But much of this movement might have little relevance to the reproduction of the population, and all that really needs to be simulated is the transfer of each animal from one relevant position to the next.

Although this may require some involved programming, the techniques may broadly speaking be derived from those described in the previous chapter.

The best approach to simulation problems of this kind is to begin with fairly simple situations in small populations, where the principles involved are well understood and familiar techniques may be applied. Once sensible models have been established, we may proceed experimentally to more complicated systems, which will often have features peculiar to themselves and which would be beyond the scope of a general discussion even if the author had sufficient experience to warrant one.

Dormancy and Perennation

The genotype simulation examples which have been discussed so far have dealt with annual plants, and have assumed no seed dormancy and consequently no overlapping of generations. Most plants are not annuals, and annuals will usually show some degree of dormancy at least, so that we should consider the ways in which dormancy and perennation may be introduced into simulation models. For the moment, attention will be confined to plants.

The easiest way of dealing with dormancy is to suppose that a fixed proportion of the available seeds will germinate in the following season, and that the remainder will remain dormant for at least one more season. If the population size is to be kept constant at n, and the proportion of the available seed which will germinate is p, the initial population will be set at n individual plants and $n(1-p)/p$ ungerminated seeds, the genotype frequencies among the seeds being the same as those among the plants. For the year's reproduction, n seeds are produced and combined with the $n(1-p)/p$ ungerminated seeds; a random choice of n or $n(1-p)/p$ (whichever is the smaller) is made from these to divide the available seeds into those which are to be the next year's plants and those which will be dormant respectively, the two groups being appropriately redistributed in the store.

This involves making random choices from a population of size n for reproduction and a population of size n/p for germination or dormancy; unless $p = 0.5$ both cannot be a power of two and one choice or the other will involve random number wastage. Since in an outbreeding population reproduction from n individuals requires at least $2n$ random choices, it is better that n should be the one which is a power of two.

This method of simulating dormancy assumes that all seeds, whether just produced or having been dormant for many years, have equal chances of germinating for the next season. Any other assumption would lengthen the procedure; if it were assumed that the chance of a seed germinating depended on its age, this could be managed by adding to the genotype of each seed the number of the generation in which it is produced. Then, at the end of any subsequent generation its age is determined by subtraction, reference to an age/germination-chance table will give the probability that it will now germinate, and this will be implemented in the usual way by comparison with a random fraction.

One consequence of this procedure would be that there would be some variability in population size from one generation to another, since there would no longer be a predetermined number of seeds germinating.

It would be easy enough to modify this procedure to allow some genotypic influence on the degree of dormancy.

Unless the age/germination-chance table is to have as many entries as possible generations for the experiment (and this may not always be known), the final entry (which will be for a maximum length of dormancy) must give a germination probability of 1.0.

Biennial plants present no difficulty. Growth to maturity of all seeds is delayed by one year, but we then have the subtle point that if dormancy is not introduced into the model we will either have a situation of one population flowering in alternate years, which is no different in practice from a population of annuals, or if we start with two sets of plants flowering in succeeding years, one which is in effect two populations occupying the same territory but isolated because they flower in different years; which is the same thing as having two isolated populations of annuals.

True perennation may be simulated in a number of different ways. Most perennials have an initial year of growth and development before flowering, sometimes more than one, but it is doubtful whether there is very much point in taking this into consideration. For the moment, we will assume no dormancy, flowering in first year of growth, and pollination and seed dispersal random throughout the population (that is, no consideration of position).

The easiest, but not very realistic way of dealing with perennation is the one used in the algebraic model described in Chapter 10. It assumes that all plants have the same life span, that the same number of plants die and are replaced each year, and consequently that all age groups contain the same numbers of plants. If the population size is n and occupies n consecutive words of store, and each plant lives a years, then n/a seeds will be produced each year and will replace a consecutive sequence of n/a plants in the store.

Each year, the plants to be replaced will follow immediately after those replaced the previous year, and this is easy enough to keep track of—either a modifier is reserved for this use only, and not reset until the end of the population is reached after a years (but great care must be taken not to forget that the use of this modifier is restricted), or a store location is used with transfers to and from a modifier when required; the only administrative actions then required are counting n/a and a, and modifier incrementation.

At the other extreme, when the year's reproduction is completed, the seeds may replace existing plants at random. This produces considerable variation in length of life span, but not very realistically. The most frequent life span will be one year, with a slow falling off in the numbers of individuals living for more years; some may live for a very long time.

If each seed is sown at random without regard to the previous occupant of its allotted position, it may fall on a position just occupied by a new seed, since there is nothing to stop the same position being chosen twice. Thus if n/a seeds are produced, there will usually be less than n/a new seeds in the population after seed dispersal and the actual mean length of life span will be longer than a years. This is corrected by producing more than n/a seeds, the extra requirement being easily calculated and not too large unless a is small. The alternative of making newly sown seeds recognizable as such, and repeating the effort to sow a seed when a position so occupied is chosen, would be rather awkward; either, at the end of sowing, the whole population would have to be scanned and the tags removed from the new seeds, or the tag would have to be year-specific which would make its recognition less simple.

A more realistic method of dealing with perennation is to use the familiar device of a frequency curve transformed into a parameter table to which random reference is made. A mean life span is decided on; this may or may not be the most frequent value in the table with longer and shorter spans appearing with lesser frequencies, but the curve need not be even approximately symmetrical. It could in fact have a second maximum at one year if it were decided to take account of the possibility that plants in their first year might not be fully established and so might be at greater risk.

A value chosen at random from the table is added in to the word carrying the genotype, where it indicates the number of years remaining for the plant to live. The starting population will need to be set with an age structure corresponding to the life span frequency table, but care will have to be taken to see that the ages are fairly distributed among the genotypes—otherwise an initial element of spurious selection will be introduced (but see also later). *Before* the year's reproduction starts, the population is scanned. For each plant, one is subtracted from the value for the number of years of life remaining, and if this is now zero the plant is to die *after* reproduction is completed; such plants are temporarily moved from the store and placed elsewhere, being counted in the process; subsequent plants not yet due to die are moved forwards so that no gaps are left. At the end of the population scan, the count of plants removed gives the number of those which will die and thus the number of seeds which will be needed to replace them (this will now differ from year to year). The fated plants are replaced in the population store, consecutively at the end. When reproduction is completed, they are replaced by the new seeds. The non-random arrangement of the plants in the store produced by these operations does not matter, since choice of parents from the store will be random.

There are other ways of determining seed requirements and replacing dead plants, but like the one given they are all rather clumsy.

This technique of perennation would allow life span to be used as an element (or even the entire expression) of fitness of an individual, and so determined at least in part by the genotype. The only real difficulty is that life span can only be conveniently dealt with in terms of an integral number of years. It is true that in nature a plant could die during the flowering period, but it would be troublesome if the population had to be scanned several times during the year's reproduction and such dead plants eliminated. The simplest way of taking life span into consideration as an element of fitness would be to assign to each genotype a fraction to be used in scaling down the life span value obtained by random choice from the table, the latter as set being related to the fittest genotype. Since the answers after scaling have to be integral, the average realized reduction in mean life span for a particular genotype may not correspond very precisely with the scaling fraction. The value of the latter therefore needs to correspond not to the required fitness reduction, but to be of such a value that the required average fitness reduction is actually realized.

The easiest assumption to make about reproductive capacity is that for any one genotype the annual reproductive capacity is constant, and not related in any way to age. This means for any one genotype that the total life span reproductive capacity is directly proportional to the length of life.

If we wished to elaborate the implementation of perennation, it would be possible to make the annual reproductive capacity of a plant vary with its age by the use of a scaling factor related to age. This would mean that the plant would need to carry its age as well as the number of years of life left, the scaling factor being determined from the age (and genotype if relevant) by table look-up. To complicate matters further, it could be arranged that the annual fertility depended not so much upon actual age as upon the proportional stage in the allotted life span; this would be relevant where life span was a substantial element of fitness, but not where death was considered to be largely a matter of chance with life span therefore having little relation to fitness.

If we wish to introduce perennation into a model which takes into account position and distance, no particular difficulty is raised if distance is considered only one-dimensionally, as in the model described in Chapter 11 with a long population arranged in rows filled serially. Scanning is row by row, and the plants in each row are rearranged so that those due to die at the end of the year are in consecutive positions following the other plants. There will be problems of administration, and it will usually be necessary to keep a tally both of the total number of plants in the row and of those due to die.

Where position and distance are considered two-dimensionally, seed dispersal (which must be into empty positions or those occupied by dead plants) is easy enough, but time consuming. It is easy because there will be no routine which sorts plants into those due to die and those not, since this is impossible because rearrangement of positions within the row is no longer permissible, and there is no practicable way of keeping a record of which positions are available. The population needs to be scanned, in order to decrease for each plant its remaining life by one year, and to determine how many plants will have to be replaced by seeds. Each seed is dispersed by random reference to a dispersal table (based on a grid of the kind shown for pollen transport in Figure 68), and the chosen position inspected to see if it is available (dead plant or unoccupied position); if not, the attempt to sow the seed must be repeated until an available position is chosen. Several attempts may have to be made on many occasions, and this is why the procedure is time-consuming. Since some seeds may fall on unoccupied spaces (the more of these the less time lost in this operation), some dead plants will not be replaced. These will have to be detected during the next population scan and removed before reproduction.

The problem of seed dispersal in this situation may be made more efficient by reversing the usual procedure, as it were, but care has to be taken to ensure that this does not produce a spurious selection effect, which will be discussed a little later.

Assuming as before that variation in population density is possible by having more places than plants, then the procedure would be to scan the population before any reproduction for the year begins and store separately the addresses of all empty positions and those with plants due to die at the end of the year. Reproduction would then proceed for each seed by making a random choice of its eventual dispersal position from the list of addresses. The chosen address is then used as the starting point for reference to the dispersal table (if we may still call it that), and by random reference to this a seed parent is chosen and a seed produced from it in the usual way, the seed being eventually dispersed to the address originally chosen.

The attempt to choose a seed parent may fall on a vacant position, or the chosen seed parent may fail the fitness test. In both cases, the initial address chosen for dispersal must be rejected. If, for the same initial address, further attempts were made to produce a seed parent, then reproductive output in any part of the population would be proportional to the number of positions available for dispersal and not to the reproductive capacity of the area. Thus in an area with lower than average plant density or lower than average mean reproductive capacity per plant, more seeds will be produced than there should be and on average the plants there would have a higher realised reproductive capacity than that proper to their fitness, and selection pressure against them would be less than it should be. It would indeed be possible for such plants of low fertility to have an actual reproductive capacity greater than that of fully fit plants in another part of the population. Pursuing the argument further, it should be clear why this procedure of dispersal in reverse will only work if there are more places than plants in the population; if all places were always occupied, plant density would remain constant and uniform, seed production would therefore remain uniform, and there would be a spurious selection effect.

So far we have not considered animals in the context of perennation. They present rather different problems from plants, because they have a wider variety of life-histories. They may reproduce more or less continuously, either with no seasonal breaks (as with man), or with several generations in a season followed by a period of little or no reproductive activity; mating may be promiscuous or not. In this context, 'generation' has little practical meaning, being recognizable only in individual lines of descent and not in the population as a whole. Or reproduction may be seasonal, and here there are several possibilities. Individuals may live for only one season, in which case the situation is the same as that for annual plants if the animals are promiscuous, not quite the same if they are not. Or they may live over several seasons, mating promiscuously in each season which is essentially the same as for perennial plants, or with a constant mate in each season but changing from one season to the next. Or they may live over several seasons but pair for life.

Unlike most plants, some animals may not begin to reproduce until they are a substantial way through their life span. If this is taken into account, there is no point in considering death during that pre-reproduction period, since an animal which fails to reach reproductive maturity may just as well never have existed, a point which has been discussed in an earlier chapter.

Where reproduction is continuous with no distinction of seasons, this can best be achieved simply by replacing an existing individual by the new one, with or without a waiting period corresponding to a juvenile non-reproductive phase. In the latter case, replacement occurs as soon as the new individual is produced; in the former, it occurs at a predetermined number of reproductions later, in general the same for all individuals. The main point is that reproduction is continuous, not in seasonal batches. Replacement could be entirely at random, or only animals above a certain age could be replaced (at random), or animals could be tagged with time still to live and replaced as soon as they are due to die. To provide a reasonable simulation in the last case, population scanning with decrease of remaining life span would have to be frequent. If no account is being taken of position and distance (mating and dispersal being random over the whole population) replacement may be effected as each dead animal is discovered during scanning.

With seasonal reproduction, perennation in animals presents no very different problems from that in plants, but it will often be desirable to take the juvenile phase into account.

Vegetative Reproduction

With perennation, the question of vegetative reproduction of plants has to be considered. This may be little more than the spreading of a perennial, which may be treated as an increase in reproductive capacity with age. Or there may be dispersal of vegetative propagules so that in effect new plants are being produced.

The latter situation may be simulated by treating reproduction simply as the copying of the genotype of an individual chosen at random or according to any other specification of the model and with the application of fitness or other tests as appropriate. Dispersal of the new individual would then take place according to the same general principles as dispersal of a seed, position and distance being considered or not as the case may be.

There is no difficulty in simulating a system which has both sexual and vegetative reproduction, but the dispersal of seeds and vegetative propagules may need to be treated in different ways since in nature they may be dispersed very differently. The ability to reproduce vegetatively may be subject to genetic control, for example in systems involving vegetative apomixis. There are so many different ways in which vegetative reproduction may be involved in evolutionary systems, that generalization would have little point. The simulation techniques required may readily be derived with or without much adaptation from procedures which have already been described in other contexts.

Multi-Allelism

A gene with several alleles may be simulated by using more than one bit. Two bits can represent four different alleles, n bits 2^n. Only a few such loci can be accommodated within a single word, and some of the better methods for segregation described in Chapter 6 are impracticable or impossible. Even if several loci could be conveniently included within a genotype, the general method for simulating gametogenesis in a multi-locus genotype will not now work. For fewer loci, the methods using random table look-up with the genotype used to direct the initial point of entry to the table are impracticable (the tables would be much too large); with two 8-allelic loci each occupying three bits, the numerical values of the possible diploid genotypes would range from 0 to 4095. One could deal with one locus at a time by this method, but this is usually uneconomical of time and effort. One has therefore to resort to methods based on some of the clumsier ones of Chapter 6.

The randomly directed jump method, avoiding or executing a shift, with masking, as described on page 151 for two independent loci may be adapted for several independent loci in a multi-allelic situation (the randomly determined shift method will also work, but involves an extra operation to multiply the 1 of the random 0 or 1 by the number of bits in the allele.)

The simplest situation is when all the loci use the same number of bits. The numerical values of some of the masks required are now very large, and to avoid possibility of error in calculating them in decimal, it is better to set them as octal parameters rather than write them directly in the masking instructions. The procedure may be illustrated by imagining a parent **AaBbCcDd** in which each locus uses 4 bits allowing up to 16 alleles. The numerical values of the masks required are (from the l.s. end) 15, 15×2^8, 15×2^{16} and 15×2^{24}.

The following subroutine, arbitrarily numbered **P30**, would simulate segregation. The parent is supplied to the subroutine in **F** and the gamete delivered in **E**.

```
P30/5;
      0; (link); 8/17; 8/7400; 8/3600000; 8/1700000000; (masks);
(0);  K15 = 4; M14 = 0; E = 0; p0P202 = (j1); J0P202;
      (H = random fraction);
(1);  F→G; H up 1; J2H<0; G down 4;
(2);  G&p1(M14)→G; M14+1; E≢G→E; K15−1; J1K15≠0;
      p0→M15; J(M15);
```

For the second gamete, the same routine is used and the resultant gamete genotype shifted up four places before fertilization.

The same method may be used if the loci do not all occupy the same number of bits, but with an important difference for the second gamete.

Suppose the four loci **A**, **B**, **C** and **D** use 4, 3, 5 and 2 bits respectively. The following variation of the preceding subroutine would now serve to produce the first gamete.

```
P31/9;
0; (link); 2; 5; 3; 4; (for shifts);
8/3; 8/760; 8/340000; 8/74000000;
(0); K15=4; M14=0; E=0; p0P202-(j1); J0P202;
(1); F→G; H up 1; J2H<0; p1(M14)→M13; G down(M13);
(2); G&p5(M14)→G; M14+1; E≢G→E; K15-1; J1K15≠0;
     p0→M15; J(M15);
```

But this will not do for the second gamete, because while a shift up of two places for fertilization would put the D bits in the correct position on addition, it will not do so for the other genes, as the reader may easily verify for himself by writing out two gametes and shifting one. In the first gamete there are for each locus two adjacent groups of bits, of which the l.s. group will carry the allele and the m.s. will be empty. If the second gamete is to mesh properly with the first on fertilization, this arrangement needs to be reversed. This can be achieved by using a second subroutine which differs from the first in that each mask is shifted up as many places as there are bits in the corresponding gene, and that **G down(M13)** becomes **G up(M13)**. The masks would become respectively **8/14; 8/37000; 8/3400000; 8/1700000000.**

A simpler method would be to have the parental gametes side by side in the genotype, **ABCDabcd**. The masks, continuing with the same example, would now be **8/3, 8/174, 8/1600** and **8/36000**. With suitable parameter amendment **P30** could be used with the shift down of **G** being 14 places instead of four. The disadvantage of this method is that if the genes have different effects on the phenotype, the latter is more awkward to determine than it would be if the two alleles of the same gene were adjacent.

It is possible to combine multi-allelic and 2-allelic loci in one genotype. If there are only one or two 2-allelic loci, they may be treated along with the others using variants of **P31** (or the alternative just suggested), differing only in the parameter lists—there being in principle no difference as far as they are concerned between a 1-bit locus and a multi-bit locus. If there are several 2-allelic loci, it is best to deal with the two groups separately, using for the 2-allelic loci the normal method for segregation of several independent loci.

It is not practicable, with multi-allelism, to deal with gametogenesis in two parents and fertilization simultaneously. Linkage may be introduced into multi-allelic systems, and may be less difficult than in 2-allelic ones for the practical reason that one cannot readily handle more than a very few loci in the former.

Unless the phenotype is capable of numerical expression directly determinable from the genotype (as for example in multi-allele incompatibility systems in plants), determination of the phenotype presents a much bigger problem in multi-allele systems than segregation does. This is not a subject on which it is useful to generalize here, since there are many possible kinds of relationship between genotype and phenotype and each situation will often need to be treated as a special case.

Gene Labelling

Gill and Clemmer (1966) devised a technique in which they labelled each individual gene in the starting population; this enabled individual genes to be traced over the whole period of an experimental run.

This can be handled for reproduction in the same way as a multi-allele situation, since in practice the addition of binary numbers as labels to single bits representing alleles is the same thing as having multiple alleles with only two different phenotypic effects determined by a single bit. Genotype/phenotype conversion is much simpler.

The population size and number of genes cannot be very large unless several words are going to be used for the genotype. Thus if in the starting population **0** and **1** alleles are equally frequent, one 32-bit word could only accommodate two genes in a population size of 128, each allele then having its own bit plus a 7-bit label.

The Breeding System

We will begin this discussion of the simulation of breeding systems by taking the simple view that inbreeding and outbreeding are to be considered only in terms of self- or cross-fertilization, and neglect for the moment such matters as sib or cousin mating.

There are then two ways of considering the genetic control of the breeding system. We may think of it as generalized in the sense that the relevant elements of the genotype determine the chance that an organism will be self-fertilized; or we can think of it in terms of a specialized genetic control of the morphological and/or physiological mechanisms of a breeding system such as sexual dimorphism or incompatibility, acting by determining whether two given individuals may or may not co-operate in sexual reproduction.

The more generalized version is relevant to hermaphrodite plants rather than animals, and examples in which the degree of self-fertilization is a constant parameter of an experimental run and has no specified representation in the genotype have been dealt with in Chapters 3 and 9. To introduce genetic control (and hence variability within an experimental run) is fairly easy, and follows lines which have already been described for other characteristics, such as fitness.

There are a number of ways in which self-pollination may be restricted, such as protandry, protogyny, and the many and various morphological devices which ensure that a visiting insect touches stigma before anthers. Whatever method of restriction one chooses to regard as operative in the system being modelled, the simulation treatment will generally be the same unless one is trying to be ultra-realistic. All that the program needs to know is the chance of a particular plant being self-pollinated, and if that is directly related to and determinable from the genotype, the biological mechanism involved is irrelevant.

Few or several genes may be chosen as the basis for genetic control, and obviously it is simplest if they all have equal effects allowing of easy conversion of genotype into phenotype, but if conversion by direct table look-up is practicable then this is less important.

The procedure is fairly simple, but depends on whether or not we choose to regard a given value for the proportion of inbreeding as applying to pollen as well as to ovules. This may sound slightly absurd, but a little thought will show that it is not. For example, suppose we decide that of a given plant's ovules, four-fifths are to be self-pollinated and one-fifth to be pollinated at random. It does not follow that because only one-fifth of the ovules are available for cross-fertilization, only one-fifth of the pollen is similarly available. If there is ample pollen production, freely available to visiting insects, the amount of its pollen which has been used for selfing may be relatively negligible and there may be practically as much pollen available for outcrossing as on a fully outbreeding plant. The actual amount of pollen involved in cross-fertilization will then depend not on the genotype of the plant, but on the mean degree of outbreeding of the rest of the population—that is, how many ovules are available to it (unavailable ones being those which are self-fertilized). An example of this situation (but in a specialized, not generalized, breeding system) occurs in homostyle primroses (Chapter 10, and Crosby, 1949) which are almost always self-fertilized but have ample pollen available for the pollination of suitable outbreeding plants in the population; in fact the selective advantage of homostyly depends on this.

If we assume that the availability of a plant's pollen for outcrossing is independent of the proportion of its ovules which are self-fertilized, the method is to choose a plant to be female parent and translate the relevant elements of its genotype into a phenotype expressing the degree of inbreeding as a fraction. Comparison of this fraction with a random fraction in the usual way will determine whether on that occasion the plant will be selfed or whether another plant should be chosen as pollen parent; in the latter case, a second plant is chosen at random and used as a pollen parent without further breeding system test.

If however it has been decided that when the phenotype of a plant involves the self-fertilization of a proportion of its ovules, this should be accompanied by a reduction in the amount of its pollen available for outcrossing, then any plant chosen as a potential pollen parent will have its breeding phenotype tested in exactly the same way as each seed parent is tested, the alternative consequences this time being rejection or use as pollen parent, the former requiring a further selection of a potential pollen parent (itself subject to test) to replace the one rejected. There is no reason why the proportions of ovules and pollen available for outcrossing should be the same for any given genotype, though there is an obvious convenience if a single genotype/phenotype table will serve for both.

If it is more convenient, the genotype/phenotype translation can be carried out once-for-all for each plant before any reproduction starts, and stored with the genotype precisely as can be done in the case of fitness.

Sexual Dimorphism

With specific breeding mechanisms the procedure is different. The easiest to deal with is sexual dimorphism. Genetic control of this in animals (and in many plants where it occurs) is typically chromosomal, but as far as consideration and simulation of this control is concerned we may treat it exactly as if it were controlled by a single gene with two alleles. Assuming male to be the heterozygous sex (precisely corresponding procedures would apply to birds and lepidoptera), then the **Y** chromosome may be treated as a dominant allele and represented by **0** and the **X** as the recessive and represented by **1**.

It is simplest if the bit used for this is always the m.s. one for each haploid set of genes, and if in using the usual type of reproduction subroutine we make sure that at fertilization the sperm genotype is placed to the left of the egg genotype, and that the zygote genotype is at the m.s. end of the word *and includes the sign bit*. If the remainder of the genotype is represented by a line, females (**XX**) will be **1**——**1**—— and males (**YX**) **0**——**1**——, since the **Y** chromosome must have been contributed by the sperm. Since the left-hand bit of the genotype is the sign bit, females will always be negative and males positive, and so the sex of any individual may be immediately recognized. In obtaining two parents for reproduction we may choose one and note its sign; if negative the program will go to a procedure which chooses further animals until it picks a positive, rejecting any which are negative; if the first parent is positive, it will go to a similar procedure which will search for a negative mate. Quicker methods which avoid or curtail time wastage through random choice of the wrong sex have been discussed in Chapter 6.

Two parents of opposite sex having been chosen, the program then has to ensure that they are put in the proper sequence for reproduction so that the sperm genotype will occupy the m.s. half of the zygote.

The sign bit may still be used for the sexual phenotype without formally including the chromosome bits in the simulation of gametogenesis. This may be particularly useful where we are dealing with only one or two gene loci and do not wish to use a generalized multi-locus reproduction subroutine. The genotype is kept clear of the sign bit, and need not be adjacent to it—it could be at the l.s. end of the word. Since in sexually dimorphic animals the expected sex ratio is 1:1, we could simply allocate sex to a new individual at the end of reproduction by generating a single random bit (**0** or **1**) and putting it in the sign position. This does not necessarily involve the generation of an extra random number since a surplus bit can sometimes be taken from one generated for an earlier operation.

Where other elements of the genotype may upset the sex ratio, then if the modified ratio is determinable from the genotype, the appropriate sign bit for the sex may be neatly added in the following way. Suppose the sex ratio is expressed as a probability p that the offspring will be female; then when p has been determined from the genotype it is subtracted from a random fraction. The sign bit of the answer will be the same as that required to indicate the sex (assuming as before that females are negative), and it may be extracted by a mask and added to the word carrying the genotype.

If we prefer to retain the sign bit for some other special use, then whatever method we use for determining the value of the sex bit, we allot one bit of the organism word to express sex with **0** or **1** and use a testing word with a single **1** in the appropriate position, an LM giving zero or non-zero according to whether the individual is male or female respectively.

With sexual dimorphism the question of sex-linked inheritance arises. To deal with more than one sex-linked locus, the difficult question of crossing over between them in the female arises. With one sex-linked locus, there is a subtlety. In the female it is treated as an independent locus, unlinked to any others in the genotype; the sex-determining bit will be homozygous and therefore irrelevant.

But in the male we have to remember that the locus is not represented at all on the **Y** chromosome, and here we are faced with a difficulty because we apparently need three values of a bit to represent differently the two alleles and absence of an allele, when only two values are possible. The absent allele needs to be represented by **1** and not by **0** for the obvious reason that in the male the absent allele has the same effect on the phenotype as the recessive. Gametogenesis in the male must be so managed that if the sperm produced is **Y**-bearing, the **0** for the **Y** chromosome is accompanied by the **1** allele of the sex-linked gene, while if the sperm is **X**-bearing the **1** for the **X** chromosome must be accompanied by the allele which was contributed to the parental genotype by the egg.

The simplest way of achieving this is to perform spermatogenesis on the autosomal genes and then with a 50 percent probability take either the two m.s. bits of the sperm contribution to the paternal genotype or the two m.s. bits of the egg contribution, and add these on to the m.s. end of the new sperm genotype.

In considering the breeding systems of animals it may be necessary to take more things into account than sexual difference. Consanguineity is an example, and we may wish to prevent or discourage sib or cousin mating. In a large population breeding at random, the chance of such mating is small enough to be ignored, but in a small population or in a model which considers position and distance with small breeding range and short-distance dispersal of progeny, the chance that sib or cousin mating will occur may be high enough to warrant action being taken to prevent it (if that is appropriate to the system being simulated). This is easier to manage if mating is permanent rather than promiscuous. If mating is permanent, then we need consider only one ancestral sex in determining relationship: sibs will have a mother in common, cousins will have at least one grandmother in common. To give effect to this, each individual needs to be tagged with a reference (relative store address is the obvious one to use) to its mother and grandmothers. If the population is large, each reference will require too much space for all to go into the same word as the genotype, and it may be necessary to carry these references separately from the genotype in words held in a parallel store.

With promiscuity, we have half-sibs to take into account, and an individual would need to be tagged with references to both parents and all four grandparents. This may now not only require two words to carry the references, but testing for parents or grandparents in common becomes involved; grandparents should be tested first, since if none of these are in common, then the parents cannot be either.

Problems of consanguineity are rather special, although they will arise when considering models of human populations. Of more general interest are cases where an individual may have mating preferences determined by its own genotype, so that when a pair of potential parents have been chosen, in addition to any fitness tests the chance that they would actually pair requires to be determined from their genotypes and implemented in the usual way by reference to a random fraction. This is easier when preferences are mutual. 'Preference' need not be taken literally; it may imply anything which affects the likelihood of pairing: mating behaviour, anatomical or physiological characteristics for example. In a situation with plants described in Chapter 11 preference took the form of being in flower at the same time (but was not implemented in the way just described).

Incompatibility in Plants

In plants, an analogy with the sexual dimorphism of animals occurs in those incompatibility systems operated by dimorphic heterostyly, of which the primrose is the best known example and has already been discussed in the context of algebraic simulation in Chapter 10.

Here, pins are **ss**, thrums are **Ss**, and if the system worked precisely (as it does in many other heterostyled plants) every reproduction would be between pin and thrum. Genotype simulation of this kind of system would be precisely the same as for sex in animals—**ss** plants would be **11** and correspond **XX**, **Ss** would be **01** and correspond to **YX**—and the whole system would be operated in the same way with the genes from the thrum parent in the m.s. position.

Where, as in the primrose, some illegitimate fertilization (mostly self-fertilization) is possible for pins, this may be realized in one of two ways. If the frequency with which pin ovules are to be self-fertilized is a, then each time a pin is chosen as seed parent a is compared with a random fraction; if the latter is larger, then the pollen parent has to be a thrum, if smaller, itself. This may be complicated by assuming that only a proportion of illegitimate fertilization is selfing. If the proportion of selfing is a and the proportion of illegitimate crossing is b, then a and (if necessary b) in turn are subtracted from the random fraction, selfing or illegitimate crossing taking place if the relevant subtraction produces a negative answer; otherwise the outcome will be legitimate crossing.

Homostyly in the primrose (Crosby, 1949) is in effect a 3-allelic system, and cannot be treated in the same way as simple heterostyly. The use of two bits as though for a 3-allelic gene comes quite naturally in this case. The **S/s** locus in *Primula* is a complex one, consisting of at least three loci so tightly linked that crossing-over must be ignored. To simulate the situation investigated by the author, we can treat the two loci affecting anther height and pollen grain size as one, since they are in their normal association in homostyles. The bits for the dominant thrum (**S**) characters, high anthers with large pollen, and short style, will be **00** respectively. The bits for the recessive pin (**s**) characters, low anthers with small pollen, and long style, will be **11** respectively. Homostyles have high anthers with large pollen (**0**) and long styles (**1**), the bits for this combination (**s′**) being **01**. The only permissible fertilizations in this system are thrum × pin, pin × thrum, pin × homostyle, pin selfed and homostyle selfed. If it is arranged that in the legitimate crosses the genes from thrum and homostyle go into the m.s. position, and that in any homostyle produced from homostyle selfing the m.s. bits are always **01**, whether the others are **01** or **11**, then thrums (which in the absence of self-fertilization are always heterozygous) will be **0011**, pins will always be

1111, and homostyles **0111** or **0101**. Then if the genotype occupies the m.s. end of the word (including the sign bit) and the operative genes are at the m.s. end of each gamete genotype if any other genes are present, pins will always be negative, thrums and homostyles positive. If the chosen seed parent is negative, it is fertilized by itself or a positive plant according to the predetermined frequency of self-fertilization. If it is positive, the second m.s. bit is tested; if this is **1**, the seed parent is a homostyle and is selfed, if not it is a thrum and is fertilized by a negative plant.

Since this is in effect a 3-allelic system, the usual methods of gametogenesis with independent genes will not serve. If no genes other than the breeding system ones are involved, then we can use the following procedure which is not so involved as it looks since most of the facts are known at the time of choosing the parents and is quicker than using the method for multi-allelic systems described in an earlier section. If the seed parent is a thrum, the seed must be pin or thrum with equal chances and **0011** or **1111** stored in consecutive locations may be chosen using a random 0 or 1 as a modifier; since no other genes are involved, a pollen parent does not actually need to be obtained. If the seed parent is a pin and selfed, the seed must be **1111**; if it is to be crossed, then a pollen parent (thrum or homostyle) has to be chosen and the two m.s. or two l.s. of the latter's four genotype bits are taken at random (using masks and shifts) and placed in the m.s. position with **11** in the next two l.s. positions. If the seed parent is a heterozygous homostyle, then from **1111**, **0111**, **0111** and **0101** in consecutive locations a seed genotype is chosen by using a random number in the range 0 to 3 as a modifier. If the seed parent is a homozygous homostyle, the seed genotype must be **0101**, the same as the parent.

If other genes are involved, then it is best to deal with these and the breeding system genes as separate operations, using orthodox segregation techniques for the former and combining the two results. In this case of course a pollen parent will always have to be produced for a thrum seed parent.

Trimorphic heterostyly may also be simulated but rather less readily, especially where inheritance is polysomic (as in *Lythrum* for example). With three forms, use of positive and negative for recognition is no longer possible, and the genes involved have to be treated like any other elements of the genotype; they will be extracted as a unit, their phenotype determined (possibly most conveniently by table look-up), and the program will simply have to make sure that the seed parent is not pollinated by a plant of identical phenotype.

Multi-allele incompatibility systems of the oppositional factor type may be simulated quite easily, and an example of this is described by Crosby (1966). This was an investigation which solved in quite a simple way a problem in *Oenothera organensis* which had become hopelessly clogged up in the mathematics and statistics of other workers. For an account of the biology of the system, the reader should refer to that paper; the account here will deal only with the simulation method used.

It was supposed that there were 64 possible alleles at the **s** locus, each occupying six bits; but the representation was not considered as a bit pattern. Instead, the genotype was treated as consisting of two integers (in the range 0 to 63) side by side; the way incompatibility worked meant that these were necessarily different. A seed parent was chosen at random, followed by a potential pollen parent. One of the latter's **s** alleles was then chosen at random. If this allele was to be effective, it could not be the same as either of the alleles in the seed parent, so it was tested against these in turn. If it differed from both of them, it was combined with one chosen at random to produce the seed. If it was the same as one of them it was rejected.

What happened next required a policy decision during construction of the model. There were two possibilities. Either the second allele of the potential pollen parent could be tested and used if it differed from both of the seed parent's alleles (it must of course differ from that identical with the rejected pollen allele); or the pollen parent could be rejected with only the one allele being tried. Both were reasonable. The former would be appropriate if one supposed that almost all the pollen carried by the pollinating insect came from the plant last visited, as it might if that insect had visited successively several flowers on that plant. The other possibility would be appropriate if one supposed that the pollinating insect carried a mixture of pollen from many plants, since then the chance of two plants crossing would differ according to whether or not they had an allele in common (that is, according to the proportion of pollen which was compatible).

No genes other than the **s** locus were involved in the experiment, and it would have made little difference which view was taken; both in fact were tried. But if other genes had been involved, there would have been a difference since rejection of the potential pollen parent if the first allele tested is rejected would to some extent reduce the possibility of sib-mating.

Mutation

Unless there are special circumstances, mutation is rarely worth bothering about in a genotype simulation model. With mutation occurring even at the relatively high rate of $1/10^5$, in a population of 2,000 mutation at a particular locus will occur about once in every 25 generations, which can have only an insignificant effect on gene frequency unless it is to an allele not otherwise present in the population. There is no point in introducing mutation for the sake of introducing it if the rate has to be unrealistically high to produce any noticeable effect.

Special circumstances will include models where the effects of mutation are being specifically considered, for example where mutation rates are high, or in multi-allele systems where mutation may perhaps produce an allele which has not existed before. One situation where it may be useful to introduce mutation (possibly at an unrealistic rate) is where one is studying rare alleles in a population and it is important to ensure that they are not permanently lost.

In a model where only two alleles are permitted at a locus (which is therefore represented by only one bit) mutation is easily executed by LA to the genotype of a word containing a single **1** in the position of the allele to be mutated. All other bits will remain unchanged; for the mutating bit, the LA will change **0** to **1** or vice versa.

How this may be effected may be illustrated by a simple example. Suppose we have a population of 2^{12} diploid individuals, with four loci, giving a genotype of eight bits which we will suppose to be at the l.s. end. Suppose the mutation rate is $1/2^{17}$ per allele per generation, and is the same for all loci. Then on average there will be one mutation in the whole population every four generations. So each generation we produce a random number in the range 0 to 3, and if this is zero a mutation is indicated and we choose one plant at random from the population. To decide which of the eight alleles is to mutate, we put a **1** at the l.s. end of an otherwise empty accumulator and shift it up n places where n is a random integer in the range 0 to 7. LA of this result to the genotype of the chosen plant will cause mutation of the allele n places from the l.s. end. This procedure is easily modified to deal with situations where the genotype is not at the l.s. end or the numbers are not so conveniently powers of two.

With multiple alleles, essentially the same or a different method may be used according to the view one chooses to take of mutation. Suppose for the sake of argument that there are 16 alleles at a locus; these may be represented by all possible values (0 to 15) of four consecutive bits. Then we could suppose that any allele could mutate to any other, in which case when the plant and the gene to be mutated have been decided, mutation can be effected by substituting that gene by a random integer in the range 0 to 15. This will give no mutation once in 16 times; this can either be accepted with the realization that the actual mutation rate is 15/16ths of that specified, or the eventuality may be looked for and the attempt repeated when it arises.

Alternatively, and probably more realistically, we could suppose that the only mutations permissible are those in which one and only one of the four bits representing the gene is changed. Then precisely the same technique may be used as with the simple 2-allele system. Suppose we have three loci, each 16-allelic and using four bits. This involves 24 bits in the diploid genotype. A random number in the range 0 to 23 can be used to shift a **1** up 0 to 23 places and so by LA cause a mutation at one of the 24 possible sites at random. With random numbers in the range 0 to 31, those above 23 would be rejected; or alternatively if there were no bits other than the genotype in use in the word carrying it, a random number in the range 0 to 31 could be used for the shift, producing a mutation rate 3/4 of that apparently specified.

Difficulty arises if the loci have different numbers of alleles and so are represented by different numbers of bits. Thus with the method described in the last paragraph, if one locus had four alleles and was represented by two bits, and another 16 alleles represented by four bits, the mutation rate of the latter would be twice that of the former.

With a locus of n bits, the population does not have to start with all 2^n possible alleles present. It could start with only two (or even only one), when early mutations would usually be to new alleles.

Chromosome Structural Change

The simulation of chromosome structural change may be quite simple or very complicated, depending on the genetical implications involved. Broadly speaking, the consequences of major viable structural change are on fertility and on linkage relationships in structural heterozygotes; among the kinds of situation which may occur are those where the heterozygote shows a lower fertility, those with polymorphism, and those where permanent heterozygosity is maintained by a balanced lethal system.

To assume heterozygosity of the relevant genes in structural homozygotes and to consider linkage in detail would be difficult, as consideration of Chapter 8 will make clear. The important relationship of linkage and structural change is that of suppression of crossing over in structural heterozygotes, which has the effect of causing blocks of genes to be inherited as a single unit; that is, those genes within the limits of an inversion, and those between centromere and point of interchange.

If one supposes that the structural homozygotes are also homozygous with respect to the relevant genes then we can treat a particular chromosome arrangement and its associated genes as a unit and represent them by a single bit. The three relevant genotypes will be **00**, **01** and **11** and these will be treated at gametogenesis just as if the bits represented alleles of a gene. Fitnesses and other phenotypic properties may be assigned to the genotypes. Often, the structural heterozygotes will have the lowest fertility and there will be selection against the rarer arrangement. In special cases, of which inversion in *Drosophila* is a well-known one, heterozygotes do not have a lower fertility, and maintenance of the different arrangements in natural populations depends on the associated genes, with the possibility of heterosis giving heterozygotes an advantage in fitness. Interchange in *Oenothera* provides an example where the structural homozygotes are lethal and only the heterozygotes survive.

Inversions on different chromosomes (and interchanges involving different chromosomes) may be treated as if they were unlinked genes, and in the bit representation of a genotype some bits may actually represent genes while others represent specific chromosome arrangements. No difficulty arises provided there is no linkage, including any between genes and structural arrangement. Overlapping inversions on the same chromosome may be treated as multiple alleles (and so require more than one bit), but non-overlapping inversions would have to be treated as linked loci. The situation becomes complicated when we have on one chromosome a series of inversions of which each overlaps at least one of the others, but among which it is possible to find two which themselves do not overlap.

The actual simulation of structural change by using the word as a model of a chromosome in detailed simulation of meiosis (along the lines of the teaching program described in Chapter 9) might be possible, but would certainly be difficult and require considerable programming ingenuity. This is something which the author has never tried, and which for that reason he does not propose to discuss further.

Tetrasomic Inheritance

This is something which the author has never seriously considered. Choosing any two from four is a more involved operation than choosing one from two, and can probably best be done by table look-up for one locus, but the table gets very large for two and virtually impossible for three. One locus may have 16 different genotypes, and there are six different combinations of bits (numbering the bits 0, 1, 2, 3, these are 01, 02, 03, 12, 13, 23), so it would need a table of 16 lines each of six gamete genotypes. For two loci, we would need a table of 256 lines each of 36 gamete genotypes.

For several loci, the general method used for diploids will not work. It might be thought that for four sets of genes $p\ q\ r\ s$ composing the genotype, it would be good enough to use the general diploid method on the sets paired at random, producing two sets for each gamete. But this will not do. Consider an individual which is **ABC ABC abc abc**, the alleles having been produced in those sets at the preceding reproduction. Then if we execute gametogenesis on the sets paired at random, the pairing **ABC/ABC abc/abc** can give only **ABC abc** gametes. The pairing **ABC/abc ABC/abc**, which would be twice as frequent, will give gametes heterozygous at all three loci (that is, any arrangement equivalent to **AaBbCc**) with a frequency of 1/8. The total frequency of such heterozygous gametes would be 10/24. But this would be wrong, since segregation in a tetraploid **AAaaBBbbCCcc** will give**AaBbCc** gametes with a frequency of only 8/27.

The best method which occurs to the author is to use a variant of the random shift and mask method for diploids. The genes will be arranged in the genotype with the alleles of each consecutive, for example **AAaaBbbBcCCC**. For each gene, two random shifts and two masks are required, for example **0001** and **0010** for **C**/**c**, and these up four and eight places for **B**/**b** and **A**/**a** respectively. If for the l.s. gene after the first random shift the mask **0001** is used, and **0010** after the second (random shifts to include zero shifts), then random choice of the shift sequences 0 & 0, 0 & 1, 0 & 2, 1 & 1, 1 & 2 and 2 & 2 will produce the correct segregation for that gene. This is then repeated with random choice from the same combinations of shifts but with shifted masks for the other genes.

The quickest way of making the random choices of shifts is to have a table of 12 entries, **0; 0; 0; 1; 1; 2; 0; 1; 2; 1; 2; 2**. If this begins in **p1**, then a random integer in the range 0 to 5 (which involves discarding 6 and 7) placed in a modifier, say **M13**, can be used to extract the two shift parameters from **p1(M13)** and **p7(M13)**. Alternatively, we could take for the shifts two random integers in the range 0 to 2, rejecting all those pairs in which the first produced one was the larger. Unfortunately, both methods are expensive on random numbers; it is best to use an economical pseudo-random number subroutine (for instance our supposed **P203**).

The following subroutine (operating the first of these alternatives) will deliver a gamete in **E** when supplied with a tetraploid parent in **F** which has the genes arranged as in **AAaaBbbBcCCC**.

```
P32/19;
0; (link);
0; 0; 0; 1; 1; 2; 0; 1; 2; 1; 2; 2; (shift parameters);
8/1; 8/20; 8/400; 8/2; 8/40; 8/1000; (masks);
(0); E=0; K15=3; M14=0;
(1); M15=3; p0P203=(j2); J0P203; (H = random integer 0 to 7);
(2); H-2; J1H<0; (H now 0 to 5); H→M13;
     p1(M13)→M12; F→D; D down(M12);
     D&p13(M14)→D; D≢E→E;
     p7(M13)→M12; F→D; D down(M12);
     D&p16(M14)→D; D≢E→E;
     M14+1; K15-1; J1K15≠0;
     p0→M15; J(M15);
```

A second gamete would be produced in the same way from the same or another parent, shifted up two places, and added to the first. The same procedure could be operated with an **ABcAbCabCaBC** type of arrangement. The possible shifts for each gene would then be 0, 3, 6 instead of 0, 1, 2, and the masks would be **1** and **1000** for the l.s. gene, **10** and **10000** for the next and **100** and **100000** for the m.s. gene. In this case, the second gamete would be shifted up six places.

Genotype/phenotype conversion is more complex than in a diploid, though the same general principles apply. If for all genes **A** is completely dominant to **aaa**, then the phenotype is determined by three LMs. This is most conveniently managed if the gene arrangement is of the type **ABcAbCabCaBC**, but the other way presents no difficulty.

With less simple dominance situations, genotype/phenotype relationships become more difficult. Again, there is little point in attempting to generalize when there are so many possibilities; each case needs treating as a separate exercise.

CHAPTER 13

Pseudorandom Numbers

It is not the purpose of this chapter to go deeply into the generation of pseudorandom numbers. The author is not sufficient of a mathematician to be able to produce a proper theoretical assessment of the efficiency or reliability of individual pseudorandom number subroutines, and the suitability of a particular subroutine will in any instance often depend on the word length, accumulator structure, available programming instructions and similar features of the computer in use. Rather, the general basic principles of pseudorandom number generation will be discussed, and one example of a generating subroutine will be considered in detail to illustrate the way in which numbers so produced may be used to provide the smaller numbers which are often required in practice.

For a more detailed discussion of pseudorandom number generation, the reader may be referred to Golenko (1964) or Hammersley and Handscomb (1964), both of which provide further references.

Before we proceed any further, it must be emphasized that the reliability of pseudorandom number subroutines should never be taken for granted and they should never be used uncritically. Before using any such subroutine, the user should either test it fully himself or should be aware of and able to evaluate critically the results of tests of its reliability, or should have available such an evaluation from a source which he knows to be reliable. It is dangerous to take pseudorandom number subroutines on trust; some are more pseudo than random, and their use can produce misleading results.

It has been pointed out earlier that truly random numbers cannot be produced by calculation, since calculation implies a precise relationship between one number and another from which it was calculated. Random numbers can be generated, so it is said, by various electronic devices making use of random electronic events; these can be used for our purposes only if they are available on-line with the computer, and there must always be an element of uncertainty about whether they are functioning properly while they are actually in use, however correct their behaviour may be shown to be by tests before and after use.

In this chapter, only pseudorandom number generation by programmed subroutines will be considered, and the term 'generator' will always refer to the procedures of such subroutines and not to random electronic devices.

Suitable pseudorandom number generators will (by definition) produce calculated sequences of numbers which may be used as if they were truly random, and while such sequences certainly have their shortcomings, if these are known and properly appreciated one is in the position of being able to prefer the devil one knows to the devil one does not know and whose behaviour one cannot perhaps always rely on. The difficulty is to know when a pseudorandom number generator is suitable.

Basically, we may say that a pseudorandom number generator will produce by calculation a cyclic sequence of p numbers $r_0\ r_1\ r_2 \ldots r_n\ r_{n+1} \ldots r_{p-1}\ r_0\ r_1$. These numbers may be considered as possibly providing a satisfactory simulation of randomness if they are what Golenko rather vaguely calls uniformly distributed, if there is no correlation between successive numbers (apart of course from that involved in generation) or between numbers taken at regular intervals, or if there is no perceivable pattern in the cycle. If the generator appears to satisfy these conditions (and this is by no means always a simple matter to establish), then the next step is to carry out detailed statistical tests to see whether its use provides the sort of variability to be expected on an assumption of randomness.

To illustrate pseudorandom number generation, we may consider a generator of the general form $r_{n+1} \equiv kr_n + c$ (modulo m), where r_{n+1} is the smallest positive integer satisfaying the congruence. For those unfamiliar with the notation, this may be translated by saying that r_{n+1} is the remainder left when $kr_n + c$ is divided by m; thus suppose $kr_n + c$ to be 18962, and m to be 100; the smallest value of r_{n+1} satisfying the congruence would be 62; if m were 47, then the value would be 21. Finding a suitable specific form of this general congruence becomes the problem of finding satisfactory values of k, c and m.

The use of such a generator would appear to involve a multiplication, an addition and a division. Two of these, especially the last, are relatively slow operations; since the number of pseudorandom numbers calculated during a single genetic simulation experiment is very high (about a million per 50 generations of the experiment described in Chapter 11), the time spent in their generation is important, and must be kept as short as is consistent with a satisfactory simulation of randomness. It would apparently help if m were an integral power of the base of the number system in use—a power of two for binary or a power of ten for decimal. Division is then unnecessary, since if m were 2^t or 10^t, r_{n+1} would be the t l.s. digits (binary or decimal respectively) of the evaluation of $kr_n + c$, and these are easily obtained by truncation.

Let us consider by way of illustration a specific example of the generating equation given above, namely $r_{n+1} \equiv 41\, r_n + 17$ (modulo 100). If $r_n = 73$, then

$41r_n + 17 = 3010$, and the remainder left on dividing by 100 is 10, the two l.s. digits of the answer. This is the generated pseudorandom number, and it forms the basis for the calculation of the next one, which will be the smallest positive integer congruent with $41 \times 10 + 17$ (modulo 100), and so on. The situation with a binary calculation is exactly analogous.

However, a sequence of this general kind may have quite serious drawbacks. One is quite apparent in the very simple example chosen as an illustration by Hammersley and Handscomb (1964)—the numbers produced are alternately odd and even. Indeed, in any example where m is a power of two or of ten the numbers will be all odd, or be all even, or alternate odd and even, according to the values of k and c; clearly such numbers cannot properly be taken as random. This is an obvious enough pattern in such a series of numbers, but there may be less obvious patterns.

TABLE 17

The sequence produced by use of the congruence $r_{n+1} \equiv 41r_n + 17$ (modulo 100). It runs along the rows and each value of r_{n+1} is the smallest positive integer satisfying the congruence

00	17	14	91	48	85	02	99	76	33	70	87	84	61	18	55	72
69	46	03	40	57	54	31	88	25	42	39	16	73	10	27	24	01
58	95	12	09	86	43	80	97	94	71	28	65	82	79	56	13	50
67	64	41	98	35	52	49	26	83	20	37	34	11	68	05	22	19
96	53	90	07	04	81	38	75	92	89	66	23	60	77	74	51	08
45	62	59	36	93	30	47	44	21	78	15	32	29	06	63	00	17

Consider the sequence generated by use of the congruence $r_{n+1} \equiv 41r_n + 17$ (modulo 100), which is shown in Table 17, beginning this time from zero and running along the rows. At first glance, the numbers look well enough scattered in a manner that might well be random, but it can quickly be seen that they alternate odd and even. We could decide that even if the units digits were not adequately random, the tens digits might be more satisfactory and we could just use these, discarding the units digits. It is generally true that the m.s. digits provide a better simulation of randomness than the l.s. digits, and as will be shown later we can sometimes get away with using an imperfect pseudorandom number generator if we discard at least some of the l.s. digits. But again, this must be approached with caution. While a casual inspection of the tens digits in Table 17 suggests that they may be dispersed in a random manner, a more careful consideration of the figures will show that although they do not alternate odd and even as did the units digits, there is a pattern of odds and evens nevertheless, the repeat being 3 odd, 3 even, 4 odd, 3 even, 3 odd, 4 even.

In fact, Table 17 was laid out in a manner calculated to mislead the reader. If he rewrites it in ten rows of ten columns, it will be immediately apparent that the 100-number sequence is full of patterns. For example, there is only one sequence of the units digits, 0 7 4 1 8 5 2 9 6 3 0 7 etc., the digit being the same in all numbers of any one column of a 10×10 table, and this sequence itself is far from providing a satisfactory simulation of randomness because each number in it is seven more than the previous one (modulo 10). In each row, the tens digits of the second and third columns would always be identical; that is, if r_n and r_{n+1} have identical tens digits, so have r_{n+10} and r_{n+11}, r_{n+20} and r_{n+21}, and so on. Also, the sequence of tens digits read down each column is always the same, 0 7 4 1 8 5 2 9 6 3, although except for the second and third columns the columns begin at different points in the sequence which, it will be noticed, is identical with the sequence of the units digits along the rows.

The temptation now arises to fiddle with the numbers. If the units digits are scattered even if not random, and the tens digits are scattered and perhaps less unrandom, we might think that we would be able to get a better approach to randomness if we added the two digits of each number together and took the units digit of the answer. But we are not any better off, as the reader will find if he does this and lays out the resultant sequence in a 10×10 table, the sequence as before running along the rows. There is an odd/even pattern with a 20-number repeat, the sequence down the columns is always the same (once again being 0 7 4 1 8 5 2 9 6 3) and although the columns do not all begin at the same point, the first and fourth columns are identical, and so are the second and eighth, fifth and seventh, and sixth and ninth.

The search for a suitable pseudorandom number generator thus becomes not so much a search for simulation of randomness but in the first place for avoidance of pattern, and this is difficult when m is a power of the base in use.

We may try to get round this difficulty by using a pseudorandom number generator with as large a cycle of numbers as possible (the principal limiting factor being the word size of the computer in use); this will produce numbers much larger than those usually required, and the latter will be obtained by using sections from the m.s. ends of the generated numbers, discarding the l.s. digits which will show patterns with small repeats. The working numbers so obtained are still liable to show patterns, but it would be hoped that these would have very large repeats, ideally so large that the pattern would not repeat itself during the course of an experiment. Thus there must certainly be more numbers in the cycle than used during any one simulation run, so that no sequence of generated numbers will be repeated during a run, and it is highly desirable that any pattern in the sequence of working numbers actually used should also be larger than the number of numbers used in a run. The problem is how to find out whether these are true.

If the cycle size is to be large, m must be large, but the converse is not necessarily true. For example, the congruence $r_{n+1} \equiv 11\,r_n + 13$ (modulo 100) produces only 50 numbers before the sequence begins to repeat itself; and the distribution of these is far from random, pairs of numbers produced by the congruence (considering them in order of magnitude from 0 to 100) alternating with pairs not produced. The congruence $r_{n+1} \equiv 7\,r_n + 5$ (modulo 100) has a cycle of only four numbers before it repeats itself.

The obvious ideal is to have a cycle in which every possible number occurs (once each, of course, since no number could occur twice in a single cycle); that is, a cycle of size m. For a congruence of the general form we are using as an example—$r_{n+1} \equiv kr_n + c$ (modulo m)—this is fortunately fairly easy when m is a power of two, since it can be shown that all possible numbers from zero to $m-1$ occur in a cycle provided that k and c have no common factor, and that $k \equiv 1$ (modulo 4). But the mere attainment of maximum cycle size is not of itself enough, since it does not mean that we have achieved the other desirable criteria, as we have seen when $k = 41$ and $c = 17$. This of course was with a small value of m, but even with a very large value of m it is still possible to get correlation patterns with small repeats. The aim therefore is to have a large value of m, with its maximum cycle size many times greater than the number of random numbers required in any one experiment, and values of k and c such that any patterns have very long repeats. Unfortunately, this is not nearly so easy to establish theoretically, and it may be necessary actually to operate the subroutine over long sequences and look for patterns. In the ultimate analysis, the only real way of testing the suitability of a pseudorandom number generator is to use it in various ways to generate variability and by statistical analysis to show whether the magnitude and kind of variability so generated agrees with what would be expected had truly random numbers been used. Clearly, the longer the cycle of numbers (which as we have seen is highly desirable), the more difficult it is to demonstrate suitable simulation of randomness over a substantial proportion of it, simply because of the time this would require.

There is one point which may be discussed here. In a pseudorandom cycle, any generated number occurs once only. As soon as we begin to use sections of generated numbers instead of the whole number we are free of this restriction. For example, suppose we are generating large pseudorandom numbers but only require numbers of five binary bits, which can of course take any of the values from zero to 31. We decide that we will obtain these 5-bit numbers by taking the five m.s. bits of each generated number; if we are using a suitable generator and enter it anywhere in the cycle, the first 32 5-bit numbers obtained are unlikely to contain each possible number once (and therefore once only), and the second 32 5-bit numbers will not coincide with the first nor will the frequencies with which the individual numbers occur be the same as in the first. Unfortunately, this does not necessarily mean that the two sequences of 32 5-bit numbers are randomly unrelated. For example, taking the simple generator $r_{n+1} \equiv 17r_n + 181$ (modulo 512) and entering it at, say, 457 and taking the five m.s. bits of each of the first 64 numbers generated, we obtain the following two consecutive 32-number sequences:

28 16 10 24 11 20 1 3 11 7 8 31 26 10 31 10
25 29 7 5 8 1 30 16 8 20 5 12 23 23 28 23 and
22 10 4 18 5 14 27 29 5 1 2 25 20 4 25 4
19 23 1 31 2 27 24 10 2 14 31 6 17 17 22 17.

At a quick glance these might appear to be satisfactory, but in fact each number in the first sequence is 6 more (modulo 32) than the number in the corresponding position in the second sequence. That is to say, $r_n \equiv r_{n+32} + 6$ (modulo 32) and also $r_{n+1} - r_n \equiv r_{n+33} - r_{n+32}$ (modulo 32).

But with larger values of k, c and m, the period becomes larger, and again the problem becomes one of choosing the right values.

We may now consider a practical pseudorandom number generator of the form we have been discussing. The generator of the English Electric KDF9 subroutine library used the congruence $r_{n+1} \equiv (2^9 + 1)\, r_n + 29741096258473$ (modulo 2^{47}), KDF9 having a 48-bit word. From the practical point of view, this is a very useful generator since it is very fast; no multiplication is involved, since $(2^9 + 1)\, r_n$ is $2^9 r_n + r_n$, and all that is required is to shift r_n up logically nine places, add the result to unshifted r_n, add 29741096258473, and remove the m.s. bit (eight bits having already been removed by the shift). This is fast.

But in this case, speed carries with it disadvantages in the shape of defects in the generator. Not only (as has been pointed out for the general case) do the l.s. bits alternate **0** and **1**, but for numbers composed of the s l.s. bits it has a cycle which repeats with a periodicity of 2^s. It is easy to see why this should be so. Whatever the modulus of the generator, the $(s+1)$th and more significant bits have no effect whatever on the production of the s l.s. bits, which would be precisely the same whether the result were modulo 2^{47} or modulo 2^s. The latter would give a period of 2^s.

Strictly speaking, this means that in a program using ten million pseudorandom numbers, the 24 l.s. bits should not be used. With one exception, the program described in detail in Chapter 11 did not use numbers of more than 12 bits and these were always taken from the m.s. end of the 48-bit word. The exception was the string of 26 m.s. bits used in gametogenesis and fertilization. The l.s. bit of this string thus occurred in a sequence which repeated itself after about four million numbers. This would seem to be of little consequence, but since in any case the generated numbers were used for several different purposes in a rather irregular pattern it is highly unlikely that there was any harmful repetition of bits sequences used in gametogenesis, and if there had been any it would only have affected the three l.s. bits.

The possibility of pattern at the m.s. end of the kind already discussed is a different and more difficult matter, and the author must admit that he does not really know what the situation is. During the preparation of this chapter he has become a little wiser, and now has some doubts about whether he might not have taken too much for granted when he used this subroutine. This is a very easy fault to fall into. One is interested in the biology of a situation and needs pseudorandom numbers, there is a fast generator which seems to have proved satisfactory in use, so why spend a lot of time (especially when one is not a mathematician) in delving into the theory of pseudorandom number generation? It is a different matter when one comes to write a textbook.

The author's growing uneasiness is however tempered by the consideration that if there was a pattern among the m.s. bits, their production was against an unpatterned and irregular background of different uses, irregular because of fertility failures, repeated efforts to sow seeds falling outside the population, seeds falling on full rows, so that one could never say that every *n*th generated number would be used for a particular purpose. The author is fairly confident that, considering any particular use of generated numbers, it was highly unlikely that there was any consistent pattern in the m.s. bits used, particularly over short periods, and feels that the advantage gained from the high speed of the pseudorandom number generator outweighed any possible disadvantage due to doubt about its complete reliability.

It is in situations like this that one is tempted to try and fiddle in order to improve the reliability of numbers obtained from a generator. Some of the things one may try are safe and effective enough. Others are dubious and dangerous.

One obvious method, which consumes a little extra time, is possible when the numbers are required to make random choices from a frequency distribution table (for example, tables such as those used for pollen transport or seed dispersal in the experiment of Chapter 11). Such a table may be constructed randomly (by writing its contents haphazardly on a sheet of squared paper and using the ensuing table when punching the program), and its contents shuffled pseudorandomly at intervals during the running of the program, either entirely or partly.

More dubious are the methods which involve fiddling with the generated numbers. For example, suppose that numbers of seven bits are required. Instead of simply taking these always from the m.s. end, they could be taken at randomly varying distances from the end. This could be done by dropping off at random any number, say, from zero to three or zero to seven of the m.s. bits by shifting the generated number up that number of places at random, and taking the seven m.s. bits of the residual string. But there is always a danger here that one may fortuitously produce short-term patterns much too frequently; one is getting into a situation in which this would be difficult or impossible to predict theoretically, and equally difficult to test in practice (even if a test seemed satisfactory one could never be sure because the method greatly increases the area which should be tested); one is getting close to the devil one does not know.

If fiddling with the generated numbers has its dangers, fiddling with the generator may be an even more dubious practice. We could use two quite different generators, alternately or in random sequence; but how could we know that they might not sometimes produce identical or simply related sequences? For the same reason, the plausible idea of logically adding two numbers produced by different generators might sometimes produce regular sequences.

Golenko (1964) suggests using two subroutines (A & B) in the following way. An initial value for r is chosen and subroutine A used to calculate a sequence of about a dozen numbers. At the end of this short sequence the current value of the number is used as the basis of a single calculation by subroutine B and the result of this is used to start a new short sequence by A, and so on. This works satisfactorily provided both subroutines generate the same number of bits (m the same for both) and provided that for each subroutine the value of r_{n+1} always has a unique derivation. There is a very remote possibility that the first use of B might produce r; if desired, this improbable event could be specially tested for; so long as the length of the A sequence is constant, no other starting value for an A sequence can be repeated until the B cycle is completed.

It is worth commenting here on the use of library subroutines for pseudorandom number generation. Two points arise. Unless the specification of a subroutine states that the generator has been satisfactorily tested for randomness, with an indication of the tests used, or is known to be theoretically sound and to have been satisfactorily independently tested, it should not be assumed that it is in fact satisfactory. Failing this, the programmer should take the necessary steps to make sure that it is suitable for his purpose.

Secondly, it should not be assumed that the library subroutine has been programmed in the most efficient way; it is always worth while for the programmer to look at it to see if he can improve it. It may well be that in its original form it does not deliver the pseudorandom numbers in the way most useful to the programmer, and it is usually not too difficult to adapt a library subroutine to that end. Some examples of adaptation are given later in the chapter.

It may happen that the subroutine program is simply inefficient, not necessarily because of bad programming but sometimes because of pointless adherence to conventions of subroutine programming. The KDF9 subroutine under discussion provides an interesting example of this. As written, it has 18 instructions.

It is a normal convention that library subroutines should leave the overflow indicator as they find it. In general, conventions are good things. A programmer using a library subroutine knows as a matter of course what to expect, and does not have to worry about non-standard or unconventional procedures which he would otherwise have to take into account. But conventions are (or should be) made for man, and where they are a positive hindrance they should be abandoned (but of course this must be made clear in the subroutine specification).

Now this KDF9 subroutine must cause overflow almost every time it is used, but this is of no significance whatever. If, before entry to the subroutine, overflow may have occurred and this would matter, it should be tested for before the subroutine is entered. If it does not matter, then there is no point in preserving the state of the overflow register. If overflow immediately after use of the subroutine matters, then the overflow register may be cleared (by a single instruction) either by the subroutine immediately before exit or by the main program immediately on return. If overflow is irrelevant during a long sequence of operations (as it normally is in genetic simulation programs then the state of the overflow register can be completely ignored until the time comes when it needs to be cleared. In any of these cases, preservation of the state of the overflow register by the subroutine is pointless. The KDF9 library subroutine devoted eight of its 18 instructions to this end, and one of them was a lengthy shift of 48 places.

There was also a small point by which another instruction was saved. Since the congruence used involved a modulus of 2^{47}, the m.s. bit of the word had to be deleted (the even more significant bits are lost off the m.s. end). The subroutine did this indirectly by operating in the 47 m.s. bits, shifting the answer down logically one place before delivery (the m.s. bit then always being zero and the 47-bit integer or fraction always positive). This is reasonable enough. But since (as has been shown) the l.s. bits of the generated numbers are unreliable, any specified number of bits wanted by the author were always removed from the m.s. end by a double length shift up the necessary number of places into an empty accumulator (the shift up being normally much shorter than would be a shift down to deliver the same number of bits), and the original shift down of one place was unnecessary and that instruction could be deleted.

The subroutine could thus be rewritten in a much faster form using only nine instructions, a saving of time worth making in a program using it about ten million times in each run.

Detailed Consideration of a 31-bit Generator

Many of the difficulties and objections which arise with subroutines having m a power of two disappear or at least become of less consequence when some other value for m is chosen. But to use other values of m increases computation time since division, which is a slow process, now replaces the rapid truncation. There is an interesting and useful exception to this, based on a somewhat different form of generator, namely $r_{n+1} \equiv kr_n$ (modulo $2^{31}-1$). If k is properly chosen, this has a period of $2^{31}-2$, zero and $2^{31}-1$ not occurring in the cycle. $2^{31}-1$ being a prime, the condition is that $k^a \not\equiv 1$ (modulo $2^{31}-1$) for $0<a<(2^{31}-2)$, but the reader is reminded that the fulfilment of the maximum possible period is no guarantee that the distribution of the numbers in the cycle provides a satisfactory simulation of randomness. A value of k which the author has used and which in his experience provides a suitable pseudorandom number generator is 455470314 (the smallest integer congruent with 13^{13}, modulo $2^{31}-1$). The l.s. bits of the generated numbers appear to provide as satisfactory a simulation of randomness as the m.s. bits.

This generator is exceptional in that division by $2^{31}-1$ can be neatly avoided even though the numbers produced are to be modulo $2^{31}-1$. If we let z be the smallest integer satisfying the congruence $z \equiv kr_n$ (modulo 2^{31}), then it can be shown that the expression $\{kr_n+(2^{31}-1)\,z\}/2^{31}$ gives on evaluation either r_{n+1} or $r_{n+1}+(2^{31}-1)$, and since this evaluation involves a division only by 2^{31}, this can be achieved by truncation. It is easy enough to determine which answer has been obtained by testing whether or not it is less than 2^{31} (since r_{n+1} must lie between zero and $2^{31}-1$ exclusively). If it is not less than 2^{31}, then subtraction from it of $2^{31}-1$ will give the required value, r_{n+1}.

With a computer whose words have 32 bits, this is all fairly simple, though it does involve a time-consuming multiplication. We will discuss the operations involved in relation to XB1 and Mendol, and treat them as being entirely concerned with integers, though we could equally well consider the operations as involving fractions.

Suppose we form the product kr_n double length in accumulators **G** and **H** (respectively m.s. and l.s.). The sign bit of **H** is not part of the product, and since we are assuming Mendol and k and r_n are always positive, it will always be zero (with a real computer this might not always be the case, and it would be necessary to make sure about this point. The operation of the subroutine which is about to be developed depends on this bit being zero).

H, being the 31 l.s. bits of the product, is clearly kr_n (modulo 2^{31}), which is z. **G** (still regarded as the m.s. half of the product) is clearly **GH** − **H**, that is kr_n-z. We can obtain $2^{31}z$ simply by regarding **H** as though it were the m.s. half of a double length number. Adding **H** to **G** then gives us $kr_n+(2^{31}-1)\,z$, and the treatment of this result as the l.s. half of a double length number is in effect dividing by 2^{31}. So the result is then $\{kr_n+(2^{31}-1)z\}/2^{31}$.

A little thought will show that all this is achieved quite simply; the product kr_n having been formed in **G** and **H**, these two accumulators are added together and the answer is treated as an integer of 32 significant bits. If this answer is $r_{n+1}+2^{31}-1$, then the addition of **G** to **H** will have caused overflow, the m.s. bit will be a **1**, and the answer will appear negative to the computer. This situation can be recognized easily either by testing for a negative result or for overflow; the former is much to be preferred, since if we use overflow as the testing criterion the main program (or the subroutine itself) will have to take steps to see that the overflow register is initially cleared; since overflow is of no consequence in most operations in a genetic simulation program (except those concerned with population analysis and related calculations), it is obviously simplest to ignore overflow entirely provided that before we embark on any subsequent calculations we remember that multiple use of this pseudorandom number subroutine is bound to have set the overflow register.

If overflow has occurred, then although the computer will treat the result as a negative 31-bit integer, we can consider it as though it were a positive 32-bit integer giving the correct value of the addition of **G** and **H**, since overflow will not affect the 31 l.s. bits and we can treat the negative sign bit as 2^{31} (but for any specific computer, it would be as well to check that this is in fact true). All we then need to do is to subtract $2^{31}-1$, or add $2^{31}+1$ (considering for our immediate purpose the word to be a 32-bit positive integer; to the computer our $2^{31}+1$ would be $1-2^{31}$). Both of these operations will cause overflow, and the author has a (probably irrational) mistrust of subtractions which cause overflow and would prefer to add $2^{31}+1$; a **1** is lost off the m.s. end of the word, the m.s. bit becomes a zero, and the 31 l.s. bits give the required value of r_{n+1}.

Overflow or not, the eventual answer is a 31-bit pseudorandom number and a Mendol program for a subroutine can be written quite simply.

In the following subroutine (which may be supposed to be the **P202** used in programs developed earlier), **p0** will carry the link, **p1** the current value of r_n, **p2** k, and **p3** $(1-2^{31})$. At the beginning of every program in which the subroutine is used, a randomly chosen starting value for r_n, not greater than $2^{31}-2$, must be set in **p1**, and this number must be different for each use of the program; it will be one of the main program parameters. The subroutine will replace r_n in **p1** with the new pseudorandom number r_{n+1} which it will also deliver in **H**.

The instruction sequence for this subroutine is

(0); p1→G; p2→H; G×H; G+H→H; J1H>0; (*whatever happens, it cannot equal zero***); H+p3→H;**
(1); H→p1; [link and exit];

The number so produced may be used as a 31-bit random positive integer (that is, an integer in the range 1 to $2^{31}-2$), a random positive fraction, or a string of 31 random bits. If we are using random fractions, then even if we do not need all the binary places we can take the generated numbers as we obtain them, since normally any superfluous bits at the l.s. end will make no practical difference.

However, with integers and strings of bits we will generally want to use integers with a smaller range (which can have a zero minimum) or smaller strings of bits than those delivered by the subroutine, and in these cases superfluous bits must be removed. This can easily be done by the main program simply by use of an appropriate mask, which can also ensure that the selected bits are in the required position in the word. But there is a great deal to be said for producing a more versatile subroutine which will carry out this operation in response to a specification on entry and deliver the required number of bits. The advantage of this is that in writing a section of the program requiring random numbers one does not have to bother with instructions for the extraction of the required number of bits from the 31-bit number generated, but can in effect simply 'order' the required number of bits and have them delivered, with no further thought. Small integers are normally required at the l.s. end of a word and they may conveniently be delivered cut off either from the l.s. end of the generated number by use of a mask of the appropriate size, or from the m.s. end by a shift which sheds unwanted bits.

The former method can only be used of course with those generators where the bits at the l.s. end can safely be assumed to provide a reliable simulation of randomness. It is probably somewhat the quicker method, since shifts are time-consuming, but it requires more storage space if the subroutine is to be entered with the number of bits directly specified; this is preferable to specification by the main program in terms of the appropriate mask, which is less neat, requires more thought, and gives more possibility of error. If the number of bits is to be directly specified, the subroutine will have to carry a permanent table of 30 masks, 1, 3, 7 ... 2^n-1 ... $2^{30}-1$ ($2^{31}-1$ is not required, since **P202** would be used for 31 bits). The bits specification is then used in a modifier to extract the appropriate mask which is used in an LM operation to delete the superfluous bits.

The author has however a preference for the following method, which requires a smaller storage space in the subroutine, but if the time required for shifting were excessive (this will depend on the computer in use) then it would certainly be better to use the faster masking method.

There are two ways of using a shift to eliminate the unwanted bits. The obvious one is to use a logical shift down (logical, since rounding must be avoided), unwanted bits being dropped off the l.s. end. For a generated word of 31 bits and a specified requirement of b bits, a logical shift down of $31-b$ places is all that is required.

Less obvious, but with possible advantages, would be to use a double length arithmetic shift up of b places into a previously cleared accumulator. The shift should be arithmetic since the sign bit of the l.s. accumulator must be skipped (rounding does not arise in shifts up); a logical shift would have to be $b+1$ places to give the same result, and this would either involve an extra instruction or a specification not the same as the number of bits required.

The choice between single length shift down and double length shift up will not usually make a great deal of difference. Where the integers or numbers of bits required are small, the single length shift down will need to be over more places than the double length shift up would require, and the latter would therefore be faster unless double length shifting of itself requires more time than single length shifting. The double length shift would require an extra instruction, to clear the m.s. accumulator. The single length shift would also require an extra instruction if the required number of bits b is specified directly, in order to convert this to $31-b$; however, $31-b$ could be specified directly, but this makes programming somewhat less simple and provides a possibility of error.

Any of the following three versions would serve as the **P200** used in many programs developed in earlier chapters. In each case, the number of bits required is specified directly in **M15** on entry. The contents of **p0** to **p3** are as in the original version, and in the masking version the table of masks begins in **p4**. Only the instruction sequences are given below. Delivery is in **H**.

1 Masking

(0); p1→G; p2→H; G×H; G+H→H; J1H>0; H+p3→H;
(1); H→p1; H&p4(M15)→H; [link and exit]**;**

2 Single length shift down

(0); M15−31; p1→G; p2→H; G×H; G+H→H; J1H>0;
H+p3→H;
(1); H→p1; H up(M15); (_this is in fact a shift down, since **M15** is now negative_**);** [link and exit]**;**

3 Double length shift up

(0); p1→G; p2→H; G×H; G+H→G; J1G>0; G+p3→G;
(1); G→p1; H=0; HG×2(M15); [link and exit]**;**

Where the program involves random choices requiring small integers, and also fertility testing and gametogenesis when it will often be the case that all the generated bits will be required (or could be used, with some bits harmlessly redundant and so not requiring preliminary elimination), it would then in the latter case be a waste of time to go through the motions of eliminating no bits, especially if this were to involve a double-length shift up of 31 places. We could avoid this contingency by using two independent subroutines (as was done in an earlier chapter), one delivering 31 random bits (the original simple version), the other specified numbers of bits. But there is something to be said for using one pseudorandom sequence for both purposes, since it improves the mixture of uses of random numbers (see earlier in this chapter). This can be achieved by having a subroutine of two sections with only one set of parameters. Thus we could modify any of the three versions just given by the addition of

(2) ; p1→G ; p2→H ; G × H ; G+H→H ; J3H>0 ; H+p3→H ;
(3) ; H→p1 ; [link and exit] ;

When all 31 bits are required, there would be no specification on entry, which would be to reference **(2)**.

We now have a good general purpose subroutine.

The same generator could be used with word lengths greater than 32, but more shift manipulations would be required in the initial calculation since the relationship between the two words of a double-length product would no longer be the factor 2^{31}, and subsequent operations would also require amendment.

A further modification of this subroutine would allow it to be regarded as though it were a producer of a continuous string of random bits, the number of bits required on any occasion being removed from the string and the latter replenished by the production of a new pseudorandom number as required. This means that all pseudorandom bits generated would be used, with some saving in time where the used pseudorandom numbers are small (though not where they are large, since the testing and extra manipulative operations required also consume time). It should also increase the number of realisable sequences of random numbers derivable from the basic generator (see next section). On the other hand, it takes the generator out of the realms of practicable predictability, which means that we can never be sure that at some stage it might not produce some highly patterned and possibility repetitive sequences. But where the numbers taken are used for different purposes and are of different lengths, and especially where success or failure tests as in selection procedures impose an irregular pattern on random number usage, the employment in this way of the pseudorandom generator should be safe enough. The author has tested such a subroutine using both the production of genetic families of various kinds and the frequencies of integers in various size ranges, and the tests on statistical analysis proved completely satisfactory.

Without going into descriptive detail, the following program for subroutine **P203** will indicate how this may be done.

p0 to **p3** are as before. In addition, **p4** will carry the number of bits unused from the last generated number, and **p5** will carry those bits at its m.s. end excepting the sign bit; **p4** and **p5** should be written as zero, that is with no bits available the first time the subroutine is used. The double length shift up method is used for this subroutine, for which the instruction sequence is as follows, the required number of bits being specified in **M15** on entry and the bits being delivered in **H**.

```
(0); H = 0; p5→G; HG×2(M15); G→p5; M15→G; J1G>p4;
     p4 − G→p4; [link and exit];
(1); G − p4→G; G→M15; p4 = 31; p4 − G→p4; H→p5;
     p1→G; p2→H; G×H; G+H→G; J2G>0; G+p3→G;
(2); G→p1; H = 0; HG×2(M15); H+p5→H; G→p5;
     [link and exit];
```

This subroutine, which is economical only for random numbers of six bits or less, could be made slightly more efficient by using an extra accumulator, but it is best to keep the number of accumulators used to a minimum. It would also have been quicker if Mendol had been designed to allow modifier contents to be used directly as criteria for jumps, and if arithmetical operations could be performed directly between modifiers and store locations.

Although this pseudorandom number generator may not be the most suitable for the machines available to many readers, it is hoped that the detailed account which has been given will have provided a satisfactory illustration of some of the general principles involved in programming pseudorandom number subroutines. It is worth pointing out here that adaptation of subroutines in the way that has just been discussed may not always be worth while, depending on the generator used. Thus it is quite easy to use the generator described on page 446 so that it delivers a specified number of bits, but it would be doubtfully worth while using it to produce a continuous string of bits in the sort of way which has just been described. This is because it involves no multiplication and is so fast that the extra administrative instructions required for such adaptation would take a disproportionate amount of time and make it considerably slower. It might however improve its reliability.

The Limited Field of Pseudorandom Number Generation

There is one point which must be mentioned which concerns all pseudorandom number generators. Earlier in this chapter it was pointed out that if for example we take the five m.s. bits from a generated number, giving a range of integers from zero to 31, then in any sequence of 32 such successive integers it will almost always be the case that the different integers will not occur with the same frequency, some occurring more than once and some not at all, and that the next sequence of 32 will differ from the first although it may be the case with some generators that it will have quite a simple relationship with it. But even with the most satisfactory generators where no such relationships exists there still remains a drastic limitation on true randomness, though to what extent this is important is a matter for argument.

Consider only integers in the range zero to 31 inclusive, each being the five m.s. bits of a generated number. If the value taken by one position in a sequence of such integers is quite independent of that of any other, the number of different 32-integer sequences is 32^{32}, or 2^{160}. But with, say, a pseudorandom generator having a cycle of 2^{31}, and with entry to the cycle at any point producing a unique 32-integer sequence, the maximum number of different 32-integer sequences is clearly the same as the cycle size, that is only 2^{31}. Such a generator can therefore at best produce only a tiny fraction, $1/2^{129}$, of the possible different 32-integer sequences of 5-bit numbers. A bigger cycle does not materially alter this situation.

In other words, a pseudorandom number generator is only capable of simulating an extremely limited section of the possible field of random variability.

The largest sequence of 5-bit numbers of which every possibility could occur at least once in a cycle of 2^{31} generated pseudorandom numbers is six, but it might be difficult to establish for any particular 2^{31}-cycle generator that each possible sequence of six integers occurred equally frequently (twice) with its occurrences in 'random' positions in the cycle. With numbers of more than five bits the position becomes progressively worse.

The proportion of the possible field of random variability which can be realized may be increased (though it will still remain small) by various methods.

If instead of simply taking the 5 m.s. bits from each generated 31-bit number we take consecutively the six possible 5-bit sections from it, or better still if we take one 5-bit section from it at random (since the next time that number appeared the random choice would probably fall on another 5-bit section, and there are 27 different possibilities), we would clearly increase the field of variability which could be created. But not by very much. In the latter case all possible 7-integer sequences could occur at least once with a generator cycle size of 2^{31}, but some would occur twice. The technique of taking integers of various sizes consecutively from a continuous string of bits (as may be done with **P203**) is a similar but possibly more effective way of increasing the field of variability.

Increase in cycle size by linking two different subroutines in some such method as that suggested by Golenko and described on page 448 not only does not help, it may make matters worse.

Consider two subroutines A and B, each with a cycle size of 2^{31} 31-bit numbers, and consider also sequences of seven 5-bit integers, each being the five m.s. bits of a generated number. There are 2^{35} possible different sequences, and even if none occurred more than once, only 2^{31} of these could be obtained in a complete cycle of A or B. Suppose A and B are linked by generating a run of 12 numbers with A, using the last one to generate one number with B, using that to start a new run of 12 with A, and so on. The maximum cycle size is now 12×2^{31}, and it is certainly possible that some new 7-integer sequences will occur. But a little thought will show that each of the 7-integer sequences obtainable by use of A alone will now occur six times in the complete cycle, while a very large number of possible sequences (at least 9×2^{31}) will still not occur at all. From the point of view of random production of sequences, this is worse than before, and is an objectionable feature of Golenko's method of linking subroutines. From this point of view, linkage of A and B is less objectionable when the run size of A is smaller, but this of course does less to increase the field of variability.

Another method which suggests itself is to use two distinct pseudorandom number generators simultaneously, logically adding the values of r_{n+1} for each to give that for the number to be used. Since for each run of a program the starting values for each generator will be chosen independently, this would have the effect over many runs of producing a cycle of a size equal to the product of the two individual cycle sizes, but with the desirable feature that individual numbers will appear many times within the cycle. Unfortunately, this method is valid only if there is no probability of any kind of relationship between any possible sequence (whatever the length) of one generator and any possible sequence of the other, a point which would seem to be impossible to establish; indeed, such a relationship of this kind is not such a very improbable contingency. The method also takes twice as long.

The reader may well by now have come to the conclusion that pseudorandom number subroutines have too many imperfections in their simulation of randomness. But it may well be that drastic limitation of the field of variability is of no consequence.

Where pseudorandom number subroutines have been properly chosen and used intelligently, there seems good reason for confidence in the reliability of the consequent results. And, except where random electronic devices are available on line, without pseudorandom number generators genetic simulation would not be possible.

References

Bateman, A. J. (1947a). 'Contamination of seed crops I. Insect pollination'. *J. Genet.*, **48,** 257–275.

Bateman, A. J. (1947b). 'Contamination in seed crops III. Relation with isolation distance'. *Heredity*, **1**, 303–336.

Bishop, J. A. and M. E. Korn (1969). 'Natural selection and cyanogenesis in white clover, *Trifolium repens*'. *Heredity*, **24**, 423–430.

Buslenko, N. P. and V. G. Sragovich (1964). 'Methods of obtaining random numbers with assigned distribution law'. In Y. A. Shreider (Ed.), *Method of statistical testing*, *Monte Carlo method.* Elsevier, Amsterdam, London, New York. Chap. VII, section 4, p. 262.

Crosby, J. L. (1949). 'The selection of an unfavourable gene-complex'. *Evolution*, **3**, 212–230.

Crosby, J. L. (1960). 'The use of electronic computation in the study of random fluctuations in rapidly evolving populations'. *Phil. Trans. Roy. Soc.* '*B*', **242**, 551–573.

Crosby, J. L. (1961). 'Teaching genetics with an electronic computer'. *Heredity*, **16**, 255–273.

Crosby, J. L. (1966). 'Self-incompatibility alleles in the population of *Oenothera organensis*'. *Evolution*, **20**, 567–579.

Crosby, J. L. (1970). 'The evolution of genetic discontinuity: computer models of the selection of barriers to interbreeding between subspecies'. *Heredity*, **25**, 253–297.

Fisher, R. A. (1930). *The Genetical Theory of Natural Selection.* Clarendon Press, Oxford.

Fraser, A. S. (1957). 'Simulation of genetic systems by automatic digital computers. I. Introduction'. *Aust. J. Biol. Sci.*, **10**, 484-491.

Fraser, A. S. (1960). 'Simulation of genetic systems by automatic digital computer. VI. Epistasis'. *Aust. J. Biol. Sci.*, **13**, 150-162.

Gill, J. L. and B. A. Clemmer (1966). 'Effects of selection and linkage on degree of inbreeding'. *Aust. J. Biol. Sci.*, **19**, 307-317.

Glass, B. (1947). 'Maupertuis and the beginnings of genetics'. *Quart. Rev. Biol.*, **22**, 196-210.

Golenko, D. I. (1964). 'Generating uniformly distributed random quantities by means of electronic computers'. In Y. A. Shreider (Ed.), *Method of statistical testing*, *Monte Carlo method.* Elsevier, Amsterdam, London, New York. Chap. VI, pp. 196-243.

Hammersley, J. M. and D. C. Handscomb (1964). *Monte Carlo methods.* Methuen, London.

Jain, S. K. and D. R. Marshall (1968). 'Simulation of models involving mixed selfing and random mating. I. Stochastic variation in outcrossing and selection parameters'. *Heredity*, **23**, 411-432.

Jones, D. A. (1962). 'Selective eating of the acyanogenic form of the plant *Lotus corniculatus* L. by various animals.' *Nature Lond.*, **193**, 1109-1110.

Kettlewell, H. B. D. (1956). 'A resume of investigations on the evolution of melanism in the Lepidoptera'. *Proc. Roy. Soc. 'B'*, **145**, 297-303.

McNeilly, T. (1968). 'Evolution in closely adjacent plant populations. III. *Agrostis tenuis* on a small copper mine'. *Heredity*, **23**, 99-108.

Moroney, M. J. (1951). *Facts from figures*. Penguin Books, Harmondsworth.

Young, S. S. Y. (1966). 'Computer simulation of directional selection in large populations. I. The programme, the additive and the dominance models'. *Genetics*, **53**, 189-205.

APPENDIX

Summary of Instructions and other Specifications for Mendol

Where the letters **c J j P M V** appear in the instructions below, they are so written in practice.

The permissible interpretation of **Q** and **R** (and in one instruction **T**) vary according to the instruction, and for each instruction are specified in the columns headed 'possible interpretation' by one or more of the letters S A K M, indicating that **Q** or **R** (as the case may be) may be interpreted respectively as store location, accumulator, counter and modifier. Where only a modifier is relevant, **M** will be used in the instruction. S may stand for any absolute address beginning with **a**, or any relative address beginning with **p s t u v w x y z**, and any of these addresses may be modified in any instruction in which it appears, the modified instruction having a form exemplified by **s***n* **(M***m***)**.

l m n may stand for any appropriate positive integer written in decimal form.

In the columns headed 'contents after operation', *Q* and *R* indicate the original contents of **Q** and **R**.

Transfer Instructions

The word is copied from the store location or register specified on the left, which remains unaltered, into that specified on the right, the previous contents of the latter being lost.

	Possible interpretation		Contents after operation	
	Q	**R**	**Q**	**R**
Q→**R**	SAKM	AKM	*Q*	*Q*
R→**Q**			*R*	*R*

(i.e. transfer may be from or into a store location, but a direct store to store transfer is not allowed).

Setting or Adding to Registers or Store Locations

	Q	R	Q	R
Q $= m$	SAKM		m	
Q $= -m$			$-m$	
Q$+m$			$Q+m$	
Q$-m$			$Q-m$	
Q $=$ **(s**m**)**	SAKM		**Q** will contain the absolute address of the word whose relative address si **s**m; **s**m may be replaced by any permissible form of address such as **t**m, **s**n**(M**m**)**, **p**n, **p**n**(M**m**)**, **p**n**P**l, **p**n**P**l**(M**m**)**.	
Q $=$ **(j**n**)** **Q** $=$ **(j**n**P**m**)**	SAKM		**Q** will contain the absolute address of the word referenced by (n) in the current subroutine or in subroutine **P**m respectively.	

In the following logical and arithmetic instructions, where two words are involved in the operation the answer appears in the store location or register to the right of the arrow. Where only one word (single or double length) is involved it is replaced by the answer.

Logical Instructions

LP = logical product; LS = logical sum

	Possible interpretation		Contents after operation	
	Q	**R**	**Q**	**R**
Q & R→Q	A	SA	LP of Q and R	R
Q & R→R			Q	LP of Q and R
Q & n	A		LP of Q and the binary form of n	
Q ≢ R→Q	A	SA	LS of Q and R	R
Q ≢ R→R			Q	LS of Q and R
bits Q	A		number of bits in **Q** which were **1**	

In the following logical shift instructions there is no rounding and overflow is ignored. The sign bit has no significance in logical instructions and is treated just like any other bit. **QR** indicates linked accumulators used for a double length shift and treated here just as though they were one accumulator of 64 bits.

	Q	R	Result of the operation
Q up n / **Q down** n	A		The contents of **Q** are shifted up or down logically n places, bits lost off one end being replaced by n zeros at the other.
Q c/up n / **Q c/down** n	A		The contents of **Q** are shifted up or down logically n places, bits lost off one end being placed in the proper sequence at the other (circular shift).
QR up n / **QR down** n	A	A	**QR** is treated as a single accumulator and its contents shifted up or down logically n places, bits lost at one end being replaced by n zeros at the other. This shift includes the sign bit of **R**.

Q up (M*m***)** **Q down (M***m***)** **Q c/up (M***m***)** **Q c/down (M***m***)** **QR up (M***m***)** **QR down (M***m***)**	As with the foregoing, the number of places being specified by the contents of the modifier **M***m*. If the integer in **M***m* is negative, the shift will be in the reverse direction from that specified in the instruction.

Arithmetic Instructions

Rounding is applied, and the overflow register will be set when appropriate.

	Possible interpretation Q	Possible interpretation R	Contents after operation Q	Contents after operation R
Q + R → Q	A	SAKM	$Q+R$	R
Q + R → R			Q	$Q+R$
Q − R → Q			$Q-R$	R
Q − R → R			Q	$Q-R$
R − Q → Q			$R-Q$	R
R − Q → R			Q	$R-Q$

	Q	**R**	**Q**	**R**
−Q	A		$-Q$	
absQ	A		$\lvert Q \rvert$	
Q × **R**	A	A	The product $Q \times R$ appears double length in **Q** plus the 31 l.s. bits of **R**, the sign bit of **R** being the same as that of **Q**.	
Q/**R**	SA	A	Quotient Q/R (rounded)	R

(In division, the computer treats both Q and R as fractions. The absolute value of R must appear to the computer to be greater than that of Q; otherwise the overflow register will be set.)

QR/**T**	A	A	Correctly signed remainder	Quotient QR/T (unrounded)

T must also be A, and is unchanged by the operation (QR is a double length number in **Q** and the 31 l.s. bits of **R**, the sign bit of **R** being immaterial. The computer treats both QR and T as fractions, and T must appear to the computer to be greater in absolute value than QR).

The following multiplications by 2^n or 2^{-n} are in effect arithmetic shifts up or down n places; shifts up may set the overflow register, shifts down are rounded.

	Q	**R**	Contents of **Q** or **QR** after operation
Q × **2**/n **Q** × **2**/$-n$	A		$Q \times 2^n$ (i.e. up n places) $Q \times 2^{-n}$ (i.e. down n places)
QR × **2**/n **QR** × **2**/$-n$	A	A	$QR \times 2^n$ (i.e. up n places) $QR \times 2^{-n}$ (i.e. down n places) (Sign bit of **R** is skipped in both cases)
Q × **2**(**M**m) **QR** × **2**(**M**m)	A A	 A	As with the preceding four instructions, the contents of **M**m specifying direction and extent of shift.

Jump Instructions

J*n* Jump unconditionally to the instruction preceded by reference (*n*) in the current subroutine (or main programme if **J***n* is a main programme instruction).

J*n***P***m* Jump unconditionally to the instruction preceded by reference (*n*) in subroutine **P***m*.

J(M*m***)** Jump unconditionally to the instruction whose absolute address is the number in the modifier **M***m*.

In the following conditional jump instructions, **J***n* may be replaced by **J***n***P***m* or **J(M***m***)**.

	Possible interpretation Q	Possible interpretation R	Meaning of instruction
J*n***Q=0**, **J***n***Q≠0**, **J***n***Q>0**, **J***n***Q⩾0**, **J***n***Q<0**, **J***n***Q⩽0**	AK		Jump to the instruction specified if the stated condition is true.
J*n***Q=R**, **J***n***Q≠R**, **J***n***Q>R**, **J***n***Q<R**	A	SA	Jump to the instruction specified if the stated condition is true.
J*n***V**			Jump to the instruction specified if overflow register is set; clear overflow register.
J*n***NV**			Jump to the instruction specified if overflow register is not set; clear overflow register.
STOP			Stop.

Form of Parameters etc. as written in the Program

Decimal numbers.	Only fractions and integers are permissible. They may be positive or negative and if negative must be preceded by the sign; a positive sign need not be written. The yare written in the ordinary way, e.g. **0.0462; −0.0462; 137; −137**. Integers must be within capacity, i.e. within the range $2^{31}-1$ to -2^{31}.
Binary patterns.	These are written in octal preceded by **8/**. The word is considered as divided into 3-bit sections from the l.s. end, and each of these is expressed as its octal equivalent. Zeros at the m.s. end are omitted, e.g. **...010110000101** would be written **8/2605**. Note than in the octal representation of a whole word, the m.s. digit cannot exceed 3.
Instructions.	Instructions may be treated as parameters, being written in their normal form, with the proviso that a **p**-store address or a jump instruction reference must include the relevant subroutine number unless it refers to an address within the subroutine in which the instruction is stored as a parameter.

In parameter lists, zeros must be written unless all the following parameters are zero, in which case they need not be.

Index

Page numbers in italics refer to flow or other figures, to tables, or to displayed programs or sections of programs.